# Table of Primes

| | | | | | | | | |
|---|---|---|---|---|---|---|---|---|
| 2 | 233 | 547 | 877 | 1229 | 1597 | 1993 | 2371 | 2749 |
| 3 | 239 | 557 | 881 | 1231 | 1601 | 1997 | 2377 | 2753 |
| 5 | 241 | 563 | 883 | 1237 | 1607 | 1999 | 2381 | 2767 |
| 7 | 251 | 569 | 887 | 1249 | 1609 | 2003 | 2383 | 2777 |
| 11 | 257 | 571 | 907 | 1259 | 1613 | 2011 | 2389 | 2789 |
| 13 | 263 | 577 | 911 | 1277 | 1619 | 2017 | 2393 | 2791 |
| 17 | 269 | 587 | 919 | 1279 | 1621 | 2027 | 2399 | 2797 |
| 19 | 271 | 593 | 929 | 1283 | 1627 | 2029 | 2411 | 2801 |
| 23 | 277 | 599 | 937 | 1289 | 1637 | 2039 | 2417 | 2803 |
| 29 | 281 | 601 | 941 | 1291 | 1657 | 2053 | 2423 | 2819 |
| 31 | 283 | 607 | 947 | 1297 | 1663 | 2063 | 2437 | 2833 |
| 37 | 293 | 613 | 953 | 1301 | 1667 | 2069 | 2441 | 2837 |
| 41 | 307 | 617 | 967 | 1303 | 1669 | 2081 | 2447 | 2843 |
| 43 | 311 | 619 | 971 | 1307 | 1693 | 2083 | 2459 | 2851 |
| 47 | 313 | 631 | 977 | 1319 | 1697 | 2087 | 2467 | 2857 |
| 53 | 317 | 641 | 983 | 1321 | 1699 | 2089 | 2473 | 2861 |
| 59 | 331 | 643 | 991 | 1327 | 1709 | 2099 | 2477 | 2879 |
| 61 | 337 | 647 | 997 | 1361 | 1721 | 2111 | 2503 | 2887 |
| 67 | 347 | 653 | 1009 | 1367 | 1723 | 2113 | 2521 | 2897 |
| 71 | 349 | 659 | 1013 | 1373 | 1733 | 2129 | 2531 | 2903 |
| 73 | 353 | 661 | 1019 | 1381 | 1741 | 2131 | 2539 | 2909 |
| 79 | 359 | 673 | 1021 | 1399 | 1747 | 2137 | 2543 | 2917 |
| 83 | 367 | 677 | 1031 | 1409 | 1753 | 2141 | 2549 | 2927 |
| 89 | 373 | 683 | 1033 | 1423 | 1759 | 2143 | 2551 | 2939 |
| 97 | 379 | 691 | 1039 | 1427 | 1777 | 2153 | 2557 | 2953 |
| 101 | 383 | 701 | 1049 | 1429 | 1783 | 2161 | 2579 | 2957 |
| 103 | 389 | 709 | 1051 | 1433 | 1787 | 2179 | 2591 | 2963 |
| 107 | 397 | 719 | 1061 | 1439 | 1789 | 2203 | 2593 | 2969 |
| 109 | 401 | 727 | 1063 | 1447 | 1801 | 2207 | 2609 | 2971 |
| 113 | 409 | 733 | 1069 | 1451 | 1811 | 2213 | 2617 | 2999 |
| 127 | 419 | 739 | 1087 | 1453 | 1823 | 2221 | 2621 | 3001 |
| 131 | 421 | 743 | 1091 | 1459 | 1831 | 2237 | 2633 | 3011 |
| 137 | 431 | 751 | 1093 | 1471 | 1847 | 2239 | 2647 | 3019 |
| 139 | 433 | 757 | 1097 | 1481 | 1861 | 2243 | 2657 | 3023 |
| 149 | 439 | 761 | 1103 | 1483 | 1867 | 2251 | 2659 | 3037 |
| 151 | 443 | 769 | 1109 | 1487 | 1871 | 2267 | 2663 | 3041 |
| 157 | 449 | 773 | 1117 | 1489 | 1873 | 2269 | 2671 | 3049 |
| 163 | 457 | 787 | 1123 | 1493 | 1877 | 2273 | 2677 | 3061 |
| 167 | 461 | 797 | 1129 | 1499 | 1879 | 2281 | 2683 | 3067 |
| 173 | 463 | 809 | 1151 | 1511 | 1889 | 2287 | 2687 | 3079 |
| 179 | 467 | 811 | 1153 | 1523 | 1901 | 2293 | 2689 | 3083 |
| 181 | 479 | 821 | 1163 | 1531 | 1907 | 2297 | 2693 | 3089 |
| 191 | 487 | 823 | 1171 | 1543 | 1913 | 2309 | 2699 | 3109 |
| 193 | 491 | 827 | 1181 | 1549 | 1931 | 2311 | 2707 | 3119 |
| 197 | 499 | 829 | 1187 | 1553 | 1933 | 2333 | 2711 | 3121 |
| 199 | 503 | 839 | 1193 | 1559 | 1949 | 2339 | 2713 | 3137 |
| 211 | 509 | 853 | 1201 | 1567 | 1951 | 2341 | 2719 | 3163 |
| 223 | 521 | 857 | 1213 | 1571 | 1973 | 2347 | 2729 | 3167 |
| 227 | 523 | 859 | 1217 | 1579 | 1979 | 2351 | 2731 | 3169 |
| 229 | 541 | 863 | 1223 | 1583 | 1987 | 2357 | 2741 | 3181 |

# ELEMENTARY
# ELEMENTARY
# ELEMENTARY
# ELEMENTARY
## SECOND EDITION ALGEBRA

ADDISON-WESLEY PUBLISHING COMPANY
READING, MASSACHUSETTS / MENLO PARK, CALIFORNIA
LONDON / AMSTERDAM / DON MILLS, ONTARIO / SYDNEY

Daniel L. Auvil KENT STATE UNIVERSITY
Charles Poluga KENT STATE UNIVERSITY

# ELEMENTARY
## ELEMENTARY
### ELEMENTARY
#### ELEMENTARY

**SECOND EDITION**

# ALGEBRA

Sponsoring Editor: Patricia Mallion
Production Manager: Karen M. Guardino
Production Editor: Laura Skinger
Text and Cover Designer: Melinda Grosser
Art Coordinator: Kristin Belanger
Cover Photographer: Four by Five, Peter Van Rhijn
Manufacturing Supervisor: Ann E. Delacey

**Library of Congress Cataloging in Publication Data**

Auvil, Daniel L.
    Elementary algebra.

    Includes index.
    1. Algebra.   I. Poluga, Charles.   II. Title.
QA152.2.A86 1984        512.9        83-17258
ISBN 0-201-11030-X

*Reprinted with corrections, June 1984*

BCDEFGHIJ-HA-8987654

# Preface

The changes in this second edition of *Elementary Algebra* reflect the many suggestions we received from users of the first edition, as well as our own perceptions gained from teaching out of the first edition for the past five years. We believe (and the reviewers agree) that these changes have transformed what was a successful first edition into a greatly improved second edition. The most significant of these changes are outlined below:

■ Every Problem Set has been reworked to provide more drill, more variety, more complexity, and more applications. In all, there are approximately 5000 problems in the second edition, as compared to approximately 3500 in the first edition.

■ A set of Calculator Problems now follows each set of regular problems. These problems generally involve the same concepts as the regular problems, but they require more complicated arithmetic calculations. They are designed to familiarize students with the hand-held calculator and to emphasize that not all problems in algebra have "nice" solutions.

■ Following each set of Calculator Problems, there is now a set of Challenge Problems. These problems extend the topics of the section in a way that is both interesting and useful, particularly to those students who plan to take subsequent courses in mathematics. They will keep the better students from becoming bored, and they will provide instructors with greater flexibility to tailor the course to their own needs.

■ Many examples have been reworked or added to correspond to the additions in the problem sets and to provide a greater range of applications throughout the text. In all, there are approximately 500 examples in the second edition, as compared to approximately 400 in the first edition.

■ Word problems and problems involving the use of formulas are now emphasized throughout the text rather than being confined to certain sections. Sixty of the 68 sections now contain realistic and useful applications. Many of these applications are unusual for an elementary algebra text, and many appear in sections that do not ordinarily contain applied problems.

■ To reflect the greater variety of applications and to assist the reader in locating them, an Index of Applications has been included.

■ The total number of problems in the Chapter Reviews has been doubled. These problems provide students with the means to review and test their understanding of the material in the entire chapter without the benefit of section headings. The Chapter Review problems are on the same level as the regular problems. That is they do not involve the complex calculations of the Calculator Problems, nor are they as difficult as the Challenge Problems.

■ The topic of sets has been moved to an appendix, thereby allowing each instructor the option of covering this topic or omitting it.

■ An optional section that covers factoring sums and differences of cubes and factoring by grouping and an optional section on equations involving radicals have been added.

■ The difficult topic of addition and subtraction of rational expressions is now covered in two sections rather than one, and there is greater attention paid to the technique of building fractions.

■ Additional historical notes have been interspersed throughout the text to heighten interest and motivation.

■ An appendix demonstrating that $\sqrt{2}$ is not a rational number and an appendix demonstrating a technique for converting repeating decimals to ratios of integers have been added.

■ The eye appeal of the text has been improved through a more generous use of illustrations and color and a larger book size.

■ There has been more attention paid to highlighting important comments, laws, hints, and warnings using boxes, color, italics, and boldface type.

The net effect of these changes is a second edition that is more interesting, more meaningful, and more challenging than the first edition. At the same time, the appealing features of the first edition have been retained. These features include:

■ Clear, carefully-sequenced examples that correspond to the problem sets.

■ Problem sets that are graded in difficulty and are constructed so that each even-numbered problem is similar to the odd-numbered problem that precedes it.

■ Answers to all of the odd-numbered problems and to all of the problems in the Chapter Reviews.

■ An optional student supplement that contains worked-out solutions to all of the even-numbered problems.

■ A step-by-step procedure for solving word problems.

■ A table of square roots, a table of prime numbers, and a table of important formulas from geometry.

■ An appendix on the metric system.

■ A logical organization of topics.

■ A spiral approach that allows students to experience the same topic several times, each time from a slightly different perspective and in slightly greater detail.

■ A writing style that is conversational and nonthreatening. Discussions are precise and mathematically correct without being too abstract or formal. Paragraphs are direct and to the point, allowing the examples to do much of the explanation. Many students who took elementary algebra from the first edition had been unsuccessful in previous attempts at algebra, and these same students told us that the first edition was the first math book that they were able to read and understand on their own.

Although the second edition has been upgraded considerably, it is still a text designed for students who have had no prior experience with algebra or for those students in need of a review. It begins with such elementary concepts as operations with common fractions and proceeds through the traditional topics of elementary algebra. Some topics of intermediate algebra are contained in the optional sections and in the challenge problems. In all, there is probably more material here than can be covered in a one-semester course.

The sections that are designated as optional are optional in the sense that (1) they are not ordinarily found in an elementary algebra text, and (2) no subsequent nonoptional section depends upon the material contained in these sections.

We owe a debt of gratitude to the many individuals who reviewed the first edition and the manuscript to the second edition and who made numerous suggestions for improvements in the book. The most notable among these are:

Rodney Chase, Oakland Community College
Kenneth Eberhard, Chabot College
Albert J. Klein, Youngstown State
    University

Marianna McClymonds, Phoenix College
H. C. Parrish, North Texas State
    University
Mark Phillips, Cypress College
Helga Schwartz, Queensborough Commu-
    nity College and
A. H. Tellez, Glendale Commu-
    nity College.

We would also like to thank our colleagues
Carole Lockwood and Bernard Richards who
lent their valuable assistance to the prepa-
ration of this text and Paul S. Wang for the
table of primes on the inside front cover.

One final note to the student who uses
this text. A mathematics text is not a novel.
It must be read much more slowly, much
more carefully, and with a pencil and paper
nearby. Keeping this in mind, we know that
you will discover as we have that the independent mastery of even a single problem of
good mathematics is an immensely satisfying
intellectual achievement of the very finest
kind.

*North Canton, Ohio*                **D.L.A.**
*Ashtabula, Ohio*                   **C.P.**
*October 1983*

# Contents
Contents
Contents
Contents

# 9 SYSTEMS OF EQUATIONS AND INEQUALITIES

# 10 ROOTS AND RADICALS

# 11 SECOND-DEGREE EQUATIONS

# 12 FUNCTIONS AND THEIR GRAPHS (OPTIONAL)

# APPENDIXES

# ANSWERS TO ODD-NUMBERED PROBLEMS AND CHAPTER REVIEWS

# INDEXES

# Chapter
## Chapter
### Chapter
#### Chapter One
## One
### One
#### One

**REAL NUMBERS**

## 1.1    RATIONAL NUMBERS

The study of algebra is an extension of the study of arithmetic.* For example, in arithmetic we might be concerned with the sum

$$5 + 3,$$

while in algebra we might be concerned with the sum

$$x + 3.$$

The number 5 in the first sum is called a **constant,** since its value is fixed. The letter $x$ in the second sum is called a **variable,** since $x$ may represent any one of a given set of numbers. Letters such as $x$, $y$, and $z$ are frequently used as variables, but actually *any* symbol can be used as a variable.

The numbers that the variable $x$ may represent in this text will always be *real numbers.* Therefore our immediate task is to develop the real numbers and discuss their properties. We shall begin this development by starting with the **natural numbers,** also called the **counting numbers.**

Natural numbers = {1, 2, 3, 4, 5, 6, 7, 8, 9, 10, 11, 12, ...}.

The three dots, read *and so on,* tell us to continue the pattern indefinitely to form an *infinite* set. It should be clear that there is no largest natural number, since no matter how large a natural number we might think of, we can always form a larger one simply by adding 1 to it.

When zero is included with the natural numbers we obtain the **whole numbers.**

Whole numbers = {0, 1, 2, 3, 4, 5, ...}.

The number 0 might be used to represent the amount of money left in your checking account after writing a check for 23 dollars, given that the original balance was 23 dollars. But what number would represent the balance had the check been written for 30 dollars? Certainly no whole number would do, so we must introduce a new kind of number called a **negative number.** For our example we introduce the number negative seven, written $-7$. The negative sign in front of the seven tells us that the account is *overdrawn* 7 dollars, in contrast to the number 7 (also written $+7$) which indicates that seven dollars *remain* in the account.

---

* For the origin of the word *algebra,* see Howard Eves' *An Introduction to the History of Mathematics.*

Note that the negative sign is identical to the symbol used for subtraction. The meaning, however, is quite different and we must rely on the context of the problem to let us know which meaning is intended. The same can be said for the positive sign in the number $+7$ and the symbol for addition.

The symbols $-$ and $+$ when placed in front of a number actually indicate a *direction* for that number. Thus while $+3$ degrees indicates a temperature of 3 degrees *above* zero, $-3$ degrees indicates a temperature of 3 degrees *below* zero. Both temperatures are the same distance from 0 degrees, but in opposite directions. Again, 5 yards might indicate the yardage *gained* on a football play, while $-5$ yards would indicate a *loss* on the play.

If we combine the whole numbers and the negatives of all the whole numbers, we obtain the **integers.**

$$\text{Integers} = \{..., -3, -2, -1, 0, 1, 2, 3, ...\}.$$

The whole number 0 is neither positive nor negative, but rather resides between the positive integers and the negative integers. In other words, $+0$ and $-0$ represent the same number.

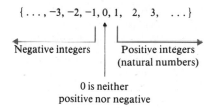

We should still be aware of a gap in our number system. For instance, suppose we were to drive into a service station and say "fill it up." It is likely that the number of gallons received would not be, say, 11 or

12 gallons but possibly some quantity *between* 11 and 12. Therefore, we use the integers to form *rational numbers* by writing ratios of integers.

---

***Definition***    A **rational number** is any number that can be written as a ratio of two integers where the divisor is not zero. That is, a rational number is any number which can be expressed in the form $a/b$ where $a$ and $b$ are integers and $b \neq 0$.

---

**EXAMPLE 1**   $\frac{1}{2}$ is a rational number since it is the ratio of the two integers 1 and 2. ☐

**EXAMPLE 2**   $\dfrac{-6}{2}$ is a rational number since it is the ratio of the two integers $-6$ and 2. ☐

**EXAMPLE 3**   $3\frac{1}{2}$ is a rational number since $3\frac{1}{2} = \frac{7}{2}$. ☐

**EXAMPLE 4**   0 is a rational number since $0 = \frac{0}{5}$. Note that 0 can also be written as $\dfrac{0}{-7}, \dfrac{0}{91},$ or $\dfrac{0}{b}$ where $b$ is any integer except 0. ☐

**EXAMPLE 5**   8 is a rational number since $8 = \frac{8}{1}$. ☐

We note that *every integer n is also a rational number* since it can be expressed as a ratio of the integers $n$ and 1; that is, $n = n/1$.

   With the inclusion of each new kind of number, we have been able to begin with the natural numbers and gradually build to the rational numbers.

   We might now inquire as to why zero was excluded as a divisor in the definition of a rational number. First, we note that $\frac{6}{2} = 3$ since $2 \cdot 3 = 6$. Here the dot means multiplication.* Now suppose we attempt to divide 6 by zero. Since we are not sure of the answer, we will call it $x$ for the time being. But if

$$\frac{6}{0} = x,$$

then

$$0 \cdot x = 6.$$

---

* In arithmetic the symbol $\times$ is used for multiplication. In algebra, however, this symbol looks too much like the letter $x$, which is often used as a variable.

However, zero times any number is zero, not 6. Therefore there is *no* value for *x* that makes this last statement true.

Moreover, if

$$\frac{0}{0} = x,$$

then

$$0 \cdot x = 0$$

and *any* value of *x* yields a true statement. This situation is certainly no better than the first, so we conclude that **division by zero is undefined.** Division *into* zero is perfectly valid, however. That is, $0 \div 6 = 0$.

**EXAMPLE 6**   The probability of getting exactly two tails in three flips of a coin is $\frac{3}{8}$. Express this rational number in decimal form.

Dividing 3 by 8 we obtain the quotient 0.375.

$$
\begin{array}{r}
0.375 \\
8\overline{)3.000} \\
2\,4\phantom{00} \\
\overline{\phantom{0}60\phantom{0}} \\
56\phantom{0} \\
\overline{\phantom{0}40} \\
40 \\
\overline{\phantom{0}0} \;\square
\end{array}
$$

The rational number $\frac{3}{8}$ has a decimal representation which is **terminating.** That is, at some point in the division process a remainder of zero was obtained. When two integers are divided, however, the result is not always a terminating decimal.

**EXAMPLE 7**   Express $\frac{1}{3}$ in decimal form.

Dividing 1 by 3 gives $0.33\overline{3}$.

$$
\begin{array}{r}
0.33\overline{3} \\
3\overline{)1.000} \\
9\phantom{00} \\
\overline{10\phantom{0}} \\
9\phantom{0} \\
\overline{10} \\
9 \\
\overline{1}
\end{array}
$$

The bar is placed over the 3 to indicate that it is repeated indefinitely. Other equivalent forms for this repeating decimal are $0.\overline{3}$, $0.3\overline{3}$, etc.  $\square$

**EXAMPLE 8**   Express $\frac{3}{11}$ in decimal form.

Dividing 3 by 11 we obtain $0.27\overline{27}$.

$$
\begin{array}{r}
0.27\overline{27} \\
11\ \overline{)\ 3.0000} \\
\underline{22}\phantom{000} \\
80\phantom{00} \\
\underline{77}\phantom{00} \\
30\phantom{0} \\
\underline{22}\phantom{0} \\
80 \\
\underline{77} \\
3 \quad \square
\end{array}
$$

These last two decimals are **nonterminating repeating** decimals.

It is beginning to appear as if every rational number has a decimal representation that is either terminating or nonterminating repeating. Let us examine the division process more closely as we convert $\frac{2}{7}$ to decimal form.

$$
\begin{array}{r}
0.285714 \\
7\ \overline{)\ 2.000000} \\
\underline{14}\phantom{00000} \\
60\phantom{0000} \\
\underline{56}\phantom{0000} \\
40\phantom{000} \\
\underline{35}\phantom{000} \\
50\phantom{00} \\
\underline{49}\phantom{00} \\
10\phantom{0} \\
\underline{7}\phantom{0} \\
30 \\
\underline{28} \\
2
\end{array}
$$

As we can see, if the division process above is continued the result will be the nonterminating repeating decimal $0.\overline{285714}$.

Note that when dividing by 7 there are 7 possible remainders, namely 0, 1, 2, 3, 4, 5, and 6. The number 7, for example, would never occur as a remainder since that would mean that we could have divided 7 into the previous dividend one more time. Now if zero occurs as a remainder, the division stops and a terminating decimal results. If zero never occurs as a remainder, then one of the other six remainders must sooner or later occur twice, and when that happens the decimal will begin to repeat. Therefore *every rational number is either a terminating decimal or a nonterminating repeating decimal.*

It can also be shown that *every terminating or nonterminating repeating decimal is a rational number.* In the case of terminating decimals, they can immediately be written as ratios of integers. For example, $0.5 = \frac{5}{10}$, $0.19 = \frac{19}{100}$, and $7.107 = \frac{7107}{1000}$. As for nonterminating repeating decimals, a method for writing them as ratios of integers is discussed in Appendix 2.

Although we will not do so here, it can be shown that decimals that are nonterminating *nonrepeating cannot* be written as ratios of integers. Therefore, such decimals are *not* rational numbers; instead, they are called *irrational* numbers. We will give some examples of irrational numbers in Section 1.4.

## Problem Set 1.1

1. Given the numbers 5, 173, 0, $5\frac{1}{2}$, $2\frac{2}{3}$, $-20$, $-1$, 0.25, $0.33\overline{3}$, $\frac{25}{3}$
   a) Which are natural numbers?
   b) Which are whole numbers?
   c) Which are integers?
   d) Which are rational numbers?

2. Given the numbers 117, 1, $-0$, $8\frac{3}{4}$, 0.5, $-10$, $0.61\overline{61}$, $\frac{7}{2}$, $-100$
   a) Which are natural numbers?
   b) Which are whole numbers?
   c) Which are integers?
   d) Which are rational numbers?

Use positive and negative numbers to represent each of the following.

3. Three strokes under par, two strokes over par
4. 750 feet above sea level, 250 feet below sea level
5. Ten seconds before blast-off, 3 seconds after blast-off
6. A rise of $1\frac{3}{8}$, a fall of $3\frac{1}{8}$ in the price of stock

3  9  15  21  27  33  39  45  51

Express each of the following rational numbers in decimal form.

7. $\frac{1}{2}$      8. $\frac{1}{4}$      9. $\frac{3}{4}$      10. $\frac{4}{5}$

11. $\frac{5}{8}$      12. $\frac{7}{8}$      13. $-\frac{3}{8}$      14. $-\frac{1}{8}$

15. $\frac{2}{3}$      16. $\frac{1}{3}$      17. $-\frac{9}{4}$      18. $-\frac{13}{4}$

19. $\frac{2}{9}$      20. $\frac{4}{9}$      21. $6\frac{4}{11}$      22. $3\frac{1}{11}$

23. $\frac{15}{22}$      24. $\frac{13}{22}$      25. $-\frac{104}{111}$      26. $-\frac{101}{111}$

27. $\frac{22}{7}$      28. $\frac{33}{7}$

In Problems 29 and 30, arrange the numbers in order from smallest to largest.

29. $\frac{9}{5}$   $1.\overline{8}$   $1.08$   $1.\overline{08}$        30. $\frac{5}{7}$   $0.714$   $0.\overline{714}$   $0.7\overline{14}$

31. Find the sum of $0.\overline{12}$ and $0.\overline{21}$.     32. Find the sum of $0.\overline{15}$ and $0.\overline{51}$.

33. Find a rational number between 5.17364 and 5.17374.

34. Find a rational number between 3.9487 and 3.9488.

35. Write each decimal as a ratio of two integers.

    a) 0.17       b) 3.181

36. Write each decimal as a ratio of two integers.

    a) 7.3        b) 0.0019

37. Given that $0.\overline{1} = \frac{1}{9}$, write each decimal below as a ratio of two integers.

    a) $0.\overline{2}$       b) $1.\overline{4}$

38. Given that $0.\overline{01} = \frac{1}{99}$, write each decimal below as a ratio of two integers.

    a) $0.\overline{05}$       b) $0.\overline{17}$

39. The batting average of a baseball player is determined by dividing the number of hits by the number of official times at bat. What is the batting average of a player with 17 hits in 51 at bats?

40. Baseball standings are determined by a percentage equal to games won divided by games played. Suppose New York has won 16 and lost 14, and Boston has won 15 and lost 13. If all other teams in the American League East are below .500, what team is in first place?

41. The probability of rolling an 8 with a pair of dice is $\frac{5}{36}$. Express this number in decimal form.

42. The probability of drawing a face card from a deck of cards is $\frac{12}{52}$. Express this number in decimal form.

43. What is the cost of $x$ pounds of coffee at 4 dollars per pound?

44. What is the value of $x$ number of quarters?
45. Bob has 37 baseball cards. If he buys five packs of gum and each pack contains $y$ number of cards, how many baseball cards does he have?

46. Amy buys 125 shares of stock A and $z$ number of shares of stock B. After she makes her purchase, there is a 3 for 1 split in stock B. How many shares of stock does she now own?

## Calculator Problems

47. Try to find $6 \div 0$ and $0 \div 0$ on your calculator.
48. In his NBA basketball career, Wilt Chamberlain made 12,681 field goals out of 23,497 attempts. What was his field goal percentage to three decimal places?
49. The slugging average of a baseball player is determined by dividing the total number of bases by the number of official times at bat. Determine the career slugging average of a player with 760 singles, 296 doubles, 136 triples, and 232 home runs in 4608 official times at bat.

## Challenge Problems

50. Express $\frac{7}{17}$ in decimal form.
51. Using the result of Problem 50, determine the 3001st digit in the decimal form of $\frac{7}{17}$.
52. If $a = 0.\overline{54}$ and $b = 0.3\overline{72}$, find $a + b$.
53. Make a list of all of the possible outcomes that can occur when a coin is flipped three times. How many of these outcomes involve exactly two tails? Does the statement of Example 6 seem reasonable now?

## 1.2  PRIME FACTORS, GCF, LCM

The integer 30 may be expressed as a product in the following way:

$$30 = 6 \cdot 5.$$

Multiple    Factors

When 30 is written in this fashion it is said to be **factored.** The natural numbers 6 and 5 are called **divisors** of, or **factors** of, 30. The number 30 is said to be a **multiple** of 6 and 5. There are other natural numbers that are also factors of 30. They are 1, 2, 3, 10, 15, and 30 itself.

Our primary interest will be in expressing numbers in **completely factored form.** When the number 30 is expressed as

$$30 = 6 \cdot 5,$$

it is *not* in completely factored form. This is because one of the factors, namely 6, can itself be factored. To express 30 in completely factored form we write

$$30 = 2 \cdot 3 \cdot 5.$$

Note that we do not include the trivial factor 1 in our factorization. This last factorization is also referred to as a **prime factorization** of 30, since the numbers 2, 3, and 5 are all *prime numbers;* that is, they do not have any natural number divisors, or factors, other than themselves and 1.

---

**Definition**  A natural number greater than 1 is called a **prime number** (or **prime**) if it has no natural number factors other than 1 and itself. A natural number greater than 1 that is not a prime number is called a **composite number** (or **composite**).

---

The first ten prime numbers are listed below:

2, 3, 5, 7, 11, 13, 17, 19, 23, 29.

The third century B.C. Greek mathematician Euclid proved in his monumental work *Elements* that there are actually an infinite number of primes. A table of primes from 2 to 3181 appears opposite the inside front cover.

**EXAMPLE 1**   Express 12 as a product of primes.

$$12 = 2 \cdot 2 \cdot 3. \quad \square$$

This is the only way that the number 12 can be factored as a product of primes (except for changing the order of the factors). Moreover, *every natural number greater than 1 is either a prime or it can be factored as a product of primes in exactly one way.*

**EXAMPLE 2**   Completely factor the number 1008.

The number 1008 is too large for us to immediately recognize all of its prime factors. It is clear, however, that the prime 2 is one of the factors of 1008, since

$$1008 = 2 \cdot 504.$$

We can now concentrate on the factors of 504. Again, 2 is one of the factors of 504, since

$$504 = 2 \cdot 252.$$

Thus, we have so far that

$$1008 = 2 \cdot 2 \cdot 252.$$

Continuing in this fashion, we can eventually arrive at a prime factorization for 1008. The most convenient way to set up our work is as follows:

$$
\begin{array}{r|r}
2 & 1008 \\ \hline
2 & 504 \\ \hline
2 & 252 \\ \hline
2 & 126 \\ \hline
3 & 63 \\ \hline
3 & 21 \\ \hline
& 7
\end{array}
$$

We must always be certain that we are dividing each new quotient by a *prime* number, and that the final quotient is itself a prime. The complete factorization for 1008 is then

$$1008 = 2 \cdot 2 \cdot 2 \cdot 2 \cdot 3 \cdot 3 \cdot 7. \quad \square$$

---

***Definition***    The **greatest common factor** (**gcf**) of a set of natural numbers is defined to be the largest natural number that is a factor of each number in the set.

---

Thus, the gcf of the set of numbers

$$\{8, 12, 16\}$$

is 4, since 4 is the largest natural number that is a factor, or divisor, of each of the numbers 8, 12, and 16.

EXAMPLE 3    Find the gcf of the set $\{144, 630, 756\}$.

In this case, the size of the numbers prevents us from determining the gcf simply by inspection. Therefore, we must begin by factoring each of the numbers completely. Using the method described in Example 2, we arrive at the factorizations below:

$$144 = 2 \cdot 2 \cdot 2 \cdot 2 \cdot 3 \cdot 3$$
$$630 = 2 \cdot 3 \cdot 3 \cdot 5 \cdot 7$$
$$756 = 2 \cdot 2 \cdot 3 \cdot 3 \cdot 3 \cdot 7.$$

Now, since the gcf must be a factor of each of the numbers 144, 630, and 756, it can contain only the factors that are in common to the three numbers. Moreover, it should contain each common factor as many times as the *least* number of times it appears in any *single* factorization. The only factors in common to the three numbers are 2 and 3. The least number of times that 2 appears is once (in 630), so it should appear once in the gcf. The least number of times that 3 appears is twice (in both 144 and 630), so it should appear twice in the gcf. Therefore,

$$\text{gcf} = 2 \cdot 3 \cdot 3 = 18. \quad \square$$

Whenever possible, the greatest common factor should be determined simply by inspection. This method, although involving some guesswork, should not be discouraged. Only when it is much too involved to try to guess at the gcf should the method of Example 3 be used.

The same can be said about finding the *least common multiple* of a set of numbers.

---

**Definition**    The **least common multiple (lcm)** of a set of natural numbers is the smallest natural number that is a multiple of each number in the set.

---

Thus, the lcm of the set of numbers

$$\{2, 3\}$$

is 6; the lcm of the set of numbers

$$\{10, 15\}$$

is 30; and the lcm of the set of numbers

$$\{4, 6, 12\}$$

is 12.


**EXAMPLE 4**   Find the lcm of the set $\{24, 90, 75\}$.

These numbers are too large to determine the lcm by inspection, so we begin by completely factoring each number.

$$24 = 2 \cdot 2 \cdot 2 \cdot 3$$
$$90 = 2 \cdot 3 \cdot 3 \cdot 5$$
$$75 = 3 \cdot 5 \cdot 5.$$

Now, since the lcm is to be a multiple of 24, 90, and 75, it must include each distinct factor as many times as the _most_ number of times it appears in any _single_ factorization. The most number of times 2 appears is three times (in 24), the most number of times 3 appears is twice (in 90), and the most number of times 5 appears is twice (in 75). Therefore, the lcm must contain three 2's, two 3's, and two 5's.

$$\text{lcm} = 2 \cdot 2 \cdot 2 \cdot 3 \cdot 3 \cdot 5 \cdot 5 = 1800. \quad \square$$

When working with fractions, it is common practice to refer to the least common multiple (lcm) of a set of denominators as the **least common denominator (lcd)**.


## Problem Set 1.2

State all of the natural number factors of each number.

| | | | | |
|---|---|---|---|---|
| 1. 6 | 2. 8 | 3. 15 | 4. 10 | 5. 7 |
| 6. 5 | 7. 24 | 8. 36 | 9. 99 | 10. 77 |

Which of the following numbers are prime numbers?

| | | | | |
|---|---|---|---|---|
| 11. 12 | 12. 18 | 13. 55 | 14. 23 | 15. 41 |
| 16. 59 | 17. 91 | 18. 119 | 19. 1 | 20. 0 |

Completely factor each natural number.

| | | | | |
|---|---|---|---|---|
| 21. 20 | 22. 45 | 23. 70 | 24. 30 | 25. 19 |
| 26. 23 | 27. 126 | 28. 168 | 29. 2520 | 30. 3780 |

Determine the greatest common factor (gcf) of each set of numbers.

31. {12, 18}    32. {12, 16}    33. {30, 6}
34. {32, 8}     35. {1, 36}     36. {1, 24}
37. {240, 84}   38. {252, 90}   39. {520, 650, 728}
40. {280, 546, 378}

Determine the least common multiple (lcm) of each set of numbers.

41. {2, 9}      42. {3, 4}      43. {27, 9}
44. {18, 6}     45. {1, 16}     46. {1, 15}
47. {8, 12}     48. {12, 16}    49. {56, 84, 90}
50. {40, 75, 84}

51. Two prime numbers that differ by 2 are called **twin primes.** For example, 3 and 5 are twin primes. Find three pairs of twin primes.

52. In 1742 a mathematician named Christian Goldbach conjectured that every even integer greater than 2 can be written as a sum of two primes. For example, $4 = 2 + 2$, $6 = 3 + 3$, and $8 = 3 + 5$. This statement has yet to be proven true or false. Verify *Goldbach's conjecture* for the number 48.

## *Calculator Problems*

53. Show that 6,700,417 is a factor of 4,294,967,297 and therefore the latter number is not prime.

54. Verify that 1,062,347 is the lcm of the set {2431, 5681, 4807}.

## *Challenge Problems*

55. A natural number is **perfect** if the sum of all of its factors is twice the number itself. Find two perfect numbers.

56. Suppose that $x$ number of oranges can be packed in boxes that hold 24 oranges each (with no oranges left over). Suppose also that the same number of oranges could be packed in boxes that hold 36 oranges each (with no oranges left over). What is the smallest number that $x$ can be?

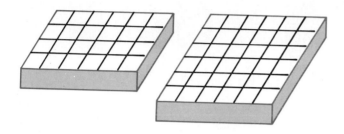

## 1.3  OPERATIONS ON RATIONAL NUMBERS

All of us recall the meaning of **fractions** such as $\frac{3}{4}$. We may have forgotten, however, the significance of the **numerator** 3 and the **denominator** 4. Consider a pie diagram of $\frac{3}{4}$.

Note that the denominator indicates the number of *equal* parts into which one whole has been divided. The numerator indicates the number of these equal parts with which we are concerned.

**EXAMPLE 1**  Make a pie diagram of $\frac{5}{3}$.

We divide one pie into 3 equal parts and note that there are not enough of these parts to shade 5 of them. Hence we divide *two* pies, each into 3 equal parts.

    $\frac{5}{3}$ or $1\frac{2}{3}$  □

The **mixed number** $1\frac{2}{3}$ is actually the sum of a whole number and a fraction: $1\frac{2}{3} = 1 + \frac{2}{3}$.

It soon becomes clear that there are many ways to express the same amount of shaded area. For example,

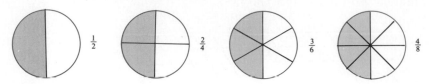

Since the amount of shaded area is the same in each diagram we conclude that

$$\frac{1}{2} = \frac{2}{4} = \frac{3}{6} = \frac{4}{8}, \text{ and so forth.}$$

Note that the second fraction can be obtained from the first by multiplying both numerator and denominator by 2, the third fraction can be obtained from the first by multiplying numerator and denominator by 3, and so on.

Generalizing this last example leads to the following rule:

---

**Fundamental Law of Fractions**

The value of a fraction is not changed when the numerator and denominator are multiplied by the same nonzero number.

---

In symbols, this rule can be stated as

$$\frac{a}{b} = \frac{a \cdot c}{b \cdot c}, \qquad \text{where } b \neq 0 \text{ and } c \neq 0.$$

**EXAMPLE 2**   Write a different fraction that is equal in value to $\frac{3}{7}$.

Multiplying both numerator and denominator by 5, we have

$$\frac{3}{7} = \frac{3 \cdot 5}{7 \cdot 5} = \frac{15}{35}. \quad \square$$

**EXAMPLE 3**   Supply the missing numerator: $\dfrac{3}{4} = \dfrac{?}{16}$.

Since $16 \div 4 = 4$, the missing numerator is $3 \cdot 4 = 12$. That is,

$$\frac{3}{4} = \frac{3 \cdot 4}{4 \cdot 4} = \frac{12}{16}. \quad \square$$

The procedure that was used in Example 3 to write $\frac{3}{4}$ as $\frac{12}{16}$ is called **building the fraction.**

If we read the rule

$$\frac{a}{b} = \frac{a \cdot c}{b \cdot c}$$

from *left to right*, it tells us that the numerator and denominator of a fraction may be *multiplied* by the same nonzero number without changing the value of the fraction. Reading from *right to left*, we see that the numerator and denominator of a fraction may be *divided* by the same nonzero number (in this case $c$) without changing its value. When this is done it is called **reducing the fraction.**

**EXAMPLE 4**   Reduce completely the fraction $\frac{30}{42}$.

We notice that a 2 may be divided evenly into both the numerator and denominator. In order to **completely reduce** the fraction, however, the *greatest* common factor must be divided out. In this case the greatest factor in common to 30 and 42 is 6. Therefore,

$$\frac{30}{42} = \frac{5 \cdot 6}{7 \cdot 6} = \frac{5}{7}. \quad \square$$

This process of dividing out factors that are common to both the numerator and the denominator is called *cancelling*. Often we indicate the common factors that are being divided out by drawing a slash mark through them.

$$\frac{30}{42} = \frac{5 \cdot \cancel{6}}{7 \cdot \cancel{6}} = \frac{5}{7}.$$

## Problem Set 1.3A

Make a pie diagram of each fraction.

1. $\frac{1}{4}$          2. $\frac{1}{3}$          3. $\frac{3}{8}$          4. $\frac{5}{6}$          5. $\frac{7}{3}$

6. $\frac{7}{2}$          7. $1\frac{3}{4}$          8. $1\frac{2}{3}$          9. $\frac{2}{6}$          10. $\frac{2}{8}$

Supply the missing numerator.

11. $\dfrac{2}{3} = \dfrac{?}{12}$     12. $\dfrac{3}{4} = \dfrac{?}{12}$     13. $\dfrac{1}{7} = \dfrac{?}{21}$     14. $\dfrac{1}{5} = \dfrac{?}{20}$     15. $\dfrac{?}{18} = \dfrac{10}{36}$

16. $\dfrac{?}{15} = \dfrac{12}{45}$     17. $\dfrac{5}{16} = \dfrac{?}{64}$     18. $\dfrac{5}{12} = \dfrac{?}{48}$     19. $\dfrac{?}{36} = \dfrac{35}{180}$     20. $\dfrac{?}{24} = \dfrac{42}{144}$

Completely reduce each fraction.

21. $\frac{6}{8}$         22. $\frac{6}{12}$         23. $\frac{10}{15}$         24. $\frac{14}{21}$         25. $\frac{12}{60}$

26. $\frac{30}{54}$       27. $\frac{16}{12}$       28. $\frac{24}{10}$       29. $\frac{48}{60}$       30. $\frac{36}{60}$

31. $\frac{96}{56}$       32. $\frac{56}{48}$       33. $\frac{240}{800}$       34. $\frac{630}{900}$

35. The residents of a town attempted to raise \$25,000 for a charity fund. They raised \$22,500. What fraction of their goal was raised?

36. Of 6000 fires in a city, 2250 were caused by smoking in bed. What part of the 6000 fires were due to this cause?

## Calculator Problems

37. $\dfrac{79}{351} = \dfrac{?}{12{,}285}$.

38. Completely reduce $\dfrac{570{,}570}{690{,}690}$.

## Challenge Problems

39. Under what conditions does $\dfrac{a}{b} = \dfrac{c}{d}$?

40. Consider the equation $\dfrac{1 + ab}{b} = 1 + a$, where $b \neq 0$. Is this equation true? Try using numerical examples to explain your thinking.

**ADDITION**

A plumber needs two pieces of pipe, one $4\frac{2}{7}$ inches long and the other $5\frac{3}{7}$ inches long. To find the total length of pipe needed requires the addition of the fractions $\frac{2}{7}$ and $\frac{3}{7}$. This addition problem can be visualized by first dividing a 1-inch length on a line into 7 equal parts. Then placing a line segment of length $\frac{3}{7}$ inch adjacent to a line segment of length $\frac{2}{7}$ inch yields a line segment of length $\frac{5}{7}$ inch. That is,

$$\frac{3}{7} + \frac{2}{7} = \frac{5}{7}.$$

Hence the plumber needs $9\frac{5}{7}$ inches of pipe.

Addition of fractions is therefore defined in the following way.

---

***Definition***    When adding fractions having the same denominator, the numerators are added and this sum is placed over that common denominator. In symbols,

$$\frac{a}{c} + \frac{b}{c} = \frac{a + b}{c}, \qquad \text{where } c \neq 0.$$

---

**EXAMPLE 1**    Find the sum $\frac{1}{8} + \frac{3}{8}$.

$$\frac{1}{8} + \frac{3}{8} = \frac{1 + 3}{8} = \frac{4}{8} = \frac{1}{2}. \quad \square$$

If the fractions to be added do *not* have the same denominator, then we must find the least common denominator (lcd). The least common denominator (lcd) of a set of fractions is the least common multiple (lcm) of the denominators of the fractions.

**EXAMPLE 2**  Find the sum $\frac{3}{4} + \frac{1}{6}$.

The lcd is 12, since 12 is the smallest natural number that is a multiple of both 4 and 6. Therefore, we write

$$\frac{3}{4} + \frac{1}{6} = \frac{?}{12} + \frac{?}{12}.$$

Supplying the missing numerators, we have

$$\frac{3}{4} + \frac{1}{6} = \frac{9}{12} + \frac{2}{12}$$
$$= \frac{11}{12}. \quad \square$$

**EXAMPLE 3**  Find the sum $\frac{1}{12} + \frac{7}{18} + \frac{2}{15}$.

Here the lcd cannot be easily determined by inspection. Therefore we begin by completely factoring each denominator.

$$12 = 2 \cdot 2 \cdot 3$$
$$18 = 2 \cdot 3 \cdot 3$$
$$15 = 3 \cdot 5.$$

Since the lcd is the lcm of 12, 18, and 15, we have

$$\text{lcd} = 2 \cdot 2 \cdot 3 \cdot 3 \cdot 5 = 180.$$

Therefore, we write

$$\frac{1}{12} + \frac{7}{18} + \frac{2}{15} = \frac{?}{180} + \frac{?}{180} + \frac{?}{180}.$$

Supplying the missing numerators, we have

$$\frac{1}{12} + \frac{7}{18} + \frac{2}{15} = \frac{15}{180} + \frac{70}{180} + \frac{24}{180}$$
$$= \frac{109}{180}. \quad \square$$

## SUBTRACTION

Since the numerators are *added* in addition, we would expect them to be *subtracted* in subtraction.

***Definition*** When subtracting fractions having the same denominator, the numerators are subtracted and this difference is placed over that common denominator. In symbols,

$$\frac{a}{c} - \frac{b}{c} = \frac{a-b}{c}, \qquad \text{where } c \neq 0.$$

**EXAMPLE 4** Find the difference $\frac{6}{7} - \frac{2}{7}$.

$$\frac{6}{7} - \frac{2}{7} = \frac{6-2}{7} = \frac{4}{7}. \quad \square$$

On a line our subtraction looks like this:

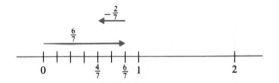

**EXAMPLE 5** Find the difference $\frac{2}{3} - \frac{1}{2}$.

Here the lcd is 6. Therefore, we write

$$\frac{2}{3} - \frac{1}{2} = \frac{?}{6} - \frac{?}{6}.$$

Supplying the missing numerators, we have

$$\frac{2}{3} - \frac{1}{2} = \frac{4}{6} - \frac{3}{6}$$

$$= \frac{1}{6}. \quad \square$$

**EXAMPLE 6** Find the difference $4 - \frac{2}{3}$.

$$4 - \frac{2}{3} = \frac{4}{1} - \frac{2}{3}.$$

The lcd is 3. Therefore, we write

$$4 - \frac{2}{3} = \frac{4}{1} - \frac{2}{3} = \frac{?}{3} - \frac{?}{3}.$$

Supplying the missing numerators, we have

$$4 - \frac{2}{3} = \frac{12}{3} - \frac{2}{3}$$
$$= \frac{10}{3}, \text{ or } 3\frac{1}{3}. \quad \square$$

## Problem Set 1.3B

Find the sum. Reduce your answer if possible.

1. $\frac{1}{4} + \frac{1}{4}$
2. $\frac{1}{8} + \frac{1}{8}$
3. $\frac{1}{8} + \frac{3}{8}$
4. $\frac{1}{4} + \frac{2}{4}$
5. $3\frac{2}{5} + 2\frac{4}{5}$
6. $4\frac{6}{7} + 5\frac{1}{7}$
7. $\frac{5}{6} + \frac{1}{12}$
8. $\frac{2}{5} + \frac{1}{15}$
9. $\frac{1}{3} + \frac{1}{4}$
10. $\frac{1}{2} + \frac{1}{5}$
11. $\frac{1}{2} + \frac{1}{3} + \frac{1}{4}$
12. $\frac{1}{2} + \frac{1}{3} + \frac{1}{5}$
13. $\frac{3}{5} + \frac{1}{8}$
14. $\frac{1}{4} + \frac{2}{7}$
15. $\frac{4}{15} + \frac{2}{9}$
16. $\frac{3}{10} + \frac{2}{15}$
17. $\frac{1}{12} + \frac{7}{30} + \frac{3}{10}$
18. $\frac{1}{12} + \frac{5}{18} + \frac{4}{15}$
19. $\frac{5}{126} + \frac{11}{168}$
20. $\frac{11}{120} + \frac{13}{378}$
21. $3\frac{5}{24} + \frac{1}{20} + 4\frac{7}{54}$
22. $5\frac{3}{80} + 2\frac{1}{36} + \frac{7}{135}$

Find the difference. Reduce your answer if possible.

23. $\frac{4}{5} - \frac{1}{5}$
24. $\frac{5}{8} - \frac{3}{8}$
25. $6\frac{4}{9} - 3\frac{2}{9}$
26. $5\frac{4}{7} - 1\frac{1}{7}$
27. $\frac{7}{18} - \frac{1}{6}$
28. $\frac{8}{15} - \frac{2}{5}$
29. $\frac{1}{2} - \frac{1}{3}$
30. $\frac{1}{4} - \frac{1}{5}$
31. $3 - \frac{2}{5}$
32. $5 - \frac{2}{3}$
33. $\frac{7}{18} - \frac{5}{24}$
34. $\frac{11}{30} - \frac{7}{45}$
35. $\frac{33}{280} - \frac{17}{210}$
36. $\frac{25}{189} - \frac{13}{252}$
37. $7\frac{1}{120} - 2\frac{7}{90}$
38. $6\frac{1}{120} - 3\frac{11}{100}$

39. A plumber needs three pieces of pipe measuring $5\frac{1}{4}$ inches, $7\frac{1}{2}$ inches, and $7\frac{2}{3}$ inches. What is the total length of pipe needed?

40. A woman must borrow $2\frac{3}{4}$ cups of flour to make a plain cake and $3\frac{1}{3}$ cups for a layer cake. How much total flour should she borrow?

41. A share of stock was worth $43\frac{1}{8}$ dollars per share on Friday. On Monday it was worth $41\frac{1}{2}$. How much did the stock fall?

42. Linda had $4\frac{3}{4}$ yards of ribbon. After tying a Christmas package, she had $2\frac{7}{8}$ yards of ribbon left. How much ribbon was used to tie the package?

43. A carpenter cut three pieces of lengths $1\frac{1}{2}$ feet, $5\frac{1}{5}$ feet, and $6\frac{7}{8}$ feet from an 18-foot board. How much is left?

44. A bolt of material contained 20 yards when full. If a sale of $6\frac{3}{4}$ yards is followed by a sale of $5\frac{1}{8}$ yards, how much material is left on the bolt?

## Calculator Problems

45. Find the sum $\frac{65}{128} + \frac{39}{80}$ in decimal form.
46. Try to guess a value for the infinite sum

$$1 + \frac{1}{2} + \frac{1}{4} + \frac{1}{8} + \frac{1}{16} + \cdots .$$

## Challenge Problems

47. In a local election, $\frac{5}{8}$ of the voters voted for Issue 1 and $\frac{5}{12}$ voted for Issue 2. What is the smallest fraction of voters that could have voted for both? The largest fraction?
48. Here are two equations. Is either equation true? Try using numerical examples to explain your thinking.

    a) $\dfrac{a}{b} + \dfrac{c}{d} = \dfrac{ad + bc}{bd}$, where neither $b$ nor $d$ is zero.

    b) $\dfrac{1}{a} + \dfrac{1}{b} = \dfrac{1}{a + b}$, where neither $a$ nor $b$ is zero.

### MULTIPLICATION

Let us now consider the operation of multiplication of fractions. Suppose we wish to find the product $5 \cdot \frac{2}{3}$. We can write

$$5 \cdot \frac{2}{3} = \frac{2}{3} + \frac{2}{3} + \frac{2}{3} + \frac{2}{3} + \frac{2}{3}$$

$$= \frac{2 + 2 + 2 + 2 + 2}{3}$$

$$= \frac{10}{3}.$$

The same answer could have been obtained by writing 5 as $\frac{5}{1}$ and multiplying numerator by numerator and denominator by denominator.

$$5 \cdot \frac{2}{3} = \frac{5}{1} \cdot \frac{2}{3} = \frac{5 \cdot 2}{1 \cdot 3} = \frac{10}{3}.$$

Of course in the example above, one of the factors was a whole number. Let us investigate multiplication further.

$$\frac{1}{2} \cdot 6 = \frac{1}{2} + \frac{1}{2} + \frac{1}{2} + \frac{1}{2} + \frac{1}{2} + \frac{1}{2} = \frac{6}{2} = 3.$$

But also

$$\frac{1}{2} \; of \; 6 = 3.$$

We see that in situations of this type the word "of" means the same as multiplication. Using this idea we can write

$$\frac{1}{3} \cdot \frac{1}{2} = \frac{1}{3} \; of \; \frac{1}{2}.$$

But the pie diagram below tells us that $\frac{1}{3}$ of $\frac{1}{2}$ equals $\frac{1}{6}$. Therefore,

$$\frac{1}{3} \cdot \frac{1}{2} = \frac{1}{3} \; of \; \frac{1}{2} = \frac{1}{6}.$$

Again we note that the product $\frac{1}{3} \cdot \frac{1}{2}$ could be obtained by multiplying numerators and multiplying denominators. These examples lead to the definition below.

---

**Definition**    Two fractions are multiplied by multiplying numerators and multiplying denominators. In symbols,

$$\frac{a}{b} \cdot \frac{c}{d} = \frac{a \cdot c}{b \cdot d}, \qquad \text{where } b \neq 0, d \neq 0.$$

---

**EXAMPLE 1**   Find the product $\frac{3}{5} \cdot \frac{2}{7}$.

$$\frac{3}{5} \cdot \frac{2}{7} = \frac{3 \cdot 2}{5 \cdot 7} = \frac{6}{35}. \quad \square$$

*Note that it is not necessary to find the lcd when multiplying fractions.*
   Sometimes our work can be shortened by cancelling common factors *before* multiplying. These common factors must appear between a numerator and a denominator, and not between two numerators or between two denominators.

**EXAMPLE 2**   Find the product $\frac{3}{5} \cdot \frac{8}{21}$.

$$\frac{3}{5} \cdot \frac{8}{21} = \frac{\overset{1}{\cancel{3}} \cdot 8}{5 \cdot \underset{7}{\cancel{21}}} = \frac{8}{35}. \quad \square$$

**EXAMPLE 3**   Find the product $1\frac{3}{5} \cdot 2\frac{1}{6}$.

$$1\frac{3}{5} \cdot 2\frac{1}{6} = \frac{8}{5} \cdot \frac{13}{6}$$

$$-\frac{\overset{4}{\cancel{8}}}{5} \cdot \frac{13}{\underset{3}{\cancel{6}}}$$

$$= \frac{52}{15}, \text{ or } 3\frac{7}{15}. \quad \square$$

**EXAMPLE 4**   How much would $1\frac{3}{4}$ pounds of onions at 44 cents per pound cost?

$$1\frac{3}{4} \cdot 44 = \frac{7}{4} \cdot \frac{44}{1}$$

$$= \frac{7}{\underset{1}{\cancel{4}}} \cdot \frac{\overset{11}{\cancel{44}}}{1}$$

$$= 77.$$

Therefore, the cost is 77¢.   $\square$

## DIVISION

Let us begin our study of division by finding the quotient of $\frac{1}{2}$ divided by $\frac{2}{3}$.

$$\frac{1}{2} \div \frac{2}{3} = \frac{\dfrac{1}{2}}{\dfrac{2}{3}}.$$

Using the fundamental law of fractions, we multiply numerator and denominator by $\frac{3}{2}$ and get

$$\frac{\dfrac{1}{2}}{\dfrac{2}{3}} = \frac{\dfrac{1}{2} \cdot \dfrac{3}{2}}{\dfrac{2}{3} \cdot \dfrac{3}{2}} = \frac{\dfrac{1}{2} \cdot \dfrac{3}{2}}{1} = \frac{1}{2} \cdot \frac{3}{2}.$$

Generalizing on this example produces the definition below.

---

**Definition**    Two fractions are divided by inverting the divisor and multiplying. In symbols,

$$\frac{a}{b} \div \frac{c}{d} = \frac{a}{b} \cdot \frac{d}{c}, \qquad \text{where } b \neq 0,\, c \neq 0,\, d \neq 0.$$

---

**EXAMPLE 5**    Find the quotient $\frac{2}{7} \div \frac{3}{4}$.

We cannot cancel between the 2 and the 4 since the operation is division. Multiplication is the only operation in which cancelling can be accomplished. Instead,

$$\frac{2}{7} \div \frac{3}{4} = \frac{2}{7} \cdot \frac{4}{3} = \frac{8}{21}. \quad \square$$

**EXAMPLE 6**    Find the quotient $\frac{1}{5} \div 2$.

$$\frac{1}{5} \div 2 = \frac{1}{5} \div \frac{2}{1} = \frac{1}{5} \cdot \frac{1}{2} = \frac{1}{10}. \quad \square$$

**EXAMPLE 7** How many boards $2\frac{1}{3}$ feet long can be cut from a board that is 20 feet long?

$$20 \div 2\frac{1}{3} = \frac{20}{1} \div \frac{7}{3}$$
$$= \frac{20}{1} \cdot \frac{3}{7}$$
$$= \frac{60}{7}$$
$$= 8\frac{4}{7}.$$

Therefore, 8 boards can be cut. □

## Problem Set 1.3C

Find the product. Reduce your answer if possible.

1. $\frac{1}{2} \cdot \frac{1}{2}$    2. $\frac{1}{9} \cdot \frac{1}{3}$    3. $\frac{3}{4} \cdot \frac{1}{5}$    4. $\frac{2}{5} \cdot \frac{1}{3}$    5. $4 \cdot \frac{2}{5}$    6. $5 \cdot \frac{3}{4}$
7. $\frac{5}{8} \cdot 40$    8. $\frac{3}{7} \cdot 21$    9. $2\frac{2}{8} \cdot \frac{2}{3}$    10. $4\frac{4}{7} \cdot \frac{3}{16}$    11. $\frac{1}{3} \cdot \frac{2}{5} \cdot \frac{5}{8}$    12. $\frac{1}{4} \cdot \frac{3}{7} \cdot \frac{7}{9}$

Find the quotient. Reduce your answer if possible.

13. $\frac{1}{4} \div 2$    14. $\frac{1}{2} \div 2$    15. $\frac{5}{8} \div \frac{2}{5}$    16. $\frac{3}{4} \div \frac{4}{9}$    17. $\frac{1}{3} \div \frac{5}{4}$    18. $\frac{4}{7} \div \frac{2}{3}$
19. $4\frac{1}{2} \div \frac{3}{2}$    20. $3\frac{1}{3} \div \frac{5}{3}$    21. $\dfrac{\frac{5}{7}}{\frac{5}{6}}$    22. $\dfrac{\frac{1}{2}}{\frac{2}{3}}$    23. $13\frac{6}{11} \div 5\frac{3}{8}$    24. $10\frac{7}{13} \div 4\frac{5}{6}$

25. If apples cost 68 cents per pound, how much would $1\frac{3}{4}$ pounds cost?
26. If 1 inch on a map represents 50 miles, how many miles are represented by $2\frac{3}{4}$ inches?
27. A lab technician must prepare 5 solutions, each containing $1\frac{1}{3}$ liters of formaldehyde. What is the total amount of formaldehyde needed?
28. If $\frac{3}{5}$ of a particular type of meat is water, what is the weight of the water in a $2\frac{1}{2}$-pound cut of that meat?
29. A recipe designed to serve five people calls for $2\frac{3}{4}$ cups of flour. If a cook wants to serve only four people, how much flour should be used?

30. A recipe for 16 brownies specifies:

    $\frac{1}{2}$ cup shortening            4 eggs
    2 ounces chocolate         1 teaspoon vanilla
    1 cup sugar                $\frac{3}{4}$ cup flour
    $\frac{3}{4}$ teaspoon salt            $\frac{1}{2}$ teaspoon baking powder

    How much of each ingredient is needed to make one dozen brownies?

31. A medic has $5\frac{1}{2}$ yards of gauze to cut into bandages. If each bandage takes $\frac{1}{6}$ of a yard, how many bandages can he make?

32. If you travel 700 miles in $12\frac{1}{2}$ hours, what is your average speed?

33. On a blueprint of a particular house $\frac{1}{2}$ inch represents 1 foot. Find the dimensions of the blueprint that will represent a room which is $11\frac{1}{2}$ feet by $15\frac{3}{4}$ feet.

34. The gasoline tank on a car holds 10 gallons. If the car averages 30 miles per gallon, how many times will the tank have to be filled to travel 1300 miles?

35. Find the number that lies midway between $\frac{3}{5}$ and $\frac{4}{9}$.

36. Three bars of iron weigh $3\frac{1}{5}$, $5\frac{1}{2}$, and $7\frac{1}{5}$ kilograms. What is their average weight?

37. A recipe for 36 peanut-butter cookies requires $\frac{3}{4}$ cup of peanut butter. How much peanut butter is in each cookie?

38. Brand $X$ toothpaste costs \$1.24 for a tube containing $5\frac{1}{3}$ ounces, while brand $Y$ costs \$1.52 for $6\frac{2}{3}$ ounces. Which is the better buy?

## *Calculator Problems*

39. Find the product $\frac{648}{282} \cdot \frac{799}{2448}$ in decimal form.

40. The probability that two persons in a random group of 40 persons will have the same birthday is $1 - \frac{364}{365} \cdot \frac{363}{365} \cdot \frac{362}{365} \cdots \cdot \frac{326}{365}$. Find this probability to the nearest hundredth. (The answer may surprise you!)

## *Challenge Problems*

41. Two holes are to be drilled in a metal plate so that the distance between the holes is $2\frac{7}{8}$ centimeters. The diameters of the holes are $\frac{3}{8}$ cm and $\frac{5}{16}$ cm. Find the distance between the centers.

42. Verify that between any two rational numbers $a/b$ and $c/d$ there exists another rational number by finding the rational number that lies midway between them.

## 1.4  IRRATIONAL NUMBERS, THE PYTHAGOREAN THEOREM

In Section 1.1 we noted that rational numbers have decimal representations that are either terminating or nonterminating repeating. We might now wonder about those decimals that are nonterminating but do *not* repeat, such as

$$0.101001000100001\cdots.$$

Decimals like the one above are called **irrational numbers.** There are actually infinitely many rational numbers and infinitely many irrational numbers.

The number $\pi$ (Greek letter pi), which is the ratio of the circumference of any circle to its diameter, is another example of an irrational number.

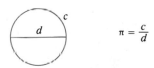

In computations, the irrational number $\pi$ is often *approximated* using either of the rational numbers 3.14 or $\frac{22}{7}$. Indeed, as early as about 240 B.C. the Greek mathematician Archimedes (287–212 B.C.) laboriously computed $\pi$ to two decimal places. Using modern computers, $\pi$ can easily be calculated to as many decimal places as one might desire. To ten places, we have

$$\pi \approx 3.1415926536.$$

The symbol $\approx$ means *approximately equals.* It wasn't until 1767 that Johann Lambert (1728–1777) *proved* that $\pi$ was irrational. Therefore, $\pi$ can never be written exactly as a decimal since it is *nonterminating nonrepeating.*

In order to give some other examples of irrational numbers, let us digress for a moment.

---

***Definition***   Let $a$ be a whole number. Then $\sqrt{a}$ is that nonnegative real number $b$ such that $b \cdot b = a$.

---

Usually $b \cdot b$ is written $b^2$ and is read $b$ *squared*. The symbol $\sqrt{\phantom{x}}$ is called a **radical sign** and $a$ is called the **radicand.** The symbol $\sqrt{a}$ is read *the principal square root of a* or simply *radical a*. The radical sign is a distortion of the letter $r$, the first letter in the Latin word *radix* (meaning root).

**EXAMPLE 1**   Find $\sqrt{25}$.

$$\sqrt{25} = 5 \quad \text{since} \quad 5^2 = 5 \cdot 5 = 25. \ \square$$

**EXAMPLE 2**   Find $\sqrt{81}$.

$$\sqrt{81} = 9 \quad \text{since} \quad 9^2 = 9 \cdot 9 = 81. \ \square$$

**EXAMPLE 3**   Find $\sqrt{0}$.

$$\sqrt{0} = 0 \quad \text{since} \quad 0^2 = 0 \cdot 0 = 0. \ \square$$

The Greek mathematician Pythagoras (ca. 572–495 B.C.) was probably the first to prove the now famous relationship between the legs of a right triangle and its hypotenuse. A **right triangle** is a triangle having a **right angle** (90° angle). The two shorter sides of a right triangle are called the **legs,** and the longest side (the side opposite the right angle) is called the **hypotenuse.**

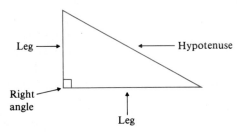

---

### The Pythagorean Theorem

In any right triangle the square of the hypotenuse equals the sum of the squares of the two legs.

---

Pictorially, we could rephrase this theorem using the diagram below.

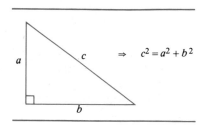

**EXAMPLE 4**   Find the hypotenuse of a right triangle whose legs are 3 feet and 4 feet.

Since we do not know the length of the hypotenuse, we shall call it $x$.

By the Pythagorean theorem,

$$x^2 = 3^2 + 4^2$$
$$x^2 = 9 + 16$$
$$x^2 = 25$$
$$x = \sqrt{25}$$
$$x = 5.$$

Therefore the hypotenuse is 5 feet in length.  ⨆

When the early Greeks attempted to apply this formula to a right triangle having legs of length 1, they discovered that the hypotenuse must be $\sqrt{2}$.

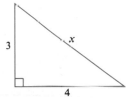

$$x^2 = 1^2 + 1^2$$
$$x^2 = 1 + 1$$
$$x^2 = 2$$
$$x = \sqrt{2}.$$

Try as they might, the Greeks could not express $\sqrt{2}$ as a ratio of two integers. The discovery of this new kind of number so disturbed the followers of Pythagoras that, for a while, efforts were made to keep the matter secret.

As was later proved, $\sqrt{2}$ is an irrational number and therefore its decimal representation is nonterminating nonrepeating. Appendix 3 gives a proof that $\sqrt{2}$ is not a rational number. Carried to three decimal places,

$$\sqrt{2} \approx 1.414.$$

You should determine the value of $(1.414)^2$ to verify that it is approximately 2.

Numbers such as $\sqrt{3}$, $\sqrt{5}$, and $\sqrt{6}$ can also be shown to be irrational numbers. More generally, the square root of any whole number that is not a *perfect square* is an irrational number. Note that numbers such as $\sqrt{4}$, $\sqrt{9}$, $\sqrt{16}$, and $\sqrt{25}$ are all *rational* numbers, since 4, 9, 16, and 25 are all perfect squares. Included on the inside front cover is a table of square roots for whole numbers from 1 to 200.

**EXAMPLE 5**   If a 25-foot ladder is placed so that the base of the ladder is 7 feet from the side of a house, how high up on the house will the ladder reach?

$$x^2 + 7^2 = 25^2$$
$$x^2 + 49 = 625$$
$$x^2 = 625 - 49$$
$$x^2 = 576$$
$$x = \sqrt{576}$$
$$x = 24.$$

Therefore, the ladder will rest on the house at a point 24 feet above ground level. □

**EXAMPLE 6**   Identify each number as being rational or irrational.

a) $\dfrac{-4}{5}$

b) $\sqrt{81}$

c) $0.475$

d) $3.878878887 \cdots$

e) $0.\overline{34}$

f) $\sqrt{12}$

The solutions are as follows:

a) $\dfrac{-4}{5}$ is a quotient of the two integers $-4$ and 5, so it is rational.

b) $\sqrt{81} = 9$, which is an integer and hence a rational number.

c) $0.475$ is a terminating decimal, so it is rational.

d) $3.878878887 \cdots$ is a nonterminating nonrepeating decimal, so it is irrational.

e) $0.\overline{34}$ is a nonterminating repeating decimal, so it is rational.

f) $\sqrt{12}$ is irrational, since 12 is not a perfect square. □

Irrational numbers and their properties will be studied further in Chapter 10.

## Problem Set 1.4

1. Given the numbers 5, $-0$, $\frac{3}{4}$, $\sqrt{2}$, $\sqrt{16}$, $0.07\overline{07}$, $\pi$, $3.14$, $-\frac{10}{3}$, $\sqrt{10}$, $0.717117111711117\cdots$

   a) Which are rational?     b) Which are irrational?

2. Given the numbers $\frac{1}{3}$, 0, $\sqrt{25}$, $\frac{22}{7}$, $-18$, $0.15$, $0.32\overline{32}$, $\pi$, $\frac{11}{4}$, $\sqrt{15}$, $0.848448444844448\cdots$

   a) Which are rational?     b) Which are irrational?

Determine the value of each square root either by inspection or by consulting the table of square roots.

3. $\sqrt{4}$       4. $\sqrt{9}$       5. $\sqrt{49}$       6. $\sqrt{36}$

7. $\sqrt{121}$      8. $\sqrt{144}$     9. $\sqrt{169}$     10. $\sqrt{196}$

11. $\sqrt{900}$     12. $\sqrt{400}$    13. $\sqrt{5}$      14. $\sqrt{7}$

15. $\sqrt{50}$      16. $\sqrt{75}$     17. $\sqrt{177}$     18. $\sqrt{185}$

Find the value of each pair of expressions and compare the results. What conclusion can be made?

19. $(2 + 3)^2$ and $2^2 + 3^2$        20. $(3 + 4)^2$ and $3^2 + 4^2$

21. $(9 - 5)^2$ and $9^2 - 5^2$       22. $(8 - 3)^2$ and $8^2 - 3^2$

Find the hypotenuse of a right triangle whose legs are:

23. 6 and 8      24. 5 and 12     25. 9 and 12     26. 7 and 24

27. 30 and 16    28. 21 and 20   29. 4 and 5      30. 5 and 7

31. 7 and 10     32. 6 and 9

Find the unknown leg of a right triangle whose hypotenuse and known leg are respectively:

33. 25 and 15     34. 26 and 24     35. 26 and 10     36. 25 and 20

37. 16 and 10     38. 14 and 10     39. $\sqrt{58}$ and 7    40. $\sqrt{85}$ and 9

41. If a 26-foot ladder is placed so that the base of the ladder is 10 feet from the side of a house, how high up on the house will the ladder reach?

42. A tunnel is to be dug under a mountain from $A$ to $B$. If $C$ is chosen on a level with $A$ and $B$ so that angle $C$ is a right angle and $AC = BC = 5$ kilometers, how long is $AB$?

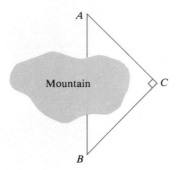

43. A house has a cross section with measurements given in the diagram. What is the length of the roof $x$ if there is an overhang of 2 feet?

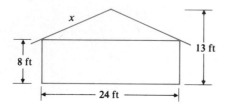

44. A TV antenna is to be braced with three cables, each attached to a point on the antenna 24 feet high. If the cables are to be fastened to the ground 10 feet from the base of the antenna, how much total cable is needed?

45. Two cars start at the same point, one traveling north at 30 mph and the other traveling west at 40 mph. How far apart are they after 30 minutes?

46. Given the box below, what is the straight-line distance from $A$ to $B$? (*Hint:* Find the straight-line distance from $A$ to $C$ first.)

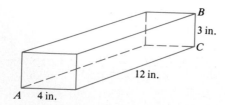

## Calculator Problems

47. Calculate to the nearest hundredth.
    a) $\sqrt{3181}$     b) $\sqrt{\sqrt{331,776}}$     c) $\pi^2$

48. Sections of railroad track are laid with a small space between them to allow for expansion when the metal becomes hot. If a 1-mile length of track expands 1 inch, and no horizontal space is allowed for this expansion, by how much (to the nearest inch) will one end of the track rise vertically? (*Hint:* 1 mi = 5280 ft.)

49. Show that a triangle whose sides are 529, 2211, and 2147 could not be a right triangle.

50. The international throwing distance for competition darts is $7'9\frac{1}{4}''$, measured horizontally from the face of the dartboard to the hockey line. Given that the dartboard is always placed so that the inner bullseye is 5'8" high, find the distance (to the nearest inch) from the hockey line to the inner bullseye.

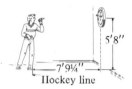

## Challenge Problems

51. True or false: The product of two irrational numbers is always an irrational number.

52. Modify the proof in Appendix 3 to prove that $\sqrt{3}$ is not a rational number.

## 1.5   REAL NUMBERS, THE NUMBER LINE, ABSOLUTE VALUE

If we combine the rational numbers with the irrational numbers, we obtain the **real numbers.** It is important to note, however, that no real number is *both* rational *and* irrational.

**Decimal Representation of Real Numbers**
1. Terminating (rational numbers)
2. Nonterminating
    a) Repeating (rational numbers)
    b) Nonrepeating (irrational numbers)

An interesting glimpse into the relationships that exist between the various types of real numbers is provided by the diagram below.

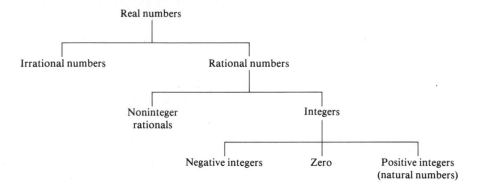

Another useful way of picturing the real numbers can be accomplished by associating each real number with a point on a line. This device, called a **number line,** enables us to visualize the arithmetic operations with positive and negative numbers, which are presented in the next chapter.

To construct a number line we begin by drawing a line (actually we cannot draw the entire line since it extends infinitely far in both directions).

An arbitrary point on the line is then selected to correspond to the number 0. This point is called the **origin** of the number line.

The *positive* real numbers are located to the *right* of 0 and the *negative* real numbers to the *left* of 0. Having chosen a *unit length,* we proceed from the origin to the right and indicate the point corresponding to the number 1.

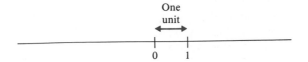

Using the same unit length we continue to the right, locating each positive integer in turn.

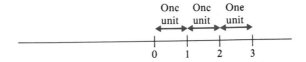

Proceeding to the left one unit at a time we locate the negative integers.

Other rational and irrational numbers are located *between* the integers. For example, $\frac{1}{2}$ would lie midway between 0 and 1. The number $\frac{1}{2}$ is called the **coordinate** of point $P$ in the diagram below. On the other hand, the point $P$ is called the **graph** of the number $\frac{1}{2}$.

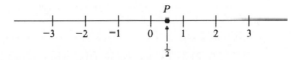

To each point on the line there corresponds a unique real number, and to each real number there corresponds a unique point on the line. We say that there is a **one-to-one correspondence** between the points on the line and the real numbers.

**EXAMPLE 1**   Graph $-1\frac{3}{4}$ on the number line.

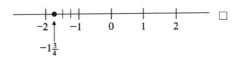

Occasionally we shall want to talk about the *size* of a real number without regard to its sign. This quantity is called the *absolute value* of the number. The **absolute value** of a number can be thought of as the distance that the point corresponding to that number lies from the origin. Thus, the absolute value of the numbers $+5$ and $-5$ are equal, since the points corresponding to each of these numbers are the same distance from the origin.

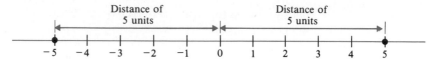

We say that each of these numbers has absolute value 5.

The absolute value of a real number is designated by enclosing the number between two vertical bars. That is,

$|x|$ is read *the absolute value of x.*

**EXAMPLE 2**  Find the absolute value of the following numbers: $-3$, $3$, $0$, $-1\frac{1}{2}$, $-\sqrt{2}$.

$$|-3| = 3$$
$$|3| = 3$$
$$|0| = 0$$
$$\left|-1\tfrac{1}{2}\right| = 1\tfrac{1}{2}$$
$$|-\sqrt{2}| = \sqrt{2}. \quad \square$$

Note that $-3 \neq +3$, but $|-3| = |+3|$.

It should be clear that *the absolute value of any real number is either a positive number or zero.* That is, $|x|$ is a *nonnegative* number.

## Problem Set 1.5

1. Graph each of the following real numbers on the number line.
   $\frac{3}{4}$, $0$, $3$, $-5$, $1.2$, $\sqrt{3}$, $-\sqrt{9}$, $-\frac{8}{3}$, $3.5$

2. Graph each of the following real numbers on the number line.
   $\frac{2}{3}$, $4$, $2\frac{1}{5}$, $-3$, $\sqrt{2}$, $-\sqrt{4}$, $\frac{7}{2}$, $10$, $4.5$

Find the absolute value of each of the following numbers.

3. 7
4. 8
5. −10
6. −3
7. 6.5
8. 10.2
9. −1$\frac{2}{3}$
10. −4$\frac{1}{3}$
11. −$\sqrt{3}$
12. −$\sqrt{5}$
13. +0
14. −0

Which number is larger?

15. −5 or 3
16. −7 or 2
17. |−5| or 3
18. |−7| or 2
19. |−5| or |3|
20. |−7| or |2|
21. |−$\sqrt{2}$| or |1|
22. |−$\sqrt{3}$| or |1|

Simplify each of the following.

23. |−7| + |7|
24. |−6| + |6|
25. |7| − |−7|
26. |6| − |−6|
27. |−2| + |−9|
28. |−3| + |−8|
29. $\frac{|-12|}{4}$
30. $\frac{|-10|}{5}$
31. |−3| − |−3|
32. |−2| − |−2|
33. −|10|
34. −|25|
35. −|−10|
36. −|−25|
37. $\frac{|-4| + |-8|}{|-2|}$
38. $\frac{|-6| + |-9|}{|-5|}$
39. |−8|$^2$
40. |−9|$^2$
41. $\frac{\sqrt{144} - |9|}{|5| - |-5|}$
42. $\frac{\sqrt{169} - |8|}{|6| - |-6|}$
43. $\frac{|7| - |7|}{\sqrt{121}}$
44. $\frac{|-8| - |8|}{-\sqrt{196}}$

Determine the distance on the number line between each pair of points whose coordinates are given below.

45. 7.1 and 4.6
46. −3.2 and −5.9
47. 8 and 19
48. 13 and −4

True or false.

49. Every natural number is a real number. T
50. Every natural number is an integer. F
51. There are irrational numbers which are not real numbers. F
52. Not every whole number is a natural number. T
53. Every integer is a positive number. F
54. Some whole numbers are not integers. F
55. Some rational numbers are negative. T
56. Not every irrational number is positive. T
57. The absolute value of a real number is always positive. F
58. To each rational number there corresponds a unique point on the number line. T
59. To each point on the number line there corresponds a unique rational number. F

60. There is a one-to-one correspondence between the points on the number line and the set of rational numbers.

## Calculator Problems

61. Calculate to two decimal places:
$$\frac{|11.796|^2 - |-23.271|}{\sqrt{13,891}}.$$

62. Determine the distance between 7.79148 and −9.61927 on the number line.

## Challenge Problems

63. True or false: $|x| = x$ for every real number $x$.
64. Using straightedge and compass, locate $\sqrt{2}$ on the number line. (*Hint:* Construct a right triangle whose legs are 1 unit each so that one leg coincides with the line segment from 0 to 1 on the number line.)

## Chapter Review

True or false.

1. 0 is a whole number.
2. 0 is a natural number.
3. $1\frac{1}{2}$ is an integer.
4. −17 is an integer.
5. −17 is a rational number.
6. $\sqrt{21}$ is a rational number.
7. $7.13\overline{13}$ is an irrational number.
8. $13.191191119 \cdots$ is an irrational number.

9. $\pi$ is a real number.
10. 0 is a prime number.
11. 1 is a prime number.
12. 77 is a composite number.
13. $\sqrt{5329} = 73$.
14. $(a + b)^2 = a^2 + b^2$.
15. $|-9|$ is larger than $|-8|$.
16. The value of a constant is fixed throughout a particular discussion.
17. The value of a variable is fixed throughout a particular discussion.
18. Division by zero is undefined.
19. Each real number is either a rational number or an irrational number, but not both.
20. There is a one-to-one correspondence between the real numbers and the points on a line.
21. Every integer is also a rational number.
22. Every terminating decimal is a rational number.
23. Every nonterminating repeating decimal is a rational number.
24. Every nonterminating nonrepeating decimal is an irrational number.

Completion.

25. Any number that can be written as a ratio of two integers where the divisor is not zero is a(n) _____?_____ number.

26. In the fraction $a/b$, $a$ is called the _____?_____ and $b$ is called the _____?_____ .

27. The statement $\dfrac{10}{27} = \dfrac{10 \cdot 8}{27 \cdot 8}$ illustrates what law? _____

28. The number 43 is a(n) _____? factor _____ of 559, and the number
    559 is a(n) _____ multiply? _____ of 43.

29. A natural number greater than 1 whose only natural number factors are 1 and itself is a(n) _____ prime? _____ number; otherwise, it
    is a(n) _____? composit _____ number.

30. The probability of getting exactly one head in three flips of a coin is $\frac{3}{8}$. Express this number in decimal form.

31. Express each number in decimal form.

   a) $-5\frac{2}{11}$          b) $\frac{10}{7}$

32. Write each decimal as a ratio of two integers in reduced form.

   a) 6.4          b) 0.023

33. Given that $0.\overline{1} = \frac{1}{9}$, write $0.\overline{5}$ as a ratio of two integers.

34. What is the value of $x$ number of dimes?

35. If $n$ is a whole number, what can be said about the number $2n + 1$?

36. Write $\frac{13}{5}$ as a mixed number.

37. Calculate the value of each expression.

   a) $\dfrac{|-3|^2 - |-3|}{|2|}$      b) $\dfrac{\sqrt{81} + \sqrt{4}}{33}$

38. Find the missing leg of the triangle.

39. A baseball diamond is actually a square 90 feet on each side. Find the distance of a throw from home plate to second base.

40. Graph $-\frac{10}{3}$ on a number line.

41. Express 420 as a product of primes.

42. Determine the gcf of {126, 630, 945}.

43. Determine the lcm of {16, 28, 36}.

44. Construct a pie diagram of $\frac{7}{3}$.

45. Completely reduce the fraction $\frac{420}{1008}$.

Perform the indicated operations and reduce your answer if possible.

46. $\frac{2}{3} + \frac{3}{10}$          47. $10 - 5\frac{2}{3}$          48. $3\frac{3}{7} \cdot \frac{5}{8}$

49. $\frac{1}{5} \div \frac{5}{9}$          50. $\frac{5}{12} + \frac{7}{8} - \frac{1}{45}$

51. How high is a stack of 12 sheets of plywood each $\frac{5}{8}$ of an inch thick?

52. A recipe for 16 cupcakes calls for $2\frac{2}{3}$ cups of sugar. How much sugar is needed to make a dozen cupcakes?

53. Determine the number that lies midway between $\frac{2}{3}$ and $\frac{3}{4}$.

# Chapter Two

## PROPERTIES OF REAL NUMBERS

## 2.1  COMMUTATIVE AND ASSOCIATIVE AXIOMS

Proven ⟨ Property
        ⟨ Law
Axiom : not
        Proven

In mathematics, as in any discipline, we must begin by making certain basic assumptions called **axioms.** On the basis of these axioms the body of mathematical knowledge is then expanded by proving other facts called **theorems.** Of course, in order to have a firm foundation on which to build these theorems, our axioms must seem as plausible as possible.

It may come as a shock that the study of something as precise as mathematics would begin with assumptions! But then how could anything at all be proved in mathematics if we had no basic assumptions from which to proceed?

As was mentioned previously, the axioms stated in this chapter will seem very plausible to the reader, almost to the point of being unnecessary even to state. These axioms, however, lie at the very heart of algebra. We shall rely heavily on them to establish rules for operations with signed numbers.

Before stating the first of these axioms, a point should be made about **grouping symbols.** Grouping symbols are often used when a combination of two or more operations appears in the same expression. For example, suppose the morning weatherman states that the temperature at 5 A.M. is 70° and that it will be rising at the rate of 2° per hour. If that is the case, what will the temperature be at noon?

The answer to this question can be obtained from the calculation

$$70 + (7 \cdot 2) = 70 + 14 = 84.$$

That is, the temperature at noon will be 84°. Note that parentheses were placed around the multiplication to indicate that it was to be done *before* the addition. However, if we *agree* that multiplication will always be done before addition whenever the two operations appear together, then we can write the calculation above more simply as

$$70 + 7 \cdot 2 = 70 + 14 = 84.$$

Of course in some situations it is *intended* that the addition be done first. To indicate this, we simply enclose the addition in grouping symbols. For example,

$$(8 + 2) \cdot 5 = 10 \cdot 5 = 50.$$

These ideas can now be summarized.

**Order of Operations**

First, perform all operations in grouping symbols.
Second, perform all multiplications and divisions from left to right.
Third, perform all additions and subtractions from left to right.

**EXAMPLE 1**   Compute $10 - 2 \cdot 4$.

$$10 - 2 \cdot 4 = 10 - 8$$
$$= 2. \quad \square$$

Note that the multiplication was performed before the subtraction.

**EXAMPLE 2**   Compute $14 \div 7 \cdot 2$.

Operating from left to right, we have

$$14 \div 7 \cdot 2 = 2 \cdot 2 = 4. \quad \square$$

Note that the answer to the example above is *not* $14 \div 14 = 1$.

**EXAMPLE 3**   Dava, who weighs 125 pounds, goes on a diet and loses 13 pounds. If she later gains 2 pounds, how much does she then weigh?

Operating from left to right, we have

$$125 - 13 + 2 = 112 + 2 = 114.$$

Dava weighs 114 pounds. $\square$

*If there is no operation symbol present, the operation is assumed to be multiplication.* That is,

$$3(5 + 2) \quad \text{means} \quad 3 \cdot (5 + 2),$$
$$2x \quad \text{means} \quad 2 \cdot x,$$

and

$$7[4 + 11(8 - 6)] \quad \text{means} \quad 7 \cdot [4 + 11 \cdot (8 - 6)].$$

*Whenever grouping symbols appear within grouping symbols, the operation in the innermost pair of grouping symbols is generally performed first.*

**EXAMPLE 4**   Compute $2(3[10 - 2(3 - 1)])$.

$$2(3[10 - 2(3 - 1)]) = 2(3[10 - 2 \cdot 2])$$
$$= 2(3[10 - 4])$$
$$= 2(3 \cdot 6)$$
$$= 2(18)$$
$$= 36. \quad \square$$

We are now ready to state the axioms for real numbers. In the statements of the axioms which follow, the letters $a$, $b$, $c$, and $d$ will represent *arbitrary* real numbers.

---

**Commutative Axiom for Addition**

$$a + b = b + a$$

**Commutative Axiom for Multiplication**

$$a \cdot b = b \cdot a$$

---

These axioms simply say that changing the *order* in which two numbers are added or multiplied will not affect the end result. For example, we observe that

$$3 + 5 = 5 + 3,$$

and

$$2 \cdot 7 = 7 \cdot 2.$$

**EXAMPLE 5**  $8 + 6 = 6 + 8$ illustrates what axiom?

Commutative axiom for addition.  $\square$

**EXAMPLE 6**  $2x = x \cdot 2$ illustrates what axiom?

Commutative axiom for multiplication.  $\square$

**EXAMPLE 7**  $4 \cdot (x + y) = (x + y) \cdot 4$ illustrates the commutative axiom for *multiplication*, since the order of multiplication is changed.
$\square$

**EXAMPLE 8**  $4 \cdot (x + y) = 4 \cdot (y + x)$ illustrates the commutative axiom for *addition*, since the order of addition is changed.  $\square$

**EXAMPLE 9**  Is division a commutative operation?

No! For example, $1 \div 2 \neq 2 \div 1$. ☐

**EXAMPLE 10**  Is the operation of putting on your shoes and putting on your socks a commutative operation?

No! Changing the order does affect the end result. ☐

**EXAMPLE 11**  Is the operation of putting on your left shoe and putting on your right shoe a commutative operation?

Yes! Changing the order does not affect the end result. ☐

The next pair of axioms state that changing the *grouping* of numbers in an addition problem or in a multiplication problem does not affect the end result.

---

**Associative Axiom for Addition**

$$a + (b + c) = (a + b) + c$$

**Associative Axiom for Multiplication**

$$a \cdot (b \cdot c) = (a \cdot b) \cdot c$$

---

**EXAMPLE 12**  $5 + (1 + 10) = (5 + 1) + 10$ illustrates the associative axiom for addition. ☐

**EXAMPLE 13**  $\frac{1}{2}(2x) = (\frac{1}{2} \cdot 2)x$ illustrates the associative axiom for multiplication. ☐

**EXAMPLE 14**  $s + (t + 8) = (t + 8) + s$ illustrates the *commutative* axiom for addition and *not* the associative axiom, since *order* of addition and *not* grouping is changed. ☐

**EXAMPLE 15**  Is subtraction an associative operation?

No! For example,

$$3 - (2 - 1) = 3 - 1 = 2,$$

but

$$(3 - 2) - 1 = 1 - 1 = 0. \; \square$$

**EXAMPLE 16**   Is the operation below an associative operation?

$$\text{paint} + \text{thinner} + \text{stirring}.$$

No!

$$(\text{paint} + \text{thinner}) + \text{stirring}$$

produces the desired result, while

$$\text{paint} + (\text{thinner} + \text{stirring})$$

does not. $\square$

The combination of the commutative axiom for addition and the associative axiom for addition allows a sum to be computed in a variety of ways. For example:

$$1 + 2 + 3 = 3 + 3 = 6,$$

or

$$1 + 2 + 3 = 1 + 5 = 6,$$

or

$$2 + 1 + 3 = 2 + 4 = 6,$$

or

$$3 + 2 + 1 = 5 + 1 = 6,$$

and so forth. The same can be said about computing products.

## Problem Set 2.1

Compute each of the following.

1. $6 + 7 \cdot 8$
2. $5 + 2 \cdot 3$
3. $(6 + 7) \cdot 8$
4. $(5 + 2) \cdot 3$
5. $\frac{1}{2}(\frac{7}{6} - \frac{4}{15})$
6. $\frac{1}{3}(\frac{2}{3} - \frac{5}{24})$
7. $\frac{1}{2} \cdot \frac{7}{6} - \frac{4}{15}$
8. $\frac{1}{3} \cdot \frac{2}{3} - \frac{5}{24}$
9. $16 \div 8 \cdot 2$
10. $12 \div 6 \cdot 2$
11. $16 \div (8 \cdot 2)$
12. $12 \div (6 \cdot 2)$
13. $18 - 5 + 3$
14. $19 - 8 + 3$
15. $18 - (5 + 3)$

16. $19 - (8 + 3)$
17. $3 + 12 \div 3 + 3$
18. $4 + 18 \div 2 + 4$
19. $3[8 - (5 + 3)]$
20. $2[6 - (4 + 2)]$
21. $4[20 - 5(3 - 1)]$
22. $3[15 - 4(4 - 2)]$
23. $4[(7 - 2) + (5 - 1)]$
24. $6[(5 - 3) + (8 - 4)]$
25. $3 + [7 + 3(2 + 5)]$
26. $7 + [4 + 2(2 + 4)]$
27. $2(2[10 - 2(4 - 2)])$
28. $3(2[12 - 4(8 - 6)])$
29. $5[(4 + 1) \cdot (3 + 7)]$
30. $6[(3 + 5) \cdot (6 + 4)]$
31. $62 \div [12 - 2(10 - 6)]$
32. $42 \div [16 - 3(18 - 14)]$
33. $92.07 - [5.2(8.6 + 4.8) - 3.5]$
34. $88.31 - [6.6(9.4 + 3.7) - 8.7]$

35. An airplane cruising at 28,100 feet loses 2500 feet of altitude and then gains 1000 feet. What is its final altitude?
36. A gambler begins with $75, triples it, and then loses $155. How much does the gambler then have?
37. Write an expression for

   a) the product of 5 and the sum of $x$ and 2.
   b) the sum of 5 times $x$ and 2.

38. Write an expression for the total value of $x$ shares of stock A at $33 per share and $y$ shares of stock B at $17\frac{3}{8}$ per share.

Name the axiom illustrated.

39. $17 + 6 = 6 + 17$
40. $0 + 9 = 9 + 0$
41. $8 \cdot 40 = 40 \cdot 8$
42. $33 \cdot 1 = 1 \cdot 33$
43. $8 + (3 + 7) = (8 + 3) + 7$
44. $2 + (5 + 15) = (2 + 5) + 15$
45. $2 \cdot (4 \cdot 5) = (2 \cdot 4) \cdot 5$
46. $x + y = y + x$
47. $\frac{1}{5}(5x) = (\frac{1}{5} \cdot 5)x$
48. $10x = x \cdot 10$
49. $t + s = s + t$
50. $\frac{1}{6}(6x) = (\frac{1}{6} \cdot 6)x$
51. $\frac{1}{3}x = x \cdot \frac{1}{3}$
52. $10 + (x + 1) = (10 + x) + 1$
53. $x + (y + z) = (x + y) + z$
54. $t(st) = (ts)t$
55. $3(x + 2) = 3(2 + x)$
56. $xy + 7 = 7 + xy$
57. $3(x + 2) = (x + 2)3$
58. $xy + 7 = yx + 7$
59. $3(x + 2) = (2 + x)3$
60. $xy + 7 = 7 + yx$
61. $r + (s + t) = (s + t) + r$
62. $(a + b) + c = (b + a) + c$

Find each sum in three different ways.

63. $3 + 5 + 2$
64. $4 + 5 + 1$
65. $10 + 4 + 12$
66. $5 + 13 + 7$

Find each product in three different ways.

67. $4 \cdot 6 \cdot \frac{1}{2}$
68. $6 \cdot 9 \cdot \frac{1}{3}$
69. $25 \cdot 6 \cdot 2$
70. $15 \cdot 7 \cdot 2$

71. Is subtraction a commutative operation? Give an example.
72. Is division an associative operation? Give an example.

## Calculator Problems

Compute each of the following to the nearest thousandth.

73. $17.689 + (14.701)(0.784)$
74. $34.165 + 621.104 - 309.747$
75. $264.1 \div 37.9 - 6.711$
76. $1.19(2.5[46 - 72.1(8 - 7.4)])$

## Challenge Problems

Suppose we define a new operation, denoted $*$, on the real numbers $a$ and $b$ as follows:

$$a * b = a \cdot b + a.$$

For example, $3 * 5 = 3 \cdot 5 + 3 = 15 + 3 = 18$.

77. Construct an example to show that $*$ is not a commutative operation.
78. Construct an example to show that $*$ is not an associative operation.

## 2.2 IDENTITY, INVERSE, AND EQUALITY AXIOMS

It is easily observed that when 0 is added to a given real number, the sum is that real number. For example, $6 + 0 = 6$, $3 + 0 = 3$, and $0 + 3 = 3$. The number 0 is called the **identity element for addition.** Also, if the number 1 is multiplied by a given real number, the product is that real number. For example, $1 \cdot 10 = 10$, $5 \cdot 1 = 5$, and $1 \cdot 5 = 5$. The number 1 is called the **identity element for multiplication.**

**Identity Axiom for Addition**

$$a + 0 = 0 + a = a$$

**Identity Axiom for Multiplication**

$$a \cdot 1 = 1 \cdot a = a$$

**EXAMPLE 1**  $7 + 0 = 7$ illustrates the identity axiom for addition.  □

**EXAMPLE 2**  $45 \cdot 1 = 45$ illustrates the identity axiom for multiplication.
 □

We might now ask whether there is a number which when *added* to 5 produces a sum of 0, the additive identity. Also, is there a number which when *multiplied* by 5 produces a product of 1, the multiplicative identity? The answer is yes to both questions.

---

**Inverse Axiom for Addition**

For each real number $a$ there is a *unique* real number called the **negative of $a$** (or **additive inverse of $a$**), written $-a$, such that

$$a + (-a) = (-a) + a = 0.$$

**Inverse Axiom for Multiplication**

For each real number $a$ (except zero) there is a *unique* real number called the **reciprocal of $a$** (or **multiplicative inverse of $a$**), written $1/a$, such that

$$a \cdot \frac{1}{a} = \frac{1}{a} \cdot a = 1.$$

---

**EXAMPLE 3**    5 is the negative of 5, and

$$(-5) + 5 = 5 + (-5) = 0. \quad □$$

**EXAMPLE 4**  $\frac{1}{5}$ is the reciprocal of 5, and

$$\frac{1}{5} \cdot 5 = 5 \cdot \frac{1}{5} = 1. \quad □$$

**EXAMPLE 5**  The reciprocal of $\frac{2}{3}$ is $1/\frac{2}{3}$, which can be written

$$\frac{1}{\frac{2}{3}} = 1 \div \frac{2}{3} = 1 \cdot \frac{3}{2} = \frac{3}{2},$$

and

$$\frac{2}{3} \cdot \frac{3}{2} = 1. \quad □$$

In general, if neither *a* nor *b* is zero, the reciprocal of *a/b* is *b/a* and the reciprocal of *b/a* is *a/b*. That is, *a/b and b/a are reciprocals of each other.*

**EXAMPLE 6**   Find the reciprocal of 0.

0 has no reciprocal since zero times any number is zero, not one.   □

According to the inverse axiom for addition, each real number has a negative. Therefore, since $-3$ is a real number *it* must have a negative, which would be written $-(-3)$. Now either we have created a *new* number, or $-(-3)$ is just a disguise for an old one.

Again by the inverse axiom for addition, the sum of a number and its negative must be 0. Therefore the sum of $-3$ and its negative, $-(-3)$, must equal 0. That is,

$$-(-3) + (-3) = 0.$$

But also

$$3 + (-3) = 0.$$

Comparing these last two statements, we see that

$$-(-3) = 3.$$

In other words, $-(-3)$ is really just another way of writing 3. That is, *the negative of a negative number is actually a positive number.* In general, if *a* is any real number, then

$$-(-a) = a.$$

**EXAMPLE 7**   Simplify $-(-[-(-5)])$.

Working from the inside out, we have

$$-(-[-(-5)]) = -(-[5])$$
$$= 5. \quad □$$

In order to solve an equation it will usually be necessary to add equal quantities to both sides of the equation and also to multiply both sides of the equation by equal quantities. As we shall see, this will be done in order to isolate the variable on one side of the equation. The following axioms state that such a maneuver can be accomplished without disturbing the balance of the equation.

---

**Addition Axiom for Equality**

If $a = b$, then $a + c = b + c$.

**Multiplication Axiom for Equality**

If $a = b$, then $a \cdot c = b \cdot c$.

---

**EXAMPLE 8**   Since $3 = 3$, then $3 + \frac{1}{2} = 3 + \frac{1}{2}$. $\square$

**EXAMPLE 9**   If $x = y$, then $x + 5 = y + 5$. $\square$

**EXAMPLE 10**   If $x = y$, then $5x = 5y$. $\square$

Let us now see how these axioms may be used to isolate a variable on one side of an equation.

**EXAMPLE 11**   Given $3x = 12$, isolate $x$.

In order to isolate $x$ we must remove the multiplier 3. This is done by multiplying both sides of the equation by the *reciprocal* of 3, namely $\frac{1}{3}$.

$$3x = 12$$
$$\frac{1}{3} \cdot 3x = \frac{1}{3} \cdot 12$$
$$1 \cdot x = 4$$
$$x = 4. \quad \square$$

**EXAMPLE 12**   Given $\frac{2}{5}x = 14$, isolate $x$.

We multiply both sides by the reciprocal of $\frac{2}{5}$, namely $\frac{5}{2}$.

$$\frac{2}{5}x = 14$$
$$\frac{5}{2} \cdot \frac{2}{5}x = \frac{5}{2} \cdot 14$$
$$1 \cdot x = 35$$
$$x = 35. \quad \square$$

**EXAMPLE 13**   Given $x + 7 = 7$, isolate $x$.

The 7 on the left-hand side is removed by *adding* to both sides the

*negative* of 7, namely −7.

$$x + 7 = 7$$
$$x + 7 + (-7) = 7 + (-7)$$
$$x + 0 = 0$$
$$x = 0. \quad \square$$

**EXAMPLE 14**    Given $(-18) + y = 5$, isolate $y$.

We add to both sides the negative of −18, namely 18.

$$(-18) + y = 5$$
$$18 + (-18) + y = 18 + 5$$
$$0 + y = 23$$
$$y = 23. \quad \square$$

## Problem Set 2.2

Name the axiom illustrated.

1. $14 + 0 = 14$
2. $0 + 10 = 10$
3. $5 + (-5) = 0$
4. $(-8) + 8 = 0$
5. $1 \cdot 9 = 9$
6. $2 \cdot 1 = 2$
7. $15 \cdot \frac{1}{15} = 1$
8. $\frac{1}{4} \cdot 4 = 1$
9. $(-x) + x = 0$
10. $b \cdot (1/b) = 1$
11. $0 + 0 = 0$
12. $0 + y = y$
13. $\frac{3}{4} \cdot \frac{4}{3} = 1$
14. $\frac{3}{2} \cdot \frac{2}{3} = 1$
15. $x \cdot 1 = x$
16. $1 \cdot y = y$
17. $(\frac{1}{3} \cdot 3)x = 1 \cdot x$
18. $(\frac{3}{2} \cdot \frac{2}{5})x = 1 \cdot x$
19. $x + [7 + (-7)] = x + 0$
20. $[18 + (-18)] + y = 0 + y$

State the negative of the given number.

21. $7$
22. $0$
23. $-4$
24. $5$
25. $-8\frac{1}{2}$
26. $-9\frac{1}{4}$
27. $-0$
28. $+0$
29. $12.5$
30. $10.2$
31. $-\sqrt{7}$
32. $-\sqrt{5}$
33. $-(-100)$
34. $-(-1000)$
35. $t$
36. $-t$

State the reciprocal of the given number.

37. $3$
38. $6$
39. $10$
40. $20$
41. $\frac{1}{5}$
42. $\frac{1}{4}$
43. $\frac{2}{3}$
44. $\frac{3}{4}$
45. $-4$
46. $-6$
47. $-1$
48. $1$
49. $2\frac{3}{4}$
50. $3\frac{1}{2}$
51. $a/b$
52. $-a/b$

*look up*

Simplify.

53. $-(-8)$  54. $-(-4)$  55. $-(-\frac{1}{5})$  56. $-(-\frac{2}{3})$
57. $-[-(-2)]$  58. $-(-[-(-10)])$  59. $-(-\sqrt{2})$  60. $-(-\sqrt{3})$
61. $-(-[-(-6.9)])$  62. $-[-(-7.1)]$
63. If $x$ is a negative integer, what kind of number is $-x$?
64. If $x$ is a negative integer, what kind of number is $(-x)$?

Use the addition axiom for equality to isolate $x$.

65. $x + 2 = 2$  66. $x + 5 = 5$  67. $x + (-3) = 1$
68. $x + (-10) = 10$  69. $(-5) + x = 3$  70. $(-7) + x = 4$
71. $(-8) + x = 8$  72. $(-6) + x = 6$  73. $x + 11 = 11$
74. $x + 13 = 13$  75. $x + (-1.7) = 4.9$  76. $x + (-2.8) = 5.7$

Use the multiplication axiom for equality to isolate $x$.

77. $5x = 10$  78. $2x = 6$  79. $4x = 12$
80. $3x = 21$  81. $\frac{1}{2}x = 4$  82. $\frac{1}{3}x = 1$
83. $4x = 15$  84. $3x = 10$  85. $\frac{2}{3}x = 8$
86. $\frac{3}{4}x = 9$  87. $10x = 0$  88. $20x = 0$
89. $0.05x = 1.2$  90. $0.14x = 3.5$

## Calculator Problems

91. Determine the reciprocal of each number.
    a) $0.0025$  b) $1949\frac{199}{727}$
92. Use the multiplication axiom for equality to isolate $x$ in the equation

$$155.4x = 0.18648.$$

## Challenge Problems

93. Isolate $x$ in each equation.
    a) $3x + (-2) = 5$  b) $\frac{1}{4}x - \frac{1}{6} = 3 - \frac{1}{3}$

94. If $x$ is a negative real number, then $|x| = $ ?
95. If $a * b = a \cdot b + a$ (see the discussion preceding Problem 77 in Problem Set 2.1), find $a * \dfrac{1}{a}$ if $a \neq 0$.

## 2.3   DISTRIBUTIVE AXIOM

Consider the rectangle below.

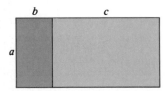

Since the area of the large rectangle is the sum of the areas of the two smaller ones, we can write

$$a \cdot (b + c) = a \cdot b + a \cdot c.$$

This property illustrates the **distributive axiom** and we shall find many uses for it throughout the rest of this text.

---

**Distributive Axiom**

$$a(b + c) = ab + ac$$

---

**EXAMPLE 1**   Compute $3(5 + 9)$ in two ways.

$$3(5 + 9) = 3 \cdot 14 = 42$$

or, using the distributive axiom,

$$3(5 + 9) = 3 \cdot 5 + 3 \cdot 9 = 15 + 27 = 42. \quad \square$$

Since multiplication is commutative, we note that the distributive axiom can also be written as

$$(b + c)a = ba + ca.$$

Moreover, multiplication can be distributed in this same fashion over any finite number of terms. That is,

$$a(b + c + d) = ab + ac + ad,$$
$$a(b + c + d + e) = ab + ac + ad + ae, \text{ and so on.}$$

The distributive axiom comes in handy when we must remove parentheses in situations where a variable is involved.

**EXAMPLE 2**   Remove parentheses from the expression $6(x + 4)$.

$$6(x + 4) = 6 \cdot x + 6 \cdot 4$$
$$= 6x + 24. \ \square$$

The distributive axiom also enables us to perform an operation known as **combining like terms.** Any collection of factors such as

$$5x^2, \quad 6ab, \quad \text{or} \quad -7y$$

is called a **term.** Thus the algebraic expression

$$10y^2 + xy + 4$$

contains the three terms $10y^2$, $xy$, and 4. Notice that *terms* are separated by addition, while *factors* are separated by multiplication. That is, the expression

$$a + b + c$$

contains the three terms $a$, $b$, and $c$; while the expression

$$abc$$

contains the three factors $a$, $b$, and $c$. **Like terms** are terms that have the same variable factor.

**EXAMPLE 3**   $5x$ and $3x$ are like terms since they have the same variable factor $x$. $\square$

**EXAMPLE 4**   $2x^2$ and $-17x^2$ are like terms since they have the same variable factor $x^2$. $\square$

**EXAMPLE 5**   $5x$ and $5y$ are *not* like terms. $\square$

**EXAMPLE 6**   $5x$ and 5 are *not* like terms. $\square$

**EXAMPLE 7**   8 and 13 are like terms. They have the same variable factor, namely none. $\square$

**EXAMPLE 8**   $6a^2b$ and $-4a^2b$ are like terms since they have the same variable factor $a^2b$. $\square$

**EXAMPLE 9**   Simplify $5x + 3x$.

We may combine these like terms by first using the distributive axiom (reading from right to left) to factor out the $x$, and then adding the numbers.

$$5x + 3x - (5 + 3) \cdot x$$
$$= 8x. \;\square$$

Usually we omit the middle step and simply write $5x + 3x = 8x$. Thus, $5x + 3x = 8x$ in the same sense that $5¢ + 3¢ = 8¢$, or that 5 apples + 3 apples = 8 apples. Note that we *cannot* combine *unlike* terms. That is, we cannot simplify the expression $5x + 3y$, since it can be taken in the same sense as 5 apples + 3 oranges, or as 5 horses + 3 cows.

In the term $5x$, the number 5 is called the **coefficient** of $x$. Similarly, 3 is the coefficient of $y$ in the term $3y$. Therefore, *like terms are added simply by adding their coefficients*. This sum is then the coefficient of the answer.

**EXAMPLE 10**   In the term $-4x^2$ the coefficient of $x^2$ is $-4$. $\square$

**EXAMPLE 11**   Combine the like terms $9y^2 + y^2$.

$$9y^2 + y^2 = 9 \cdot y^2 + 1 \cdot y^2$$
$$= (9 + 1) \cdot y^2$$
$$= 10 \cdot y^2$$
$$= 10y^2,$$

or simply

$$9y^2 + y^2 = 10y^2. \;\square$$

**EXAMPLE 12**   Forty-five couples plan to attend a formal dance. Each boy will purchase a bouquet for \$15.50, and each girl a carnation for \$2.50. Using two different methods, calculate the total cost of the 45 bouquets and 45 carnations.

**METHOD I**

$$45(15.50) + 45(2.50) = 697.50 + 112.50 = 810.$$

**METHOD II**

$$45(15.50) + 45(2.50) = 45(15.50 + 2.50) = 45(18) = 810.$$

The total cost is \$810. □

## Problem Set 2.3

Compute each of the following in two ways.

1. $3(1 + 2)$       2. $4(5 + 7)$       3. $6(2 + \frac{1}{3})$       4. $8(1 + \frac{1}{4})$
5. $6(17 + 8)$       6. $9(11 + 4)$       7. $13(5 + 5)$       8. $17(5 + 5)$
9. $12(\frac{1}{3} + \frac{1}{4})$       10. $15(\frac{1}{3} + \frac{1}{5})$       11. $30(\frac{17}{24} + \frac{14}{15})$       12. $24(\frac{7}{12} + \frac{11}{45})$

Use the distributive axiom to remove parentheses.

13. $3(x + 1)$       14. $5(x + 2)$       15. $6(2y + 4)$       16. $7(3y + 2)$
17. $5(z + \frac{1}{6})$       18. $6(z + \frac{1}{2})$       19. $12(\frac{1}{3}s + \frac{1}{4})$       20. $15(\frac{1}{3}s + \frac{1}{5})$
21. $20\left(\dfrac{t}{5} + \dfrac{2}{5}\right)$       22. $16\left(\dfrac{t}{4} + \dfrac{3}{4}\right)$       23. $12r(\frac{1}{3} + \frac{7}{24})$       24. $12r(\frac{1}{6} + \frac{7}{15})$

State the coefficient of each term.

25. $8x$       26. $4.3x$       27. $-4.3x$       28. $-8x$
29. $y$       30. $-y$       31. $-\sqrt{7}t^2$       32. $\sqrt{5}t^7$
33. $\frac{4}{5}xy^2$       34. $\frac{7}{3}s^2y$       35. $\pi s$       36. $0s$

Indicate whether each collection of terms should be classified as like terms or unlike terms.

37. $6x, 7x$       38. $14y, 8y$       39. $-3mn, 12mn$       40. $5nm, -nm$
41. $25x, -x^2$       42. $-20y, y^2$       43. $6, 7, -8$       44. $-13, 0, 1$
45. $\frac{1}{3}s, 89s, s$       46. $t, 39t, \frac{2}{5}t$       47. $-2xy^2, 3xy^2$       48. $11ab^2c, -ab^2c$
49. $4r, 4$       50. $8, 8w$       51. $5a^2b, -3ab^2$       52. $-4ab^2, 7a^2b$

Combine the like terms.

53. $7x + 2x$       54. $4x + 6x$       55. $8y + 11y$       56. $10y + 10y$
57. $4s + s$       58. $8s + s$       59. $3z + 4z + z$       60. $5z + 7z + z$
61. $1.2t + 7t + 1$       62. $1.3t + 6t + 1$       63. $10x + 10x + 10$       64. $5x + 5x + 5$
65. $89b^2 + 26b + 11b^2$       66. $47c^2 + 98c + 63c^2$       67. $\frac{3}{4}s + \frac{17}{10}s$       68. $\frac{7}{6}r + \frac{5}{9}r$

69. Suppose that a reserved seat ticket to the opera costs $15.75 and a general admission ticket costs $8.50. Using two different methods, calculate the total cost of 37 tickets of each kind.
70. A rectangle has width 5.3 cm and length 7.8 cm. Using two different methods, calculate the perimeter of the rectangle.

71. The area of a trapezoid with bases of lengths $b_1$ and $b_2$ and height $h$ is $\frac{1}{2}h(b_1 + b_2)$.* Write this expression without parentheses.
72. The amount that a principal of $P$ dollars will amount to if invested for $t$ years at a simple interest rate of $r$ is $P(1 + rt)$. Write this expression without parentheses.

## Calculator Problems

73. Compute each of the following in two ways.
    a) $1.17(19.72 + 413.57)$    b) $496(17.012 + 19.763)$
74. Use the distributive axiom to remove parentheses.
    a) $89.8(0.15x + 6.6)$    b) $0.079(536,000y + 8899)$
75. Combine the like terms.
    a) $7196.8x + 337.5x$    b) $0.0173y + 1.9984y$

## Challenge Problems

76. Use the distributive axiom to find the product $(x + y) \cdot (b + c)$.
77. If $a * b = a \cdot b + a$ (see the discussion preceding Problem 77 in Problem Set 2.1), find $5 * (3 + 4)$ and $5 * 3 + 5 * 4$. Does $5 * (3 + 4) = 5 * 3 + 5 * 4$?

---

* We differentiate between the two bases of the trapezoid by writing $b_1$ and $b_2$ read *b subscript one* and *b subscript two*, respectively. For brevity, $b_1$ and $b_2$ are often read *b sub one* (or simply *b one*) and *b sub two* (or *b two*), respectively.

## 2.4    OPERATIONS WITH SIGNED NUMBERS

### ADDITION

Suppose that on a particular football play 4 yards are gained. If on the next play 3 additional yards are gained, the total yardage for the two plays is 7 yards.

On a number line these computations can be visualized using arrows. Arrows pointed to the *right* will indicate *positive* numbers, while arrows pointed to the *left* will indicate *negative* numbers.

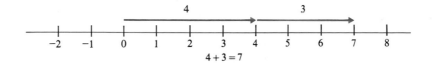

A gain of 4 yards followed by a *loss* of 3 is the same as a gain of 1 yard.

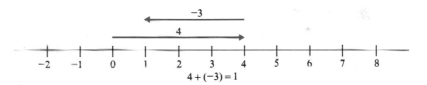

If a gain of 4 yards is followed by a loss of 6 yards, the total yardage is −2 yards.

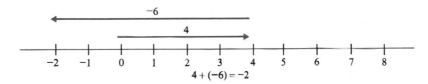

Finally, if a loss of 3 yards is followed by a loss of 5 yards, the total yardage is −8 yards.

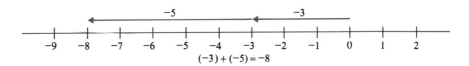

Note that when two positive numbers are added, the sum is positive, and when two negative numbers are added, the sum is negative. When two numbers of different sign are added, the sum may be positive or negative, depending upon which of the two numbers is larger in absolute value.

$$
\begin{array}{rrrr}
+4 & -3 & +4 & +4 \\
+3 & -5 & -3 & -6 \\
\hline
\text{SUM} \rightarrow \quad +7 & -8 & +1 & -2
\end{array}
$$

---

### Rule for Adding Signed Numbers

To add two numbers having

like signs: Add the absolute values of the numbers and then prefix the common sign.

unlike signs: Subtract the smaller absolute value from the larger absolute value and prefix the sign of the number having the larger absolute value.

---

**EXAMPLE 1**   Find the sum $(-7) + (-10)$.

Since these numbers have *like* signs, we first find the sum of their absolute values.

$$|-7| + |-10| = 7 + 10 = 17.$$

Then we prefix their common sign.

$$(-7) + (-10) = -17. \ \square$$

**EXAMPLE 2**   Find the sum $2 + (-9)$.

Since these numbers have *unlike* signs, we first subtract the smaller absolute value from the larger absolute value.

$$|-9| - |2| = 9 - 2 = 7.$$

Then we prefix a *negative* sign to the answer since $-9$ has the larger absolute value.

$$2 + (-9) = -7. \ \square$$

**EXAMPLE 3**   Find the sum $8 + (-3)$.

Find the difference of the absolute values.

$$|8| - |-3| = 8 - 3 = 5.$$

Prefix a *positive* sign to the answer since 8 has the larger absolute value.

$$8 + (-3) = +5. \quad \square$$

The examples above were intended to illustrate the mechanics of adding signed numbers. In actual practice, the operations involving absolute values should not be written. Rather, they should be performed mentally. Thus, for this last example we would simply write

$$8 + (-3) = 5.$$

**EXAMPLE 4**   The temperature at 7 A.M. is $-10$ degrees. If it rises at the rate of 4 degrees per hour, what will the temperature be at noon?

Since there are 5 hours between 7 A.M. and noon, we write

$$-10 + 5 \cdot 4 = -10 + 20 = 10.$$

The temperature at noon will be 10 degrees. $\square$

**EXAMPLE 5**   The Dow Jones Industrial Average posted the following results during one particular week: up 7.68 on Monday, up 4.13 on Tuesday, down 6.24 on Wednesday, up 1.87 on Thursday, down 9.05 on Friday. What was the net change in the Dow from Monday's opening to Friday's closing?

$$7.68 + 4.13 + (-6.24) + 1.87 + (-9.05)$$
$$= [7.68 + 4.13 + 1.87] + [(-6.24) + (-9.05)]$$
$$= 13.68 + (-15.29)$$
$$= -1.61.$$

The Dow was down 1.61 points. $\square$

Notice that when adding several numbers, some of which are positive and some of which are negative, it is often helpful to collect all of the positive numbers in one group and all of the negative numbers in another. This procedure generally produces the simplest calculation.

## Problem Set 2.4A

Draw a number line diagram of each of the following.

| | | |
|---|---|---|
| 1. $2 + 3$ | 2. $3 + 4$ | 3. $(-5) + (-2)$ |
| 4. $(-1) + (-4)$ | 5. $8 + (-5)$ | 6. $7 + (-3)$ |
| 7. $(-4) + (-6)$ | 8. $(-2) + (-3)$ | 9. $(-11) + 4$ |
| 10. $(-9) + 5$ | 11. $4 + (-6) + 8$ | 12. $3 + (-5) + 7$ |
| 13. $1 + 5 + (-3)$ | 14. $4 + 5 + (-2)$ | |

Find the sum without the aid of a number line.

| | |
|---|---|
| 15. $(-8) + (-6)$ | 16. $(-5) + (-7)$ |
| 17. $(-4) + 7$ | 18. $(-23) + 10$ |
| 19. $19 + (-6)$ | 20. $18 + (-4)$ |
| 21. $6 + (-9)$ | 22. $5 + (-17)$ |
| 23. $(-11) + (-9)$ | 24. $(-12) + (-8)$ |
| 25. $(+5) + (+7)$ | 26. $(+6) + (+9)$ |
| 27. $(+5) + 0$ | 28. $(+6) + 0$ |
| 29. $0 + (-5)$ | 30. $0 + (-6)$ |
| 31. $8 + (-8) + 25$ | 32. $4 + (-4) + 10$ |
| 33. $-(-9) + (-6)$ | 34. $-(-7) + (-5)$ |
| 35. $(-14) + 9$ | 36. $(-17) + 8$ |
| 37. $18 + (-3) + (-3)$ | 38. $19 + (-5) + (-5)$ |
| 39. $-(-\frac{2}{7}) + (-\frac{3}{7})$ | 40. $-(-\frac{1}{5}) + (-\frac{3}{5})$ |
| 41. $\frac{1}{5} + (-\frac{3}{4})$ | 42. $(-\frac{2}{3}) + \frac{1}{4}$ |
| 43. $(-4.1) + 3.6$ | 44. $2.3 + (-0.7)$ |
| 45. $(-9.2) + (5.7) + (-3.3)$ | 46. $(-8.5) + (6.6) + (-3.7)$ |
| 47. $(-4) + 7 + [-(-10)]$ | 48. $14 + (-30) + [-(-16)]$ |
| 49. $-(-10) + (-12) + 20$ | 50. $15 + [-(-5)] + (-11)$ |

51. Ken bet on all nine horse races at a nearby track with the following results: won $16.20, won $18.60, lost $14, lost $2, lost $6, lost $10, won $12.60, lost $2, lost $4. What were his net earnings for the day?

52. Sharon played nine holes of golf with the following results: $+2$, par, $+1$, $-1$, $-3$, $-2$, par, $-1$, $+3$. What was her score for the nine holes in relation to par?

53. A party of spelunkers (cave explorers) begins its ascent from the bottom of a cave at an elevation of $-457$ feet. They ascend 110 feet, descend 68 feet, and then ascend 95 feet. What is their elevation at that point?

54. A used car dealer sold three cars in one week, one for a profit of $343.80, one for a loss of $132.50, and one for a loss of $155.60. Determine the dealer's net profit for the week.
55. The temperature at 7 A.M. is $-3$ degrees. If it rises at the rate of 2 degrees per hour, what will the temperature be at noon?
56. The temperature at 8 A.M. is $-2$ degrees. If it rises at the rate of 3 degrees per hour, what will the temperature be at noon?
57. During the course of a football game a halfback carried the ball 7 times with the following results: loss 2 yd, gain 6 yd, gain 4 yd, gain 13 yd, loss 1 yd, gain 4 yd, loss 3 yd. Find his total yardage and average gain per carry.
58. In a certain city, the following temperatures were recorded at 7 A.M. each day of the first week in January: Monday 5°, Tuesday 3°, Wednesday 1°, Thursday 0°, Friday $-4$°, Saturday $-2$°, Sunday 4°. Find the average temperature at 7 A.M. for the week.
59. Given the information below,

| Teacher's age $T$ | Student's age $S$ |
|---|---|
| 30 | 12 |
| 31 | 13 |
| 32 | 14 |
| 33 | 15 |

   write a formula relating $T$ and $S$.
60. Using the formula from Problem 59, find

   a) the teacher's age when the student is 20 years old.
   b) the teacher's age when the student was 5 years old.
   c) the teacher's age when the student was born.
   d) the teacher's age 5 years before the student was born.

## Calculator Problems

61. The progress of the Dow Jones Industrial Average was charted over a three-week period with the following results: up 3.67, up 4.19, down 1.12, down 1.91, up 2.78, up 6.43, up 0.92, down 0.37, up 6.79, up 7.88, up 3.64, down 2.72, up 3.99, up 1.06, down 8.23.

What was the net change in the Dow from the beginning to the end of the three-week period?

62. Compute the sum $(-50) + (-49) + (-48) + \cdots + (-2) + (-1)$.

## Challenge Problems

63. Show it is false that $|a + b| = |a| + |b|$ for *all* real numbers $a$ and $b$. Under what conditions *does* $|a + b| = |a| + |b|$?
64. Find a pattern that enables the sum of Problem 62 to be found by computing a single product.

### SUBTRACTION

We are already familiar with subtraction problems such as $7 - 3$, where the first number is larger than the second. The difference $7 - 3$ equals 4, since 4 is the number which added to 3 gives 7.

$$7 - 3 = 4, \text{ since } 4 + 3 = 7.$$

Let us now consider the problem of subtracting 5 from 2. Here we are looking for the number which when added to 5 gives 2.

$$2 - 5 = -3, \text{ since } (-3) + 5 = 2.$$

**EXAMPLE 1**   Find the difference $(-4) - 2$.

$$(-4) - 2 = -6, \text{ since } (-6) + 2 = -4. \quad \square$$

**EXAMPLE 2**   Find the difference $(-5) - (-1)$.

$$(-5) - (-1) = -4, \text{ since } (-4) + (-1) = -5. \quad \square$$

We shall now look for a general rule that describes the subtraction process. Consider the problem of subtracting the number $b$ from the number $a$. That is, consider the difference $a - b$. We note that the answer, when added to $b$, must produce $a$. It turns out that the desired answer is the sum of $a$ and the negative of $b$, that is $a + (-b)$. Checking this answer by adding it to $b$ gives

$$a + (-b) + b = a + 0 = a.$$

Therefore our **rule for subtraction** is

$$a - b = a + (-b).$$

In other words, *subtracting b* from *a* is the same as *adding* the *negative* of *b* to *a*.

**EXAMPLE 3** Find the difference $5 - 3$.

$$5 - 3 = 5 + (-3) = 2. \quad \square$$

**EXAMPLE 4** Find the difference $3 - 5$.

$$3 - 5 = 3 + (-5) = -2. \quad \square$$

**EXAMPLE 5** Find the difference $(-10) - 4$.

$$(-10) - 4 = (-10) + (-4) = -14. \quad \square$$

**EXAMPLE 6** Find the difference $(-9) - (-7)$.

$$(-9) - (-7) = (-9) + [-(-7)] = (-9) + 7 = -2. \quad \square$$

**EXAMPLE 7** Find the difference $8 - (-4)$.

$$8 - (-4) = 8 + 4 = 12. \quad \square$$

With a little practice, it should not be difficult to distinguish between the symbols that are negative signs and those that stand for the operation of subtraction.

---

**Rule for Subtracting Signed Numbers**

To subtract the number *b* from the number *a*, change the sign of *b* and then proceed as in addition.

---

**EXAMPLE 8** Determine the 1984 age of an urn that was made in 157 B.C.

Subtracting the year the urn was made from the year 1984, we have

$$1984 - (-157) = 1984 + 157 = 2141.$$

The 1984 age of the urn is 2141 years. $\square$

## Problem Set 2.4B

Find the difference.

1. $6 - 2$
2. $7 - 3$
3. $3 - 7$
4. $2 - 6$
5. $(-5) - 4$
6. $(-4) - 6$
7. $(-1) - (-8)$
8. $(-5) - (-2)$
9. $4 - 8$
10. $6 - 12$
11. $10 - 15$
12. $15 - 20$
13. $8 - 2$
14. $9 - 3$
15. $(-5) - 5$
16. $(-10) - 10$
17. $(-6) - 3$
18. $(-5) - 6$
19. $7 - (-2)$
20. $8 - (-5)$
21. $(-1) - (-4)$
22. $(-3) - (-2)$
23. $(-12) - (-10)$
24. $0 - 9$
25. $0 - (-8)$
26. $(-1) - 5$
27. $9 - (-3)$
28. $8 - (-4)$
29. $0 - 15$
30. $0 - (-10)$
31. $(-11) - 4$
32. $(-9) - 6$
33. $(-10) - (-4)$
34. $(-13) - (-5)$
35. $-8 - (-18)$
36. $-7 - (-17)$
37. $(4 - 6) + 14$
38. $(5 - 7) + 15$
39. $3 - (10 - 1)$
40. $2 - (8 - 1)$
41. $\frac{1}{3} - \frac{1}{2}$
42. $\frac{1}{4} - \frac{1}{3}$
43. $6.7 - 7.54$
44. $-8.1 - 4.3$
45. $-5.7 - 3.1$
46. $4.99 - 8.3$
47. $1\frac{2}{7} - 4$
48. $1\frac{3}{5} - 6$
49. $-1.9 - (-2.3)$
50. $-2.4 - 5.1$

51. What number is 13 less than 5?
52. How much greater is 16 than $-7$?
53. If the temperature was $-28°$ and then it fell $14°$, what is it now?
54. Sally's checking account is already overdrawn $37, and she writes another check for $56. What will her balance be if the check clears?
55. If Pikes Peak is 14,110 feet above sea level and Death Valley is 280 feet below sea level, find the difference in altitude by subtracting the lower altitude from the higher.

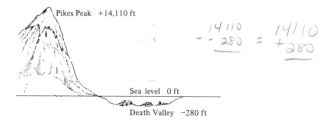

56. The temperature at 4 P.M. is $6°$. If it falls at the rate of $7°$ per hour, what will the temperature be at 9 P.M.?
57. An experiment was observed and the following data recorded:

| After $h$ hours | Temperature $T$ was |
| --- | --- |
| 0 | 10 |
| 1 | 8 |
| 2 | 6 |
| 3 | 4 |

Write a formula relating $T$ and $h$.

58. Using the formula from Problem 57, find
    a) the temperature after 5 hours.
    b) the temperature after 6 hours.
    c) the temperature after 10 hours.

## Calculator Problems

59. Compute.
    a) $34.165 - 621.104 - 309.747$
    b) $57.14 + (-4.54) - (16.85 - 25.16)$
60. Determine $\sqrt{2.5} - \sqrt{3.4}$ to four decimal places.

## Challenge Problems

61. Determine the *exact* value of $|2 - \pi|$.
62. Use the addition axiom for equality to prove that if $a = b$, then
    $a - 8 = b - 8$.
63. True or false: $|a - b| = |b - a|$ for all real numbers $a$ and $b$.

### MULTIPLICATION

We are already familiar with the problem of finding the product of two *positive* numbers. Now suppose we wanted to find the product of 5 and $-3$. One way to look at this problem is in terms of repeated addition. That is, since

$$5 \cdot 3 = 3 + 3 + 3 + 3 + 3$$
$$= 15,$$

then it should also be true that

$$5 \cdot (-3) = (-3) + (-3) + (-3) + (-3) + (-3)$$
$$= -15.$$

Also,

$$(-5) \cdot 3 = (-5) + (-5) + (-5)$$
$$= -15.$$

We conclude that *the product of a positive number and a negative number is a negative number.* A formal proof that $5 \cdot (-3) = -15$ lies below.

| Statement | Reason |
|---|---|
| $3 + (-3) = 0$ | Inverse axiom for addition. |
| $5 \cdot [3 + (-3)] = 5 \cdot 0$ | Multiplication axiom for equality. |
| $5 \cdot 3 + 5 \cdot (-3) = 0$ | Distributive axiom and fact that $5 \cdot 0 = 0$. |
| $15 + 5 \cdot (-3) = 0$ | Fact that $5 \cdot 3 = 15$. |

But also

| | |
|---|---|
| $15 + (-15) = 0$ | Inverse axiom for addition. |

Comparing these last two statements, we see that $5 \cdot (-3) = -15$.

Let us now turn our attention to finding the product of two *negative* numbers. Consider the following products.

$$(+3) \cdot (-3) = -9 \qquad 0 \cdot (-3) = 0$$
$$(+2) \cdot (-3) = -6 \qquad (-1) \cdot (-3) = ?$$
$$(+1) \cdot (-3) = -3 \qquad (-2) \cdot (-3) = ?$$

According to the pattern which has been established, it appears that

$$(-1) \cdot (-3) = +3$$

and that

$$(-2) \cdot (-3) = +6.$$

We shall now prove this last statement, that is that $(-2) \cdot (-3) = 6$.

| Statement | Reason |
|---|---|
| $3 + (-3) = 0$ | Inverse axiom for addition. |
| $(-2) \cdot [3 + (-3)] = (-2) \cdot 0$ | Multiplication axiom for equality. |
| $(-2) \cdot 3 + (-2) \cdot (-3) = 0$ | Distributive axiom and fact that $(-2) \cdot 0 = 0$. |
| $(-6) + (-2) \cdot (-3) = 0$ | Fact that $(-2) \cdot 3 = -6$. |

But also

| | |
|---|---|
| $(-6) + 6 = 0$ | Inverse axiom for addition. |

Comparing these last two statements we see that

$$(-2) \cdot (-3) = 6.$$

It is interesting to note that while the axioms stated at the beginning of this chapter seemed intuitively obvious, they can be used to prove a statement that is not, namely that *the product of two negative numbers is a positive number.*

---

**Rule for Multiplying Signed Numbers**

To find the product of two numbers, multiply their absolute values. If the numbers have like signs, the product is positive; if they have unlike signs, the product is negative.

---

The example that follows will help to further illustrate the multiplication of signed numbers. Let us agree that if someone handles money, a gain will be represented by a positive number and a loss by a negative number. Also, time in the future will be represented by a positive number and time in the past by a negative number. Signed numbers can now be used to calculate the increase or decrease in the person's wealth.

If a man gains five dollars a day, then three days in the future he will be fifteen dollars richer.

$$(+5)(+3) = 15$$

If he loses five dollars a day, then three days in the future he will be fifteen dollars poorer.

$$(-5)(+3) = -15.$$

If he gains five dollars a day, then three days ago he was fifteen dollars poorer.

$$(+5)(-3) = -15.$$

Finally, if he loses five dollars a day, then three days ago he was fifteen dollars richer.

$$(-5)(-3) = 15.$$

**EXAMPLE 1**    Simplify $6 + 4[2(-7 + 5) - 1]$.

Using the order of operations and the rules for operating with signed numbers, we have

$$6 + 4[2(-7 + 5) - 1] = 6 + 4[2(-2) - 1]$$
$$= 6 + 4[-4 - 1]$$
$$= 6 + 4[-5]$$
$$= 6 + (-20)$$
$$= -14. \ \square$$

**EXAMPLE 2**   A retailer sells two items at a loss of $27 per item, three items at a loss of $13 per item, and seven items at a profit of $32 per item. Determine the net profit on the 12 sales.

We set up our work as follows:

$$2(-27) + 3(-13) + 7(32) = (-54) + (-39) + 224$$
$$= 131.$$

The net profit is $131.  $\square$

## Problem Set 2.4C

Find the following products and observe the pattern.

| | | | |
|---|---|---|---|
| 1. $(+3) \cdot (+5) =$ | 2. $(+3) \cdot 10 =$ | 3. $(+3) \cdot (-1) =$ | 4. $(+3) \cdot (-2) =$ |
| $(+2) \cdot (+5) =$ | $(+2) \cdot 10 =$ | $(+2) \cdot (-1) =$ | $(+2) \cdot (-2) =$ |
| $(+1) \cdot (+5) =$ | $(+1) \cdot 10 =$ | $(+1) \cdot (-1) =$ | $(+1) \cdot (-2) =$ |
| $0 \cdot (+5) =$ | $0 \cdot 10 =$ | $0 \cdot (-1) =$ | $0 \cdot (-2) =$ |
| $(-1) \cdot (+5) =$ | $(-1) \cdot 10 =$ | $(-1) \cdot (-1) =$ | $(-1) \cdot (-2) =$ |
| $(-2) \cdot (+5) =$ | $(-2) \cdot 10 =$ | $(-2) \cdot (-1) =$ | $(-2) \cdot (-2) =$ |
| $(-3) \cdot (+5) =$ | $(-3) \cdot 10 =$ | $(-3) \cdot (-1) =$ | $(-3) \cdot (-2) =$ |

Find the product.

| | | |
|---|---|---|
| 5. $5(-4)$ | 6. $(-10)3$ | 7. $(-6)(-5)$ |
| 8. $(-4)(-8)$ | 9. $(-3)(4)$ | 10. $(-3)(5)$ |
| 11. $(-3)(-4)$ | 12. $(-3)(-5)$ | 13. $4 \cdot 2 \cdot (-11)$ |
| 14. $5 \cdot 2 \cdot (-12)$ | 15. $(-9) \cdot 0$ | 16. $(-8) \cdot 0$ |
| 17. $(-6)(-1)2$ | 18. $(-5)(-1)4$ | 19. $(-1)(-2)(-4)$ |
| 20. $(-1)(-3)(-5)$ | 21. $(15)(-17)$ | 22. $(13)(-19)$ |
| 23. $(-21)(-33)$ | 24. $(-23)(-35)$ | 25. $\frac{1}{2}(-\frac{1}{3})$ |

26. $(-\frac{2}{7})(\frac{3}{2})$
27. $5(-\frac{1}{5})$
28. $(-7)(-\frac{1}{7})$
29. $(-2.5)(-2.5)$
30. $(-1.1)(-1.1)$
31. $6(-\frac{2}{3})4$
32. $8(-\frac{3}{4})2$
33. $(-2)(-2)(-2)$
34. $(-3)(-3)(-3)$
35. $(-4)^2$
36. $(-6)^2$
37. $(-\frac{1}{3})^2$
38. $(-\frac{2}{5})^2$
39. $(-1)(-1)(-1)(-1)$
40. $(-1)(-1)(-1)(-1)(-1)$
41. $13.9(-6.7)$
42. $15.3(-4.8)$
43. $(-31.4)(-85.29)$
44. $(-93.6)(-24.72)$

Compute.

45. $4 + 3[2(-5) + 1]$
46. $6 + 2[3(-4) + 1]$
47. $2(3[4 - 5 \cdot 2])$
48. $3(4[6 - 7 \cdot 2])$
49. $8[6 - 2(-4)]$
50. $7[3 - 5(-5)]$
51. $(-3)[10(-2) - 40]$
52. $(-2)[10(-3) - 50]$
53. $2 - [4(-5 + 3) - 2]$
54. $5 - [6(-8 + 7) - 3]$

55. The Dow Jones Industrial Average declines 2.85 points on each of three consecutive days of trading. What is the total change in the Dow for the three-day period?

56. A golfer shoots two strokes under par each day of a four day tournament. How did the golfer stand in relation to par at the end of the tournament?

57. A football team ran eight plays with the following results: two 4-yard gains, two 5-yard losses, one 22-yard gain, three 8-yard losses. What was the total yardage for the eight plays?

58. Alice plays a 50¢ slot machine 23 times. She wins a $5 jackpot twice and a $1 jackpot three times. Find her net profit.

59. Given that $F = \frac{9}{5}C + 32$, determine the Fahrenheit temperature, F, that corresponds to a Celsius temperature of $-15°C$.

60. Given that $C = \frac{5}{9}(F - 32)$, determine the Celsius temperature, C, that corresponds to a Fahrenheit temperature of $-4°F$.

61. An experiment was observed and the following data recorded:

| After $h$ hours | Temperature $T$ was |
| --- | --- |
| 0 | 10 |
| 1 | 14 |
| 2 | 18 |
| 3 | 22 |

Write a formula relating $T$ and $h$. Using this formula, find

a) the temperature after 12 hours.
b) the temperature 2 hours before the observation began.
c) the temperature 3 hours before the observation began.

62. An experiment was observed and the following data recorded:

| After $h$ hours | Temperature $T$ was |
|:---:|:---:|
| 0 | 10 |
| 1 | 13 |
| 2 | 16 |
| 3 | 19 |

Write a formula relating $T$ and $h$. Using this formula, find
a) the temperature after 10 hours.
b) the temperature 2 hours before the observation began.
c) the temperature 4 hours before the observation began.

## Calculator Problems

63. Compute.
    a) $3.4[7.01 + 60(6.8 - 7.001)]$
    b) $3.44(0.5[6.13 - 4(4.7 - 8.11)])$

64. A retailer sells 23 items at a loss of $2.73 per item, 19 items at a loss of $1.37 per item, 64 items at a profit of $13.49 per item, and 18 items at a profit of $28.62 per item. Determine the net profit on the 124 sales.

## Challenge Problems

65. True or false: $|ab| = |a| \, |b|$ for all real numbers $a$ and $b$.
66. Supply the reason for each step in the proof below.

| Statement | Reason |
|:---:|:---:|
| $(-b) + b = 0$ | ? |
| $a \cdot [(-b) + b] = a \cdot 0$ | ? |
| $a \cdot (-b) + a \cdot b = 0$ | ? |

But also

$$-(ab) + ab = 0 \qquad \underline{\qquad ? \qquad}$$

Comparing these last two statements, we see that $a \cdot (-b) = -(ab)$.

### DIVISION

The rules that were just developed for *multiplying* signed numbers can now be used to formulate rules for *dividing* signed numbers.

**EXAMPLE 1**   Find the quotient $(-6) \div (-2)$.

$$(-6) \div (-2) = 3 \quad \text{since} \quad 3 \cdot (-2) = -6. \quad \square$$

**EXAMPLE 2**   Find the quotient $-6/2$.

$$\frac{-6}{2} = -3 \quad \text{since} \quad (-3) \cdot 2 = -6. \quad \square$$

**EXAMPLE 3**   Find the quotient $6/-2$.

$$\frac{6}{-2} = -3 \quad \text{since} \quad (-3) \cdot (-2) = 6. \quad \square$$

---

**Rule for Dividing Signed Numbers**

To find the quotient of two numbers, find the quotient of their absolute values. If the numbers have like signs, the quotient is positive; if they have unlike signs, the quotient is negative.

---

**EXAMPLE 4**   Eight people formed an investment club in which the profits and losses were shared equally. Determine each member's share of a total club loss of $2993.20.

Since

$$(-2993.20) \div 8 = -374.15,$$

each member lost $374.15. $\square$

**EXAMPLE 5**   Compute $\left[ \dfrac{4(-7) + 5(-1)}{-2 - 1} \right]\left[ \dfrac{8 + (-14)}{6 - 9} \right]$.

The fraction bar is considered a grouping symbol. Therefore operations within numerators and within denominators should be performed before the division operation.

$$\left[ \frac{4(-7) + 5(-1)}{-2 - 1} \right]\left[ \frac{8 + (-14)}{6 - 9} \right] = \left[ \frac{-28 + (-5)}{-3} \right]\left[ \frac{-6}{-3} \right]$$

$$= \left[ \frac{-33}{-3} \right]\cdot 2$$

$$= 11 \cdot 2$$

$$= 22. \ \square$$

Very often we shall want to *reposition* the sign that occurs in front of a fraction. From Example 2 and Example 3 above we see that both

$$\frac{-6}{2} \quad \text{and} \quad \frac{6}{-2}$$

have a value of $-3$. The fraction $-\frac{6}{2}$ also has the value $-3$. Since these three fractions all have the same value, we can write

$$-\frac{6}{2} = \frac{-6}{2} = \frac{6}{-2}.$$

More generally,

$$-\frac{a}{b} = \frac{-a}{b} = \frac{a}{-b}, \quad \text{if } b \neq 0.$$

**EXAMPLE 6**   By repositioning the negative sign, express $-3/4$ in two other forms.

$$\frac{-3}{4} = -\frac{3}{4} = \frac{3}{-4}. \ \square$$

It should be pointed out that both of the forms $-\dfrac{a}{b}$ and $\dfrac{-a}{b}$ are generally preferred over the form $\dfrac{a}{-b}$.

**EXAMPLE 7**   Simplify $-\dfrac{-7}{9}$.

$$-\frac{-7}{9} = \frac{-(-7)}{9} = \frac{7}{9}. \ \square$$

**EXAMPLE 8**   Simplify $-\dfrac{10}{5}$ and $\dfrac{-10}{-5}$.

$$-\frac{10}{5} = -2, \text{ but } \frac{-10}{-5} = +2. \quad \square$$

Note that $-\dfrac{a}{b}$ is *not* equal to $\dfrac{-a}{-b}$ (unless $a = 0$).

## Problem Set 2.4D

Find the following quotients and observe the pattern.

1. $(+3) \div (+1) =$
$(+2) \div (+1) =$
$(+1) \div (+1) =$
$0 \div (+1) =$
$(-1) \div (+1) =$
$(-2) \div (+1) =$
$(-3) \div (+1) =$

2. $(+15) \div (+5) =$
$(+10) \div (+5) =$
$(+5) \div (+5) =$
$0 \div (+5) =$
$(-5) \div (+5) =$
$(-10) \div (+5) =$
$(-15) \div (+5) =$

3. $(+15) \div (-5) =$
$(+10) \div (-5) =$
$(+5) \div (-5) =$
$0 \div (-5) =$
$(-5) \div (-5) -$
$(-10) \div (-5) =$
$(-15) \div (-5) =$

4. $(+3) \div (-1) =$
$(+2) \div (-1) =$
$(+1) \div (-1) =$
$0 \div (-1) =$
$(-1) \div (-1) =$
$(-2) \div (-1) =$
$(-3) \div (-1) =$

Find the quotient.

5. $12 \div (-3)$

6. $14 \div (-7)$

7. $(-32) \div (-8)$

8. $(-25) \div (-5)$

9. $(-9) \div 3$

10. $(-34) \div 2$

11. $(-51) \div (-3)$

12. $(-14) \div (-14)$

13. $(-12.5) \div (-1.25)$

14. $24 \div (-1.2)$

15. $\dfrac{-17}{17}$

16. $\dfrac{-34}{17}$

17. $\dfrac{-18}{-6}$

18. $\dfrac{27}{-9}$

19. $\dfrac{0}{-3}$

20. $\dfrac{-24}{8}$

21. $\dfrac{20}{-2}$

22. $\dfrac{0}{-4}$

23. $-\dfrac{-280}{-20}$

24. $-\dfrac{-240}{-40}$

25. $\dfrac{21.44}{-6.7}$

26. $\dfrac{44.52}{-5.3}$

27. $\dfrac{-10.8}{-0.72}$

28. $\dfrac{-9.5}{-0.38}$

Compute.

29. $\dfrac{-50}{6-11}$

30. $\dfrac{-100}{6-(-4)}$

31. $\dfrac{4(-1)+3(-2)}{-1-1}$

32. $\dfrac{5(-2)+3(-1)}{-6-7}$

33. $-\dfrac{3(-8)+4}{-6+1}$

34. $-\dfrac{2(-12)+4}{-5+1}$

35. $64 \div [-12 - 11(6-10)]$

36. $42 \div [-6 - 5(14-18)]$

37. $\dfrac{(-3)(-2)-5(-1)}{-3-8}$

38. $\dfrac{(-4)(-1)-5(-2)}{-1-1}$

39. $\left[\dfrac{4(-3) - 12}{-3 + 6}\right]\left[\dfrac{6 + (-10)}{-3 + 5}\right]$    40. $\left[\dfrac{4(-5) - (-8)}{-4 + 1}\right]\left[\dfrac{28 + (-10)}{2 - 8}\right]$

Simplify.

41. $\dfrac{-6}{-12}$ and $-\dfrac{6}{12}$    42. $\dfrac{-10}{-15}$ and $-\dfrac{10}{15}$    43. $-\dfrac{-2}{5}$    44. $-\dfrac{-6}{7}$

45. $-\dfrac{4}{-9}$    46. $-\dfrac{3}{-10}$    47. $-\dfrac{-2}{-4}$    48. $-\dfrac{-6}{-8}$

49. $-\dfrac{-x}{5}$    50. $-\dfrac{-x}{10}$    51. $-\dfrac{y}{-11}$    52. $-\dfrac{y}{-8}$

Perform the indicated operation and simplify.

53. $\dfrac{-1}{2} \cdot \left(-\dfrac{3}{5}\right)$    54. $\dfrac{-1}{4} \cdot \left(-\dfrac{2}{3}\right)$    55. $\left(-\dfrac{1}{2}\right)\left(\dfrac{-1}{3}\right)\left(-\dfrac{1}{4}\right)$

56. $\left(-\dfrac{1}{2}\right)\left(\dfrac{-2}{3}\right)\left(-\dfrac{3}{4}\right)$    57. $\dfrac{-4}{7} \cdot \dfrac{1}{8}$    58. $\dfrac{2}{9} \cdot \dfrac{-3}{5}$

59. $\dfrac{1}{2} \div \left(-\dfrac{3}{5}\right)$    60. $\dfrac{1}{4} \div \left(-\dfrac{2}{3}\right)$    61. $\left(\dfrac{1}{-7}\right) \div \left(-\dfrac{1}{2}\right)$

62. $\left(\dfrac{1}{-5}\right) \div \left(-\dfrac{1}{2}\right)$

63. Al played 16 hands of poker and lost a total of $54.40. What was his average loss per hand?
64. In 4 hours the temperature dropped from 18° above zero to 17° below zero. What was the average drop per hour?
65. In a certain city, the following temperatures were recorded at 6 A.M. each day of the last week of December: Monday 1°, Tuesday −3°, Wednesday −3°, Thursday −5°, Friday −6°, Saturday 0°, Sunday 2°. Find the average temperature at 6 A.M. for the week.
66. During the course of a football game a fullback carried the ball 4 times with the following results: no gain, loss 3 yd, gain 2 yd, loss 5 yd. Find his total yardage and average gain per carry.

## Calculator Problems

67. Calculate to the nearest thousandth. $\dfrac{\dfrac{5}{8}\left(\dfrac{3}{11} - \dfrac{8}{7}\right)}{-\dfrac{3}{2}\left(\dfrac{4}{7} + \dfrac{5}{11}\right)}$

68. Calculate to the nearest tenth.

   a) $[0.439 \div (-0.5) + (-0.06)] \div 1.6$

   b) $\left[\dfrac{4.7(-6.9) + 3.2(13.8)}{-7.23 - 0.19}\right]\left[\dfrac{17.23 + (-21.89)}{8.77 - 6.23}\right]$

---

## Challenge Problems

69. True or false: $\left|\dfrac{a}{b}\right| = \dfrac{|a|}{|b|}$ for all real numbers $a$ and $b$ except $b = 0$.

70. Just as subtraction can be defined in terms of addition (that is, $a - b = a + (-b)$), so can division be defined in terms of multiplication. Write $a/b$ in terms of multiplication.

## 2.5    REMOVING PARENTHESES

In order to solve equations in the next chapter, it will often be necessary to remove parentheses that contain a sum or a difference. This must be done so that like terms may then be combined. We have already seen a few examples of removing parentheses by using the distributive axiom.

**EXAMPLE 1**   Remove parentheses in $3(2x + 5)$.

$$3(2x + 5) = 6x + 15. \quad \square$$

Before looking at other examples, we first note that a negative sign in front of an expression has exactly the same effect as multiplying that expression by $-1$. That is,

$$-5 = (-1) \cdot 5,$$
$$-x = (-1) \cdot x,$$

and

$$-(x + 2) = (-1) \cdot (x + 2).$$

**EXAMPLE 2**    Remove parentheses in $-(x + 2)$.

$$
\begin{aligned}
-(x + 2) &= (-1) \cdot (x + 2) \\
&= (-1) \cdot x + (-1) \cdot 2 \\
&= (-x) + (-2) \\
&= -x - 2. \ \square
\end{aligned}
$$

Note that $-x - 2 = (-x) + (-2)$ by the rule for subtraction.

In practice, most of the steps in Example 2 are usually omitted. Instead, when a negative sign appears alone in front of parentheses, we simply visualize multiplying each term inside the parentheses by $-1$. This has the effect of changing the sign of each of these terms.

**EXAMPLE 3**    Remove parentheses in $-(3x + 5)$.

$$-(3x + 5) = -3x - 5. \ \square$$

**EXAMPLE 4**    Remove parentheses in $-2(x + \frac{1}{2})$.

$$-2\left(x + \frac{1}{2}\right) = -2x - 1. \ \square$$

**EXAMPLE 5**    Remove parentheses in $-4(-3x + 1)$.

$$-4(-3x + 1) = 12x - 4. \ \square$$

The procedure is similar when the parentheses contain a *difference* instead of a sum.

**EXAMPLE 6**    Remove parentheses in $-(x - 5)$.

$$
\begin{aligned}
-(x - 5) &= (-1) \cdot (x - 5) \\
&= (-1) \cdot [x + (-5)] \\
&= (-1) \cdot x + (-1) \cdot (-5) \\
&= -x + 5. \ \square
\end{aligned}
$$

As before, many of the steps that were performed in the example above may be omitted.

**EXAMPLE 7**    Remove parentheses in $-(8x - 4)$.

$$-(8x - 4) = -8x + 4. \ \square$$

Recall that the distributive axiom is also used to combine like terms.

**EXAMPLE 8**   Combine the like terms $6a + 7a$.
$$6a + 7a = (6 + 7)a$$
$$= 13a. \quad \square$$

**EXAMPLE 9**   Combine the like terms $10x - x$.
$$10x - x = (10 - 1)x$$
$$= 9x. \quad \square$$

**EXAMPLE 10**   Combine the like terms $8x - 10x$.
$$8x - 10x = (8 - 10)x$$
$$= -2x. \quad \square$$

**EXAMPLE 11**   Combine the like terms $-5y - y$.
$$-5y - y = (-5 - 1)y$$
$$- -6y. \quad \square$$

Again, we can add or subtract like terms simply by adding or subtracting their coefficients.

**EXAMPLE 12**   Combine the like terms $11a - 15a$.
$$11a - 15a = -4a. \quad \square$$

**EXAMPLE 13**   Combine the like terms $-2z - 8z$.
$$-2z - 8z - -10z. \quad \square$$

**EXAMPLE 14**   Remove parentheses and combine the like terms in $2(x + 5) - (x - 3)$.
$$2(x + 5) - (x - 3) = 2x + 10 - x + 3$$
$$= (2x - x) + (10 + 3)$$
$$= x + 13. \quad \square$$

**EXAMPLE 15**   Remove parentheses and combine the like terms in $-3(4a - 1) - (a + 5)$.
$$-3(4a - 1) - (a + 5) = -12a + 3 - a - 5$$
$$= -13a - 2. \quad \square$$

**EXAMPLE 16** Remove parentheses and combine the like terms in $3 + 2(x - 1) + 5(-2x) - (-3x)(4)$.

$$3 + 2(x - 1) + 5(-2x) - (-3x)(4) = 3 + 2x - 2 - 10x + 12x$$
$$= 4x + 1. \quad \square$$

**EXAMPLE 17** Simplify $(-9)\dfrac{-3y + 5}{12}$.

$$(-9)\frac{-3y + 5}{12} = \frac{\overset{-3}{-\cancel{9}}}{1} \cdot \frac{-3y + 5}{\underset{4}{\cancel{12}}}$$

$$= \frac{-3(-3y + 5)}{1 \cdot 4}$$

$$= \frac{9y - 15}{4}. \quad \square$$

## Problem Set 2.5

Remove parentheses.

1. $5(5x + 3)$
2. $7(3x + 4)$
3. $-(x + 6)$
4. $-(x + 11)$
5. $-(a - 9)$
6. $-(a - 6)$
7. $-(-y + 5)$
8. $-(-y + 3)$
9. $-(-z - 1)$
10. $-(-z - 4)$
11. $-2(b + 4)$
12. $-3(b + 6)$
13. $-4(c - 5)$
14. $-5(c - 1)$
15. $6(y - \frac{1}{3})$
16. $8(y - \frac{1}{4})$
17. $6(\frac{2}{3}x - \frac{1}{3})$
18. $4(\frac{3}{4}x - \frac{1}{4})$
19. $\frac{1}{2}(\frac{1}{3}x - \frac{1}{5})$
20. $-\frac{1}{3}(\frac{1}{4}x - \frac{2}{3})$
21. $-5(-x + 2y - 3)$
22. $-10(2x - y - 1)$
23. $2.7(3.1r - 0.09s + t)$
24. $4.6(5.1u + 0.11v - w)$

Combine the like terms.

25. $6x + 2x$
26. $7x + 3x$
27. $-4x + 6x$
28. $-3x + 8x$
29. $9a - 11a$
30. $16a - 20a$
31. $-2y - 8y$
32. $-5y - 5y$
33. $3z + (-6z)$
34. $14z + (-18z)$
35. $2x + (-2x)$
36. $4x + (-4x)$
37. $3x + (-x)$
38. $5x + (-x)$
39. $-14b + b$
40. $-12b + b$
41. $(-10x) + 10x$
42. $(-13x) + 13x$

43. $-y + 7y$      44. $-y + 9y$      45. $-y - 4y$
46. $-y - 3y$      47. $-13.8q + 6.9q$      48. $-19.4p + 7.6p$

Simplify by removing parentheses and combining the like terms.

49. $7(x - 4) - (x - 6)$
50. $3(x - 5) - (x + 8)$
51. $-(y + 1) + \frac{1}{2}(4y - 6)$
52. $-(y - 2) + \frac{1}{3}(9y + 3)$
53. $-4(2z - 6) - 3(-z + 1)$
54. $\frac{1}{2}(8z + 8) - \frac{2}{3}(3z - 6)$
55. $3(a - 2b) - 7(3a - b)$
56. $5(2a - b) - 2(4a - 2b)$
57. $-6(-x + 2) - \frac{3}{4}(4x + 8)$
58. $-3(-x - 7) - 5(2x - 1)$
59. $-(11x + 9y) - (x - 14y)$
60. $-(-x + 4y) - (19x + 15y)$
61. $4 + 2(x - 13) + 3(-3x)$
62. $3 + 2(x - 12) + 4(-4x)$
63. $5 + 5(x + 1) - 6(2x)$
64. $6 + 4(x + 2) - 2(5x)$
65. $-4 + 8a - 4(3a + 2) - (17 + 5a - 9a)$
66. $-3 + 9a - 2(a + 1) - (14 + 6a - 8a)$
67. $9 - 4(a \quad 8a) + 6 - (13 + 7a) - (-a)(3)$
68. $10 - 5(a - 4a) + 8 - (15 + 9a) - (2)(-a)$
69. $(5)(6a) - (4a)(-8) + (-9a)(-4) + (6b)(2)$
70. $(3)(8a) - (7a)(-4) + (-10a)(-6) + (7)(2b)$
71. $(-1)(13a) - (a)(-12) + (6a)(-2) - (-5)(-3a)$
72. $(-1)(17a) \quad (-a)(14) + (7a)(-2) - (-4a)(-6)$

Simplify.

73. $(-3)\dfrac{-y + 1}{5}$      74. $(-2)\dfrac{-x + 1}{9}$      75. $-\dfrac{(-x \quad 4)}{10}$       76. $+\dfrac{+y \quad 3}{11}$

77. $(-5)\dfrac{-x \quad 1}{7}$      78. $(-3)\dfrac{-x + 1}{13}$      79. $(-2)\dfrac{x - 4}{9}$      80. $(-4)\dfrac{x - 2}{3}$

81. $(-12)\dfrac{-x - 6}{6}$      82. $(-16)\dfrac{-x - 4}{4}$      83. $(-15)\dfrac{-2x + 1}{10}$      84. $(\quad 9)\dfrac{-3x + 1}{6}$

## Calculator Problems

85. Remove parentheses. $4.18(6.77c - 0.98d + 0.015)$
86. Combine the like terms. $857.23r - 901.007r + 38.087r$
87. Remove parentheses and combine the like terms.

$$\frac{1}{2}(37.4x + 67.008) - \frac{1}{6}(126.42x + 468)$$

## Challenge Problems

88. True or false: $a + (b \cdot c) = (a + b) \cdot (a + c)$ for all real numbers $a$ and $b$. In other words, does addition distribute over multiplication?
89. Supply the reason for each step in the proof below.

| Statement | Reason |
|---|---|
| $a(b - c) = a \cdot [b + (-c)]$ | ? |
| $= a \cdot b + a \cdot (-c)$ | ? |
| $= ab + [-(ac)]$ | ? |
| $= ab - ac$ | ? |

Therefore $a(b - c) = ab - ac$, which means that *multiplication distributes over subtraction.*

## Chapter Review

True or false (Problems 1–22).

1. $-\dfrac{x}{3} = \dfrac{-x}{\times 3}$.
2. The reciprocal of $-\frac{3}{4}$ is $\frac{4}{3}$.
3. The number 0 has no reciprocal.
4. The number 0 is the identity element for addition.
5. The number 1 is the identity element for multiplication.
6. The coefficient of $y$ in the term $4y$ is 4.
7. Like terms are combined by combining their coefficients.
8. If $x + 4 = 7$, then $(x + 4) + (-4) = 7 + (-4)$ illustrates the addition axiom for equality.
9. $0 + 8 = 0$ illustrates the identity axiom for addition.
10. $4x$ and $-x$ are like terms.
11. $9s$ and $9t$ are like terms.
12. $17st$ and $-17s^2t$ are like terms.
13. Division is a commutative operation.
14. Subtraction is an associative operation.
15. $3x + 7x = (3 + 7)x$ illustrates the distributive axiom.
16. $(x + y) \cdot 5 = 5 \cdot (x + y)$ illustrates the commutative axiom for multiplication.

17. $[x + (-3)] + 3 = x + [(-3) + 3]$ illustrates the associative ax-iom for addition.
18. $x + [(-3) + 3] = x + 0$ illustrates the inverse axiom for addition.
19. $ab + 8 = ba + 8$ illustrates the commutative axiom for addition.
20. $4 + (x + y) = (x + y) + 4$ illustrates the associative axiom for addition.
21. The expression $-a + b - c$ can be written as $-(a - b + c)$.
22. If no grouping symbols are present, multiplications are performed before subtractions.

Completion.

23. Terms having the same variable factor are _____?_____ terms.

24. In simplest form, the reciprocal of $-2.3$ is _____?_____.
25. In simplest form, the negative of the number $-(-(-14))$ is

_____?_____.

26. In the term $-x$, the coefficient of $x$ is _____?_____.

27. If $a(b + c) = -10$ and $ac = -2$, then $ab =$ _____?_____.

Perform each operation.

28. $(-15) + 4$     29. $(-9) + (-11)$     30. $-7 - 4$          31. $(-\frac{1}{3}) - (-\frac{1}{2})$

32. $(-2)(-6)$     33. $\dfrac{-13}{13}$                34. $(-\frac{2}{3}) \div (-\frac{1}{4})$     35. $\dfrac{0}{-10}$

Compute each of the following.

36. $(-8)[9 + (-1)]$          37. $7[10 - 4(5 - 2)]$          38. $(-9)(1.1 - 2.2)$

39. $\dfrac{4(-3) - 12}{6 + (-3)} + (-3)^2$     40. $18 \div 6 \cdot (-3)$          41. $6.8 - [3.5(-8.2 + 4.4) - 7.9]$

Simplify.

42. $-(-x + 5)$          43. $(-8)\dfrac{-x + 6}{6}$          44. $6\left(\dfrac{t}{2} + \dfrac{2}{3}\right)$

Combine the like terms.

45. $69b^2 + b + 48b^2$          46. $-7.1k + 13.9k$

Isolate $x$ in each equation.

47. $x + (-6) = 9$          48. $\frac{2}{3}x = 12$

Remove parentheses and combine the like terms.

49. $-2(x - 3y) + 7(3x - 4y)$
50. $(a - 2b + c) + (2a - b + c) + (a \mp b \mp 2c) = 2a - 4b$
51. $4 + 7(x - 3) + 2(-3x) - (-5x)(-2)$

52. If $n$ is a positive integer, what kind of number is $-(-n)$?
53. A bowling team held a banquet at which members could order either chicken or salisbury steak. If $x$ chicken dinners at \$3.75 each and $y$ steak dinners at \$4.25 each were ordered, write an expression for the total amount of money spent on dinners.
54. The total surface area of a cylinder of radius $r$ and height $h$ is $2\pi r(r + h)$. Write this expression without parentheses.
55. A clothing store sold 24 skirts at a profit of \$9 per skirt, 3 sweaters at a loss of \$2.75 per sweater, and 5 hats at a loss of \$1.55 per hat. Determine the average profit per item for the 32 items.

Supply the axiom that justifies each step.

| Statement | Reason |
|---|---|
| $3x = 3$ | Given |
| 56. $\frac{1}{3} \cdot (3x) = \frac{1}{3} \cdot 3$ | ? |
| 57. $(\frac{1}{3} \cdot 3)x = \frac{1}{3} \cdot 3$ | ? |
| 58. $1 \cdot x = 1$ | ? |
| 59. $x = 1$ | ? |

axiom for equality
Associative
inverse
Identity

# Chapter Chapter Chapter Chapter Three Three Three Three

## FIRST-DEGREE EQUATIONS

## 3.1   SOLVING FIRST-DEGREE EQUATIONS

Suppose that in order to get an A in a course, you are required to have a final average of 93. The grades on your first three tests were 87, 88, and 96. Only the final exam remains, but it will be counted twice as much as any previous test. What score must you get on the exam to get an A in the course?

We do not know what score must be attained on the final exam so let us denote this number by $x$. Noting that the exam counts the same as *two* tests, we write the following statement:

$$\frac{87 + 88 + 96 + x + x}{5} = 93.$$

Since the statement above involves an equals sign, it is called an **equation.** The expression to the left of the equals sign is called the **left-hand side** of the equation, and the expression to the right of the equals sign is called the **right-hand side.** Our purpose in this chapter is to outline a systematic approach to *solving* first-degree equations. That is, we will develop a method for finding a number which when substituted for the variable of the equation produces a true statement.

We shall solve the equation above in Section 3.3, but let us begin in this section by looking at some of the different types of equations that we may encounter. Note that the equation

$$8 = 9$$

is never true, while the equation

$$8 = 8$$

is always true. Also the equation

$$x + 3 = x + 3$$

is always true no matter what real number is substituted for the variable $x$. Equations that are true for all values of the variables for which the expressions involved have meaning are called **identical equations,** or **identities.** Therefore

$$a + b = b + a$$

and

$$\frac{5}{x - 2} = \frac{5}{x - 2}$$

are identities. The first equation is true for all real numbers $a$ and $b$, and the second equation is true for all real numbers $x$ except $x = 2$ (since $5/(x - 2)$ is undefined when $x = 2$).

The equation

$$x + 3 = 5$$

is called a **conditional equation,** since it is a true statement only under the condition that $x$ is replaced by 2. It is a false statement if $x$ is replaced by any other number. The number 2 is therefore called the **solution** to the equation $x + 3 = 5$. We also say that the number 2 *satisfies* the equation $x + 3 = 5$. The number 7 on the other hand does *not* satisfy the equation $x + 3 = 5$.

To *solve* an equation means to find its solutions.

**EXAMPLE 1**  Solve $x + 3 = 7$.

The solution is 4.  ⊓

**EXAMPLE 2**  Solve $x = 8$.

The solution is 8.  □

**EXAMPLE 3**  Solve $2x + 3 = 13$.

The solution is 5.  ⊔

At this point we are finding the solution of an equation by guessing. Obviously this method is not a good method when the equation is complicated, such as the one at the beginning of this chapter.

Recall that the *addition axiom for equality* allows us to add equal quantities to both sides of an equation; and the *multiplication axiom for equality* allows us to multiply both sides of an equation by equal quantities. Using these two properties, as well as the other axioms, we shall change the *form* of an equation without changing its solution.

Now, in what way should the form of an equation be changed? That is, what should be the end result? Examining the three examples above, it is clear that the solution was easiest to find for the second equation, $x = 8$. This is because the variable $x$ is isolated on one side of the equation and the constant 8 on the other. Therefore *to solve the equations in this chapter, we shall isolate the variable on one side of the equation.* Although the left-hand side is often chosen, the variable may actually be isolated on *either* side of the equation.

**EXAMPLE 4**  Solve $x + 2 = 6$.

In order to isolate $x$ on one side of the equation, we must remove the 2 from the left-hand side. This is done by adding the negative of 2, namely $-2$, to both sides.

$$x + 2 = 6$$
$$x + 2 + (-2) = 6 + (-2)$$
$$x + 0 = 4$$
$$x = 4.$$

The solution is 4.

The solution, 4, can be checked simply by substituting it for the variable.

$$\text{CHECK:}\quad 4 + 2 \overset{?}{=} 6$$
$$6 = 6. \quad \square$$

In the example above, the number 2 was removed from the left-hand side by adding the negative of 2, namely $-2$, to each side. The same result could have been achieved by *subtracting* a positive 2 from each side. This is because $a + (-b)$ is the same as $a - b$; that is, *adding* $-b$ *is equivalent to subtracting* $b$. Solving the equation in this manner, we have

$$x + 2 = 6$$
$$x + 2 - 2 = 6 - 2$$
$$x = 4.$$

**EXAMPLE 5**   Solve $5x = 10$.

Again we wish to isolate the variable $x$ on one side of the equation. Therefore, we must remove the coefficient 5. To do this we multiply both sides of the equation by the reciprocal of 5, namely $\frac{1}{5}$.

$$5x = 10$$
$$\frac{1}{5} \cdot 5x = \frac{1}{5} \cdot 10$$
$$1 \cdot x = \frac{10}{5}$$
$$x = 2.$$

The solution is 2.

$$\text{CHECK:}\quad 5 \cdot 2 \overset{?}{=} 10$$
$$10 = 10. \quad \square$$

In this last example, the number 5 was removed from the left-hand side by multiplying each side by the reciprocal of 5, namely $\frac{1}{5}$. The same result could have been achieved by *dividing* each side of the equation by 5. This is because $\frac{1}{b} \cdot a$ is the same as $\frac{a}{b}$; that is, *multiplying by* $\frac{1}{b}$ *is the same as dividing by b*. Solving the equation in this manner, we have

$$5x = 10$$
$$\frac{5x}{5} = \frac{10}{5}$$
$$x = 2.$$

In some cases it may be easier to solve an equation by adding the same number to each side. In other cases, it may be easier to subtract the same number from each side. The same can be said about the multiplication and division of each side of an equation by the same number.

**EXAMPLE 6**   Solve $-4x = 32$.

To isolate $x$, we divide each side of the equation by $-4$.

$$-4x = 32$$
$$\frac{-4x}{-4} = \frac{32}{-4}$$
$$x = -8.$$

The solution is $-8$.

$$\text{CHECK:} \quad -4(-8) \stackrel{?}{=} 32$$
$$32 = 32. \quad \square$$

**EXAMPLE 7**   Solve $\frac{5}{3}x = 2$.

We multiply each side of the equation by $\frac{3}{5}$.

$$\frac{5}{3}x = 2$$
$$\frac{3}{5} \cdot \frac{5}{3}x = \frac{3}{5} \cdot 2$$
$$x = \frac{6}{5}.$$

The solution is $\frac{6}{5}$.

$$\text{CHECK:} \quad \frac{5}{3} \cdot \frac{6}{5} \stackrel{?}{=} 2$$
$$\frac{6}{3} \stackrel{?}{=} 2$$
$$2 = 2. \quad \square$$

We shall now solve an equation utilizing *both* the addition and multiplication axioms for equality.

**EXAMPLE 8**   Solve $-x - 4 = 17$.

First, we add 4 to each side.

$$-x - 4 = 17$$
$$-x - 4 + 4 = 17 + 4$$
$$-x = 21.$$

Then the negative sign is removed by multiplying each side by $-1$.

$$(-1) \cdot (-x) = (-1) \cdot 21$$
$$x = -21.$$

The solution is $-21$.

$$\text{CHECK:} \quad -(-21) - 4 \overset{?}{=} 17$$
$$21 - 4 \overset{?}{=} 17$$
$$17 = 17. \quad \square$$

**EXAMPLE 9**   Solve $7x + 6 = 27$.

First, we subtract 6 from each side.

$$7x + 6 = 27$$
$$7x + 6 - 6 = 27 - 6$$
$$7x = 21.$$

Then we divide each side by 7.

$$\frac{7x}{7} = \frac{21}{7}$$
$$x = 3.$$

The solution is 3.

$$\text{CHECK:} \quad 7 \cdot 3 + 6 \overset{?}{=} 27$$
$$21 + 6 \overset{?}{=} 27$$
$$27 = 27. \quad \square$$

**EXAMPLE 10**   Solve $8x = 0$.

$$8x = 0$$
$$\frac{8x}{8} = \frac{0}{8}$$
$$x = 0$$

The solution is 0.

CHECK:   $8 \cdot 0 \stackrel{?}{=} 0$

$0 = 0.$ ☐

**EXAMPLE 11**   Twice a certain number $x$ plus 7 equals 18. Write this statement as an equation involving $x$. Then solve the equation to find the number $x$.

The equation is

$$2x + 7 = 18.$$

Solving this equation, we have

$$2x + 7 - 7 = 18 - 7$$
$$2x = 11$$
$$\frac{2x}{2} - \frac{11}{2}$$
$$x = \frac{11}{2}.$$

The number is $\frac{11}{2}$, or $5\frac{1}{2}$.

CHECK:   $2\left(\dfrac{11}{2}\right) + 7 \stackrel{?}{=} 18$

$11 + 7 \stackrel{?}{=} 18$

$18 = 18.$ ☐

## Problem Set 3.1

Solve each of the following equations.

1. $x + 2 = 5$
2. $x + 4 = 7$
3. $4x = 8$
4. $3x = 15$
5. $x - 7 = 4$
6. $x - 6 = 8$
7. $3x = -18$
8. $5x = -20$
9. $5x = 0$
10. $4x = 0$
11. $2x = 7$
12. $2x = 9$
13. $-8x = 32$
14. $-7x = 21$
15. $x + 22 = 10$
16. $x + 24 - 10$
17. $-2x = -14$
18. $-2x = -16$
19. $-x = 5$
20. $-x = 7$
21. $6 - x = 8$
22. $4 - x = 9$
23. $-x = -10$
24. $-x = -6$
25. $14 - x = 2$
26. $18 - x = 13$
27. $-5x = 17$

28. $-3x = 7$
29. $x - 7 = -3$
30. $x - 8 = -2$
31. $-17x = -13$
32. $-19x = -11$
33. $\frac{3}{2}x = 8$
34. $\frac{4}{3}x = 9$
35. $-\frac{2}{3}x = 8$
36. $-\frac{3}{4}x = 9$
37. $\frac{11}{6}x = -11$
38. $\frac{13}{8}x = -13$
39. $-\frac{1}{4}x = -\frac{2}{3}$
40. $-\frac{1}{6}x = -\frac{3}{5}$
41. $5x - 10 = -15$
42. $4x - 6 = -10$
43. $2x - 7 = 13$
44. $5x - 3 = 12$
45. $4x + 7 = -17$
46. $3x + 2 = -19$
47. $3x + 9 = 21$
48. $2x + 8 = 18$
49. $2x - 11 = 11$
50. $2x - 13 = 13$
51. $2x - 5 = -6$
52. $3x - 5 = -6$
53. $-7x - 8 = 7$
54. $-6x - 4 = 15$
55. $-10 - 4x = -7$
56. $-12 - 4x = -9$
57. $-9x + 10 = 10$
58. $-7x + 10 = 10$

Write each statement as an equation involving $x$. Then solve the equation to find the number $x$.

59. A certain number $x$ minus 5 equals 21.
60. A certain number $x$ plus 27 equals 8.
61. Four times a number $x$ equals 36.
62. One-half a number $x$ equals 19.
63. Three times a number $x$ plus 14 equals 5.
64. Five times a number $x$ minus 11 equals 15.

## Calculator Problems

Solve each equation.

65. $927x = 62201.7$
66. $0.0528x = -17.16$
67. $-41.51x = -95.473$
68. $4.017x - 22.049 = 39.4111$

69. Solve the equation $8.317x + 32.648 = 89.4114$ to the nearest hundredth.

## Challenge Problems

Solve each equation.

70. $3x - 6 = 2x + 1$
71. $3 - x = 2x - 5$
72. $10 - 2x - 4x = 4 - 6x$
73. $5x - x + 7 = 4x + 13 - 6$

## 3.2 EQUATIONS INVOLVING LIKE TERMS

When an equation involves two or more like terms on the same side, these like terms should be combined as the first step in solving the equation.

**EXAMPLE 1**  Solve $2x + 3x + 1 = 21$.

We begin by combining the like terms $2x$ and $3x$.

$$2x + 3x + 1 = 21$$
$$5x + 1 = 21.$$

Then, proceeding as before, we have

$$5x + 1 - 1 = 21 - 1$$
$$5x = 20$$
$$\frac{5x}{5} = \frac{20}{5}$$
$$x = 4.$$

The solution is 4.

$$\text{CHECK:}\quad 2 \cdot 4 + 3 \cdot 4 + 1 \stackrel{?}{=} 21$$
$$8 + 12 + 1 \stackrel{?}{=} 21$$
$$21 = 21. \quad \square$$

**EXAMPLE 2**  Solve  $3x + 5 = 19 - 20$.

We begin by combining the like terms 19 and 20.

$$-3x + 5 = 19 - 20$$
$$-3x + 5 = -1.$$

Then, proceeding as before, we have

$$-3x + 5 - 5 = -1 - 5$$
$$-3x = -6$$
$$\frac{-3x}{-3} = \frac{-6}{-3}$$
$$x = 2.$$

The solution is 2.

$$\text{CHECK:}\quad -3(2) + 5 \stackrel{?}{=} 19 - 20$$
$$-6 + 5 \stackrel{?}{=} -1$$
$$-1 = -1. \quad \square$$

If the like terms appear on *opposite* sides of the equation, they should be brought together on the same side of the equation so that they may be combined.

**EXAMPLE 3**   Solve $3x + 5 = 2x + 12$.

The like terms $3x$ and $2x$ are on opposite sides of the equation. We bring them together on the left-hand side by subtracting $2x$ from each side.

$$3x + 5 = 2x + 12$$
$$3x - 2x + 5 = 2x - 2x + 12$$
$$x + 5 = 12.$$

Then, subtracting 5 from each side gives the solution.

$$x + 5 - 5 = 12 - 5$$
$$x = 7.$$

The solution is 7.

$$\text{CHECK:}\quad 3 \cdot 7 + 5 \overset{?}{=} 2 \cdot 7 + 12$$
$$21 + 5 \overset{?}{=} 14 + 12$$
$$26 = 26. \ \square$$

If the equation involves parentheses, these parentheses should be removed first. Then if any like terms are present, they should be combined.

**EXAMPLE 4**   Solve $x - (3x - 4) = -15$.

We begin by removing parentheses. Since a negative sign precedes the parentheses, we remove parentheses by changing the sign of each term inside the parentheses. We are actually multiplying each term inside the parentheses by $-1$.

$$x - (3x - 4) = -15$$
$$x - 3x + 4 = -15.$$

The like terms $x$ and $-3x$ are then combined.

$$-2x + 4 = -15.$$

Then 4 is subtracted from each side.

$$-2x + 4 - 4 = -15 - 4$$
$$-2x = -19.$$

Finally, each side is divided by the coefficient $-2$.

$$\frac{-2x}{-2} = \frac{-19}{-2}$$

$$x = \frac{19}{2}.$$

The solution is $\frac{19}{2}$ .

$$\text{CHECK:} \quad \frac{19}{2} - \left(3 \cdot \frac{19}{2} - 4\right) \overset{?}{=} -15$$

$$\frac{19}{2} - \left(\frac{57}{2} - \frac{8}{2}\right) \overset{?}{=} -15$$

$$\frac{19}{2} - \frac{49}{2} \overset{?}{=} -15$$

$$-\frac{30}{2} \overset{?}{=} -15$$

$$-15 = -15. \quad \square$$

Although we have always isolated $x$ on the left-hand side in the examples thus far, the variable may actually be isolated on *either* side of the equation.

**EXAMPLE 5**   Solve $4 - (2x + 3) = 7x + (2x + 12)$.

In order to combine like terms we must first remove parentheses.

$$4 - (2x + 3) = 7x + (2x + 12)$$

$$4 - 2x - 3 = 7x + 2x + 12$$

$$1 - 2x = 9x + 12$$

$$1 - 2x + 2x = 9x + 12 + 2x$$

$$1 = 11x + 12$$

$$1 - 12 = 11x + 12 - 12$$

$$-11 = 11x$$

$$\frac{-11}{11} = \frac{11x}{11}$$

$$-1 = x.$$

The solution is $-1$.

$$\text{CHECK:} \quad 4 - [2(-1) + 3] \overset{?}{=} 7(-1) + [2(-1) + 12]$$

$$4 - [-2 + 3] \overset{?}{=} -7 + [-2 + 12]$$

$$4 - 1 \overset{?}{=} -7 + 10$$

$$3 = 3. \quad \square$$

**EXAMPLE 6**   Four times a number is 18 more than twice the number. Find the number.

Since we don't know the number, we shall represent it by the variable *x*. We then write the following equation involving *x*:

$$4x = 18 + 2x.$$

Solving this equation, we have

$$4x - 2x = 18 + 2x - 2x$$
$$2x = 18$$
$$\frac{2x}{2} = \frac{18}{2}$$
$$x = 9.$$

The number is 9.

$$\text{CHECK:}\quad 4 \cdot 9 \overset{?}{=} 18 + 2 \cdot 9$$
$$36 \overset{?}{=} 18 + 18$$
$$36 = 36. \quad \square$$

## Problem Set 3.2

Solve each of the following equations.

1. $2x + 5 = 9 + 4$
2. $2x + 8 = 5 + 9$
3. $5x + 3x = -24$
4. $4x + 3x = -21$
5. $3x - 2x = 6 - 7$
6. $5x - 4x = 2 - 3$
7. $-x + 2x = 19$
8. $-x + 2x = 14$
9. $8x - 9x = -10 - 1$
10. $7x - 8x = -12 - 3$
11. $7x - 11x + 3 = 15$
12. $6x - 11x + 2 = 22$
13. $4x + 7 = 3x - 2$
14. $8x + 4 = 7x - 6$
15. $9x - 1 = -6x - 31$
16. $5x - 1 = -6x - 23$
17. $-x + 14 = x + 9$
18. $-x + 10 = x + 3$
19. $x + 7 = 2x - 6$
20. $x - 4 = 2x + 1$
21. $7x - 4 = x - 4$
22. $6x + 5 = -x + 5$
23. $4x - 4 = 8x - 4$
24. $x + 1 = 6x + 1$
25. $5(x - 1) = 3x - 7$
26. $3(x - 2) = x + 8$
27. $3x - 2(x + 1) = 5(x + 2)$
28. $7(x - 3) = 4 + 3(3x - 5)$
29. $5 - (x - 1) = 4x + 8$
30. $8 - (x - 4) = 3x + 13$

31. $15 - (x - 6) = 6 - (3x + 5)$
32. $7x - (9x - 16) = 14 - (-x + 19)$
33. $3(x + 5) + 4(x + 5) = 21$
34. $5(x + 1) - (x - 18) = 11$
35. $x - (2x + 1) = 3 + (4x + 10)$
36. $x - (5x + 1) = 4 + (x + 7)$
37. $x - (3x - 1) = -x + 16$
38. $x - (4x - 3) = -2x + 17$

39. Three times a number is 17 more than twice the number. Find the number.
40. Five times a number is 12 more than four times the number. Find the number.
41. Four times a number minus 6 is 13 less than the number. Find the number.
42. Three times a number plus 9 is 14 less than the number. Find the number.

$4x - 16 = x - 13$   $3x + 9 = x - 14$

$5x = 12 + 4x$

## Calculator Problems

43. Solve $3.7x - (2.41x + 6.5) = 0.014 + (0.28x - 4.393)$.
44. Solve $4.117(6.872x - 8.989) = -0.213x + 17.211$ to the nearest hundredth.

## Challenge Problems

Solve each equation.

45. $2x - 3(x - 1) = 13 - (x + 9)$
46. $7(2x - 1) + 1 = 16x - 2(x + 3)$

---

## 3.3   EQUATIONS INVOLVING FRACTIONS

Equations involving fractions are solved using the same techniques that were employed in the two previous sections. The only difference lies in the fact that fractions are harder to work with than integers and hence the solving process is more prone to error. For this reason it is usually advisable to clear the equation of fractions in the first step. This is done by multiplying both sides of the equation by the lcd.

**EXAMPLE 1**   Solve $\dfrac{x}{2} + \dfrac{x}{4} = 6$.

We begin by multiplying both sides of the equation by the lcd 4.

$$\frac{x}{2} + \frac{x}{4} = 6$$

$$4 \cdot \left( \frac{x}{2} + \frac{x}{4} \right) = 4 \cdot 6$$

$$4 \cdot \frac{x}{2} + 4 \cdot \frac{x}{4} = 24$$

$$2x + x = 24.$$

The equation is now cleared of fractions and we may proceed as before.

$$3x = 24$$

$$x = 8.$$

The solution is 8.  □

**EXAMPLE 2**   Solve $\dfrac{y}{2} = 7 - \dfrac{2y}{3}$.

We multiply both sides by the lcd 6.

$$\frac{y}{2} = 7 - \frac{2y}{3}$$

$$6 \cdot \frac{y}{2} = 6\left( 7 - \frac{2y}{3} \right)$$

$$3y = 6 \cdot 7 - 6 \cdot \frac{2y}{3}$$

$$3y = 42 - 4y.$$

The equation has been cleared of fractions. Hence

$$7y = 42$$

$$y = 6.$$

The solution is 6.  □

**EXAMPLE 3**   Solve $.6z - .4z = 3.2$.

Both sides are multiplied by 10 to remove the decimal fraction.

$$.6z - .4z = 3.2$$
$$10(.6z - .4z) = 10(3.2)$$
$$6z - 4z = 32$$
$$2z = 32$$
$$z = 16.$$

The solution is 16. □

**EXAMPLE 4**  Solve $\dfrac{2m - 3}{4} - 1 = \dfrac{m - 5}{3}$.

The lcd is 12.

$$\frac{2m - 3}{4} - 1 - \frac{m - 5}{3}$$

$$12\left[\frac{2m - 3}{4} - 1\right] = 12 \cdot \frac{m - 5}{3} \quad \text{cancel}$$

(Be careful in this step!)

$$3(2m - 3) - 12 = 4(m - 5)$$
$$6m - 9 - 12 = 4m - 20$$
$$6m - 21 = 4m - 20$$
$$6m = 4m + 1$$
$$2m = 1$$
$$m = \frac{1}{2}.$$

The solution is ½. □

**EXAMPLE 5**  A couple puts 20% down on a house and secures a 30-year mortgage for the remaining $54,000. What was the price of the house?

Let $p = $ the price of the house. Then we can write the equation

$$\text{price minus downpayment} = 54,000, \text{ or}$$
$$p - .20p = 54,000.$$

Solving this equation gives

$$10p - 2p = 540,000$$
$$8p = 540,000$$
$$p = 67,500.$$

The price of the house was $67,500. □

We are now able to solve the equation presented at the beginning of this chapter.

$$\frac{87 + 88 + 96 + x + x}{5} = 93$$

$$\frac{271 + 2x}{5} = 93$$

$$5 \cdot \frac{271 + 2x}{5} = 5 \cdot 93$$

$$271 + 2x = 465$$

$$2x = 194$$

$$x = 97.$$

Therefore a grade of 97 or better must be made on the final exam in order to receive an A for the course.

## Problem Set 3.3

Solve each of the following equations.

1. $\dfrac{x}{3} + \dfrac{x}{6} = 2$

2. $\dfrac{x}{4} + \dfrac{x}{8} = 3$

3. $\dfrac{x}{2} - \dfrac{x}{3} = -1$

4. $\dfrac{x}{9} - \dfrac{2}{3} = \dfrac{4}{3}$

5. $\dfrac{3}{2} - \dfrac{y}{3} = 5 + \dfrac{y}{6}$

6. $\dfrac{2y}{3} = 5 + \dfrac{y}{4}$

7. $\dfrac{x}{6} + 1 = \dfrac{x}{4} + \dfrac{7}{12}$

8. $\dfrac{5a}{4} - 1 = \dfrac{3a}{4} + \dfrac{1}{2}$

9. $\dfrac{1}{8}x - 1 = \dfrac{1}{3}x + \dfrac{1}{4}$

10. $\dfrac{1}{9}x - 1 = \dfrac{1}{2}x + \dfrac{1}{6}$

11. $\dfrac{1}{3}x - \dfrac{1}{9} = 4 - \dfrac{2}{3}$

12. $\dfrac{1}{4}x - \dfrac{1}{6} = 3 - \dfrac{1}{3}$

13. $2.3x - 4.25 = 0.35$

14. $3.5x - 5.15 = 1.85$

15. $m + \dfrac{16}{3} = \dfrac{3m}{2} + \dfrac{25}{6}$

16. $m - \dfrac{7}{5} = \dfrac{m}{3} + \dfrac{7}{15}$

17. $4.1x - .7 = -8.9$

18. $0.9x + 1.1 = 0.2$

19. $.15x + .40(25 - x) = .20(25)$
20. $.90x + .65(10 - x) = .80(10)$
21. $.07y + .08(500 - y) = 37.75$
22. $.06y + .09(450 - y) = 34.95$
23. $\dfrac{t - 1}{5} + \dfrac{t - 4}{2} + 5 = 0$
24. $\dfrac{2t - 7}{5} + \dfrac{t + 2}{3} = 0$
25. $\dfrac{p - 3}{8} - \dfrac{p - 10}{12} - \dfrac{5}{12} = 0$
26. $\dfrac{p - 1}{6} - \dfrac{p - 2}{9} - \dfrac{5}{18} = 0$
27. $\dfrac{h + 7}{2} - \dfrac{1}{3} = \dfrac{1}{2} - \dfrac{h + 9}{9}$
28. $\dfrac{h + 5}{4} - \dfrac{1}{8} = 1 - \dfrac{h + 8}{16}$
29. $\dfrac{5r}{3} - \dfrac{2r + 7}{2} = 1$
30. $\dfrac{4r}{5} - \dfrac{2r + 3}{4} = 1$
31. $\dfrac{2s - 8}{4} - \dfrac{1}{5} = \dfrac{7s + 1}{20}$
32. $\dfrac{2s - 3}{2} - \dfrac{1}{3} = \dfrac{4s - 1}{6}$

33. If 38% of a number is 20.9, what is the number?
34. If 42% of a number is 27.3, what is the number?
35. A worker's salary is decreased by $\frac{3}{8}$. If the new salary is $1345, what was the original salary?
36. A company states that its light beer has $\frac{1}{3}$ fewer calories than its regular beer. If a 12-ounce bottle of its light beer has 96 calories, how many calories does a 12-ounce bottle of its regular beer have?
37. The population of a town increases 7% to 5992. What was the original population?
38. The price of a book plus a 6% tax is $18.02. What was the price of the book itself?
39. A retail store has a standard markup of 30%. What did the store pay for an item that it has priced at $49.40?
40. A sofa is marked down 20% to $650. What was the original price?

$x + 30\% = 49.40$

## Calculator Problems

41. Solve to the nearest thousandth $q = \dfrac{q}{149} + \dfrac{607}{751}$.
42. The price of an automobile including a 5.5% tax was $10,210.29. What was the price of the automobile itself?

## Challenge Problems

Solve each equation.

43. $\dfrac{3x}{5} - 3 = \dfrac{x}{2} + \dfrac{x}{10}$

44. $\dfrac{y + 1}{6} - \dfrac{y}{4} = \dfrac{1}{6} - \dfrac{y}{12}$

45. $\dfrac{2}{3} + \dfrac{4}{a} = 1$

46. $\dfrac{5}{6b} = \dfrac{1}{2b} + \dfrac{2}{3}$

## 3.4 FORMULAS

Very often when solving practical problems we must know how to work with *formulas*. A **formula** is a rule that relates two or more variables. For example,

$$C = \frac{5}{9}(F - 32)$$

is a formula which gives the relationship between Fahrenheit temperature $F$ and the corresponding Celsius* temperature $C$.

**EXAMPLE 1**  What is the Celsius temperature when the Fahrenheit temperature is 14°?

Substituting the number 14 for $F$ in the formula above, we have

$$C = \frac{5}{9}(14 - 32)$$

$$C = \frac{5}{9}(-18)$$

$$C = 5(-2)$$

$$C = -10.$$

The Celsius temperature is $-10°$. □

The formula $d = r \cdot t$ describes the relationship between distance, rate, and time.

---

* Named after the Swedish astronomer Anders Celsius, who established the Celsius temperature scale in 1742.

**EXAMPLE 2**   If a car travels at a rate of 55 miles per hour for 4 hours, how far has it traveled?

Letting $r = 55$ and $t = 4$ in the formula above, we have

$$d = 55 \cdot 4$$
$$d = 220.$$

The car has traveled 220 miles.   □

**EXAMPLE 3**   How long would it take to travel 375 miles if an average rate of 50 miles per hour is maintained?

$$d = r \cdot t.$$

In this case, we let $d = 375$ and $r = 50$.

$$375 = 50t$$
$$\frac{375}{50} = t$$
$$t = 7\frac{1}{2}.$$

It would take $7\frac{1}{2}$ hours.   □

Simple interest $I$ can be calculated using the formula

$$I = Prt,$$

where $P$ represents the principal, $r$ the annual rate of interest *expressed as a decimal*, and $t$ the time in years.

**EXAMPLE 4**   Compute the simple interest on $300 invested at an annual rate of 5% for 1 year and 6 months.

$$I = Prt$$
$$I = (300)(.05)(1.5)$$
$$I = 22.50.$$

The interest is $22.50.   □

Due to the curvature of the earth's surface the distance $d$ *in miles* that a person can see over an unobstructed area is related to that person's height $h$ *in feet* above the surface. The relation is given by the formula

$$d = \sqrt{1.5h}.$$

**EXAMPLE 5**  If a person stands on a cliff, 100 feet above an ocean below, how far away is the horizon?

$$d = \sqrt{1.5h}$$
$$d = \sqrt{1.5(100)}$$
$$d = \sqrt{150} \approx 12.25.$$

The horizon is approximately 12 miles away. □

When an object with little air resistance is projected vertically upward with an initial velocity of $r$ feet per second, its velocity $v$ after $t$ seconds is given by the formula

$$v = -32t + r.$$

**EXAMPLE 6**  An arrow is shot vertically upward with an initial velocity of 128 feet per second. What is its velocity

a) after 2 seconds?
b) after 4 seconds?
c) after 6 seconds?
d) after 8 seconds?

The formula above, with $r = 128$, becomes $v = -32t + 128$. Using this formula with the appropriate values for $t$, we get

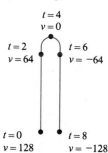

a) $v = (-32) \cdot 2 + 128$
    $= -64 + 128$
    $= 64.$
    Velocity is 64 feet per second.
b) $v = (-32) \cdot 4 + 128$
    $= -128 + 128$
    $= 0.$
    Velocity is 0 feet per second.
c) $v = (-32) \cdot 6 + 128$
    $= -192 + 128$
    $= -64.$
    Velocity is $-64$ feet per second.
d) $v = (-32) \cdot 8 + 128$
    $= -256 + 128$
    $= -128.$
    Velocity is $-128$ feet per second. □

Note that a *negative* value for velocity indicates that the arrow is moving in a *downward* direction.

A description of frequently used formulas from geometry can be found inside the back cover of the text. It may be necessary to refer to these formulas to solve some of the exercises in the next problem set.

**EXAMPLE 7**  Determine the total area $A$ of the Norman window pictured below.

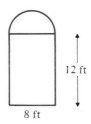

Total area — area of rectangle + $\frac{1}{2}$(area of circle)

$$A = \ell w + \frac{1}{2}(\pi r^2).$$

Using $\pi \approx 3.14$, we have

$$A \approx (12)(8) + \frac{1}{2}(3.14)(4^2)\frac{16}{2}$$
$$A \approx 96 + (3.14)(8)$$
$$A \approx 96 + 25.12$$
$$A \approx 121.$$

The total area is approximately 121 square feet. □

Occasionally, a formula is more convenient when it is written in a different form. The perimeter $P$ of a rectangle is related to the width $w$ and the length $\ell$ by the formula $P = 2w + 2\ell$. In this form the formula is said to be *solved for P*. This is because the variable $P$ is isolated on one side of the equation.

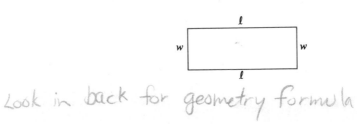

Look in back for geometry formula

**EXAMPLE 8**   Solve the formula $P = 2w + 2\ell$ for $w$.

To solve a formula for a specified variable means to isolate that variable on one side of the equation. In this case, we want to isolate the variable $w$. Therefore, we begin by subtracting $2\ell$ from each side.

$$P = 2w + 2\ell$$
$$P - 2\ell = 2w + 2\ell - 2\ell$$
$$P - 2\ell = 2w.$$

Then we divide each side by 2.

$$\frac{P - 2\ell}{2} = \frac{2w}{2}$$
$$\frac{P - 2\ell}{2} = w,$$

or

$$w = \frac{P - 2\ell}{2}. \quad \square$$

**EXAMPLE 9**   Solve $C = \frac{5}{9}(F - 32)$ for $F$.

We isolate $F$ on one side of the equation using the same techniques we used to solve equations in one variable.

$$C = \frac{5}{9}(F - 32)$$
$$9 \cdot C = 9 \cdot \frac{5}{9}(F - 32)$$
$$9C = 5(F - 32)$$
$$\frac{9C}{5} = \frac{5(F - 32)}{5}$$
$$\frac{9}{5}C = F - 32$$
$$\frac{9}{5}C + 32 = F - 32 + 32$$
$$\frac{9}{5}C + 32 = F,$$

or

$$F = \frac{9}{5}C + 32. \quad \square$$

## Problem Set 3.4

Use the formula and the values of the variables which are given to find the value of the variable that is not given.

1. $P = 2w + 2\ell$: $w = 5$, $\ell = 6$
2. $V = \ell wh$: $\ell = 5$, $w = 3$, $h = 2$
3. $A = \frac{1}{2}h(b_1 + b_2)$: $h = 4$, $b_1 = 8$, $b_2 = 10$
4. $A = \frac{1}{2}h(b_1 + b_2)$: $h = 6$, $b_1 = 10$, $b_2 = 12$
5. $A = \frac{1}{2}bh$: $A = 120$, $h = 15$
6. $d = rt$: $d = 630$, $r = 45$
7. $A = P + Pr$: $A = 1040$, $P = 1000$
8. $A = P + Pr$: $A = 800$, $P = 750$
9. $V = \frac{1}{3}\pi r^2 h$ : $\pi \approx 3.14$, $r = 3$, $h = 5$
10. $V = \pi r^2 h$: $\pi \approx 3.14$, $r = 2$, $h = 4$
11. $S = \dfrac{a}{1 - r}$: $S = 50$, $r = -\dfrac{1}{2}$
12. $S = \dfrac{a}{1 - r}$: $S = 75$, $r = -\dfrac{1}{3}$
13. $W = \dfrac{11(h - 40)}{2}$: $W = 132$
14. $C = \dfrac{5}{9}(F - 32)$: $C = 20$
15. $S = 2\pi r(r + h)$: $S = 47.1$, $\pi \approx 3.14$, $r = 1.5$
16. $S = 2\pi r(r + h)$: $S = 345.4$, $\pi \approx 3.14$, $r = 5.5$

17. What is the Celsius temperature when the Fahrenheit temperature is
    a) 23°?    b) 32°?    c) −4°?

18. What is the Fahrenheit temperature when the Celsius temperature is
    a) 20°?    b) −15°?    c) −40°?

19. The boiling point of water is 100° Celsius. What is it in Fahrenheit degrees?

20. The melting point of gold is 1948° Fahrenheit. What is it in Celsius degrees?

21. If a woman walks 4 miles per hour for a period of 20 minutes, how far has she walked?
22. How long would it take to drive 260 miles at a speed of 50 miles per hour?
23. The distance from New York to Southampton is approximately 2900 nautical miles. In order for the *Queen Elizabeth II* to make the trip in 5 days, what must be the average speed?
24. You see lightning strike a building 4 seconds before you hear the thunder. If the speed of sound is 1100 feet per second, how far away is the building?
25. Find the simple interest on $150 invested at an annual rate of $8\frac{1}{2}$% for 2 years.
26. How long must $1000 be invested at an annual rate of 12% to accrue $100 of simple interest?
27. How far could a man whose eyes were six feet from the ground see over land if his view were unobstructed?
28. If a sailor is positioned in a crow's nest 50 feet above the sea, how far away is the horizon?
29. A stone is thrown vertically upward with an initial velocity of 80 feet per second. What is its velocity

    a) after 1 second?         b) after 2 seconds?
    c) after 3 seconds?         d) after 4 seconds?

    When does the stone reach its maximum height? When does the stone strike the ground?

30. Repeat Problem 29 if the initial velocity is 112 feet per second.
31. How much would it cost to carpet the L-shaped living room below if carpeting is $16.00 per square yard while installation and padding is $3.75 per square yard? (*Hint:* 1 square yard = 9 square feet.)

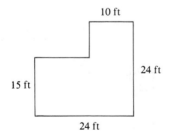

32. Which skillet has the greater frying surface, a circular one of diameter 9 inches or a square one of side 8 inches?

33. How many feet of fencing are needed to enclose a circular flower garden which is 16 feet in diameter?
34. How many times should you run around a block that is 825 feet long and 275 feet wide in order to run 5 miles? One mile is 5280 feet.
35. To determine the amount of wool which must be dyed to make the ring-shaped wall hanging below, its area must be found. If the diameter of the inner circle is 6 inches and the diameter of the outer circle is 24 inches, find the area of the wall hanging.

36. How many square feet of sod are needed to cover the lawn whose dimensions are given below?

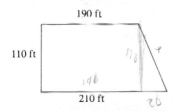

37. How many gallons of water will it take to fill an aquarium which is 21 inches by 11 inches and 8 inches deep? One gallon contains 231 cubic inches.
38. How many cubic feet of water will it take to fill a cylindrical wading pool which is 10 feet across and 3 feet deep?
39. What area of paint coverage is needed to paint 200 plastic balls, each having a radius of 3 inches?
40. How many square inches of paper are needed to label 100 cans of fruit juice if the height of each can is 10 inches and the radius of each base is 3 inches?
41. A conical pile of grain is 15 meters in diameter and 10 meters high. What is the volume of the grain?
42. A spherical weather balloon has a diameter of 20 feet. If each cubic foot of helium gas it contains has a lifting power of 1.11 ounces, what is the maximum weight the balloon can lift?

Find the area of each shaded region below.

43.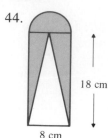

14 cm

6 cm

44.

18 cm

8 cm

Solve each of the following formulas for the specified variable.

45. $V = -32t + r$   for   $r$

46. $T = \dfrac{n}{4} + 40$   for   $n$

47. $P = 2\ell + 2w$   for   $\ell$

48. $P = 2\ell + 2w$   for   $w$

49. $d = rt$   for   $r$

50. $d = rt$   for   $t$

51. $A = \ell w$   for   $w$

52. $A = \ell w$   for   $\ell$

53. $A = \dfrac{1}{2}bh$   for   $h$

54. $A = \dfrac{1}{2}bh$   for   $b$

55. $A = P + Pr$   for   $r$

56. $V = -32t + r$   for   $t$

57. $W = \dfrac{11(h - 40)}{2}$   for   $h$

58. $C = \dfrac{5}{9}(F - 32)$   for   $F$

59. $I = Prt$   for   $P$

60. $I = Prt$   for   $t$

61. $V = \dfrac{1}{3}Bh$   for   $h$

62. $V = \dfrac{1}{3}Bh$   for   $B$

63. $A = \dfrac{1}{2}h(b_1 + b_2)$   for   $b_1$

64. $A = \dfrac{1}{2}h(b_1 + b_2)$   for   $b_2$

65. $3x + y - 12 = 0$   for   $y$

66. $5x + y - 10 = 0$   for   $y$

67. $3y + 6x = 9$   for   $y$

68. $5y + 10x = 15$ for $y$

69. $2y - x = 8$   for   $y$

70. $4y - x = 16$   for   $y$

71. $7x - 2y + 1 = 0$   for   $y$

72. $3x - 7y + 1 = 0$   for   $y$

73. $A = a + (n - 1)d$   for   $n$

74. $B = b - p(1 - r)$   for   $r$

## *Calculator Problems*

75. Determine the average speed in mph of a runner who completes the Boston Marathon (26 miles 385 yards) in 2 hours 39 minutes.

76. What is the simple interest on $14,758 at an annual rate of $15\frac{3}{4}\%$ for two years and three months?
77. How much larger is the surface area of the earth than the surface area of the moon if the diameter of the earth is 7926 miles and the diameter of the moon is 2160 miles?
78. The area $A$ of a triangle can be determined from the lengths of its sides $a$, $b$, and $c$ using **Heron's formula**

$$A = \sqrt{s(s-a)(s-b)(s-c)},$$

where $s$ is one-half the perimeter.* Find the area to the nearest tenth of a square meter of the triangle pictured below.

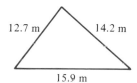

12.7 m   14.2 m

15.9 m

## Challenge Problems

79. Find the area of the shaded region below if the diameter of each circle is 10 cm.

$100 \ cm^2$

$\div 3\frac{3}{4}$

$15.70$

80. Determine the grazing area of a horse that is tied with a 50-foot rope to one corner of a shed that is 25 feet by 25 feet.
81. Solve

$$\frac{x}{a} + \frac{y}{b} = 1 \quad \text{for} \quad y.$$

* Named after Heron of Alexandria (ca. 75 A.D.).

## 3.5   APPLIED PROBLEMS

In previous sections of this chapter we were given equations and asked to solve them. In this section it will be left to us to read the problem and write an equation that fits the information given in the problem. Solving our own equation then will give us the desired answer to the problem.

Since it will be necessary for us to translate word phrases into mathematical phrases, let us practice with a few examples. In each of the following, the variable $x$ will be used to represent the unknown quantity, but actually any symbol would do.

| Word phrase | Mathematical phrase |
|---|---|
| Three more than a number | $x + 3$ |
| Three times a number | $3x$ |
| Half a number | $x/2$, or $\frac{1}{2}x$ |
| Two-thirds of a number | $\frac{2}{3}x$ |
| Thirty-five percent of a number | $.35x$ |
| One more than twice a number | $2x + 1$ |
| Five less than a number | $x - 5$ |
| A person's age in years | $x$ |
| The person's age in six years | $x + 6$ |
| The person's age four years ago | $x - 4$ |
| Seven times the person's age four years ago | $7(x - 4)$ |
| A number of dimes | $x$ |
| The value of the dimes in cents | $10x$ |
| A number of quarters | $x$ |
| The value of the quarters in cents | $25x$ |
| Consecutive integers | $x$ and $x + 1$ |
| Consecutive even integers | $x$ and $x + 2$ |
| Two numbers whose sum is 400 | $x$ and $400 - x$ |

Too often, a student reads a word problem and, not being able to see the solution immediately, gives up. Word problems are generally too involved to rush directly into a solution. Eating an entire meal in one bite would be extremely difficult, but the task is accomplished quite easily if it is taken a small bite at a time. So it is with word problems. We should take them one step at a time.

---

**Steps in Solving Word Problems**

1. Choose a variable, say $x$, and use it to represent one of the unknown quantities in the problem.
2. If there are other unknown quantities in the problem, represent each of them in terms of $x$.
3. Translate a statement in the problem into an equation involving $x$. Sometimes a diagram can be helpful here.
4. Solve the equation.
5. Check your solution.

---

We are now ready to consider some examples of word problems.

**EXAMPLE 1**   A 38-foot rope is cut into two pieces so that one piece is 5 feet longer than the other. Find the length of each piece.

**Step 1:**   *The two unknown quantities are the lengths of each piece of rope. Represent one of them by x.*

Let

$$x = \text{the number of feet in the shorter piece.}$$

**Step 2:**   *Represent the other unknown quantity in terms of x.*

Then

$$x + 5 = \text{the number of feet in the longer piece.}$$

**Step 3:**   *Translate a statement in the problem,*

length of shorter piece + length of longer piece = 38 feet,

*into an equation involving x.*

$$x + (x + 5) = 38.$$

**Step 4:**   *Solve the equation.*

first step combine likes

$$2x + 5 = 38 \quad -5$$
$$2x = 33$$
$$x = \frac{33}{2} = 16\frac{1}{2},$$
$$x + 5 = 21\frac{1}{2}.$$

The shorter piece is $16\frac{1}{2}$ feet and the longer piece is $21\frac{1}{2}$ feet.

**Step 5:**   *Check your solution.*

CHECK:   $16\frac{1}{2}$ feet $+ 21\frac{1}{2}$ feet $= 38$ feet.  $\square$

**EXAMPLE 2**  John is six years older than Jim. In two years John will be twice as old as Jim. Find their present ages.

**Step 1:**  *The two unknown quantities are the ages of Jim and John. Represent one of them by x.*

Let
$$x = \text{Jim's age.}$$

**Step 2:**  *Represent the other unknown quantity in terms of x.*

Then
$$x + 6 = \text{John's age.}$$

**Note:**  $(x + 6) + 2 = $ John's age in two years.
**Note:**  $x + 2 = $ Jim's age in two years.

*This is 2 times* **Step 3:**  *Translate a statement in the problem,*

John's age in two years $=$ twice Jim's age in two years,

*into an equation involving x.*

$$(x + 6) + 2 = 2(x + 2).$$

**Step 4:**  *Solve the equation.*

*need to combine x*
$$\begin{aligned} x + 8 &= 2x + 4 \\ x &= 2x - 4 \\ -x &= -4 \\ x &= 4, \\ x + 6 &= 10. \end{aligned}$$

Jim is 4 and John is 10.

**Step 5:**  *Check your solution.*

CHECK:   In two years Jim will be 6 and John will be 12, which is twice as old.  $\square$

These same five steps should be used to solve each word problem in this section.

**EXAMPLE 3**  The length of a rectangle is 3 feet more than twice the width. If the perimeter of the rectangle is 30 feet, find the dimensions of the rectangle.

Let
$$w = \text{the number of feet in the width.}$$

Then

$$2w + 3 = \text{the number of feet in the length.}$$

Using the formula for the perimeter of a rectangle,

$$2w + 2\ell = P,$$

we have

$$2w + 2(2w + 3) = 30$$
$$2w + 4w + 6 = 30$$
$$6w + 6 = 30$$
$$6w = 24$$
$$w = 4,$$
$$2w + 3 = 11.$$

The width is 4 feet and the length is 11 feet.

CHECK:   2(4 ft) + 2(11 ft) = 30 ft, which is the perimeter.  □

**EXAMPLE 4**   A collection of coins consists of 29 nickels and dimes. If the total value of the collection is $2.10, how many nickels and how many dimes are there?

Let

$$x = \text{the number of dimes.}$$

Then

$$29 - x = \text{the number of nickels,}$$
$$10x = \text{the value of the dimes in cents,}$$
$$5(29 - x) = \text{the value of the nickels in cents.}$$

Value of dimes + value of nickels = total value

$$10x + 5(29 - x) = 210$$
$$10x + 145 \quad 5x = 210$$
$$5x + 145 = 210$$
$$5x = 65$$
$$x = 13,$$
$$29 - x = 16.$$

There are 13 dimes and 16 nickels in the collection.

CHECK:   13 dimes are worth $1.30 and 16 nickels
are worth $.80, making a total value of $2.10.  □

**EXAMPLE 5**   One solution is 15% acid, while a second is 40% acid. How many ounces of each should be used to make 25 ounces of a solution which is 20% acid?

Let

$$x = \text{the number of ounces of 15\% solution needed.}$$

Then

$$25 - x = \text{the number of ounces of 40\% solution needed.}$$

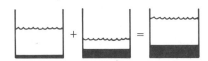

$$
\begin{array}{c}
\text{Amount of acid} \\
\text{in 15\% solution}
\end{array}
+
\begin{array}{c}
\text{amount of acid} \\
\text{in 40\% solution}
\end{array}
=
\begin{array}{c}
\text{amount of acid} \\
\text{in 20\% solution}
\end{array}
$$

$$.15x + .40(25 - x) = .20(25)$$
$$15x + 40(25 - x) = 20(25)$$
$$15x + 1000 - 40x = 500$$
$$1000 - 25x = 500$$
$$-25x = -500$$
$$x = 20,$$
$$25 - x = 5.$$

Therefore, 20 ounces of 15% solution and 5 ounces of 40% solution should be used.

CHECK:   20 ounces of 15% solution contains 3 ounces of acid, 5 ounces of 40% solution contains 2 ounces of acid, and 25 ounces of 20% solution contains 5 ounces of acid.   □

**EXAMPLE 6**   Tom leaves Los Angeles at 8 A.M. and drives north at a speed of 50 miles per hour. Jerry leaves Los Angeles at 8:30 A.M. and drives north on the same highway at a speed of 60 miles per hour. At what time will Jerry overtake Tom?

Let

$$t = \text{the number of hours Tom travels before being overtaken by Jerry.}$$

Then

$$t - \frac{1}{2} = \text{the number of hours Jerry travels,}$$
$$50t = \text{the distance traveled by Tom,}$$
$$60\left(t - \frac{1}{2}\right) = \text{the distance traveled by Jerry.}$$

Distance traveled by Tom = distance traveled by Jerry

$$50t = 60\left(t - \frac{1}{2}\right)$$
$$50t = 60t - 30$$
$$-10t = -30$$

Therefore, Tom travels 3 hours before he is overtaken by Jerry at 11 A.M.

CHECK:   At 11 A.M., Tom has traveled 3 hours at 50 miles per hour for a distance of 150 miles, and Jerry has traveled $2\frac{1}{2}$ hours at 60 miles per hour for a distance of 150 miles also.  □

## Problem Set 3.5

Write a mathematical phrase corresponding to each word phrase below.

1. Five more than a number
2. Seven less than a number
3. Twice a number
4. One-third of a number
5. Nine less than three times a number
6. Four more than twice a number
7. Two numbers whose sum is 23
8. Two numbers whose sum is 5500
9. Consecutive integers
10. Consecutive odd integers
11. The value of $3y$ nickels in cents
12. The value of $y$ quarters in cents
13. Five percent of a number
14. Fifteen percent of a number
15. A person's age four years ago if they are $s$ years old today

16. A person's age in three years if they are $2s$ years old today
17. Twice a girl's age in three years if she is $r + 4$ years old today
18. Three times a boy's age six years ago if he is $r + 2$ years old today
19. The number of liters of pure acid in $30 - z$ liters of a 35% acid solution
20. The number of liters of pure alcohol in $z$ liters of a 60% alcohol solution
21. The distance in miles traveled in $t$ hours at 55 miles per hour
22. The distance in miles traveled in $t - \frac{1}{2}$ hours at 40 miles per hour
23. One-half the sum of three consecutive even integers
24. Twice the sum of three consecutive integers

Solve each word problem.

25. One number is 4 more than another number. The sum of the two numbers is 30. Find the numbers.
26. One number is 3 more than another number. The sum of the two numbers is 27. Find the numbers.
27. The sum of two numbers is 39, and one of the numbers is twice the other. Find the numbers.
28. The sum of two numbers is 36, and one of the numbers is three times the other. Find the numbers.
29. Two consecutive integers have a sum of 155. Find the integers.
30. Two consecutive odd integers have a sum of 108. Find the integers.
31. One-half the sum of three consecutive even integers is 66. Find the integers.
32. One-fourth the sum of three consecutive integers is 42. Find the integers.
33. The grades on Tina's first four tests were 95, 84, 83, and 92. What must she score on the final exam, which is counted as three tests, to bring her average up to 93?
34. The grades on Bill's first three tests were 74, 78, and 79. What must he score on the final exam, which is counted as two tests, to bring his average up to 85?
35. A roofer laid shingles for four days. Each day he laid two more bundles than the previous day. If he laid 92 bundles in all, how many bundles did he lay the first day?
36. A student has 720 pages to be read in 5 days. Figuring that she may become fatigued, she wants to arrange her reading so that

each day she will read 20 pages less than the previous day. How many pages should she read the first day?

37. Kathy is three times as old as Sue. The sum of their ages is 24 years. Find their present ages.

38. Ted is twice as old as Mike. The sum of their ages is 54 years. Find their present ages.

39. Steve is twice as old as his brother. Four years ago he was four times as old as his brother. Find their present ages.

40. Jill is six years older than her sister. In two years she will be twice as old as her sister. Find their present ages.

41. Nancy is ten years older than Lisa. In two years she will be twice as old as Lisa. Find their present ages.

42. Dave is twice as old as Mark. Seven years ago he was three times as old as Mark. Find their present ages.

43. The length of a rectangle is 7 inches more than the width. If the perimeter is 34 inches, find the dimensions of the rectangle.

44. The length of a rectangle is 9 inches more than the width. If the perimeter is 34 inches, find the dimensions of the rectangle.

45. The length of a rectangle is 5 meters less than three times the width. If the perimeter is 54 meters, find the dimensions of the rectangle.

46. The length of a rectangle is 6 meters less than three times the width. If the perimeter is 76 meters, find the dimensions of the rectangle.

47. A collection of 40 nickels and dimes has a total value of $3.15. How many of each kind of coin are in the collection?

48. A piggy bank contains $7.45 in nickels, dimes, and quarters. If it contains 3 more dimes than nickels and twice as many quarters as nickels, how many of each kind of coin does it contain?

49. The total receipts for a basketball game were $1355 for 830 tickets sold. If adults paid $2.50 for admission and students paid $1.50, how many of each kind of ticket were sold?

50. The total receipts for a school play were $850 for 450 tickets sold. If adults paid $2.75 for admission and students paid $1.50, how many of each kind of ticket were sold?

51. How many liters each of a 60% alcohol solution and a 20% alcohol solution must be mixed together to form 40 liters of a 35% alcohol solution?

52. One solution is 12% acid while another is 30% acid. How many liters of each should be used to make 72 liters of a 20% acid solution?

53. How many grams of pure gold should be melted with 60 grams of an alloy containing 45% gold to obtain an alloy which is 50% gold?
54. How many ounces of pure alcohol should be added to 5 ounces of a 40% alcohol solution to obtain a 50% alcohol solution?
55. How can $6300 be invested, one part at 8% and the remainder at 12%, so that the interest will be the same on each investment?
56. A man invests $3600, part at 15% and the rest at 9%. His annual interest is $399. How much did he invest at each rate?
57. An executive leaves home at 7 A.M. driving 40 miles per hour. Fifteen minutes later, his wife finds the briefcase which he left behind, and starts after him at 60 miles per hour. When will she catch up with him?
58. A car starts out on a trip and travels 35 miles per hour. A half hour later a second car leaves from the same point and travels the same route at 50 miles per hour. How long does it take the second car to overtake the first?
59. One runner finishes a race in 1 hour. A second runner finishes 20 minutes later. If the rate of the faster runner is 2 mph more than the rate of the slower runner, find the rate of each.
60. Do Problem 59 if the rate of the faster runner is 3 mph faster than the rate of the slower runner.

## Calculator Problems

61. Two machines together weigh 71.361 kilograms. If one weighs 12.609 kilograms more than the other, find the weight of each.
62. A sum of $35,750 is to be invested, part in a high-risk fund paying 14.78% interest and the rest in a low-risk fund paying 9.37% interest. How much should be invested at each rate so that the total yearly interest is $3725?

## Challenge Problems

63. If $n$ is an integer, write an expression that represents
    a) an even integer.        b) an odd integer.

64. Think of a number. Add 3. Multiply by 2. Add 4. Multiply by 3. Divide by 6. Subtract your original number. The result is 5! Now, write a mathematical explanation for this puzzle.
65. How long will it take a runner who travels at 11 mph to lap a runner who travels at 8 mph on a 1-mile oval track?
66. A man says to his young bride of 27, "When you are my age I'll be 89." How old is the man?

## Chapter Review

True or false.

1. A first-degree equation is solved by isolating the variable on either side of the equation.
2. The formula $d = rt$ solved for $t$ is $t = rd$.
3. Adding $-3$ to each side of an equation is equivalent to subtracting 3 from each side.
4. Multiplying each side of an equation by $\frac{1}{2}$ is equivalent to dividing each side by 2.
5. The expressions $x$ and $x + 1$ may be used to represent consecutive odd integers.
6. The expression $55t$ represents the number of miles driven in $t$ hours at 55 mph.
7. If Richele will be $m$ years old in two years, then three years ago she was $m - 5$ years old.

Completion.

8. A statement that involves an equals sign is called a(n) _____?_____.
9. An equation that is true only for certain values of the variable is called a(n) _____?_____ equation.
10. The equation $3(x + 4) = 3x + 12$ is an example of a(n) _____?_____ equation.
11. The left-hand side of the equation $2x + 5 = 7$ is _____?_____.
12. A value for the variable of an equation that causes the equation to be a true statement is called a(n) _____?_____ to the equation.

13. A rule that relates two or more variables is called a(n)

_____?_____ .

Solve each equation.

14. $2x - 11 = 5$     15. $6x + 3 = 20$     16. $7x + 10 = 10x - 17$

17. $-3x + 8 = -x + 8$     18. $8(x - 3) = 4 + 3(3x - 5)$     19. $x - (3x - 2) = 6(x + 1)$

20. $\dfrac{y}{9} - \dfrac{2}{3} = \dfrac{4}{3}$     21. $\dfrac{3t}{4} - 3 = \dfrac{t}{3} + \dfrac{1}{3}$     22. $\dfrac{5r}{12} - \dfrac{3r + 4}{16} = \dfrac{r - 48}{48}$

Use the formula and the values of the variables which are given to find the value of the variable that is not given.

23. $P = 2w + 2\ell$: $P = 26$, $\ell = 8$

24. $S = \dfrac{a}{1 - r}$: $S = 90$, $r = -\dfrac{1}{2}$

25. $A = P + Pr$: $A = 1120$, $P = 1000$

Solve each formula for the specified variable.

26. $2a + b = 10$   for   $a$

27. $M = \dfrac{a + bc}{2}$   for   $b$

28. $D = c + (n - 1)d$   for   $n$

29. Write an equation describing each of the following conditions:
   a) A number added to 5 equals 27.
   b) Three times two more than a number equals 18.

30. If the outside temperature is reported as 20° Celsius, what is it in Fahrenheit degrees?

31. Determine the area of the region shown below.

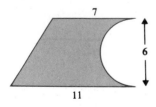

32. How many minutes will it take to run a 10-km race if a constant speed of 16 km/hr is maintained?

33. One number is twice as large as another. If the sum of the two numbers is 52.5, find the numbers.

34. A 43-foot rope is cut into three pieces so that the second piece is 3 feet longer than the first piece, and the third piece is 1 foot longer than the second. Find the length of each piece.
35. Three consecutive integers have a sum of 204. Find the integers.
36. A furniture store has a standard markup of 55%. What did the store pay for a lamp that it has priced at $41.85?
37. Hamburgers cost 95 cents each and hotdogs cost 80 cents each. If Terri was able to buy 15 sandwiches for $13.50, how many of each did she buy?
38. A tennis court for singles play is 24 feet longer than twice its width. If its perimeter is 210 feet, find its dimensions.
39. Lory is three times as old as Georganne. In two years she will only be twice as old as Georganne. Find the present ages of Lory and Georganne.
40. A ship averaging 20 mph steams out of port heading east. Forty-five minutes later, another ship leaves the same port and heads east averaging 25 mph. How long will it take the second ship to overtake the first?

# Chapter Chapter Chapter Chapter Four Four Four Four

## FIRST-DEGREE INEQUALITIES

## 4.1  THE ORDER RELATION

There are many situations that can be described more effectively in terms of **inequalities** rather than equations. We agree to say that the real number $a$ **is greater than** the real number $b$ if the graph of $a$ lies to the *right* of the graph of $b$ on the number line. For example, 6 is greater than 3 since the graph of 6 lies to the right of the graph of 3 on the number line.

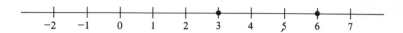

We denote this by writing

$$6 > 3, \quad \text{read} \quad 6 \text{ is greater than } 3.$$

We could also write

$$3 < 6, \quad \text{read} \quad 3 \text{ is less than } 6.$$

One way to keep the symbols $>$ and $<$ straight is to remember that *the symbol always points to the smaller number.*

**EXAMPLE 1**   Which is greater, $-1$ or $-5$?

$-1 > -5$ since $-1$ lies to the right of $-5$ on the number line.

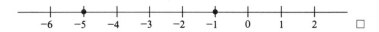

It may seem strange to say that $-1$ is greater than $-5$, but remember that a temperature of $-1$ degree is warmer, or higher, than a temperature of $-5$ degrees. However, it is true that $-5$ is greater *in absolute value* than $-1$.

**EXAMPLE 2**   In the diagram below, which is greater, $x$ or $y$?

$y > x$ since $y$ lies to the right of $x$ on the number line.  □

**EXAMPLE 3**   Which is greater, $\frac{2}{3}$ or $\frac{3}{5}$?

These fractions are difficult to compare because their denominators are not the same. Therefore we find the lcd and then write each fraction as an equivalent fraction having that lcd.

$$\frac{2}{3} = \frac{2 \cdot 5}{3 \cdot 5} = \frac{10}{15}$$

$$\frac{3}{5} = \frac{3 \cdot 3}{5 \cdot 3} = \frac{9}{15}.$$

Therefore, $\frac{10}{15} > \frac{9}{15}$ or $\frac{2}{3} > \frac{3}{5}$. □

**EXAMPLE 4**   Which is greater, $-\frac{3}{4}$ or $-\frac{5}{7}$?

Writing each fraction as a fraction with denominator 28, we have

$$-\frac{3}{4} = -\frac{21}{28}$$

$$-\frac{5}{7} = -\frac{20}{28}.$$

Since $-\frac{20}{28}$ lies to the right of $-\frac{21}{28}$ on the number line,

$$-\frac{5}{7} > -\frac{3}{4}. \quad \square$$

Just as the symbol $\neq$ means *is not equal to*, the symbol $\not<$ means *is not less than*. Therefore,

$8 \not< 4$ is read 8 *is not less than* 4.

Similarly,

$10 \not> 20$ is read 10 *is not greater than* 20.

When we write the statement $5 \leqslant 6$, which is read 5 *is less than or equal to* 6, we are saying that either 5 is less than 6 *or* 5 is equal to 6. Only one of these conditions could be true. Both conditions could not possibly hold. In this case we have $5 < 6$. We can also write the statement $5 \leqslant 5$. This is because the condition $5 = 5$ is true. On the other hand, we would *not* write $7 \leqslant 5$ because *neither* the condition $7 < 5$ *nor* the condition $7 = 5$ is true.

Now, suppose that a department store is having a sale on sweaters. One of their advertisements announces savings from \$6 to \$10. If $S$ represents the amount that may be saved on a sweater, then $S$ must be at least 6. That is,

$$S \geqslant 6 \quad (\text{or } 6 \leqslant S).$$

Also, $S$ is at most 10. That is,

$$S \leqslant 10.$$

The two inequalities

$$6 \leqslant S \quad \text{and} \quad S \leqslant 10$$

can be combined by writing

$$6 \leqslant S \leqslant 10.$$

This last statement is called a **double inequality.** It is read 6 *is less than or equal to S and S is less than or equal to* 10. Very simply, it means that the savings can be any amount between \$6 and \$10 inclusive. On the other hand, the double inequality

$$6 < S < 10$$

means that $S$ may be any amount between 6 and 10 (*not including 6 or 10*).

Therefore, we can write

$$0 < 4 < 5$$

because 4 is a number between 0 and 5. We *cannot* write

$$0 < 6 < 5,$$

because 6 is *not* a number between 0 and 5. That is, while $0 < 6$ it is *not* true that $6 < 5$.

The inequality

$$0 < 4 < 5$$

can also be written as

$$5 > 4 > 0.$$

However, *we shall never write a statement such as* $6 < 8 > 2$. While it is true that $6 < 8$ and also that $8 > 2$, it is *not* true that $6 < 2$.

Finally, it is possible to write a double inequality that includes one end value or the other, but not both. Examples of inequalities of this form are

$$3 < x \leqslant 8 \quad \text{and} \quad 0 \leqslant x < 7.$$

**EXAMPLE 5**   Find all numbers $x$ that satisfy the conditions $-3 \leqslant x < 5$ and $x$ is an integer.

The numbers that satisfy these conditions are the integers between $-3$ and 5, including $-3$ but not including 5. That is,

$$\{-3, -2, -1, 0, 1, 2, 3, 4\}. \quad \square$$

**EXAMPLE 6**  A car with a fuel capacity of 15 gallons gets 19 mpg in the city and 28 mpg on the highway. If $d$ denotes the distance in miles the car can travel on a full tank, write a double inequality that describes the values that $d$ may assume.

If the driving is done entirely in the city, then

$$d = 15 \cdot 19 = 285.$$

If the driving is done entirely on the highway, then

$$d = 15 \cdot 28 = 420.$$

Therefore,

$$285 \le d \le 420,$$

and the range of the car on a tankful of gas is 285 miles to 420 miles, inclusive. $\square$

## Problem Set 4.1

Replace the comma with the symbol $<$ or the symbol $>$.

1. 5, 3
2. 4, 1
3. $-7, 0$
4. $-6, 0$
5. $-2, -8$
6. $-3, -5$
7. $-10, 4$
8. $-15, 9$
9. $\sqrt{2}, 1$
10. $\sqrt{3}, 2$
11. $-\sqrt{2}, -1$
12. $-\sqrt{3}, -2$
13. $-1001, -1000$
14. $-1000, -999$
15. $\pi, 3.14$
16. $\pi, \frac{22}{7}$
17. $\frac{4}{5}, \frac{7}{9}$
18. $\frac{3}{4}, \frac{5}{7}$
19. $\frac{5}{12}, \frac{7}{16}$
20. $\frac{7}{12}, \frac{9}{16}$
21. $-\frac{3}{4}, -\frac{4}{5}$
22. $-\frac{2}{3}, -\frac{3}{4}$
23. $-\frac{5}{7}, -\frac{7}{10}$
24. $-\frac{4}{9}, -\frac{5}{11}$

True or false.

25. Every positive number is greater than every negative number.
26. Every negative number is less than every positive number.
27. Zero is less than every positive number.
28. Zero is greater than every negative number.

29. Given the number line diagram below, order each of the numbers
$a$, $b$, $c$, and $d$ from smallest to largest.

30. Given the number line diagram below, order each of the numbers
$x$, $y$, $s$, and $t$ from largest to smallest.

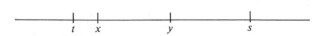

Find all numbers $x$ satisfying the given conditions.

31. $x > 2$ and $x$ is an integer
32. $x > 3$ and $x$ is an integer
33. $x \leq 5$ and $x$ is an integer
34. $x \leq 4$ and $x$ is an integer
35. $x < 5$ and $x$ is a whole number
36. $x < 4$ and $x$ is a whole number
37. $x \leq -1$ and $x$ is a whole number
38. $x \leq -2$ and $x$ is a whole number
39. $x \geq -3\frac{1}{3}$ and $x$ is an integer
40. $x \geq -4\frac{1}{2}$ and $x$ is an integer
41. $0 < x < 6$ and $x$ is an integer
42. $0 < x < 8$ and $x$ is an integer
43. $1 \leq x \leq 11$ and $x$ is an even integer
44. $2 \leq x \leq 12$ and $x$ is an odd integer
45. $0 \geq x > -5$ and $x$ is an integer
46. $0 \geq x > -4$ and $x$ is an integer
47. $x \geq 6$ and $x \leq -6$ and $x$ is an integer
48. $x \geq 4$ and $x \leq -4$ and $x$ is an integer
49. $x \geq -6$ and $x \leq 6$ and $x$ is an integer
50. $x \geq -4$ and $x \leq 4$ and $x$ is an integer

Describe each set of numbers using an inequality.

51. {5, 6, 7, 8, 9, 10, 11, ...}
52. {7, 8, 9, 10, 11, 12, 13, ...}
53. {..., −6, −5, −4, −3, −2}
54. {..., −8, −7, −6, −5, −4}
55. {−3, −2, −1, 0, 1, 2}
56. {−2, −1, 0, 1, 2, 3, 4, 5}
57. {4, 6, 8, 10, 12, 14}
58. {5, 7, 9, 11, 13}
59. {13, 15, 17, 19, 21, 23, ...}
60. {14, 16, 18, 20, 22, 24, ...}

Use an inequality to express the requirement that

61. $x$ be a positive number.
62. $x$ be a negative number.
63. $x$ be a nonnegative number.
64. $x$ be a nonpositive number.
65. $x$ be at least 7.
66. $x$ be at most 2.
67. $x + 3$ be less than 9.
68. $x - 5$ be greater than 6.
69. $r$ be between 5 and 6.
70. $r$ be between −2 and 0.
71. $y$ be at least −3 but less than 15.
72. $y$ be larger than 4 but no larger than 17.
73. a miler's time $t$ is less than 4 minutes.
74. a person's salary $s$ is more than $100,000.
75. a U.S. President's age $a$ must be at least 35 years.
76. a policeman's height $h$ must be at least 5'8".

77. A turnpike has a minimum speed of 35 mph and a maximum speed of 55 mph. A motorist travels for 3 hr on the turnpike while staying within these legal limits. Write a double inequality that describes the distance $d$ the motorist has traveled.

78. The diameter $d$ of a metal rod must be 3 cm, with no more than a 4% error. Write a double inequality that describes the values that $d$ may assume.

79. In 1983 the cost of sending a letter first-class was 20¢ for the first ounce and 17¢ for each ounce (or part of an ounce) after the first (up to and including 12 ounces). You have $1.65 to spend for postage. If $w$ denotes the weight of the letter you are mailing, write a double inequality which describes the values that $w$ may assume.

80. The charge for a particular long-distance phone call is $4.87 for the first 3 minutes and $1.57 for each additional minute. You have $19 to spend on a phone call whose length will be denoted by $\ell$. Write a double inequality which describes the values that $\ell$ may assume.

## Calculator Problems

81. True or false: $\sqrt{11} + \sqrt{17} < \sqrt{13} + \sqrt{15}$.
82. True or false: $\frac{691}{1427} > \frac{967}{1993}$.
83. A couple is willing to spend between $63,750 and $71,250 to build a new house on a lot they received as a wedding gift. If the cost of building is $39 per square foot, what size house (in terms of the number of square feet $n$) can they build?

## Challenge Problems

84. Find all integers $x$ such that
    a) $|x| \le 4$.       b) $|x| > 4$.
85. True or false: If $ab < 0$ and $a < -3$, then $b > 0$.
86. The markup on a particular calculator must be at least 30% of the cost. The cost of the calculator is $12. If a competitor is selling the same calculator for $24, what can the price $p$ of the calculator be if the competitor is to be undersold?

## 4.2   PROPERTIES OF INEQUALITIES

When an inequality involving a variable is complicated, it will be necessary to isolate the variable in order to interpret the inequality in a useful way. We were able to do this for equations by using the addition and multiplication axioms for equality. The obvious question is then, do the same laws apply for inequalities? The answer is — almost.

Let us first consider the effect of adding equal quantities to both sides of an inequality. Adding 3 to both sides of the inequality

$$2 < 4,$$

produces the inequality

$$5 < 7.$$

On the number line this transaction appears as follows:

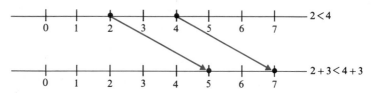

Adding $-3$ to both sides of the inequality

$$2 < 4,$$

produces

$$-1 < 1.$$

This can be diagramed as follows:

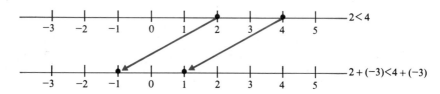

These two examples illustrate the following property.

---

**Addition Property of Inequality**

If $a < b$, then $a + c < b + c$.

---

Similar properties hold for the inequalities $a \leq b$, $a > b$, and $a \geq b$. In other words, *equal quantities may be added to both sides of an inequality.* Moreover, since *subtracting d* is equivalent to *adding −d*, we may also *subtract* equal quantities from both sides of an inequality.

**EXAMPLE 1**    Given the inequality $x + 4 < 10$, isolate the variable $x$ on one side.

To isolate $x$ on the left-hand side, we either add $-4$ to each side or subtract 4 from each side. Both methods are illustrated below.

| **Solve by adding −4** | **Solve by subtracting 4** |
|---|---|
| $x + 4 < 10$ | $x + 4 < 10$ |
| $x + 4 + (-4) < 10 + (-4)$ | $x + 4 - 4 < 10 - 4$ |
| $x < 6.$ | $x < 6.$ |

The solution consists of all numbers less than 6.  ⊔

It should be clear that any number less than 6 satisfies the original inequality $x + 4 < 10$.

   We now consider the effect of multiplying both sides of an inequality by the same quantity. Multiplying both sides of

$$-3 < 4$$

by $+2$ produces

$$-6 < 8.$$

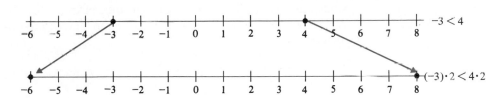

On the other hand, multiplying both sides of the inequality

$$-3 < 4$$

by $-2$ produces

$$+6 > -8.$$

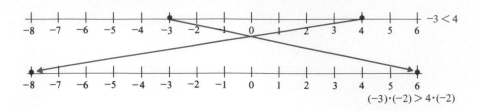

$$-3 < 4$$
$$(-3)\cdot(-2) > 4\cdot(-2)$$

Note that when both sides of the inequality were multiplied by a *negative* number, the direction of the inequality was reversed. Therefore, when solving an inequality we must *reverse* the inequality symbol whenever we multiply each side by a *negative* number.

---

**Multiplication Property of Inequality**

If $a < b$ and $c$ is positive, then $a \cdot c < b \cdot c$.
If $a < b$ and $c$ is negative, then $a \cdot c > b \cdot c$.

---

Similar properties hold for the inequalities $a \le b$, $a > b$, and $a \ge b$.

Again, since *dividing* by $d$ is the same as *multiplying* by $1/d$, we may also *divide* both sides of an inequality by any nonzero number. Further, since $1/d$ is positive or negative according to whether $d$ is positive or negative, we also must reverse the direction of an inequality when we *divide* by a negative number.

**EXAMPLE 2**   Given the inequality $4x < 12$, isolate $x$.

To isolate $x$ each side is multiplied by the reciprocal of 4, which is $\frac{1}{4}$. Since $\frac{1}{4}$ is a positive number, the direction of the inequality is not changed. We may also isolate $x$ by dividing each side by 4. Both methods are illustrated below.

| Solve by multiplying by $\frac{1}{4}$ | Solve by dividing by 4 |
|---|---|
| $4x < 12$ | $4x < 12$ |
| $\frac{1}{4} \cdot 4x < \frac{1}{4} \cdot 12$ | $\frac{4x}{4} < \frac{12}{4}$ |
| $x < 3.$ | $x < 3.$ |

The solution consists of all numbers less than 3. □

**EXAMPLE 3**   Given the inequality $-2x < 10$, isolate $x$.

To isolate $x$ we divide each side by $-2$ and reverse the direction of the inequality.

$$-2x < 10$$
$$\frac{-2x}{-2} > \frac{10}{-2}$$
$$x > -5.$$

The solution consists of all numbers greater than $-5$. □

**EXAMPLE 4**   A salesperson earns \$125 per week plus a 15% commission on all sales. What must the total sales $s$ in a particular week be for the salesperson to earn at least \$305 that week?

$$125 + 15\% \text{ of } s \geqslant 305$$
$$125 + .15s \geqslant 305$$
$$125 - 125 + .15s \geqslant 305 - 125$$
$$.15s \geqslant 180$$
$$\frac{.15s}{.15} \geqslant \frac{180}{.15}$$
$$s \geqslant 1200.$$

Total sales must be at least \$1200. □

## Problem Set 4.2

Add 5 to each side of the following inequalities and observe that the direction of the inequality remains the same. Then do the same with $-5$.

| | | | |
|---|---|---|---|
| 1. $1 < 2$ | 2. $5 < 10$ | 3. $0 < 6$ | 4. $-4 < 0$ |
| 5. $-10 > -20$ | 6. $4 > 3$ | 7. $-8 < 5$ | 8. $-1 < 1$ |

Multiply each side of the following inequalities by 2 and observe that the direction of the inequality remains the same.

| | | | |
|---|---|---|---|
| 9. $1 < 2$ | 10. $5 < 10$ | 11. $0 < 6$ | 12. $-4 < 0$ |
| 13. $-10 > -20$ | 14. $4 > 3$ | 15. $-8 < 5$ | 16. $-1 < 1$ |

Multiply each side of the following inequalities by $-2$ and observe that the direction of the inequality is reversed.

17. $1 < 2$
18. $5 < 10$
19. $0 < 6$
20. $-4 < 0$
21. $-10 > -20$
22. $4 > 3$
23. $-8 < 5$
24. $-1 < 1$

Isolate $x$ on one side of the inequality.

25. $x - 6 < 4$
26. $x + 4 > 1$
27. $x + 7 \geq 0$
28. $x - 3 \leq 0$
29. $2x < 4$
30. $4x > 12$
31. $5x \leq 0$
32. $\frac{1}{2}x \geq 0$
33. $-6x \leq 6$
34. $-x \leq -1$
35. $5x > 25$
36. $\frac{1}{4}x < 8$
37. $-2x \leq 7$
38. $-3x \geq 5$
39. $x - 8 > 5$
40. $x + 10 < 14$
41. $-x \geq -1$
42. $-5x \leq -20$
43. $\frac{1}{3}x \leq -6$
44. $8x \geq -24$
45. $-5x < -12$
46. $-7x > -19$
47. $2x + 6 < 0$
48. $3x - 12 > 0$
49. $5x - 1 \geq 9$
50. $4x + 1 \leq 13$

51. A salesperson earns $175 per week plus a 5% commission on all sales. What must the total sales $s$ in a particular week be for the salesperson to earn at least $240 that week?

52. The cost of renting a car for one day is $28 plus 18¢ per mile. How many miles $m$ can the car be driven that day if the bill is to be less than $55?

53. No more than 100 meters of fencing are available to construct a rectangular pasture whose width must be 23 meters. What are the possibilities for the length $\ell$?

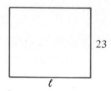

54. In 1983, the U.S. Post Office would not mail a rectangular package parcel post if the sum of its length ($\ell$) and girth ($2w + 2h$) exceeded 108 inches. If the width and length of a package are 18 and 26 inches, respectively, what are the possibilities for the height $h$?

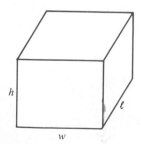

## Calculator Problems

Isolate $x$.

55. $-29.178x < 189.657$    56. $0.174x - 92.94 \geq 37.56$

## Challenge Problems

57. True or false: If $a < b$ then $|a| < |b|$.
58. Isolate $x$ if $x/a < 5$. (*Hint:* You must consider two separate cases here.)

<table>
<tr><td>**4.3**</td><td>**SOLVING INEQUALITIES**</td></tr>
</table>

Recall that a solution of an equation is a value for the variable that causes the equation to be a true statement; that is, a value that satisfies the equation. The solution of the equation

$$5x + 3 - 23$$

is 4, since the number 4 satisfies the equation.

Similarly, a **solution of an inequality** is a value for the variable that satisfies the inequality. Therefore, the solutions of the inequality

$$x + 4 < 10$$

consist of all real numbers less than 6, since these numbers, and only these numbers, satisfy the inequality. For example, the numbers 5, $\frac{1}{2}$, and $-10$ satisfy the inequality since

$$5 + 4 < 10,$$

$$\frac{1}{2} + 4 < 10,$$

and

$$-10 + 4 < 10.$$

The numbers 6 and 8 *do not* satisfy the inequality since

$$6 + 4 \not< 10,$$

and

$$8 + 4 \not< 10.$$

Note that the equation $5x + 3 = 23$ has one solution, namely 4. But the inequality $x + 4 < 10$ has an *infinite* number of solutions, namely all those real numbers less than 6.

Most inequalities are too complicated for us to immediately write their solutions. However, using the addition and multiplication properties of inequality, we can isolate the variable in almost exactly the same fashion as we did when solving equations. The only difference is that we must remember to reverse the direction of the inequality symbol whenever we multiply or divide each side by a negative number.

**EXAMPLE 1**   Solve the inequality $4x - 9 \leq 3$.

Using the addition property of inequality, we add 9 to each side.

$$4x - 9 \leq 3$$
$$4x - 9 + 9 \leq 3 + 9$$
$$4x \leq 12.$$

Using the multiplication property of inequality, we multiply each side by $\frac{1}{4}$ (or, equivalently, divide each side by 4). Since $\frac{1}{4}$ is a positive number, we do not reverse the inequality symbol.

$$\frac{1}{4} \cdot 4x \leq \frac{1}{4} \cdot 12$$
$$x \leq 3.$$

The solution consists of all those numbers less than or equal to 3. □

**EXAMPLE 2**   Solve $4x - 3 < 2x + 5$.

$$4x - 3 < 2x + 5$$
$$4x - 3 + 3 < 2x + 5 + 3$$
$$4x < 2x + 8$$
$$4x - 2x < 2x - 2x + 8$$
$$2x < 8$$
$$\frac{2x}{2} < \frac{8}{2}$$
$$x < 4.$$

The solution consists of all those numbers less than 4. □

**EXAMPLE 3**   Solve $6 - 3(y + 1) > 5y + 7$.

Our first step is to remove parentheses. Then we proceed as before.

$$6 - 3(y + 1) > 5y + 7$$
$$6 - 3y - 3 > 5y + 7$$
$$-3y + 3 > 5y + 7$$
$$-3y > 5y + 4$$
$$-8y > 4.$$

Our last step is to divide each side by $-8$. Since $-8$ is a negative number, we reverse the direction of the inequality.

$$y < -\frac{4}{8}$$

$$y < -\frac{1}{2}.$$

The solution consists of all those numbers less than $-\frac{1}{2}$. □

**EXAMPLE 4**   Solve $\frac{3}{4}t - 3 \le \frac{1}{2} + t$.

Since this inequality involves fractions, we begin by multiplying both sides by the lcd 4. This will clear the inequality of fractions.

$$\frac{3}{4}t - 3 \le \frac{1}{2} + t$$

$$4\left(\frac{3}{4}t - 3\right) \le 4\left(\frac{1}{2} + t\right)$$

$$3t - 12 \le 2 + 4t$$

$$3t \le 14 + 4t$$

$$-t \le 14.$$

To remove the negative sign, each side is multiplied by $-1$. Since $-1$ is a negative number, we must reverse the inequality symbol.

$$(-1) \cdot (-t) \ge (-1) \cdot 14$$
$$t \ge -14.$$

The solution consists of all those numbers greater than or equal to $-14$. □

**EXAMPLE 5**   Solve the double inequality $7 \le 3x - 8 \le 11$.

**METHOD I**

We can split the double inequality

$$7 \le 3x - 8 \le 11$$

into the *two* inequalities

$$7 \le 3x - 8 \quad and \quad 3x - 8 \le 11,$$

and solve each inequality separately.

$$
\begin{array}{ccc}
7 \le 3x - 8 & \text{and} & 3x - 8 \le 11 \\
15 \le 3x & \text{and} & 3x \le 19 \\
5 \le x & \text{and} & x \le \dfrac{19}{3}.
\end{array}
$$

These last two inequalities may then be written as the double inequality

$$5 \le x \le \frac{19}{3}.$$

**METHOD II**

A double inequality may often be solved without splitting it into two separate inequalities. We simply must be certain that when an operation is performed, it is performed in each of the three parts of the inequality.

$$7 \le 3x - 8 \le 11.$$

Add 8 to each part.

$$
\begin{array}{l}
7 + 8 \le 3x - 8 + 8 \le 11 + 8 \\
15 \le 3x \qquad\qquad \le 19.
\end{array}
$$

Divide each part by 3.

$$\frac{15}{3} \le \frac{3x}{3} \le \frac{19}{3}$$

$$5 \le x \le \frac{19}{3}.$$

Using either method, we find that the solution consists of all those numbers from 5 to $\frac{19}{3}$, inclusive. □

**EXAMPLE 6**   The freezing point of water is 0°C while the boiling point is 100°C. What is the corresponding range on the Fahrenheit scale?

Since $C = \frac{5}{9}(F - 32)$, we have

$$0 \leqslant C \qquad\qquad \leqslant 100$$

$$0 \leqslant \frac{5}{9}(F - 32) \qquad \leqslant 100$$

$$\frac{9}{5} \cdot 0 \leqslant \frac{9}{5} \cdot \frac{5}{9}(F - 32) \leqslant \frac{9}{5} \cdot 100$$

$$0 \leqslant F - 32 \qquad\quad \leqslant 180$$

$$32 \leqslant F \qquad\qquad\quad \leqslant 212.$$

The corresponding Fahrenheit range is 32°F to 212°F, inclusive. ☐

The *profit* $P$ of a company is determined by subtracting cost $C$ from revenue $R$. That is,

$$P = R - C.$$

**EXAMPLE 7**   A company can produce an item at a cost of $15 per item plus a monthly overhead of $1000. How many items must be manufactured and sold each month at $19 per item for the company's monthly profit to be greater than $2500?

Let $x$ = the number of items manufactured and sold each month. Then the monthly cost $C$ is given by

$$C = 15x + 1000.$$

The monthly revenue $R$ is given by

$$R = 19x.$$

The monthly profit $P$ is

$$P = R - C = \overset{R}{19x} - (\overset{C}{15x} + 1000) = 4x - 1000.$$

Since the monthly profit is to be greater than $2500, we write

$$P > 2500$$
$$4x - 1000 > 2500$$
$$4x > 3500$$
$$x > 875.$$

That is, in excess of 875 items must be manufactured and sold monthly if the monthly profit is to be greater than $2500. ☐

## Problem Set 4.3

Solve each of the following inequalities.

1. $2x - 4 < 6$
2. $3x - 2 < 7$
3. $5x + 4 > 9$
4. $4x + 1 > 5$
5. $-2x - 5 \geqslant 3$
6. $-3x - 5 \geqslant 7$
7. $-x - 4 \leqslant 3$
8. $-x - 5 \leqslant 2$
9. $-7x + 8 < -6$
10. $-6x + 11 < -1$
11. $8 - 3x \geqslant 20$
12. $15 - 5x \geqslant 30$
13. $7x - 4 < 4x + 17$
14. $8x - 9 < 3x + 16$
15. $3x + 9 \leqslant x + 9$
16. $5x + 2 > 3x + 2$
17. $5x - 10 < 6x - 10$
18. $6x - 12 \leqslant 7x - 12$
19. $11 - 3x \geqslant 7x - 19$
20. $17 - 6x \leqslant 9x - 13$
21. $8x + 13 \leqslant 4x + 22$
22. $10x + 11 \geqslant 6x + 22$
23. $4(x + 1) \leqslant 12 - 3(x - 2)$
24. $6(x + 1) \leqslant 7 - 5(x - 2)$
25. $3x - (5x + 15) < x$
26. $2x - (4x + 18) < x$
27. $x - (11x - 30) > 0$
28. $x - (16x - 30) > 0$
29. $4(2x - 1) > 5 - 2(x - 8)$
30. $3(2x - 3) > 9 - 2(x - 1)$
31. $\dfrac{y}{3} - 1 \leqslant y + 1$
32. $\dfrac{y}{4} - 1 \leqslant y + 2$
33. $\dfrac{1}{2}t + 5 \geqslant t + \dfrac{1}{4}$
34. $\dfrac{1}{3}t + 5 \geqslant t + \dfrac{1}{6}$
35. $s - \dfrac{2}{5} < \dfrac{s}{2} + \dfrac{1}{5}$
36. $s + \dfrac{1}{2} < \dfrac{s}{3} - \dfrac{2}{3}$
37. $10 < 1 - \dfrac{3r - 6}{5}$
38. $15 < 1 - \dfrac{2r - 4}{3}$
39. $12 - \dfrac{m - 2}{3} \geqslant \dfrac{m}{6}$
40. $21 - \dfrac{m + 1}{2} \geqslant \dfrac{m}{4}$

Solve each double inequality.

41. $3 < x - 4 < 5$
42. $2 < x - 3 < 6$
43. $0 \leqslant x + 8 < 8$
44. $0 \leqslant x + 7 < 7$
45. $3 < 3x \leqslant 15$
46. $2 < 2x \leqslant 16$
47. $-4 \leqslant x - 10 \leqslant 4$
48. $-5 \leqslant x - 10 \leqslant 5$
49. $1 \leqslant 2x - 9 \leqslant 3$
50. $1 \leqslant 2x - 3 \leqslant 5$
51. $2 \leqslant 3x + 1 \leqslant 3$
52. $2 \leqslant 4x + 1 \leqslant 4$
53. $-6 \leqslant -5x - 11 \leqslant 14$
54. $-7 \leqslant -3x - 10 \leqslant 20$
55. $15 < 6n + 3 < 22$
56. $21 < 8n + 5 < 30$
57. $-4 < \dfrac{3p - 9}{2} < 3$
58. $-2 < \dfrac{5p - 3}{4} < 1$

59. $-\dfrac{2}{3} \leqslant \dfrac{1-q}{6} \leqslant -\dfrac{1}{2}$

60. $-\dfrac{3}{4} \leqslant \dfrac{1-q}{12} \leqslant -\dfrac{1}{3}$

61. The percentage $P$ of bacteria left in a culture depends upon the number of minutes $t$ it is exposed to ultraviolet rays. For a particular culture this relationship is

$$P = 100 - \dfrac{15}{2}t.$$

If this culture is not deemed safe to use unless there is less than 25 percent bacteria remaining in it, what lengths of time render the culture safe?

62. The percentage $P$ of toxic gas left in a laboratory after an experiment depends upon the number of minutes $t$ an exhaust fan operates. For a particular room this relationship is

$$P = 100 - \dfrac{19}{2}t.$$

If the room is not deemed safe to use unless the air contains less than 24 percent of the toxic gas, what lengths of time render the laboratory safe?

63. Organizers of a banquet estimate the cost to be anywhere from $450 to $600. If 40 persons are to share the cost equally, what can each person expect to pay?

64. The **Intelligence Quotient** IQ of an individual is given by the formula

$$IQ = \dfrac{MA}{CA} \cdot 100,$$

where $MA$ is *mental age* and $CA$ is *chronological age.*[*] If the IQ's for a class of 12-year-olds range from 85 to 115, what is the range in mental ages for the class?

65. In Leningrad one day in November the temperature ranged from a low of $-15°C$ to a high of $15°C$. What is the corresponding range on the Fahrenheit scale?

66. The velocity $V$ of sound is 1087 ft/sec at $0°$ Celsius, and under normal atmospheric conditions it increases approximately 2 ft/sec for each Celsius degree increase in temperature. That is,

$$V = 1087 + 2C.$$

---

[*] This formula is due primarily to the work of Alfred Binet (1857–1911), Lewis Terman (1877–1956), and Wilhelm Stern (1871–1938).

For what Celsius temperatures is the velocity of sound between 1079 feet per second and 1125 feet per second?

67. A company can produce an item for a cost of $3.50 per item plus a monthly overhead of $700. How many items must be manufactured and sold each month at $4.75 per item for the company's monthly profit to be greater than $1500?

68. Ritz Rent-A-Car charges $25 per day plus 22¢ per mile, while Royal Rent-A-Car charges $30 per day but only 18¢ per mile. For what daily mileages is Royal the better deal?

69. An object's weight on the moon is $\frac{1}{6}$ its weight on earth. Suppose that the total weight of an astronaut and his space suit should be no more than 50 pounds on the moon. If the space suit cannot be made to weigh less than 120 pounds on earth, what limitation must be placed on the weight of the astronaut?

70. Tickets for a father-son banquet are priced at $4.50 for each father and $3.50 for each son. If the cost of staging the banquet is $280, how many father-son pairs are needed in order for the banquet to show a profit?

## Calculator Problems

71. Solve $15.789x - 37.746 \leq 18.714x - 42.426$.
72. Solve $14.709 < (6.718x + 19.373)/0.8140 < 26.998$ to the nearest thousandth.

## Challenge Problems

73. Devise a method for checking the solution to an inequality.
74. The rate of the current in a river is 2 mph. How far upstream can a motorboat that goes 5 mph in still water travel and still return within 3 hours?
75. The cost of publication of each copy of a certain magazine is 20¢. It is sold to dealers for 18¢ a copy, and the publishers receive from advertisers 6¢ for each copy over 10,000 that is sold. Find

the number of magazines that must be sold by the publisher to
ensure a profit.

76. Solve each absolute value inequality.

   a) $|x| < 4$      b) $|x - 2| < 4$      c) $|x + 3| < 4$

## 4.4   GRAPHING INEQUALITIES

An inequality involving one variable can generally be pictured using a
*graph*. The graph of an inequality consists of a set of points on the
number line.

**EXAMPLE 1**   Graph on a number line all those numbers $x$ that satisfy
the following conditions:

$$x < 2 \quad \text{and} \quad x \text{ is a whole number.}$$

The graph consists of the two points on the number line corresponding
to the numbers 0 and 1.

**EXAMPLE 2**   Graph on a number line:

$$x < 2 \quad \text{and} \quad x \text{ is an integer.}$$

The integers that are less than 2 are graphed below.

**EXAMPLE 3**   Graph on a number line: $x < 2$.

When it is not stipulated otherwise, we shall assume that $x$ is a *real*
number. Therefore, the graph of $x < 2$ consists of all points to the left
of 2 on the number line.

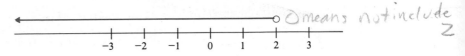

○ means not include

This graph is called an **open half-line.** The arrow indicates the graph continues infinitely far to the left. The open circle above the number 2 indicates that the point corresponding to 2 is not included in the graph. The graph has been drawn *above* the number line so that it does not coincide with the number line itself, making it difficult to read. □

If we wanted to *include* the number 2 in the example above we would have written

$$x \leqslant 2$$

or, equivalently,

$$2 \geqslant x.$$

**EXAMPLE 4**   Graph $x \leqslant 2$.

This graph is called a **closed half-line.** □

**EXAMPLE 5**   Graph $0 \leqslant x \leqslant 4$.

This graph consists of all those real numbers between 0 and 4, inclusive.

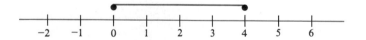

This graph is called a **closed interval.** The points corresponding to the two end values 0 and 4 are called the **endpoints** of the interval. □

**EXAMPLE 6**   Graph $1 < x < 5$.

In this case, the endpoints of the interval are *not* included.

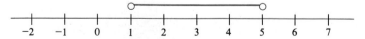

This graph is called an **open interval.** □

It is also possible for the graph of an interval to include one of the endpoints but not the other.

**EXAMPLE 7**    Graph $-2 < x \leq 2$.

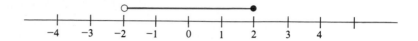

This graph is called a **half-open interval.** ☐

**EXAMPLE 8**    Graph $-6 < y < 6$ and $y$ is an integer.

This graph consists of only the integers between $-6$ and $6$.

**EXAMPLE 9**    Graph $3t - 7 \leq 14$.

In order to graph this inequality, we must first solve the inequality.

$$3t - 7 \leq 14$$
$$3t \leq 21$$
$$t \leq 7.$$

Therefore, the graph is the closed half-line below.

Two inequalities may be stated together to form a **compound inequality.**

**EXAMPLE 10**    Graph the following compound inequality:

$$-1 < x < 3 \quad \text{and} \quad x \geq 1.$$

The word "and" indicates that we are looking for all those numbers $x$ that satisfy *both* inequalities simultaneously. The graph of $-1 < x < 3$ is the open interval below.

The graph of $x \geq 1$ is the closed half-line below.

Therefore, those numbers $x$ that satisfy *both* inequalities are given by $1 \leq x < 3$. The graph of this double inequality is the half-open interval below.

**EXAMPLE 11**   Graph the following compound inequality:

$$-1 < x < 3 \quad \text{or} \quad x \geq 1.$$

The word "or" indicates that we are looking for all those numbers $x$ that satisfy *either* the first inequality, *or* the second inequality, *or* perhaps both inequalities. Those numbers $x$ satisfying at least one of the inequalities are given by $x > -1$. The graph is the open half-line below.

## Problem Set 4.4

Graph on a number line all those numbers $x$ that satisfy the conditions of each problem.

1. $x < 4$ and $x$ is a whole number
2. $x < 3$ and $x$ is a whole number
3. $x < 4$ and $x$ is an integer
4. $x < 3$ and $x$ is an integer
5. $x < 4$
6. $x < 3$
7. $x > 3$
8. $x > 2$
9. $x < 5$
10. $x < 6$
11. $x \geq -2$
12. $x \leq -1$
13. $x \leq 0$
14. $x \geq 0$

15. $x > \frac{1}{3}$

16. $x < \frac{1}{3}$

17. $x > \frac{1}{3}$ and $x$ is an integer

18. $x < \frac{1}{3}$ and $x$ is an integer

19. $0 \leq x \leq 3$

20. $0 \leq x \leq 4$

21. $0 < x < 3$

22. $0 < x < 4$

23. $-4 < x \leq 4$

24. $-1 < x \leq 1$

25. $-2 \leq x < 1$

26. $-3 \leq x < 2$

27. $-3 > x > -6$

28. $-2 > x > -5$

29. $-\frac{5}{3} \leq x \leq \frac{5}{3}$

30. $-\frac{5}{2} \leq x \leq \frac{5}{2}$

31. $-5 < x < 5$ and $x$ is an integer

32. $-4 < x < 4$ and $x$ is an integer

Graph each inequality and name the graph.

33. $5t - 1 < 14$

34. $4t - 1 < 15$

35. $-3t - 8 \geq 1$

36. $-2t - 9 \geq 1$

37. $-6 \leq 2t + 4 \leq 14$

38. $-7 \leq 3t + 5 \leq 17$

39. $0 < -t + 2 < 4$

40. $0 < -t + 3 < 6$

For each of the following problems, graph the compound inequality that results when the comma is replaced by

    a) the word "and."      b) the word "or."

41. $1 \leq x \leq 4, 0 \leq x \leq 2$

42. $0 \leq x \leq 3, 1 \leq x \leq 5$

43. $x \geq 0, x \leq 2$

44. $x \geq 0, x \leq 3$

45. $x \leq 3, x \geq 3$

46. $x \leq 2, x \geq 2$

47. $0 < y < 1, 1 \leq y < 2$

48. $0 < y < 2, 2 \leq y < 4$

49. $-2 \leq t < 2, 2 < t \leq 6$

50. $-1 < t < 1, 1 < t \leq 3$

51. $s \geq -\frac{1}{3}, s > \frac{7}{3}$

52. $s < -\frac{1}{2}, s \leq \frac{5}{2}$

53. Graph each equation or inequality.

    a) $|x| = 3$    b) $|x| < 3$    c) $|x| > 3$

54. Graph each equation or inequality.

    a) $|x| = 4$    b) $|x| < 4$    c) $|x| > 4$

## Calculator Problems

55. Graph the inequality $59.674x + 57.019 \leq -12.34x + 345.075$.

56. A car with a fuel capacity of $13\frac{1}{8}$ gallons gets 29.60 mpg in the city and 41.60 mpg on the highway. Determine the range of the car on a tankful of gas and then graph this range on a number line.

## Challenge Problems

Graph each inequality.

57. $2(x + 3) - 8 > -5 + 2x$

58. $3 + 5x \geqslant 2x + 1 > 4x - 6$

59. $\dfrac{1}{2} + \dfrac{4x - 1}{6} < \dfrac{2x}{3}$

60. $\dfrac{-10}{4x - 10} < 0$

## Chapter Review

True or false.

1. $-1000 > -999$

2. $\frac{5}{9} > \frac{9}{16}$

3. If $a < b$, then $a + 10 < b + 10$.

4. If $a + 4 \geqslant b + 4$, then $a \geqslant b$.

5. If $x \leqslant y$, then $-5x \leqslant -5y$.

6. If $-x < 0$, then $x > 0$.

7. If $xy > 0$ and $x < -2$, then $y < 0$.

8. If $a > b$, then $|a| > |b|$.

9. The real number $a$ is greater than the real number $b$ if the graph of $a$ lies to the right of the graph of $b$ on the number line.

10. The endpoints of the interval $-4 \leqslant x \leqslant 3$ are the points corresponding to the numbers $-4$ and $3$.

Completion.

11. A statement involving any of the symbols $>$, $<$, $\geqslant$, or $\leqslant$ is called a(n) _____?_____.

12. The inequality $a < x < b$ is a(n) _____?_____ inequality.

13. The addition property of inequality states that if $a < b$, then _____?_____.

14. According to the multiplication property of inequality, if $a < b$ and $c < 0$, then _____?_____.

15. According to the multiplication property of inequality, if $a < b$ and $c > 0$, then _____?_____.

16. Graph on a number line all those numbers $x$ that satisfy the conditions $0 < x \leqslant 5$ and $x$ is an integer.

17. Describe the set $\{..., -3, -2, -1, 0, 1, 2\}$ using an inequality.

18. Use an inequality to express the requirement that
    a) $r$ be a number between $-2$ and 7.
    b) $s$ be greater than 4 but not greater than 5.
    c) the horizontal distance $d$ from the face of a dartboard to the hockey line must be at least $7'6''$.

Solve each inequality.

19. $4x - 1 \le 15$

20. $1 - 3x < 4$

21. $13x - 10 > 10x - 10$

22. $4(8 - 3x) \ge 32 - 8(x + 2)$

23. $\dfrac{r}{5} - 1 < \dfrac{1}{3}$

24. $\dfrac{s}{6} > \dfrac{1}{3} - \dfrac{s - 2}{5}$

Solve each double inequality.

25. $2 \le 5x - 8 \le 17$

26. $0 < 11 - x < 10$

27. $-\dfrac{3}{2} \le \dfrac{1 - 4h}{10} \le \dfrac{1}{5}$

Graph each inequality and name the graph.

28. $x \ge 0$

29. $-3 \le t < 0$

30. $x - \pi < 0$

31. $-3 < 2y < 3$

32. $|y| \le \frac{3}{2}$

Graph each compound inequality.

33. $0 \le t \le 3$  and  $-2t + 10 < 4$

34. $0 \le t \le 3$  or  $2t + 10 < 4$

35. $r > \frac{1}{2}$  and  $r > \frac{1}{3}$

36. $r > \frac{1}{2}$  or  $r > \frac{1}{3}$

37. The taxi fare in a certain city is \$1.20 for the first $\frac{1}{8}$-mile and \$.20 for each additional $\frac{1}{4}$-mile. You have a maximum of \$8.40 to spend for your fare. If $d$ represents the distance you can travel in a taxi, write a double inequality that describes the values that $d$ may assume.

38. The relationship between Fahrenheit and Celsius temperatures can be written as $F = \frac{9}{5}C + 32$. Within what range must the temperature be in Celsius degrees for the temperature in Fahrenheit degrees to be between $-4°$ and $+50°$?

39. A salesperson earns \$150 per week plus a 25% commission on all sales. What must the total sales $s$ in a particular week be for the salesperson to earn at least \$415 that week?

40. A firm can produce an item at a cost of 4¢ per item plus a daily overhead of \$550. How many items must be manufactured and sold each day at a price of 6¢ per item for the firm's daily profit to be greater than \$600?

# Chapter
# Chapter
# Chapter
# Chapter Five
# Five
# Five
# Five

*EXPONENTS*
*AND*
*POLYNOMIALS*

## 5.1  EXPONENTS

As we have already seen, the expression $a^2$ is a shorthand way of writing $a \cdot a$. The number 2 in this case is called the **exponent** and the letter $a$ is called the **base.** The expression $a^2$ is read *a squared* (since it is the area of a square whose side is $a$), or *a to the second power*. If we wanted to introduce a shorthand way of writing $a \cdot a \cdot a$ it seems natural to simply write an exponent of 3 on the base $a$. Thus $a \cdot a \cdot a$ is written $a^3$ and read *a cubed* (since it is the volume of a cube whose edge is $a$), or *a to the third power*. Similarly,

$$a^{25} = \underbrace{a \cdot \cdots \cdot a}_{\text{twenty-five } a\text{'s}}$$

and is read *a to the twenty-fifth power*. The three center dots in this last example take the place of the twenty-three $a$'s which were not written.

---

**Definition**   Let $a$ be any real number and $n$ any natural number. Then

$$a^n = a \cdot \cdots \cdot a$$

where the number of factors of the base $a$ equals the exponent $n$. The expression $a^n$ is read *a to the nth power.*

---

From this definition we have that

$$a^1 = a,$$
$$a^2 = a \cdot a,$$
$$a^3 = a \cdot a \cdot a,$$
$$a^4 = a \cdot a \cdot a \cdot a,$$

and so forth. The expression $a^4$ is said to be in **exponential form,** and the expression $a \cdot a \cdot a \cdot a$ is in **expanded form.**

The French mathematician and philosopher René Descartes (1596–1650) is generally credited with being the first to use this exponential notation.

**EXAMPLE 1**   Find the value of $2^5$.

$$2^5 = 2 \cdot 2 \cdot 2 \cdot 2 \cdot 2 = 32. \quad \square$$

**EXAMPLE 2**   Find the value of $(-3)^2$ and $-3^2$.

The base in the expression $(-3)^2$ is $-3$. Therefore,
$$(-3)^2 = (-3) \cdot (-3) = 9.$$
However, the base in the expression $-3^2$ is 3. Therefore,
$$-3^2 = -(3^2) = -(3 \cdot 3) = -9. \quad \square$$

From this last example we see that an exponent acts only on the object immediately to its left, unless parentheses indicate otherwise. Therefore, when we write $3x^2$ we mean $3(x^2)$ and *not* $(3x)^2$.

**EXAMPLE 3**   Find the value of $5(-\frac{1}{5})^3$.

$$5\left(-\frac{1}{5}\right)^3 = 5\left(-\frac{1}{5}\right)\left(-\frac{1}{5}\right)\left(-\frac{1}{5}\right)$$
$$= -1\left(\frac{1}{25}\right)$$
$$= -\frac{1}{25}. \quad \square$$

**EXAMPLE 4**   Write $y \cdot y \cdot y \cdot y \cdot y \cdot y \cdot y$ in exponential form.
$$y \cdot y \cdot y \cdot y \cdot y \cdot y \cdot y = y^7. \quad \square$$

An expression involving exponents may contain more than one base.

**EXAMPLE 5**   Write $5 \cdot 5 \cdot a \cdot a \cdot a \cdot b \cdot b$ in exponential form.
$$5 \cdot 5 \cdot a \cdot a \cdot a \cdot b \cdot b = 5^2 a^3 b^2. \quad \square$$

**EXAMPLE 6**   Write $(x + 2)(x + 2)(x + 2)$ in exponential form.
$$(x + 2)(x + 2)(x + 2) = (x + 2)^3. \quad \square$$

**EXAMPLE 7**   Write $xxxyy + 3xy$ in exponential form.
$$xxxyy + 3xy = x^3 y^2 + 3xy. \quad \square$$

The terms in this last example cannot be added since they are not *like* terms.

## Problem Set 5.1

State the base and the exponent of each expression.

| | | | | |
|---|---|---|---|---|
| 1. $4^3$ | 2. $5^2$ | 3. $(-6)^2$ | 4. $(-2)^4$ | 5. $-6^2$ |
| 6. $-2^4$ | 7. $-x^5$ | 8. $-y^3$ | 9. $5^p$ | 10. $3^q$ |
| 11. $(r+2)^8$ | 12. $(s-1)^{10}$ | 13. $(u/3)^4$ | 14. $(v/2)^6$ | 15. $(6a)^{11}$ |
| 16. $(7b)^9$ | 17. $-\pi^{n+1}$ | 18. $-\pi^{2n-3}$ | 19. $(abc)^{1-3k}$ | 20. $(5xyz)^{1-k}$ |

Find the value of each of the following.

| | | |
|---|---|---|
| 21. $4^3$ | 22. $5^3$ | 23. $(-\frac{1}{2})^5$ |
| 24. $(-\frac{1}{3})^4$ | 25. $(-0.7)^3$ | 26. $(-0.4)^3$ |
| 27. $3 \cdot 5^2$ | 28. $2 \cdot 4^2$ | 29. $3 \cdot (\frac{1}{9})^4$ |
| 30. $2 \cdot (\frac{1}{8})^4$ | 31. $(-10)^2$ and $-10^2$ | 32. $(-8)^2$ and $-8^2$ |
| 33. $12(-\frac{1}{4})^3$ | 34. $10(-\frac{1}{5})^3$ | 35. $(-2)^7$ and $-2^7$ |
| 36. $(-3)^5$ and $-3^5$ | 37. $(-5)^4$ and $-5^4$ | 38. $(-6)^4$ and $-6^4$ |
| 39. $(-5)^3$ and $-5^3$ | 40. $(-6)^3$ and $-6^3$ | 41. $3^2 + 3^4$ and $3^2 \cdot 3^4$ |
| 42. $2^3 + 2^5$ and $2^3 \cdot 2^5$ | 43. $17^3 - 17^2$ and $17^3 \div 17^2$ | 44. $29^3 - 29^2$ and $29^3 \div 29^2$ |
| 45. $(2^3)^2$ and $2^{(3^2)}$ | 46. $(3^2)^3$ and $3^{(2^3)}$ | |

Write in exponential form.

| | |
|---|---|
| 47. $9 \cdot 9 \cdot 9 \cdot 9 \cdot 9$ | 48. $6 \cdot 6 \cdot 6 \cdot 6 \cdot 6$ |
| 49. $4 \cdot 4 \cdot x \cdot x \cdot x$ | 50. $5 \cdot 5 \cdot b \cdot b \cdot b$ |
| 51. $a \cdot a \cdot a \cdot b \cdot b \cdot b \cdot b$ | 52. $x \cdot x \cdot x \cdot y \cdot y \cdot y \cdot y$ |
| 53. $(x+1)(x+1)$ | 54. $(y-4)(y-4)$ |
| 55. $(x-2)(x-2)(x-2)$ | 56. $(y+5)(y+5)(y+5)$ |
| 57. $3aa - 2bbb$ | 58. $13aaa - 7bb$ |
| 59. $xxy + xyy$ | 60. $abb + aab$ |
| 61. $(3x)(3x)(3x)(3x)$ | 62. $(2x)(2x)(2x)(2x)$ |
| 63. $(5a)(5a) - aab$ | 64. $(7b)(7b) - abb$ |
| 65. $\dfrac{a}{b} \cdot \dfrac{a}{b} \cdot \dfrac{a}{b}$ | 66. $\dfrac{x}{y} \cdot \dfrac{x}{y} \cdot \dfrac{x}{y} \cdot \dfrac{x}{y}$ |
| 67. $\dfrac{n}{2} \cdot \dfrac{n}{2} \cdot \dfrac{n}{2} \cdot \dfrac{n}{2} \cdot \dfrac{n}{2}$ | 68. $\dfrac{m}{3} \cdot \dfrac{m}{3} \cdot \dfrac{m}{3}$ |
| 69. $(x^2)(x^2)(x^2)$ | 70. $(y^2)(y^2)(y^2)$ |
| 71. $(a^3)(a^3)(a^3)(a^3)$ | 72. $(b^4)(b^4)(b^4)(b^4)(b^4)$ |

## Calculator Problems

73. Find each value to the nearest thousandth.

   a) $(0.817)^5$    b) $(\sqrt{2})^3$    c) $\pi^{10}$    d) $\dfrac{1}{(-4)^5}$

74. Compute.

   a) $9 \cdot 57^4$    b) $93^4 - 93^3$

75. Show that $(2^3)^3 \neq 2^{(3^3)}$.

76. In about 1640 the French mathematician Pierre de Fermat conjectured that if $n$ were a positive integer, then $2^{(2^n)} + 1$ was a prime number. This conjecture was disproved by the Swiss mathematician Leonhard Euler in 1732, who showed that $2^{(2^n)} + 1$ is divisible by 641 when $n = 5$. Verify Euler's calculation.

## Challenge Problems

77. Find $x$ if $4^x \cdot 4^{225} = 4^{235}$.

78. Observe the following pattern:

   $1$                          $= 1$
   $1 + 3$                      $= 4$
   $1 + 3 + 5$                  $= 9$
   $1 + 3 + 5 + 7$              $= 16$
   $1 + 3 + 5 + 7 + 9 = 25$, and so on.

   Now formulate a rule for the sum of the first $n$ odd positive integers.

## 5.2   LAWS OF EXPONENTS

Suppose we wanted to find the product of $a^2$ and $a^3$. We could proceed as follows:

$$a^2 \cdot a^3 = (a \cdot a) \cdot (a \cdot a \cdot a)$$
$$= a^5.$$

Note that the exponent of the product $a^5$ is simply the *sum* of the exponents of the factors $a^2$ and $a^3$. That is, $a^2 \cdot a^3 = a^{2+3} = a^5$.

---

**First Law of Exponents**

$$a^m \cdot a^n = a^{m+n}$$

---

**EXAMPLE 1**   Find the product of $x^{27}$ and $x^{33}$.

$$x^{27} \cdot x^{33} = x^{27+33} = x^{60}. \quad \square$$

Note that the exponents were added (*not* multiplied) and the sum became the exponent of the common base $x$ to give the answer $x^{60}$.

**EXAMPLE 2**   Find the product of $3^2$ and $3^4$.

$$3^2 \cdot 3^4 = 3^{2+4} = 3^6. \quad \square$$

**EXAMPLE 3**   Find the product of $2x^2$ and $3x^7$.

$$(2x^2)(3x^7) = (2 \cdot 3)(x^2 \cdot x^7) = 6x^9. \quad \square$$

**EXAMPLE 4**   Find the product $a^r \cdot a^{r+1}$.

$$a^r \cdot a^{r+1} = a^{r+(r+1)} = a^{2r+1}. \quad \square$$

Now suppose we wanted to find the quotient of $a^5$ divided by $a^2$.

$$\frac{a^5}{a^2} = \frac{\cancel{a^2} \cdot a^3}{\cancel{a^2}}$$
$$= a^3.$$

This quotient could have been obtained by simply *subtracting* exponents. That is,

$$\frac{a^5}{a^2} = a^{5-2} = a^3.$$

---

**Second Law of Exponents**

$$\frac{a^m}{a^n} = a^{m-n}, \text{ where } m > n \text{ and } a \neq 0.$$

---

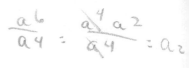

**EXAMPLE 5**   Find the quotient $x^{15}/x^5$.

$$\frac{x^{15}}{x^5} = x^{15-5} = x^{10}. \quad \square$$

Note that the exponents were subtracted, *not* divided.

**EXAMPLE 6**   Find the quotient $2^6/2^3$.

$$\frac{2^6}{2^3} = 2^{6-3} = 2^3. \quad \square$$

**EXAMPLE 7**   Find the quotient $(b^{p+2})/b$.

$$\frac{b^{p+2}}{b} = b^{(p+2)-1} = b^{p+1}. \quad \square$$

Let us now consider raising a power to a power. For example, consider $a^2$ raised to the third power, written $(a^2)^3$. We have

$$(a^2)^3 = (a^2) \cdot (a^2) \cdot (a^2)$$
$$= a^6.$$

This result could have been obtained more simply by *multiplying* exponents.

---

**Third Law of Exponents**

$$(a^m)^n = a^{m \cdot n}$$

---

**EXAMPLE 8**   Remove parentheses in $(x^4)^3$.

$$(x^4)^3 = x^{4 \cdot 3} = x^{12}. \quad \square$$

**EXAMPLE 9**   Remove parentheses in $(a^{r-1})^2$.

$$(a^{r-1})^2 = a^{2 \cdot (r-1)} = a^{2r-2}. \quad \square$$

The next law of exponents concerns raising a product to a power. For example, consider $(ab)^3$. We can write

$$(ab)^3 = (ab) \cdot (ab) \cdot (ab)$$
$$= (a \cdot a \cdot a) \cdot (b \cdot b \cdot b)$$
$$= a^3 b^3.$$

---

**Fourth Law of Exponents**

$$(ab)^n = a^n b^n$$

---

**EXAMPLE 10**　Remove parentheses in $(xy)^5$.

$$(xy)^5 = x^5 y^5. \quad \square$$

**EXAMPLE 11**　Remove parentheses in $(3x)^3$ and simplify.

$$(3x)^3 = 3^3 x^3 = 27x^3. \quad \square$$

**EXAMPLE 12**　Remove parentheses in $(ab)^{3r}$.

$$(ab)^{3r} = a^{3r} b^{3r}. \quad \square$$

Finally, let us consider raising the quotient $a/b$ to the third power.

$$\left(\frac{a}{b}\right)^3 = \frac{a}{b} \cdot \frac{a}{b} \cdot \frac{a}{b}$$

$$= \frac{a \cdot a \cdot a}{b \cdot b \cdot b}$$

$$= \frac{a^3}{b^3}.$$

---

**Fifth Law of Exponents**

$$\left(\frac{a}{b}\right)^n = \frac{a^n}{b^n}, \text{ where } b \neq 0.$$

---

**EXAMPLE 13**　Remove parentheses in $(x/y)^{10}$.

$$\left(\frac{x}{y}\right)^{10} = \frac{x^{10}}{y^{10}}. \quad \square$$

**EXAMPLE 14**　Remove parentheses in $(x/4)^2$ and simplify.

$$\left(\frac{x}{4}\right)^2 = \frac{x^2}{4^2} = \frac{x^2}{16}. \quad \square$$

**EXAMPLE 15**   Remove parentheses in $(u/v)^{n+1}$.

$$\left(\frac{u}{v}\right)^{n+1} = \frac{u^{n+1}}{v^{n+1}}. \quad \square$$

Very often it will be necessary to use a combination of the laws of exponents in the same problem.

**EXAMPLE 16**   Remove parentheses and simplify $(4x/y^2)^3$.

$$\left(\frac{4x}{y^2}\right)^3 = \frac{(4x)^3}{(y^2)^3} = \frac{4^3 x^3}{y^6} = \frac{64x^3}{y^6}. \quad \square$$

**EXAMPLE 17**   Remove parentheses and simplify $(6r^3 s^4)(-2rs^2)^3(r^5 s^6)^4$.

$$(6r^3 s^4)(-2rs^2)^3(r^5 s^6)^4 = 6r^3 s^4(-2)^3 r^3(s^2)^3(r^5)^4(s^6)^4$$
$$= 6r^3 s^4(-8)r^3 s^6 r^{20} s^{24}$$
$$= 6 \cdot (-8)(r^3 \cdot r^3 \cdot r^{20})(s^4 \cdot s^6 \cdot s^{24})$$
$$= -48r^{26} s^{34}. \quad \square$$

*Look at sign*
*Pos · neg · Pos = —*

---

## Problem Set 5.2

Use the first law of exponents to find each product.

1. $x^2 \cdot x^5$
2. $x^4 \cdot x^5$
3. $a^3 \cdot a^6$
4. $a^8 \cdot a^7$
5. $b \cdot b^7$
6. $b \cdot b^5$
7. $y^2 \cdot y^4 \cdot y^6$
8. $y^3 \cdot y^5 \cdot y^7$
9. $5^2 \cdot 5^4$
10. $7^2 \cdot 7^4$
11. $3^4 \cdot 3^5 \cdot 3^9$
12. $4^3 \cdot 4^5 \cdot 4^8$
13. $(x + 2)^2(x + 2)^4$
14. $(y + 3)^3(y + 3)^5$
15. $(r - 1)^{99}(r - 1)$
16. $(s - 4)^{100}(s - 4)$
17. $(2x)(4x^2)$
18. $(3x^2)(5x)$
19. $(2a^2)(a^3)(2a)$
20. $(3a)(a^2)(4a^3)$
21. $(3a^2 b)(2ab^2)(4ab)$
22. $(4ab^2)(5a^2 b)(2ab)$
23. $(-5p^3 q^2)(6pq^4)(p^3 q^3)$
24. $(-3pq^3)(p^2 q^2)(7p^5 q^4)$
25. $x^n \cdot x$
26. $a^{n+1} \cdot a^{n+2}$

Use the second law of exponents to find each quotient.

27. $x^5/x^3$
28. $x^7/x^4$
29. $a^{10}/a^2$
30. $a^8/a^2$
31. $y^5/y$
32. $y^6/y$
33. $a^3 b^{20}/ab^4$
34. $a^4 b^{16}/ab^4$
35. $5^6/5^2$
36. $7^9/7^3$
37. $101^{99}/101^{33}$
38. $707^{66}/707^{11}$
39. $(x + 2)^6/(x + 2)^2$
40. $(y + 3)^9/(y + 3)^3$
41. $(5n - 3)^{55}/(5n - 3)^{54}$

42. $(3m - 1)^{100}/(3m - 1)^{99}$    43. $a^{3q}/a^q$       44. $x^{n+1}/x$

Use the third law of exponents to remove parentheses.

45. $(x^2)^3$    46. $(x^3)^2$    47. $(a^4)^5$    48. $(a^3)^5$    49. $(b^{20})^3$
50. $(b^{10})^7$    51. $(x^n)^2$    52. $(y^m)^3$    53. $(a^{r+1})^3$    54. $(b^{r-1})^2$

Use the fourth law of exponents to remove parentheses.

55. $(xy)^3$    56. $(xy)^4$    57. $(ab)^{10}$    58. $(ab)^{20}$    59. $(5xy)^3$
60. $(10xy)^3$    61. $(-4pq)^2$    62. $(-3pq)^4$    63. $(ab)^{r+1}$    64. $(ab)^{2r}$

Use the fifth law of exponents to remove parentheses.

65. $(x/y)^5$    66. $(x/y)^6$    67. $(a/b)^{15}$    68. $(a/b)^{25}$    69. $(3/b)^4$
70. $(2/b)^7$    71. $(p/-5)^3$    72. $(q/-2)^5$    73. $(u/v)^{3s}$    74. $(u/v)^{s+2}$

Remove parentheses and simplify.

75. $(xy^2)^3$           76. $(x^2y)^3$           77. $(a^2b^3)^4$
78. $(a^3b^2)^5$        79. $(3x^2y^3)^4$       80. $(5x^3y^4)^3$
81. $(x^2/y)^5$        82. $(x/y^2)^4$        83. $(3x^4/y^2)^3$
84. $(2x^3/y^4)^3$      85. $(2x^6/5y^3)^4(x^2/y)^2$    86. $(3x^4/4y^2)^4(x/y^3)^2$
87. $(2x^2)^3(5x)^2$     88. $(4x^3)^2(3x^4)^3$      89. $(3x^2y)(4xy)^2$
90. $(2x^3y)^2(5xy^4)$    91. $(7r^2s)(-3r^3s^3)^3(r^{10}s^8)^4$    92. $(-2r^4s^5)^3(8r^3s^2)(r^6s^6)^5$

## Calculator Problems

Remove parentheses and simplify.

93. $(2x^{471}y^{938})^{23}$     94. $(-3a^{727}/b^{333})^{13}$     95. $3r^{2819}s^{1929}(-2r^{94}s^{129})^{16}$

## Challenge Problems

96. Find $x$ if

    a) $(7^3)^x = 7^{12}$.    b) $\dfrac{5^{2x+1}}{5^2} = 125$.    c) $4^x \cdot 2^{20} = 4^{17}$.

97. Remove parentheses and simplify $\dfrac{2a^n(-2a^nb^{m+1})^3a}{b^2}$.

98. Show that $a^m \cdot a^n = a^{m+n}$ for all positive integers $m$ and $n$.

## 5.3 ZERO AND NEGATIVE EXPONENTS (OPTIONAL)

In this section we shall extend the concept of an exponent to include *zero* and *negative* exponents. We shall define these exponents so that the laws of exponents apply to them as well as to the positive exponents previously discussed.

Consider the fraction $5^2/5^2$. If the second law of exponents is to apply, then

$$\frac{5^2}{5^2} = 5^{2-2} = 5^0.$$

But also

$$\frac{5^2}{5^2} = \frac{25}{25} = 1.$$

Therefore it is natural to define $5^0$ as 1. It should also be clear that we could have used *any* base (except zero) in place of the base 5 in the discussion above. Hence we make the definition below.

---

**Definition**   Let $a$ be any real number except zero.* Then

$$a^0 = 1.$$

---

**EXAMPLE 1**   Simplify each of the following: $325^0$, $1^0$, $(\frac{1}{2})^0$, $x^0$ $(x \neq 0)$, $(7x^2y^3)^0$ $(x \neq 0, y \neq 0)$, $(-5)^0$, $-5^0$.

$$325^0 = 1$$
$$1^0 = 1$$
$$\left(\frac{1}{2}\right)^0 = 1$$
$$x^0 = 1 \quad \text{if } x \neq 0$$
$$(7x^2y^3)^0 = 1 \quad \text{if } x \neq 0, y \neq 0$$
$$(-5)^0 = 1$$
$$-5^0 = -1 \quad (\text{since the base is 5, } not -5). \quad \square$$

---

* The expression $0^0$ shall be left undefined.

Now consider the fraction $5^2/5^5$. If the second law of exponents is to apply, then

$$\frac{5^2}{5^5} = 5^{2-5} = 5^{-3}.$$

But also

$$\frac{5^2}{5^5} = \frac{5^2}{5^2 \cdot 5^3} = \frac{1}{5^3}.$$

Therefore it is natural to define $5^{-3}$ as $1/5^3$. Again, *any* real number (except zero) could have been used in place of the base 5 in the discussion above.

---

**Definition**   Let $a$ be any real number except zero and $n$ any natural number. Then

$$a^{-n} = \frac{1}{a^n}.$$

---

Therefore,

$$a^{-1} = \frac{1}{a^1},$$

$$a^{-2} = \frac{1}{a^2},$$

$$a^{-3} = \frac{1}{a^3}, \quad \text{and so forth.}$$

The English mathematician John Wallis (1616–1703) was the first to fully explain the meaning of the zero exponent and of negative exponents.

**EXAMPLE 2**   Simplify each of the following: $10^{-2}$, $x^{-8}$ $(x \neq 0)$, $(\tfrac{1}{3})^{-2}$.

$$10^{-2} = \frac{1}{10^2} = \frac{1}{100}, \text{ or } 0.01$$

$$x^{-8} = \frac{1}{x^8} \quad \text{if } x \neq 0$$

$$\left(\frac{1}{3}\right)^{-2} = \frac{1}{\left(\frac{1}{3}\right)^2} = \frac{1}{\frac{1}{9}} = 9. \quad \square$$

We can observe certain patterns that occur with negative exponents. For example,

*multiply by Reciprocal*

$$\left(\frac{a}{b}\right)^{-n} = \frac{1}{(a/b)^n} = \frac{1}{a^n/b^n} = \frac{b^n}{a^n} = \left(\frac{b}{a}\right)^n.$$

*See it changes*

$$\div \mid \frac{b^n}{a^n}$$

$$a^{-n}_b = \frac{b^n}{a}$$

Hence the rule

$$\left(\frac{a}{b}\right)^{-n} = \left(\frac{b}{a}\right)^n, \text{ where } a \neq 0 \text{ and } b \neq 0.$$

In other words, *a negative exponent on a fraction may be replaced by the corresponding positive exponent simply by inverting the fraction.*
    Also,

$$\frac{1}{a^{-n}} = \frac{1}{1/a^n} = a^n.$$

Hence the rule

$$\frac{1}{a^{-n}} = a^n, \text{ where } a \neq 0.$$

**EXAMPLE 3**   Simplify each of the following: $(\frac{1}{2})^{-5}$, $(\frac{2}{5})^{-3}$, $1/10^{-2}$, $7/x^{-9}$ $(x \neq 0)$, $2^{-1} + 4^{-1}$.

$$\left(\frac{1}{2}\right)^{-5} = \left(\frac{2}{1}\right)^5 = 32 \qquad \left(\frac{1}{2}\right)^{-5} = 2^5$$

$$\left(\frac{2}{5}\right)^{-3} = \left(\frac{5}{2}\right)^3 = \frac{125}{8}$$

$$\frac{1}{10^{-2}} = 10^2 = 100$$

$$\frac{7}{x^{-9}} = 7 \cdot \frac{1}{x^{-9}} = 7x^9 \quad \text{if } x \neq 0$$

$$2^{-1} + 4^{-1} = \frac{1}{2} + \frac{1}{4} = \frac{3}{4}. \quad \square$$

**EXAMPLE 4**   Write $x^{-2}/y^{-3}$ with positive exponents.

$$\frac{x^{-2}}{y^{-3}} = \frac{\frac{1}{x^2}}{\frac{1}{y^3}} = \frac{1}{x^2} \cdot \frac{y^3}{1} = \frac{y^3}{x^2}. \quad \square$$

**EXAMPLE 5**   Write $10^{-5}$ in decimal form.

$$10^{-5} = \frac{1}{10^5}$$

$$= \frac{1}{100,000}$$

$$= 0.00001. \quad \square$$

Since negative exponents were defined with the laws of exponents in mind, we may use these laws to simplify expressions containing negative exponents.

**EXAMPLE 6**   Write $(10^{-2} \cdot 10^3)/(10^7 \cdot 10^{-5})$ as a power of ten.

$$\frac{10^{-2} \cdot 10^3}{10^7 \cdot 10^{-5}} = \frac{10^{-2+3}}{10^{7+(-5)}}$$

$$= \frac{10^1}{10^2}$$

$$= 10^{1-2}$$

$$= 10^{-1}. \quad \square$$

**EXAMPLE 7**   Simplify $x^{-8} \cdot x^3 \cdot x$ and write your answer using a positive exponent.

Using the first law of exponents, we have

$$x^{-8} \cdot x^3 \cdot x = x^{-8+3+1} = x^{-4} = \frac{1}{x^4}. \quad \square$$

**EXAMPLE 8**   Simplify $(3r^{-2}s^3)^4$ and write your answer using positive exponents.

Using the fourth law of exponents, we have

$$(3r^{-2}s^3)^4 = 3^4(r^{-2})^4(s^3)^4.$$

Then, using the third law of exponents, we have

$$= 3^4 r^{(-2) \cdot 4} s^{3 \cdot 4}$$

$$= 3^4 r^{-8} s^{12}$$

$$= 3^4 \cdot \frac{1}{r^8} \cdot s^{12}$$

$$= \frac{3^4 s^{12}}{r^8}, \quad \text{or} \quad \frac{81 s^{12}}{r^8}. \quad \square$$

**EXAMPLE 9** Simplify $(a^3b^{-1}/c^{-2})^{-3}$ and write your answer using positive exponents.

$$\left(\frac{a^3b^{-1}}{c^{-2}}\right)^{-3} = \frac{(a^3)^{-3}(b^{-1})^{-3}}{(c^{-2})^{-3}}$$

$$= \frac{a^{-9}b^3}{c^6}$$

$$= \frac{\left(\frac{1}{a^9} \cdot b^3\right)}{c^6}$$

$$= \frac{\frac{b^3}{a^9}}{\frac{c^6}{1}}$$

$$= \frac{b^3}{a^9} \cdot \frac{1}{c^6}$$

$$= \frac{b^3}{a^9c^6}. \quad \square$$

## Problem Set 5.3

Simplify each of the following.

1. $8^0$
2. $13^0$
3. $999^0$
4. $1,000,000^0$
5. $t^0$, $t \neq 0$
6. $y^0$, $y \neq 0$
7. $(5a^2b^3)^0$, $a \neq 0, b \neq 0$
8. $(-3a^3b^2)^0$, $a \neq 0, b \neq 0$
9. $(-4)^0$ and $-4^0$
10. $(-3)^0$ and $-3^0$
11. $(t - 2)^0$, $t \neq 2$
12. $(y + 4)^0$, $y \neq -4$

Write with positive exponents and simplify.

13. $10^{-1}$
14. $10^{-2}$
15. $10^{-3}$
16. $10^{-4}$
17. $x^{-5}$, $x \neq 0$
18. $x^{-6}$, $x \neq 0$
19. $(\frac{1}{2})^{-3}$
20. $(\frac{1}{3})^{-2}$
21. $(\frac{2}{7})^{-2}$
22. $(-\frac{2}{5})^{-3}$
23. $(-\frac{3}{5})^{-3}$
24. $(\frac{4}{9})^{-2}$
25. $1/4^{-4}$
26. $1/3^{-4}$
27. $1/y^{-8}$
28. $1/y^{-7}$
29. $1/(\frac{1}{3})^{-2}$
30. $1/(\frac{1}{2})^{-3}$
31. $2^{-1} + 3^{-1}$
32. $3^{-1} + 4^{-1}$
33. $12^{-1} - 6^{-1} + 1^{-1}$
34. $15^{-1} - 5^{-1} + 1^{-1}$
35. $3^{-2} + 4^{-3}$
36. $2^{-3} + 3^{-4}$
37. $5x^{-2}$
38. $7x^{-3}$
39. $-13a^{-13}$
40. $-19a^{-19}$
41. $10/t^{-4}$
42. $15/t^{-9}$

43. $(-1)/b^{-1}$
44. $(-10)/b^{-1}$
45. $x^{-5}/y^{-2}$
46. $x^{-4}/y^{-6}$
47. $a^{-12}b^4/c^{-6}$
48. $a^5b^{-15}/c^{-10}$

Write each power of ten in decimal form.

49. $10^3$
50. $10^4$
51. $10^{-2}$
52. $10^{-3}$
53. $10^{-1}$
54. $10^{-4}$
55. $10^9$
56. $10^7$
57. $10^{-11}$
58. $10^{-14}$
59. $10^{-18}$
60. $10^{-17}$

Write as a power of tcn.

61. $10^4 \cdot 10^{-6}$
62. $10^5 \cdot 10^{-7}$
63. $10^{-3}/10^2$
64. $10^{-4}/10^3$
65. $10^5/10^{-9}$
66. $10^6/10^{-10}$
67. $(10^{23} \cdot 10^{-10})/10^{-2}$
68. $(10^{22} \cdot 10^{-11})/10^{-3}$
69. $(10^{17} \cdot 10^{-18})/(10^{-6} \cdot 10^3)$
70. $(10^{-15} \cdot 10^{14})/(10^8 \cdot 10^{-11})$
71. $(10^{-3} \cdot 10^8)/(10^2 \cdot 10^{-2})$
72. $(10^{-4} \cdot 10^9)/(10^3 \cdot 10^{-3})$

Simplify each of the following. Write your answer using positive exponents.

73. $x^{10} \cdot x^{-5} \cdot x$
74. $x^{12} \cdot x^{-8} \cdot x$
75. $(t^{-1} \cdot t^5)/(t^3 \cdot t^{-4})$
76. $(t^6 \cdot t^{-1})/(t^{-5} \cdot t^2)$
77. $(3p^{-3})^4$
78. $(2p^{-2})^5$
79. $(4r^{-3}s^3)^{-3}$
80. $(5r^{-2}s^4)^{-3}$
81. $(3a^{-4})^2/a^{-5}$
82. $(2a^{-2})^5/a^{-8}$
83. $(5x^{-3}y^6/4z^2)^{-2}$
84. $(6x^5y^{-3}/5z^3)^{-2}$

## Calculator Problems

85. Compute to the nearest ten-thousandth.
    a) $(4.6135)^{-2}$  b) $\pi^{-3}$  c) $3^{-4} + 4^{-4}$

86. Compute $\dfrac{(1.93)^{-2}(1.85)^{-3}}{0.297}$ to the nearest hundredth.

87. Compute $3958^0$ on your calculator.

## Challenge Problems

88. Simplify.
    a) $y^{k+6}(y^{-2k})^{-2}(y^{k+1})^{-1}$  b) $\dfrac{(2m^2)^4(-3m^{-2})^2}{4m^{-6}(9^{-1}m^{-3})^{-1}}$

89. Show it is *false* that $(a + b)^{-1} = a^{-1} + b^{-1}$.

## 5.4 APPLICATIONS OF EXPONENTS (OPTIONAL)

Extremely large positive numbers may be written in a more compact way using powers of ten. For example, the sun is approximately 93,000,000 miles from the earth. We may write this number as

$$9.3 \times 10,000,000, \quad \text{or} \quad 9.3 \times 10^7.$$

Note that we have written our number in the form

$$a \times 10^n,$$

where $1 \le a < 10$ and $n$ is an integer. When a positive number is written in this way, it is said to be written in **scientific notation.** In our example $a = 9.3$ and $n = 7$. The exponent 7 on the ten indicates the number of places the decimal point in 9.3 is to be moved to the *right*.

Extremely small positive numbers are often written in scientific notation as well. Here we make use of *negative* exponents. For example, the mass of one water molecule is 0.00000000000000000000003 grams. This can be written as

$$3 \times 0.00000000000000000000001, \text{or } 3 \times 10^{-23}.$$

The negative exponent $-23$ on the ten indicates the number of places the decimal point in 3 is to be moved to the *left*.

**EXAMPLE 1**  Write each number in scientific notation: 5, 750, 0.075, 435,000,000, 0.0000068, 1000.

$$5 = 5 \times 10^0$$
$$750 = 7.5 \times 10^2$$
$$0.075 = 7.5 \times 10^{-2}$$
$$435,000,000 = 4.35 \times 10^8$$
$$0.0000068 = 6.8 \times 10^{-6}$$
$$1000 = 1 \times 10^3, \quad \text{or simply } 10^3. \quad \square$$

*Negative* numbers may also be written in scientific notation. In that case we would have $-10 < a \le -1$. For example, $-0.0701$ in scientific notation would be $-7.01 \times 10^{-2}$. Note here that $a = -7.01$.

**EXAMPLE 2**  Write $\dfrac{(0.27)(840)}{(21,000,000)(0.0012)}$ in scientific notation and simplify. Express your answer in scientific notation.

$$\frac{(0.27)(840)}{(21,000,000)(0.0012)} = \frac{(2.7 \times 10^{-1})(8.4 \times 10^2)}{(2.1 \times 10^7)(1.2 \times 10^{-3})}$$

$$= \frac{(2.7)(8.4)}{(2.1)(1.2)} \times \frac{(10^{-1})(10^2)}{(10^7)(10^{-3})}$$

$$= 9 \times \frac{10}{10^4}$$

$$= 9 \times 10^{-3}. \quad \square$$

Many calculators will use scientific notation to display the answer to a computation when that answer is too large or too small to fit on the display in decimal form. When this is done, only the number $a$ and the exponent $n$ in the notation $a \times 10^n$ are shown. Thus, the computation $(2,500,000)^2$ would be displayed as

which means that

$$(2,500,000)^2 = 6.25 \times 10^{12}.$$

**EXAMPLE 3** Light travels at a fast but finite speed (approximately 186,000 miles per second). How long does it take the sun's rays to reach the earth?

$$d = rt, \text{ so}$$

$$t = \frac{d}{r}$$

$$t = \frac{93,000,000 \text{ miles}}{186,000 \text{ miles/sec}}$$

$$t = \frac{9.3 \times 10^7}{1.86 \times 10^5} \cdot \frac{\text{miles}}{1} \cdot \frac{\text{sec}}{\text{miles}}$$

$$t = 5 \times 10^2 \text{ sec}$$

$$t = 500 \text{ sec}, \quad \text{or } 8\frac{1}{3} \text{ min.} \quad \square$$

Exponents provide us with a simple way of writing repeated products. In addition, many interesting formulas are easily expressed using exponents. For example, in attempting to pick the winner of a basketball game you have two choices: the home team or the visiting team. If you are attempting to pick the winner in both of *two* basketball games you have $2^2$ (or 4) choices. These choices are enumerated in the following table.

|          | Game 1   | Game 2   |
|----------|----------|----------|
| Choice 1 | Home     | Home     |
| Choice 2 | Visiting | Visiting |
| Choice 3 | Home     | Visiting |
| Choice 4 | Visiting | Home     |

If you are attempting to pick a *three*-team parlay you have $2^3$ (or 8) choices. You should verify this yourself by constructing a table similar to the one above. A *ten*-team parlay offers $2^{10}$ (or 1024) choices. In other words, your chance of making the correct choice is 1 out of 1024. This is an interesting statistic in light of the fact that your local bookmaker is likely to pay off at the rate of only 150 to 1 on a ten-team parlay.

Large numbers that have been given a standardized name are actually powers of ten.

| | | |
|---|---|---|
| hundred | $10^2$ | $= 100$ |
| thousand | $10^3$ | $= 1000$ |
| million | $10^6$ | $= 1,000,000$ |
| billion | $10^9$ | $= 1,000,000,000$ |
| trillion | $10^{12}$ | $= 1,000,000,000,000$ |
| quadrillion | $10^{15}$ | $= 1,000,000,000,000,000$ |
| quintillion | $10^{18}$ | $= 1,000,000,000,000,000,000$ |
| sextillion | $10^{21}$ | $= 1,000,000,000,000,000,000,000$ |
| septillion | $10^{24}$ | $= 1,000,000,000,000,000,000,000,000$ |
| octillion | $10^{27}$ | $= 1,000,000,000,000,000,000,000,000,000$ |
| nonillion | $10^{30}$ | $= 1,000,000,000,000,000,000,000,000,000,000$ |
| decillion | $10^{33}$ | $= 1,000,000,000,000,000,000,000,000,000,000,000$ |
| googol | $10^{100}$ | $= 10,000,000,000,000,000,000,000,000,000,000,000,$ $000,000,000,000,000,000,000,000,000,000,$ $000,000,000,000,000,000,000,000,000,000,000$ |

The name *googol* was coined by the nine-year-old nephew of the American mathematician Edward Kasner, who made the name popular in 1940 with his book *Mathematics and the Imagination.* You may wonder why mathematicians would even bother to name a number as large as a googol, particularly when the number of grains of sand needed to fill a sphere as large as the earth is only about $10^{32}$. For the answer, consider the first transatlantic telephone cable, which was completed in 1956 and connected Newfoundland with Scotland. Spaced somewhat evenly along its length were 51 amplifiers, each of which increased the signal strength by approximately one million times in order to keep the sound loud enough to hear. Therefore the total amplification along the cable was (one million)$^{51}$ = $(10^6)^{51}$ = $10^{306}$! This is a number that dwarfs even the mighty googol!

There are actually many quantities that under certain conditions will experience what is known as **exponential growth.** Among these are population growth, bacteria growth, the growth of rumors and disease, and the growth of money in a savings account that compounds interest. A formula for this last type of exponential growth is

$$V = P(1 + r)^t,$$

where $V$ is the value of the account after $t$ years, $P$ is the original principal, and $r$ is the annual interest rate (compounded annually) *expressed as a decimal.*

**EXAMPLE 4**   Suppose that $1000 is deposited in a savings account paying an annual interest rate of 8% compounded annually. What is the value of the account after two years?

Using $P = 1000$, $r = 0.08$, and $t = 2$ in the formula

$$V = P(1 + r)^t,$$

we have

$$V = 1000(1 + 0.08)^2$$
$$= 1000(1.08)^2$$
$$= 1000(1.1664)$$
$$= 1166.40.$$

The value of the account is $1166.40. □

Just as some quantities experience exponential *growth*, other quantities experience **exponential decay.** Radioactive decay is an example of exponential decay. For example, the substance radium-226 is present in radioactive wastes. Since it takes approximately 1600 years for a given quantity of radium-226 to decay to half of its original quantity, we say that the **half-life** of radium-226 is 1600 years. Using this fact, it can be shown that the quantity $Q$ of radium-226 that remains after $t$ years is given by the formula

$$Q = Q_0 2^{-t/1600},$$

where $Q_0$ is the original quantity of radium-226.

**EXAMPLE 5**   What quantity of radium-226 will remain after 3200 years if the original quantity was 250 grams?

Using $Q_0 = 250$ and $t = 3200$ in the formula

$$Q = Q_0 2^{-t/1600},$$

we have

$$Q = 250 \cdot 2^{-3200/1600}$$
$$= 250 \cdot 2^{-2}$$
$$= 250 \cdot \frac{1}{2^2}$$
$$= 250 \cdot \frac{1}{4}$$
$$= 62.5.$$

Therefore, 62.5 grams of radium-226 will remain.  □

## Problem Set 5.4

Write each number in decimal form.

1. $3 \times 10^2$
2. $5 \times 10^2$
3. $8 \times 10^{-2}$
4. $9 \times 10^{-2}$
5. $4.1 \times 10^5$
6. $8.6 \times 10^6$
7. $5.2 \times 10^{-7}$
8. $7.1 \times 10^{-5}$
9. $1.79 \times 10^{-4}$
10. $7.13 \times 10^{-3}$
11. $2.14 \times 10^8$
12. $6.78 \times 10^6$
13. $3.76 \times 10^0$
14. $5.15 \times 10^0$

Write each number in scientific notation.

15. 70
16. 60
17. 5000
18. 3000
19. 73,000,000
20. 1,200,000
21. 0.09
22. 0.007
23. 0.0000714
24. 0.000346
25. 0.00000404
26. 0.0606
27. 110,000,000
28. 321,000,000
29. 6,835,000,000
30. 8,760,000,000
31. 0.0000000114
32. 0.00000173
33. 7.23
34. 8.91

Write in scientific notation and simplify. Express your answer in scientific notation.

35. (40,000)(0.002)
36. (300,000)(0.0003)
37. (0.00003)(300)
38. (0.000002)(4000)
39. (900)(0.00002)
40. (500)(0.00003)
41. (0.0046)(0.2)(40,000)
42. (0.0054)(0.3)(20,000)
43. $\dfrac{0.00018}{0.006}$

44. $\dfrac{0.000049}{0.007}$
45. $\dfrac{(0.000039)(350)}{(130,000)(0.0015)}$
46. $\dfrac{(0.00036)(240)}{(12,000,000)(0.18)}$

47. $\dfrac{(81,000,000)(0.000016)}{(0.0009)(120,000)}$
48. $\dfrac{(250,000)(0.0004)}{(0.00005)(20,000)}$

49. Other than the sun, the nearest star to the earth is Proxima Centauri, which is about $2.5 \times 10^{13}$ miles away. Write this number in decimal form.
50. The average lifespan of a human is about $2.4 \times 10^9$ seconds. Write this number in decimal form.
51. In 1939, immediately prior to World War II, one U.S. dollar bought 3.38 Hungarian pengös. By 1946, however, inflation of the currency in Hungary was so bad (the worst in history) that one dollar bought 500,000,000,000,000,000,000 pengös. Write this last number in scientific notation.
52. It would take 3,000,000,000,000,000,000,000,000,000 candles to yield as much light as the sun. Write this number in scientific notation.
53. Radio waves travel at the speed of light. If an astronaut on the moon 238,000 miles away sends a radio message, how long will it take to reach the earth?
54. If radio waves travel at the speed of light, how long would it take a radio message from the earth to reach a spaceship 2,418,000 miles away?
55. How many possible choices are there in a three-team parlay?

Construct a table like the one in this section to verify your answer.

56. How many possible choices are there in a four-team parlay? Construct a table like the one in this section to verify your answer.

57. Suppose that $10,000 is deposited in an account that pays an annual interest rate of 10% compounded annually. What is the value of the account after   (a) 1 year?   (b) 2 years?   (c) 3 years?   (d) 4 years?

58. Suppose that a piece of property is purchased for $20,000 and it subsequently appreciates at a rate of 20% per year. What is the value of the property after (a) 1 year? (b) 2 years? (c) 3 years? (d) 4 years?

59. How much of 140 grams of the radioactive substance radium-226 will remain after   (a) 0 years?   (b) 1600 years?   (c) 3200 years?   (d) 4800 years?

60. How much of 220 grams of the radioactive substance radium-226 will remain after   (a) 0 years?   (b) 1600 years?   (c) 3200 years?   (d) 4800 years?

61. A chain letter is begun on Saturday when a girl mails a letter to each of five friends who in turn are to mail a letter to five of their friends on the following Saturday. If the chain is not broken, how many letters will be mailed on the sixth Saturday? On the tenth Saturday?

62. Under certain conditions, a bacteria known as *Escherichia coli* can double its number every 20 minutes. If one of these bacteria is placed at 9 A.M. in a culture maintained at such conditions, how many bacteria will there be at 6 P.M.? At midnight?

63. An old legend has it that the inventor of the game of chess was invited by the king to name his own reward. What the inventor requested did not seem like much. He asked that he be given one grain of wheat for the first square on the chessboard, two grains for the second, four for the third, eight for the fourth, and so on. How many grains of wheat would the king have to supply for the final square of the chessboard? (Incidentally, the total amount of wheat would be enough to cover the entire state of California with a layer over a foot deep!)

64. The Christian era began about 60 generations ago. Assuming that you have 2 parents, 4 grandparents, 8 great-grandparents, etc., and there are no incestuous combinations, how many ancestors of yours were part of the first generation of the Christian era? (The answer is greater than the current world population!)

65. The speed of light $c$ can be converted from 186,000 miles per second to miles per hour as follows:

$$\frac{186,000 \text{ mi}}{1 \text{ sec}} \cdot \frac{60 \text{ sec}}{1 \text{ min}} \cdot \frac{60 \text{ min}}{1 \text{ hr}} = c \frac{\text{mi}}{\text{hr}}.$$

Write $c$ in scientific notation.

66. The velocity of sound $V$ can be converted from 1100 feet per second to miles per hour as follows:

$$\frac{1100 \text{ ft}}{1 \text{ sec}} \cdot \frac{60 \text{ sec}}{1 \text{ min}} \cdot \frac{60 \text{ min}}{1 \text{ hr}} \cdot \frac{1 \text{ mi}}{5280 \text{ ft}} = V \frac{\text{mi}}{\text{hr}}.$$

Write $V$ in scientific notation.

## Calculator Problems

67. If you must guess the answer to every question on a 20-question true-false test, then you have one chance out of $2^{20}$ of having a perfect score. Are your chances better than one in a million?

68. On the day of your birth, your grandparents deposit $2500 into an account in your name. The account pays an annual interest rate of 14% compounded annually. What is the value of the account when you are ready to attend college 18 years later?

69. Like the number $\pi$, the number $e^*$ is an irrational number. While $\pi \approx 3.1416$, the number $e$ is approximately 2.7183. It can be shown that the value $V$ of an account after $t$ years when the interest is compounded *continuously* is given by the formula

$$V = P \cdot e^{rt},$$

where $P$ is the original principal and $r$ is the annual interest rate *expressed as a decimal.* Do Problem 68 if the interest is compounded continuously.

70. The distance $d$ that light travels in one year is called a **light year.** We can calculate this distance as follows:

$$\frac{186,000 \text{ mi}}{1 \text{ sec}} \cdot \frac{60 \text{ sec}}{1 \text{ min}} \cdot \frac{60 \text{ min}}{1 \text{ hr}} \cdot \frac{24 \text{ hr}}{1 \text{ day}} \cdot \frac{365 \text{ days}}{1 \text{ yr}} = d \frac{\text{mi}}{\text{yr}}.$$

Find $d$.

* Named by the Swiss mathematician Leonhard Euler.

## Challenge Problems

71. While a googol is a 1 followed by one hundred zeros, a **googolplex** is a 1 followed by a googol's worth of zeros. Write a googolplex using only the numerals 1 and 0.

72. An **annuity** is a sequence of equal payments made at equal time intervals. The value $V$ of an annuity consisting of yearly payments of size $p$, after $t$ years, is given by the formula

$$V = p\frac{(1 + r)^t - 1}{r},$$

where $r$ is the annual interest rate (compounded annually) *expressed as a decimal.* Suppose you open an Individual Retirement Account (IRA) on your 18th birthday, and deposit $500 per year (about $10 per week) into this account. What will be the value of your account when you retire at age 68 if the annual interest rate remains at 12% compounded annually? How much money did you actually deposit into the account? (You will need a calculator to complete this problem.)

## 5.5   POLYNOMIALS

Consider a rectangle whose length is three times the width. If we denote the width of the rectangle by $x$, then the length would be $3x$. The area of the rectangle would then be

$$3x \cdot x = 3x^2.$$

The expression $3x^2$ is called a *second-degree monomial in x.* It is said to be of the second degree since the exponent that appears on the variable $x$ is 2. It is called a *monomial* because it consists of only *one* term. The number 3 is called the *coefficient* of $x^2$.

---

**Definition**   An **nth-degree monomial in x** is an expression of the form $ax^n$, where $n$ is a whole number and $a$ is not zero. The number $a$ is called the **coefficient** of $x^n$.

---

**EXAMPLE 1** $17x^3$ is a third-degree monomial in $x$. The coefficient of $x^3$ is 17. □

**EXAMPLE 2** $-\frac{1}{2}y$ is a first-degree monomial in $y$. The coefficient of $y$ is $-\frac{1}{2}$. □

**EXAMPLE 3** $z^5$ is a fifth-degree monomial in $z$. The coefficient of $z^5$ is 1. □

**EXAMPLE 4** The number 5 is a monomial of degree zero, since $5 = 5 \cdot 1 = 5 \cdot x^0$. □

The number 0 is a special case. It is also a monomial, but no degree is assigned to it since 0 can be written in any of the forms $0 \cdot x^0$, $0 \cdot x^1$, $0 \cdot x^2$, etc.

Of course, not all algebraic expressions consist of only one term.

---

*Definition* A **polynomial in $x$** is either a monomial in $x$ or a finite sum of monomials in $x$. The **degree** of the polynomial is the degree of the highest-degree monomial in the polynomial. The coefficient of the highest-degree monomial is called the **leading coefficient** of the polynomial. The coefficient of $x^0$ is called the **constant term** of the polynomial.

---

**EXAMPLE 5** $5x^2 - 3x + 12$ is a polynomial in $x$ since it is the sum of the monomials $5x^2$, $-3x$, and 12. It is a second-degree polynomial since the highest-degree monomial, $5x^2$, is of the second degree. The leading coefficient of the polynomial is 5, and the constant term is 12 (since $12 = 12 \cdot x^0$). □

**EXAMPLE 6** $3x^5 - x^7 - \frac{1}{2}x^3 - 10$ is a polynomial of degree 7 whose leading coefficient is $-1$ and whose constant term is $-10$. □

Polynomials cannot contain terms such as $6/x$ or $\sqrt{x}$. From the discussion in Section 5.3 we know that

$$\frac{6}{x} = 6x^{-1}.$$

And as we will see in Section 10.6,

$$\sqrt{x} = x^{1/2}.$$

Since only *whole*-number exponents may appear on the *variable* factor in a monomial, neither $6x^{-1}$ nor $x^{1/2}$ is a monomial. In general, no *variable* in a polynomial appears under a radical sign *or* in a denominator. This last statement does *not* apply to *constants*, however, and expressions such as

and

$$x^3 + \frac{1}{3} = x^3 + (3^{-1}) \text{ —constant}$$

$$x^2 + \sqrt{5}x + 4 = x^2 + 5^{1/2}x + 4$$

*are* polynomials.

As we have already noted, a polynomial of one term is also called **a monomial.** Moreover, a polynomial of *two* terms is also called a **binomial,** and a polynomial of *three* terms a **trinomial.** Polynomials of four or more terms are not given any special name. Therefore, the polynomials

$$5x, \qquad 10x^3, \qquad -17y^9$$

are all monomials; the polynomials

$$2z + 7, \qquad 8x^2 + 11x, \qquad x^3 - 4$$

are all binomials; and the polynomials

$$x^2 + 5x + 6, \qquad 3x^7 - 10x^3 + \sqrt{2}x, \qquad t^4 + 6t^2 + 100$$

are all trinomials.

The **value of a polynomial** in $x$ at a particular value of the variable $x$, say $x = 2$, is determined by substituting 2 for $x$ wherever $x$ appears in the polynomial. This process is called *evaluating the polynomial at* $x = 2$.

**EXAMPLE 7**   Evaluate the polynomial $x^3 - 3x^2 + 5x + 1$ at $x = 2$.

$$(2)^3 - 3(2)^2 + 5(2) + 1 = 8 - 3 \cdot 4 + 10 + 1$$
$$= 8 - 12 + 10 + 1$$
$$= 7. \quad \square$$

Polynomials appear naturally in many equations and formulas. For example, suppose an object with little air resistance is projected vertically upward with an initial velocity of $r$ feet per second from an initial height of $s$ feet. It can be shown using the laws of physics that the height $h$ of the object in *feet* after $t$ *seconds* is given by the formula

$$h = -16t^2 + rt + s.$$

This formula is due largely to the work of the Italian astronomer and mathematician Galileo Galilei (1564–1643) and the English mathematician and physicist Isaac Newton (1642–1727).

**EXAMPLE 8**   An arrow is shot vertically upward from the top of a building 100 feet high with a bow that gives the arrow an initial velocity of 112 feet per second. Write an expression for the height of the arrow at any time $t$. Then find the height of the arrow 3 seconds after it is shot.

Using the formula above with $r = 112$ and $s = 100$, we can write the height $h$ of the arrow in feet after $t$ seconds as

$$h = -16t^2 + 112t + 100.$$

The right-hand side of this last equation is actually a second-degree trinomial in the variable $t$. To determine the height of the arrow after 3 seconds, we simply evaluate this polynomial at $t = 3$.

$$h = -16(3)^2 + 112(3) + 100 = -16 \cdot 9 + 336 + 100$$
$$= -144 + 336 + 100$$
$$= 292.$$

The height of the arrow at $t = 3$ seconds is 292 feet. $\square$

<hr>

## Problem Set 5.5

1. Which of the following algebraic expressions are polynomials? State the degree, leading coefficient, and constant term of each polynomial. If the polynomial is also a monomial, a binomial, or a trinomial, identify it as such.

a) $5x^3 + x^2 - 7x + 1$      b) $x^2 + 2x - \dfrac{6}{x}$      c) $x^7 - 1$

d) $\sqrt{x} + 9$      e) $8$      f) $\dfrac{5}{x + 1}$

g) $7 - y$      h) $x^6 - x^{-3}$      i) $\sqrt{x} - 5$

j) $3^4z^3 - 32$      k) $\dfrac{3x^2 + 1}{x + 3}$      l) $\pi t^5 + t^2 + \sqrt{2}t$

m) $8x^4$      n) $x + 2$      o) $\dfrac{1}{3} + \dfrac{x^{50}}{5} - \dfrac{x^{100}}{10}$

2. Which of the following algebraic expressions are polynomials? State the degree, leading coefficient, and constant term of each polynomial. If the polynomial is also a monomial, a binomial, or a trinomial, identify it as such.

a) $x^3 - 3x^2 + x + 5$

b) $\sqrt{x} + 1$

c) $x^3 - x^5$

d) $x^2 + 1 + \dfrac{7}{x}$

e) $10$

f) $\dfrac{3}{x - 2}$

g) $3y + 4$

h) $\sqrt{x + 4}$

i) $x^3 - x^{-2}$

j) $t^6 + \sqrt{3}t + \pi$

k) $\dfrac{x^2 + x + 1}{3x - 2}$

l) $9z^2$

m) $x - 3$

n) $81y^3 + 2^5$

o) $\dfrac{1}{2} + \dfrac{x^{33}}{3} - \dfrac{x^{99}}{6}$

Evaluate each polynomial at the given value.

3. $x^2 + 3x + 5$   at   $x = 0$
4. $x^2 - 2x + 7$   at   $x = 0$
5. $2x^2 - 4x + 1$   at   $x = 1$
6. $3x^2 - 10x + 2$   at   $x = 1$
7. $y^3 + y^2 - 5y - 3$   at   $y = -2$
8. $y^3 - 2y^2 - 10y + 2$   at   $y = -2$
9. $y^4 + 7$   at   $y = 3$
10. $y^5 - 3$   at   $y = 3$
11. $z^3 + z^2 + z + 1$   at   $z = 5$
12. $z^3 - z^2 + z - 1$   at   $z = 5$
13. $z^5 - z^2$   at   $z = 4$
14. $z^4 + z$   at   $z = 4$
15. $x^3 - 5x^2 + 3x - 2$   at   $x = \frac{1}{2}$
16. $x^3 + 5x^2 - 3x + 2$   at   $x = \frac{1}{2}$
17. $-x^2 + 7x + 3$   at   $x = 2$
18. $-x^2 + 4x + 8$   at   $x = 2$
19. $-x^2 - x + 1$   at   $x = -10$
20. $-x^2 + x - 1$   at   $x = -10$
21. $x^3 - x^2 + 6x$   at   $x = 1.2$
22. $x^3 - x^2 + 9x$   at   $x = 1.4$
23. $t^2 + 15$   at   $t = \sqrt{2}$
24. $t^2 + 13$   at   $t = \sqrt{3}$
25. $5r^3 - r^2 + r - 2$   at   $r = \frac{3}{5}$
26. $5r^3 - r^2 + r - 3$   at   $r = \frac{4}{5}$

27. The cost of producing $x$ units of a particular product can often be expressed as a polynomial in $x$. Suppose it costs $0.01x^3 - 0.02x^2 + 350x + 2500$ dollars for a company to produce $x$ gadgets. What is the cost of producing 60 gadgets?

28. The profit derived from $x$ units of a particular product can often be expressed as a polynomial in $x$. Suppose the profit realized by a company from $x$ widgets is $-0.03x^2 + 9.96x - 210$ dollars. What is the profit realized from 50 widgets?

29. The sum of the first $n$ positive integers is given by the polynomial $\frac{1}{2}n^2 + \frac{1}{2}n$. Use this polynomial to find the sum of the first 100 positive integers.

30. The sum of the squares of the first $n$ positive integers is given by the polynomial $\frac{1}{3}n^3 + \frac{1}{2}n^2 + \frac{1}{6}n$. Use this polynomial to find the sum of the squares of the first 20 positive integers.

31. A psychologist conducts an experiment in which a rat repeatedly runs a maze. After each of the eight trials, a score is assigned. The score for trial $t$ is $6t^2 - 0.5t^3$. Determine the score after (a) the second trial. (b) the fifth trial.

32. Suppose that the number of persons having a contagious disease $t$ days after an epidemic begins is $250 + 39t^2 - t^3$. How many persons have the disease after (a) 3 days? (b) 10 days?

33. An arrow is shot upward with an initial velocity of 48 feet per second from a height of 64 feet. Write an expression for the height of the arrow at any time $t$. Then find its height

   a) after 1 second.      b) after 2 seconds.
   c) after 3 seconds.      d) after 4 seconds.

Draw a picture of your results.

34. A stone is thrown upward with an initial velocity of 32 feet per second from a height of 48 feet. Write an expression for the height of the stone at any time $t$. Then find its height

   a) after 1 second.      b) after 2 seconds.
   c) after 3 seconds.

Draw a picture of your results.

## Calculator Problems

35. Evaluate $5x^3 - 17x^2 + 8x + 0.99184$  at  $x = 2.48$.
36. Evaluate $3t^3 + 4t^2 - t + 35$  at  $t = 2 + \sqrt{3}$ to the nearest hundredth.
37. In Problem 27, what is the cost of producing 179 gadgets?
38. Check the answer to Problem 30 by calculating the sum $1^2 + 2^2 + 3^2 + \cdots + 19^2 + 20^2$.

## Challenge Problems

39. Find the *maximum* height attained by the arrow of Example 8.
40. Write 756 as a second-degree trinomial in 10.

## 5.6 ADDITION AND SUBTRACTION OF POLYNOMIALS

Consider the triangle below. Finding the perimeter involves adding the three first-degree binomials $2x + 5$, $3x + 4$, and $6x - 1$. This is really nothing more than combining like terms. Recall that like terms are terms with the same variable factor. We may set up our work in *vertical form* as follows:

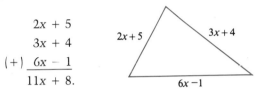

$$
\begin{array}{r}
2x + 5 \\
3x + 4 \\
(+)\ \underline{6x - 1} \\
11x + 8.
\end{array}
$$

The same calculation would be done in *horizontal form* as

$$(2x + 5) + (3x + 4) + (6x - 1) = (2x + 3x + 6x) + (5 + 4 - 1)$$
$$= 11x + 8.$$

The first method probably seems easier since the like terms are arranged in the same column. Most of the work in algebra, however, appears on line as in the second method, so the student should learn to feel comfortable with both.

**EXAMPLE 1**   Add the two polynomials $5x^3 - x^2 + 1$  and  $3x^3 + 4x^2 + x - 6$.

$$
\begin{array}{r}
5x^3 - \ x^2 \quad\ + 1 \\
(+)\ \underline{3x^3 + 4x^2 + x - 6} \\
8x^3 + 3x^2 + x - 5. \ \square
\end{array}
$$

**EXAMPLE 2**   Using the previous example, subtract the lower polynomial from the upper polynomial.

$$
\begin{array}{r}
5x^3 - \ x^2 \quad\ + 1 \\
(-)\ \underline{3x^3 + 4x^2 + x - 6} \\
2x^3 - 5x^2 - x + 7. \ \square
\end{array}
$$

Since $a - b = a + (-b)$, the subtraction in Example 2 could be done by changing the sign of each term in the lower polynomial and then *adding.* In that case we would write

$$5x^3 - x^2 \quad\ + 1$$
$$(+)\ \underline{-3x^3 - 4x^2 - x + 6}$$
$$2x^3 - 5x^2 - x + 7.$$

**EXAMPLE 3**   Subtract the lower polynomial from the upper polynomial.

$$2x^2 - 3x \quad\ 9$$
$$(-)\ \underline{5x^2 - 8x - 4.}$$

We change the problem to

$$2x^2 - 3x - 9$$
$$(+)\ \underline{-5x^2 + 8x + 4}$$

and then add.

$$2x^2 - 3x - 9$$
$$(+)\ \underline{-5x^2 + 8x + 4}$$
$$-3x^2 + 5x - 5. \ \square$$

Once the knack of changing the sign of each term in the lower polynomial is mastered, the student can perform this operation mentally and does not need to rewrite the problem.

In the next example, the two polynomials are added on line without arranging the like terms in the same column.

**EXAMPLE 4**   Find the sum $(6y^3 + 14y^2 - 5y + 3) + (7y^3 - 10y - 8).$

$$(6y^3 + 14y^2 - 5y + 3) + (7y^3 - 10y - 8) = 13y^3 + 14y^2 - 15y - 5. \ \square$$

Notice that when two polynomials are added or subtracted, the result is yet another polynomial.

A polynomial may involve more than one variable. Each polynomial in parentheses below contains the *two* variables $x$ and $y$.

**EXAMPLE 5**   Remove parentheses and simplify $2(x^2 - 4xy + y^2) - 5(x^2 + 3xy - 2y^2).$

$$2(x^2 - 4xy + y^2) - 5(x^2 + 3xy - 2y^2)$$
$$= 2x^2 - 8xy + 2y^2 - 5x^2 - 15xy + 10y^2$$
$$= -3x^2 - 23xy + 12y^2. \ \square$$

## Problem Set 5.6

Find the sum of each pair of polynomials.

1. $4x^2 - 2x + 6$
   $3x^2 + 8x - 7$

2. $5x^2 - 4x + 1$
   $2x^2 + 9x - 3$

3. $6y^3 - 4y^2 + y - 10$
   $5y^3 - y^2 - 2y + 4$

4. $7y^3 - y^2 + 4y - 11$
   $3y^3 + 6y^2 - y + 7$

5. $a^3 - 8a + 1$
   $a^3 \quad\;\; - 1$

6. $a^3 + 9a^2 - 5$
   $a^3 \qquad\;\; + 3$

7. $9m^3 - 5m^2 + 4m - 8$
   $3m^3 + 6m^2 + 8m - 6$

8. $5m^3 - 2m^2 + m - 10$
   $6m^3 + 4m^2 - m + 5$

9. $3x^2 - 4xy + 2y^2$
   $7x^2 + 5xy - 11y^2$

10. $5x^2 + xy + 3y^2$
    $4x^2 - 10xy - y^2$

Subtract the lower polynomial from the upper polynomial.

11. $10x^2 + 3x + 2$
    $6x^2 - 2x + 1$

12. $9x^2 + 5x + 4$
    $3x^2 - 4x + 3$

13. $4y^2 - 9y + 7$
    $5y^2 + y - 3$

14. $3y^2 - 7y + 5$
    $6y^2 + y - 5$

15. $a^3 + 2a^2 \quad\;\; - 5$
    $-a^3 \qquad\;\; - a + 1$

16. $a^3 \qquad\;\; + 3a - 8$
    $-a^3 + 4a^2 \qquad\; + 2$

17. $2m^5 - 4m^2 + 6$
    $3m^5 + 7m^2 + 5$

18. $9m^4 - 3m^2 + 11$
    $2m^4 - m^2 - 1$

19. $3x^3 - x^2y^2 + 8y^3$
    $x^3 - x^2y^2 - 8y^3$

20. $x^3 + x^2y^2 - 6y^3$
    $7x^3 + x^2y^2 + 6y^3$

Remove parentheses and simplify.

21. $(8x^2 + 4x - 7) + (12x^2 - 3x + 10)$
22. $(7x^2 - 2x + 9) + (13x^2 - 6x - 4)$
23. $(15x^3 + 2x^2 - x + 10) + (4x^3 - 7x^2 - 1)$
24. $(12x^3 - x^2 + 4x) + (x^3 - 6x^2 + 2x + 9)$
25. $(a^2 - 2a - 6) - (3a^2 - 5a + 1)$
26. $(a^2 + 4a - 4) - (5a^2 - 2a + 8)$
27. $(7x^3 - 2x^2 + x - 4) - (3x^3 - x^2 + 6x - 2)$
28. $(10x^3 - x^2 + 6x - 1) - (2x^3 + 4x^2 - 2x + 9)$
29. $5(b^2 - 2b - 1) - 3(b^2 + b + 7)$

30. $6(b^2 + b + 5) - 2(b^2 - 4b + 1)$
31. $3(x^2 + 4xy - y^2) - 4(x^2 - xy + y^2)$
32. $2(4x^2 - 6xy - y^2) - 5(x^2 + xy - 3y^2)$
33. $-3(a^2 + ab + 2b^2) + 6(2a^2 - 2ab - b^2)$
34. $-7(4a^2 - ab + 2b^2) + 3(a^2 - ab + 8b^2)$

35. If the sides of a triangle are $3x + 1$, $4x - 5$, and $x + 7$, write an expression for its perimeter.
36. If the sides of a triangle are $5x - 3$, $x + 8$, and $2x + 9$, write an expression for its perimeter.
37. If the length of a rectangle is $3x - 5$ and the width is $2x + 4$, write an expression for its perimeter.
38. If the width of a rectangle is $4x - 3$ and the length is $5x + 7$, write an expression for its perimeter.
39. If you have $n$ nickels, and 4 more dimes than nickels, and 3 times as many quarters as dimes, how much money in cents do you have?
40. If you have $n$ dimes, and 7 fewer nickels than dimes, and 6 more than twice as many quarters as dimes, how much money in cents do you have?
41. The sum of the measures of the interior angles of any triangle is 180°. If the measure of angle $A$ in the diagram below is $m$ and the measure of angle $B$ is 17° more than twice the measure of angle $A$, write an expression for the measure of angle $C$.

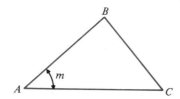

42. Do Problem 41 if the measure of angle $B$ is 13° less than three times the measure of angle $A$.

## Calculator Problems

43. Subtract the lower polynomial from the upper polynomial.

$73.184a^2 + 15.111a - 106.872$
$\underline{48.967a^2 - 18.843a -\ \ 37.188}$

44. Simplify $4.7(6.15k^2 - 8.75k + 4.55) + 2.5(6.878k^2 + 16.45k - 0.034)$.

## Challenge Problems

45. Add the polynomials $\pi x^2 + \sqrt{2}x + \frac{1}{3}$ and $\pi x^2 + 3x - \frac{1}{5}$.
46. Write each of the numbers 132 and 546 as a second-degree trinomial in 10. Then add the two polynomials in 10. Finally, write this sum in decimal form.

## Chapter Review

True or false.

1. $10^{-3} = 0.001$
2. $-(-5)^0 = -1$
3. $6^{15}/3^5 = 2^{10}$
4. The first law of exponents states that $a^m \cdot a^n = a^{m \cdot n}$. m+n
5. The fourth law of exponents states that $(a + b)^n = a^n + b^n$. $ab^n = a^n b^n$
6. If $a \neq 0$ and $n$ is a natural number, then $1/a^{-n} = a^n$.
7. If neither $a$ nor $b$ is zero and $n$ is a natural number, then $(a/b)^{-n} = (b/a)^n$.
8. The number 2,001,000 written in scientific notation is $20.01 \times 10^5$.
9. The number 13 is a monomial of degree zero.
10. The number 0 is a monomial of degree zero.
11. The expression $x^2 \quad 4x + 8$ is called a trinomial.
12. The expression $x^2 - 4x + 8$ is called a polynomial.
13. The expression $10x^6 + 1$ is a binomial.
14. The expression $8x^3y^2$ is a monomial.
15. The number 4 in the expression $4x^3$ is called the coefficient of $x^3$.
16. In a polynomial, the expressions that are separated by addition are called factors.
17. The expression $\dfrac{x^2 + x + 1}{x - 6}$ is a polynomial.
18. The expression $x^2 + \sqrt{x} + 1$ is a polynomial.

Completion.

19. If $a \neq 0$, then $a^0 = $ _____?_____ .

20. The exponent of the expression $\pi^{n+2}$ is _____?_____ .

21. The base of the expression $-1^3$ is _____?_____ .

22. The degree of the polynomial $7x^2 - 2x^4 + 3$ is _____?_____ .

23. The leading coefficient of the polynomial $7x^2 - 2x^4 + 3$ is

_____?_____ .

24. The constant term of the polynomial $7x^2 - 2x^4 + 3$ is

_____?_____ .

Find each value.

25. $-5^4$      26. $10^3(-\frac{1}{2})^{10}$      27. $(2^2)^3$      28. $2^{(2^3)}$

Write in exponential form.

29. $3 \cdot 3 \cdot x \cdot x \cdot x \cdot x \cdot y \cdot y - x \cdot x \cdot y \cdot y$      30. $(5x - 1)(5x - 1)(5x - 1)$

Find each product.

31. $x^8 \cdot x^4 \cdot x^6 \cdot x$      32. $(6x^3y)(-2xy)(3xy^2)$

Find each quotient.

33. $(x + 10)^{100}/(x + 10)^{99}$      34. $x^5y^2z^3/xy^2z$

Remove parentheses and simplify.

35. $(2x^2y^5/z^4)^7(x^3/z)^2$      36. $(3x^5y^2)^2(10x^3y)^4$

37. $-(4t)^2(2t)^3$

Simplify.

38. $8000^0 \cdot 10^2$      39. $6y^{-5}$      40. $(-\frac{2}{7})^{-2}$      41. $11/x^{-3}$

Write in decimal form.

42. $3.04 \times 10^{-3}$      43. $(10^{-5} \cdot 10^{11} \cdot 10^{-10})/(10^{-4} \cdot 10^{-3})$

Write in scientific notation.

44. $513{,}000$      45. $0.0000609$

46. Write $\dfrac{(0.000012)(9{,}000{,}000)}{(40{,}000)(0.0006)}$ in scientific notation and simplify. Express your answer in scientific notation.

Use the appropriate law of exponents to rewrite each expression.

47. $x^n \cdot x^n$     48. $(b^s)^3$     49. $(xy)^{k+1}$

50. $(5/v)^{2m}$     51. $\dfrac{(3a + 4)^r}{3a + 4}$

Write with positive exponents and simplify.

52. $2^{-2} + 3^{-2}$     53. $x^{-3}/y^{-2}$

Simplify each expression. Write your answer using positive exponents.

54. $(5r^4 r^{-1} s^{-3})^{-1}$     55. $(a^2 b^{-2} c/c^{-1})^{-4}$

56. The cost in dollars of producing $x$ units of a particular product is given by the polynomial $0.01x^2 + 5x + 300$. Find the cost of producing 40 units.
57. Evaluate the polynomial $3x^3 - 5x^2 + 4x + 1$ at $x = \frac{2}{3}$.
58. Subtract the lower polynomial from the upper polynomial.

$$3x^3 + 5x^2 \qquad - 10$$
$$6x^3 - \ x^2 + 4x + 10$$

59. Combine the like terms: $x^2yz + xy^2z + 3yzx^2 - 2xy^2z$.

Remove parentheses and simplify.

60. $(x^3 + 4x^2 - 10) - (-x^3 + x^2 - x)$
61. $7(4a^3 - 3ab + b) - 8(2a^3 - ab + 5b)$
62. $(-3x^3y)(y^2) - (-2x^2y)(-2xy^2)$

63. If the width of a rectangle is $3x + 8$ and the length is $5x - 2$, write an expression for its perimeter.
64. Suppose that $50,000 is deposited in an account that pays an annual interest rate of 12% compounded annually. What is the value of the account after three years?

# Chapter
# Chapter
# Chapter
# Chapter Six
# Six
# Six
# Six

## PRODUCTS, FACTORS, AND QUOTIENTS OF POLYNOMIALS

## 6.1   MULTIPLICATION OF POLYNOMIALS

Consider a rectangle whose length is two units longer than its width. We can denote the width by $x$ and the length by $x + 2$. The area of the rectangle is therefore the product of $x$ and $x + 2$. Using the distributive axiom we can write the area as

$$x \cdot (x + 2) = x \cdot x + 2 \cdot x$$
$$= x^2 + 2x.$$

**EXAMPLE 1**   Find the product $7x(3x^2 - 1)$.

$$7x(3x^2 - 1) = 7x \cdot 3x^2 - 7x \cdot 1$$
$$= 21x^3 - 7x. \quad \square$$

Actually the distributive axiom can be used to find the product of *any* two polynomials.

**EXAMPLE 2**   Find the product $(x + 3) \cdot (x + 2)$.

In order to calculate this product, we note that the distributive axiom allows us to write that

$$(\quad) \cdot (x + 2) = (\quad) \cdot x + (\quad) \cdot 2.$$

This equation is true for any number we might choose to place inside the empty parentheses. If we place the number $x + 3$ inside these parentheses, we get

$$(x + 3) \cdot (x + 2) = (x + 3) \cdot x + (x + 3) \cdot 2.$$

We then use the distributive axiom again to calculate both products on the right-hand side of this last equation. From beginning to end, our work would appear as follows:

$$(x + 3) \cdot (x + 2) = (x + 3) \cdot x + (x + 3) \cdot 2$$
$$= x \cdot x + 3 \cdot x + 2 \cdot x + 3 \cdot 2$$
$$= x^2 + 5x + 6. \quad \square$$

If we look closely at the next-to-the-last step in the example above, we observe that *the product is simply the result of multiplying each term of the first polynomial by each term of the second polynomial.* The result is then simplified by combining like terms. We shall apply this rule to calculate the product in the next example.

**EXAMPLE 3**   Find the product $(x + 2)(x^2 - 5x + 4)$.

First we multiply $x$ by each term in the second polynomial, and then we multiply $+2$ by each term in the second polynomial.

$$(x + 2)(x^2 - 5x + 4) = x^3 - 5x^2 + 4x + 2x^2 - 10x + 8.$$

Combining like terms gives the final result.

$$= x^3 - 3x^2 - 6x + 8. \quad \square$$

Note that the answers in the three examples above have been written so that the terms are in *decreasing powers of x*. While the terms can be written in *any* order, writing them in this fashion does make for easy reading.

The product of Example 3 can also be determined by arranging the factors in vertical form. Our work would appear as follows:

$$
\begin{array}{r}
x^2 - 5x + 4 \\
x + 2 \\
\hline
x^3 - 5x^2 + 4x \qquad \leftarrow x \text{ times } x^2 - 5x + 4 \\
2x^2 - 10x + 8 \quad \leftarrow 2 \text{ times } x^2 - 5x + 4 \\
\hline
x^3 \quad 3x^2 - \quad 6x + 8 \quad \leftarrow \text{combine the like terms.}
\end{array}
$$

Note that the like terms are aligned in the same column so that they can be combined easily.

The student should learn to feel comfortable finding products using either the horizontal form or the vertical form.

**EXAMPLE 4**   Find $(5x - 3)^2$.

$$
\begin{aligned}
(5x - 3)^2 &= (5x - 3)(5x - 3) \\
&= 25x^2 - 15x - 15x + 9 \\
&= 25x^2 - 30x + 9. \quad \square
\end{aligned}
$$

Note that $(5x - 3)^2$ does *not* equal $25x^2 + 9$. In general, $(t + a)^2 \neq t^2 + a^2$.

**EXAMPLE 5**   A box without a top is to be made by cutting equal squares from the corners of a piece of cardboard that is 12 in. by 12 in. and then turning up the sides. What will be the volume $V$ of the box if the side of each square cut is $x$ in.?

The volume of a rectangular box is given by the formula $V = \ell wh$.

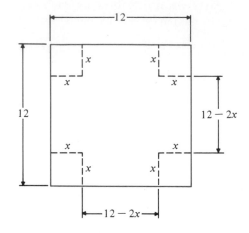

From the diagram we see that $\ell = 12 - 2x$, $w = 12 - 2x$, and $h = x$. Therefore,

$$
\begin{aligned}
V &= (12 - 2x)(12 - 2x)x \\
&= (144 - 24x - 24x + 4x^2)x \\
&= (144 - 48x + 4x^2)x \\
&= 144x - 48x^2 + 4x^3.
\end{aligned}
$$

The volume $V$ of the box is $144x - 48x^2 + 4x^3$ cubic inches.  □

Note that the terms of the answer to the last example were written in *increasing powers of x.*

## Problem Set 6.1

Find each product.

1. $x(x + 5)$            2. $x(x + 3)$
3. $3x(2x - 1)$          4. $2x(3x - 1)$
5. $x^2(x - 4)$          6. $x^2(x - 6)$
7. $4x^2(2x + 1)$        8. $5x^2(3x + 2)$

9.  $-5xy(x^2 + x + 1)$
10. $-2xy(x^2 - x + 1)$
11. $x^2y(x^2 + 2xy - y)$
12. $x^2y(x^2 - 3xy + y)$
13. $-7a^3(ab - b^2 + 3)$
14. $-8b^3(ab - a^2 + 6)$
15. $(x + 2)(x + 5)$
16. $(x + 2)(x + 4)$
17. $(x + 4)(x - 3)$
18. $(x + 5)(x - 7)$
19. $(2x - 3)(3x - 2)$
20. $(4x - 2)(3x - 2)$
21. $(5x + 1)^2$
22. $(4x + 1)^2$
23. $(x + y)^2$
24. $(x - y)^2$
25. $(2x - 5y)^2$
26. $(2x + 5y)^2$
27. $(x + 2)(x^2 - 2x + 4)$
28. $(x - 2)(x^2 - 2x + 4)$
29. $(y - 5)(3y^2 - y - 1)$
30. $(y + 5)(2y^2 + y - 1)$
31. $(a + 3)(a^2 - 5a + 7)$
32. $(a + 4)(a^2 + 3a - 5)$
33. $(a - 1)(a^3 - 2a^2 + a + 1)$
34. $(a - 1)(a^3 + a^2 - 2a + 1)$
35. $(a - 1)(a + 1)(a + 2)$
36. $(a + 2)(a - 2)(a + 1)$
37. $(a + 2b)(a - 2b)(a + b)$
38. $(5a - b)(5a + b)(a + b)$
39. $(4c + 3)(5c^3 - 4c^2 + c - 5)$
40. $(2c - 5)(3c^3 - c^2 + 6c + 1)$
41. $(6m - 5)(2m^3 + 5m^2 - m + 3)$
42. $(4m + 3)(5m^3 - 4m^2 + m - 5)$
43. $(k + 1)^3$
44. $(k - 1)^3$
45. $(p - 2q)^3$
46. $(p + 3q)^3$

47. Find an expression for the area of a triangle whose base is $4x + 6$ and whose altitude is $3x - 1$.

48. Find an expression for the area of a triangle whose base is $2x + 8$ and whose altitude is $5x - 7$.

49. A cake pan is to be made by cutting equal squares from the corners of a piece of metal that is 19 in. by 24 in. and then turning up the sides. What will be the volume $V$ of the pan if the side of each square cut is $x$ in.?

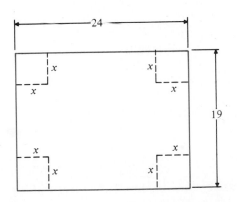

50. Determine the total area $A$ of a picture and its mat iı the picture is 14 in. by 16 in. and the width of the mat is $x$ in.

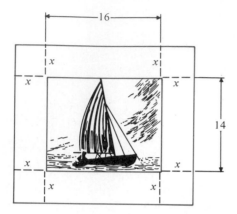

## Calculator Problems

51. Find each product.

    a) $2.50x^3(3.64x^2 + 2.78x - 7.76)$    b) $(198a + 127b)(296a - 137b)$

52. Determine the volume $V$ of the box described in Example 5 for various values of $x$ by completing the table below.

| $x$ in. | $V$ cu. in. |
| --- | --- |
| 1 | |
| 2 | |
| 3 | |
| 4 | |
| 5 | |

## Challenge Problems

53. Find each product.

    a) $2x^n(3x^{2n} - 5x^{n+1} + 6)$    b) $(a^k - 4)(a^{2k} + 2a^k - 1)$

54. The number of ways to roll a total of $n$ with a pair of dice is the same as the coefficient of $x^n$ in the product $(x + x^2 + x^3 + x^4 +$

$x^5 + x^6)^2$. Use this fact to determine the number of ways to roll a 7 with a pair of dice.

## 6.2    MULTIPLYING BINOMIALS MENTALLY

Using the distributive law, we showed in Section 6.1 that the product of two polynomials can be found by multiplying each term of one polynomial by each term of the other polynomial. The resulting polynomial can then sometimes be simplified by combining like terms.

A topic that appears frequently enough to deserve special attention involves finding the product of two first-degree binomials. Let us examine the multiplication process while finding the product of $x + 3$ and $x + 5$. Multiplying each term in the first polynomial by each term in the second gives

$$(x + 3)(x + 5) = x \cdot x + x \cdot 5 + 3 \cdot x + 3 \cdot 5$$
$$= x^2 + 5x + 3x + 15$$
$$= x^2 + 8x + 15.$$

The first term $x^2$ is the product of the two first terms.

$$\overset{x^2}{\overbrace{(x + 3)(x + 5)}}$$

The last term 15 is the product of the two last terms.

$$\overset{15}{\underset{(x + 3)(x + 5)}{\phantom{x}}}$$

The middle term $8x$ is actually the sum of the two like terms $5x$ and $3x$. The term $5x$ is the product of the two outer terms,

$$\underset{5x}{\underbrace{(x + 3)(x + 5)}}$$

and the term $3x$ is the product of the two inner terms.

$$\underset{3x}{(x + 3)(x + 5)}$$

Therefore, we multiply two binomials by multiplying their first terms (**F**), their outer terms (**O**), their inner terms (**I**), and their last terms

(**L**). By remembering the key word **FOIL** and by adding the outer product and inner product mentally, we can perform the multiplication in one step.

$$(x + 3)(x + 5) = x^2 + 8x + 15.$$

**EXAMPLE 1**   Find the product $(x - 3)(x + 7)$.

$$(x - 3)(x + 7) = x^2 + 4x - 21. \quad \square$$

**EXAMPLE 2**   Find the product $(x - 4)(x + 4)$.

$$(x - 4)(x + 4) = x^2 - 16. \quad \square$$

The middle term of this last example was zero and hence *dropped out* of the answer, because the inner product and the outer product were equal in absolute value but opposite in sign.

This same procedure is used to multiply binomials whose first terms have coefficients other than 1.

**EXAMPLE 3**   Find the product $(2x - 8)(x + 3)$.

$$(2x - 8)(x + 3) = 2x^2 - 2x - 24. \quad \square$$

Normally all of the work in multiplying two binomials is done mentally, and the problem is simply written as in the next two examples.

**EXAMPLE 4**   Find the product $(5x - 1)(2x - 7)$.

$$(5x - 1)(2x - 7) = 10x^2 - 37x + 7. \ \square$$

**EXAMPLE 5**   Find the product $(3x - y)(6x + 5y)$.

$$(3x - y)(6x + 5y) = 18x^2 + 9xy - 5y^2. \ \square$$

## *Problem Set 6.2*

Multiply each pair of binomials mentally.

1. $(x + 2)(x + 3)$
2. $(x + 3)(x + 4)$
3. $(x + 4)(x + 5)$
4. $(x + 2)(x + 6)$
5. $(x + 9)(x + 11)$
6. $(x + 7)(x + 8)$
7. $(x - 5)(x - 6)$
8. $(x - 4)(x - 7)$
9. $(x - 2)(x - 9)$
10. $(x - 3)(x - 8)$
11. $(x - 7)(x - 8)$
12. $(x - 9)(x - 11)$
13. $(y + 4)(y - 2)$
14. $(y + 5)(y - 3)$
15. $(y - 8)(y + 3)$
16. $(y - 9)(y + 4)$
17. $(y - 12)(y + 10)$
18. $(y - 11)(y + 10)$
19. $(a - 5)(a + 5)$
20. $(a - 6)(a + 6)$
21. $(a - 10)(a + 10)$
22. $(a - 9)(a + 9)$
23. $(b + 1)(b - 1)$
24. $(h + 8)(b - 8)$
25. $(b + 7)(b + 7)$
26. $(b + 5)(b + 5)$
27. $(b - 3)^2$
28. $(b - 6)^2$
29. $(x + a)(x - a)$
30. $(y + b)(y - b)$
31. $(x + a)^2$
32. $(y + b)^2$
33. $(9 - y)(9 + y)$
34. $(4 - b)(4 + b)$
35. $(2x + 1)(x + 3)$
36. $(3x + 1)(x + 2)$
37. $(5x - 4)(x + 2)$
38. $(4x - 3)(x + 5)$
39. $(y + 1)(3y - 2)$
40. $(y + 3)(2y - 1)$
41. $(y - 10)(2y + 9)$
42. $(y - 8)(3y + 5)$
43. $(3x + 1)^2$
44. $(2x + 1)^2$
45. $(5x - 1)^2$
46. $(4x - 1)^2$
47. $(6y - 5)(6y + 5)$
48. $(3y - 7)(3y + 7)$
49. $(3x - y)(2x + y)$
50. $(5x - y)(2x + y)$
51. $(2a + 3b)(5a - b)$
52. $(2a + 3b)(4a - b)$
53. $(a - 2b)^2$
54. $(a + 2b)^2$
55. $(5x + 2y)^2$
56. $(4x - 3y)^2$
57. $(\frac{1}{5}k - \frac{1}{2})(\frac{3}{5}k + \frac{7}{2})$
58. $(\frac{1}{3}k - \frac{1}{5})(\frac{2}{3}k + \frac{7}{5})$
59. $(t^2 - 1)(t^2 - 9)$
60. $(t^2 - 4)(t^2 - 16)$

61. Simplify $(x - y)^2 - (x + y)^2$.
62. Simplify $(x + y)^2 - (x - y)^2$.
63. Find an expression for the area of a rectangle whose width is $2x - 3$ and whose length is $3x + 4$.

64. Find an expression for the area of a rectangle whose width is $4x - 8$ and whose length is $5x + 1$.
65. Find $51 \cdot 49$ by writing this product as $(50 + 1)(50 - 1)$ and then multiplying these two binomials mentally.
66. Find $42 \cdot 38$ by writing this product as $(40 + 2)(40 - 2)$ and then multiplying these two binomials mentally.

## Calculator Problems

Find each product.

67. $(47p - 724)(68p + 96)$　　　68. $(1.28q + 544)(2.6875q - 1.5625)$

## Challenge Problems

69. Find the product $(x^n - 2)(x^n + 5)$ mentally.
70. By calculating the area of the large square below using two different methods, show that
$$(x + a)^2 = x^2 + 2ax + a^2.$$

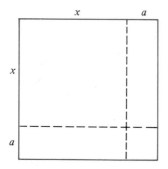

71. Prove that the product of the smallest and the largest of any four consecutive even integers when subtracted from the product of the middle two always produces 8. (*Hint:* Denote the smallest of the four integers by $2n$.)

## 6.3   COMMON FACTORS

Suppose we wished to solve the equation

$$x^2 - 5x + 6 = 0.$$

If we were able to recognize that $x^2 - 5x + 6$ is actually the product of $(x - 2)$ and $(x - 3)$, we could write this equation as

$$(x - 2) \cdot (x - 3) = 0.$$

When the equation is in this form we can see that both 2 and 3 satisfy the equation, since 2 causes the first factor to be 0 and 3 causes the second factor to be 0.

The key to solving this equation lies in recognizing the fact that $x^2 - 5x + 6 = (x - 2) \cdot (x - 3)$. When a polynomial is expressed as a product we say that the polynomial has been **factored.** Thus factoring polynomials is essentially the opposite of multiplying polynomials.

We shall study several types of factoring. The first type of factoring involves searching a polynomial for a **common factor** that is present in every term. Once found, this common factor is then *factored out* of the polynomial.

**EXAMPLE 1**   Factor $3x^2 + 6x$.

The two terms $3x^2$ and $6x$ both have the common factor $3x$. Using the distributive law we have

$$3x^2 + 6x = 3x \cdot x + 3x \cdot 2$$
$$= 3x(x + 2).$$

The given polynomial has the two factors $3x$ and $x + 2$.   □

*A factorization can always be checked by multiplying the factors to see if the original polynomial is obtained.*

**EXAMPLE 2**   Factor $12x^4 - 8x^3 + 20x^2$.

$$12x^4 - 8x^3 + 20x^2 = 4x^2 \cdot 3x^2 - 4x^2 \cdot 2x + 4x^2 \cdot 5$$
$$= 4x^2(3x^2 - 2x + 5).$$   □

Note that when factoring polynomials, we usually do not bother to factor monomials. That is why in the example above we did not write $4x^2$ as

$$2 \cdot 2 \cdot x \cdot x.$$

EXAMPLE 3   Factor $a^2 + a$.

$$a^2 + a = a(a + 1). \quad \square$$

EXAMPLE 4   Factor $4x^4y^3 - 10x^3y^2 + 2x^2y$.

$$4x^4y^3 - 10x^3y^2 + 2x^2y = 2x^2y(2x^2y^2 - 5xy + 1). \quad \square$$

EXAMPLE 5   The total surface area of a cylindrical can of radius $r$ and height $h$ is given by $2\pi r^2 + 2\pi rh$. Write this expression in factored form.

$$2\pi r^2 + 2\pi rh = 2\pi r(r + h).$$

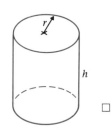

## Problem Set 6.3

Factor each of the following polynomials.

1. $5x^2 + 5$
2. $7x^2 + 7$
3. $4x^2 + 8x$
4. $3x^2 + 9x$
5. $8x^2 - 72x$
6. $5x^2 - 30x$
7. $10x + 5y$
8. $15x + 5y$
9. $-3x^2 - 6x$
10. $-4x^2 - 12x$
11. $a^2 + ab$
12. $a^2 - ab$
13. $-12x - 24y$
14. $-8x - 16y$
15. $4y^3 - 2y^2 + 2y$
16. $6y^3 - 6y^2 + 9y$
17. $3x^4 - 6x^3 + 12x^2$
18. $2x^4 - 4x^3 + 10x^2$
19. $b^2 - b$
20. $a^2 - a$
21. $y^5 + y$
22. $3y^4 + 3y$
23. $x^6 - 5x^4 + x^2$
24. $x^5 - 7x^3 + x$
25. $5x^4 + 15x^3 - 10x^2$
26. $3x^3 - 6x^2 + 9x$
27. $x^6 + x^5 + x^4 + x^3$
28. $2x^6 - 4x^5 + 6x^4 - 8x^3$
29. $10z^{73} - 100z^{72}$
30. $99z^{55} + 11z^{53}$
31. $xy + xz$
32. $7x - xz$
33. $12xy - 24y$
34. $8x^2y + 16y$
35. $3x^2y^3 + 21x^4y^2$
36. $25x^3y^4 - 10x^2y^2$
37. $a^2bc + ab^2c + abc^2$
38. $x^2y^2z - xy^2z + xy^2z^2$
39. $-xy^5 - xy^4 + 8xy^2$
40. $-x^4y - x^3y + 4x^2y$
41. $4\pi r^3 + 6\pi r^2h$
42. $3\pi r^2 + 6\pi rh$

43. The cost of an item to a retailer is $c$ dollars. If the *markup* on the item is $r$ percent (expressed as a decimal) of the cost, determine the selling price. Then write the selling price in factored form.
44. The normal selling price of an item is $p$ dollars. If during a sale there is a *discount* of $r$ percent (expressed as a decimal) of the price, determine the sale price of the item. Then write the sale price in factored form.

## Calculator Problems

45. Factor $119x^3 - 2261x^2 + 5117x$.
46. Show that both the factored form and the unfactored form of the expression in Example 5 produce the same surface area for a cylindrical can of radius 3.175 cm and height 10.16 cm.

## Challenge Problems

Factor each polynomial.

47. $x(x + y) + 5(x + y)$     48. $P(1 + r) + P(1 + r)r$     49. $x^{n+5} + x^{n+3} + x^3$

## 6.4   DIFFERENCE OF TWO SQUARES

If the two binomials $x - 5$ and $x + 5$ are multiplied, the product is the difference of the two perfect squares $x^2$ and 25.

$$(x - 5)(x + 5) = x^2 - 25.$$

Note that the middle term in the product drops out since the outer product and the inner product are equal in absolute value but opposite in sign.

Given any **difference of two squares,** say $a^2 - b^2$, it can always be immediately factored into the two binomials $a - b$ and $a + b$. The factorization is given by

$$a^2 - b^2 = (a - b)(a + b).$$

**EXAMPLE 1**   Factor $x^2 - 4$.

$$x^2 - 4 = x^2 - 2^2$$
$$= (x - 2)(x + 2), \quad \text{or} \quad (x + 2)(x - 2). \ \square$$

**EXAMPLE 2**   Factor $25x^2 - 9$.

$$25x^2 - 9 = (5x)^2 - 3^2$$
$$= (5x - 3)(5x + 3). \ \square$$

**EXAMPLE 3**   Factor $x^2 + 4$.

This polynomial is *not* a difference of two squares but rather a *sum* of two squares. It cannot be factored using real numbers.* We shall call this polynomial a **prime polynomial.** $\square$

This last example illustrates the fact that not all polynomials are factorable. This should come as no surprise since the same is true for natural numbers. That is, while the number 6 may be factored as $2 \cdot 3$, the number 7 cannot be written as a product of two other natural numbers. As such, 7 is a prime *number*.

**EXAMPLE 4**   Factor $x^4 - 81$.

$$x^4 - 81 = (x^2)^2 - 9^2$$
$$= (x^2 - 9)(x^2 + 9).$$

But the factor $x^2 - 9$ is *itself* a difference of two squares and can be factored.

---

* The student should verify that plausible factorizations such as $(x + 2)(x + 2)$, $(x - 2)(x - 2)$, and $(x + 2)(x - 2)$ do not work.

$$x^4 - 81 = (x^2)^2 - 9^2 \quad \text{— Difference of 2 squares}$$
$$= (x^2 - 9)(x^2 + 9) \text{— Prime same as } x^2 + 4$$
$$= (x - 3)(x + 3)(x^2 + 9).$$

Since $x - 3$, $x + 3$, and $x^2 + 9$ are all prime polynomials, the polynomial $x^4 - 81$ is said to be in **completely factored form** when it is expressed as the product $(x - 3)(x + 3)(x^2 + 9)$. □

When factoring any polynomial *we should always look for a common factor before attempting any other type of factorization.*

**EXAMPLE 5** Factor $15x^5y - 15xy$.

First, the common factor $15xy$ is factored out.

$$15x^5y - 15xy = 15xy(x^4 - 1).$$

Then, the difference of two squares $x^4 - 1$ is factored.

$$15x^5y - 15xy = 15xy(x^4 - 1)$$
$$= 15xy(x^2 - 1)(x^2 + 1).$$

Finally, in order to *completely* factor the polynomial, the difference of two squares $x^2 - 1$ is factored.

$$15x^5y - 15xy = 15xy(x^4 - 1)$$
$$= 15xy(x^2 - 1)(x^2 + 1)$$
$$= 15xy(x - 1)(x + 1)(x^2 + 1). \quad \square$$

## Problem Set 6.4

Factor each of the following polynomials.

1. $x^2 - 16$
2. $x^2 - 9$
3. $x^2 - 81$
4. $x^2 - 49$
5. $a^2 - 100$
6. $a^2 - 144$
7. $9y^2 - 4$
8. $16y^2 - 25$
9. $x^2 + 16$   no
10. $x^2 + 9$   no
11. $64x^2 - 9$ $(8x - 3)(8x + 3)$
12. $121x^2 - 9$ $(11x + 3)(11x - 3)$
13. $49a^2 - 144b^2$
14. $25a^2 - 81b^2$
15. $z^2 - 1$
16. $4z^2 - 1$
17. $25x^2 - 121$
18. $36x^2 - 625$
19. $4x^2 - y^2$
20. $9x^2 - y^2$
21. $x^4 - 81$ $(x^2 + 9)(x^2 - 9)$ $(x + 3)(x - 3)$
22. $x^4 - 256$
23. $x^4y^4 - 625$ $(x^2y^2 - 25)(x^2 - y^2 + 25)$ $(xy + 5)(xy - 5)$
24. $49x^6 - y^4$ $(7x^3 - y^2)$

*[handwritten: $x^2 - y^2 = (x+y)(x-y)$]*
*[handwritten: difference of 2 squares]*

25. $1 - 100a^2b^2$     26. $1 - 144a^2b^2$     27. $(a + b)^2 - c^2$

28. $(a - b)^2 - c^2$     29. $(2x + 1)^2 - (3x - 5)^2$     30. $(3x - 4)^2 - (4x + 1)^2$

Factor out a common factor and then factor the difference of two squares that remains.

*[handwritten: $7(x^2 - 9)$]*

31. $7x^2 - 63$     32. $5x^2 - 5$     33. $x^6y - 4y$

34. $3x^4 - 48y^4$     35. $2x^4 - 2$     36. $x^3y^3 - xy$

37. $25xy^2 - 49x^3$     38. $4a^3 - 121ab^2$     39. $x^4y - x^2y$

40. $x^3y^2 - xy^2$     41. $6r^7 - 96rs^2$     42. $r^2s^9 - 9r^2s^3$

*[handwritten: $\frac{s^9}{s^3} = s^6$]*

43. Calculate $25^2 - 15^2$ by first factoring this expression.

*[handwritten: $r^2s^3(s^6 - 9)$]*

44. Calculate $55^2 - 35^2$ by first factoring this expression.

*[handwritten: $r^2s^3(s^3 - 3)(s^3 + 3)$]*

*[handwritten: $s^3 - (\sqrt{3})^3$ ___ later]*

## Calculator Problems

45. Factor $1369x^2 - 9801y^2$.

46. Factor $2178\pi r^6 - 4418\pi$.

## Challenge Problems

47. Factor $a^{4m} - b^{2n}$.     48. Factor $x^2 - 3$.

49. Find the incorrect step in the "proof" below.

$$a = b$$
$$a^2 = ab$$
$$a^2 - b^2 = ab - b^2$$
$$(a + b)(a - b) = b(a - b)$$
$$a + b = b$$
$$b + b = b$$
$$2b = b$$
$$2 = 1 \quad ?!?$$

## 6.5    SECOND-DEGREE TRINOMIALS

Let us examine what happens when the two binomials $x + 2$ and $x + 3$ are multiplied.

$$(x + 2)(x + 3) = x^2 + 5x + 6.$$

The result is a second-degree trinomial whose middle term $5x$ is the sum of $2x$ and $3x$.

More generally, if $x + a$ is multiplied by $x + b$, we have

$$(x + a)(x + b) = x^2 + ax + bx + ab,$$

or

$$(x + a)(x + b) = x^2 + (a + b)x + ab.$$

We would now like to reverse this process. That is, given a second-degree trinomial that is a product of two binomials, we would like to find the binomials.

Let's try to write $x^2 + 7x + 12$ as a product of two binomials. Since the coefficient of $x^2$ is 1, we can start by writing

$$x^2 + 7x + 12 = (x + a)(x + b).$$

We must now find integers $a$ and $b$ such that $a \cdot b = 12$ and $a + b = 7$. We first consider combinations of integers whose product is 12.

$$x^2 + 7x + 12 = (x \quad 1)(x \quad 12) \qquad \text{wrong}$$
$$x^2 + 7x + 12 = (x \quad 2)(x \quad 6) \qquad \text{wrong}$$
$$x^2 + 7x + 12 = (x \quad 3)(x \quad 4) \qquad \text{right.}$$

The third choice is the correct one since $3 + 4 = 7$. The final step is to insert the proper signs.

$$x + 7x + 12 = (x + 3)(x + 4).$$

The polynomial $x^2 + 7x + 12$ is now factored. The factorization should then be checked by mentally computing the product on the right to see if $x^2 + 7x + 12$ is obtained.

**EXAMPLE 1**   Factor $x^2 + 3x - 10$.

First we consider combinations of integers whose product is 10.

$$x^2 + 3x - 10 = (x \quad 1)(x \quad 10) \qquad \text{wrong}$$
$$x^2 + 3x - 10 = (x \quad 2)(x \quad 5) \qquad \text{right.}$$

Then we select the one that gives us the correct middle term. This would be the second one since $(-2) + 5 = 3$. Finally, we insert the proper signs.

$$x^2 + 3x - 10 = (x - 2)(x + 5). \ \square$$

**EXAMPLE 2**   Factor $x^2 - 6x - 16$.

$$x^2 - 6x - 16 = (x \quad 1)(x \quad 16) \qquad \text{wrong}$$
$$x^2 - 6x - 16 = (x \quad 2)(x \quad 8) \qquad \text{right}$$
$$x^2 - 6x - 16 = (x \quad 4)(x \quad 4) \qquad \text{wrong.}$$

Inserting the proper signs, we have

$$x^2 - 6x - 16 = (x + 2)(x - 8). \ \square$$

**EXAMPLE 3**   Factor $y^2 - 12y + 36$.

*Perfect square trinomial*

$$y^2 - 12y + 36 = (y \quad 1)(y \quad 36) \qquad \text{wrong}$$
$$y^2 - 12y + 36 = (y \quad 2)(y \quad 18) \qquad \text{wrong}$$
$$y^2 - 12y + 36 = (y \quad 3)(y \quad 12) \qquad \text{wrong}$$
$$y^2 - 12y + 36 = (y \quad 4)(y \quad 9) \qquad \text{wrong}$$
$$y^2 - 12y + 36 = (y \quad 6)(y \quad 6) \qquad \text{right.}$$

Inserting the proper signs, we have

$$y^2 - 12y + 36 = (y - 6)(y - 6), \quad \text{or} \quad (y - 6)^2. \ \square$$

Since the two factors in Example 3 are actually the same factor, we call $y^2 - 12y + 36$ a **perfect square trinomial.** More generally,

$$x^2 + 2ax + a^2 = (x + a)^2$$

and thus $x^2 + 2ax + a^2$ is a perfect square trinomial. So is the trinomial

$x^2 - 2ax + a^2$, since

$$x^2 - 2ax + a^2 = (x - a)^2.$$

**EXAMPLE 4**   Factor $a^2 + 10a - 24$.

$a^2 + 10a - 24 = (a \quad 1)(a \quad 24)$     wrong
$a^2 + 10a - 24 = (a \; \sim 2)(a + 12)$     right
$a^2 + 10a - 24 = (a \quad 3)(a \quad 8)$     wrong
$a^2 + 10a - 24 = (a \quad 4)(a \quad 6)$     wrong.

At first it may appear that *both* the second trial *and* the fourth trial are correct. Upon further investigation, however, we see that no choice of signs for the fourth trial will yield *both* the correct middle term *and* the correct constant term. That is,

$a^2 + 10a - 24 = (a + 4)(a - 6)$     wrong
$a^2 + 10a - 24 = (a - 4)(a + 6)$     wrong
$a^2 + 10a - 24 = (a - 4)(a - 6)$     wrong
$a^2 + 10a - 24 = (a + 4)(a + 6)$     wrong.

Instead, the second trial with the proper signs inserted produces the correct factorization.

$$a^2 + 10a - 24 = (a - 2)(a + 12). \quad \square$$

**EXAMPLE 5**   Factor $x^2 + 10x + 12$.

$x^2 + 10x + 12 = (x \quad 1)(x \quad 12)$     wrong
$x^2 + 10x + 12 = (x \quad 2)(x \quad 6)$     wrong
$x^2 + 10x + 12 = (x \quad 3)(x \quad 4)$     wrong.

This trinomial cannot be factored using only integers. Therefore we shall simply say that the polynomial is *prime*. $\square$

**EXAMPLE 6**   Factor $5x^2 - 55x + 50$.

First the common factor 5 is factored out, and then the remaining trinomial is factored.

$$5x^2 - 55x + 50 = 5(x^2 - 11x + 10)$$
$$= 5(x - 1)(x - 10). \quad \square$$

*when multiply together*
*= 10*
*when added together*
*= 11*
*Sum so both go in same direction*

Skill at factoring is usually the result of extensive practice. As the student becomes familiar with the procedure, more of the work is done mentally and often the solution can be written immediately.

## Problem Set 6.5

Factor each of the following polynomials.

1. $x^2 + 3x + 2$
2. $x^2 + 5x + 6$
3. $x^2 + 7x + 12$
4. $x^2 + 6x + 8$
5. $x^2 + 12x + 35$
6. $x^2 + 10x + 21$
7. $x^2 + 2x + 1$ $(x+1)^2$
8. $x^2 + 4x + 4$
9. $x^2 + 5x + 3$
10. $x^2 + 7x + 5$
11. $y^2 - 9y + 20$
12. $y^2 - 11y + 18$
13. $y^2 - 5y + 6$
14. $y^2 - 7y + 12$
15. $y^2 - 12y + 32$
16. $y^2 - 15y + 54$
17. $a^2 + 3a - 10$ $(a+5)(a-2)$
18. $a^2 + 4a - 21$
19. $a^2 + 3a - 54$
20. $a^2 + 2a - 8$
21. $a^2 + 2a - 30$
22. $a^2 + 2a - 45$
23. $b^2 - b - 42$
24. $b^2 - b - 20$
25. $b^2 - 2b - 48$
26. $b^2 - 6b - 27$
27. $b^2 - 10b - 11$
28. $b^2 - 12b - 13$
29. $x^2 - 44x - 45$
30. $x^2 - 35x - 36$
31. $x^2 - 14x - 51$
32. $x^2 - 9x - 52$
33. $y^2 + 8y - 24$
34. $y^2 + 6y - 18$
35. $y^2 - 26y + 25$
36. $y^2 - 46y + 45$

Factor out a common factor and then factor the second-degree trinomial that remains.

37. $5x^2 + 50x + 105$
38. $2x^2 + 18x + 28$
39. $2x^2 - 22x + 20$
40. $3x^2 - 33x + 30$
41. $3y^2 - 6y - 24$
42. $2y^2 + 6y - 20$
43. $4y^2 - 40y + 100$
44. $5y^2 - 60y + 180$

45. If the area of a rectangle is $40 + 13r + r^2$ and the width is $r + 5$, find the length.
46. If the area of a rectangle is $30 + 11s + s^2$ and the length is $s + 6$, find the width.

## Calculator Problems

47. If the product of two numbers is $x^2 + 122x + 3577$ and one number is $x + 49$, find the other number.

48. If the area of a rectangle is $x^2 + 152x + 5292$ and the width is $x + 54$, find the length.

## Challenge Problems

Factor each polynomial.

49. $t^4 + 2t^2 - 24$

50. $x^{2n} + 5x^n + 6$

51. $k^5 - 8k^3 - 9k$

## 6.6   MORE TRINOMIALS

In the previous section we considered only trinomials whose leading coefficient was 1, such as

$$x^2 + 5x + 6.$$

In this section we will consider trinomials whose leading coefficient may be an integer other than 1, such as

$$2x^2 + 11x + 15.$$

The same procedure is used to factor these trinomials, but the presence of a leading coefficient other than 1 introduces more combinations to be tried.

**EXAMPLE 1**   Factor $2x^2 + 11x + 15$.

In this case we must have $2x^2 + 11x + 15 = (2x + a)(x + b)$ for some choice of integers $a$ and $b$. Since

$$\overset{\displaystyle ab}{\underset{\displaystyle 2bx}{\underset{\displaystyle ax}{(2x + a)(x + b)}}} = 2x^2 + ax + 2bx + ab = 2x^2 + (a + 2b)x + ab,$$

we must look for a pair of integers whose product is 15 such that one added to twice the other is 11. Let's consider the possible combinations.

$$2x^2 + 11x + 15 = (2x \quad 1)(x \quad 15) \qquad \text{wrong}$$
$$2x^2 + 11x + 15 = (2x \quad 15)(x \quad 1) \qquad \text{wrong}$$
$$2x^2 + 11x + 15 = (2x \quad 3)(x \quad 5) \qquad \text{wrong}$$
$$2x^2 + 11x + 15 = (2x \quad 5)(x \quad 3) \qquad \text{right.}$$

The last trial is the correct one since the outer product is $2x \cdot 3 = 6x$, and the inner product is $5 \cdot x = 5x$. The sum of this outer product and this inner product gives the desired middle term of $11x$. Inserting the proper signs completes the factorization.

$$2x^2 + 11x + 15 = (2x + 5)(x + 3). \quad \square$$

Note that the product

$$(2x + 5)(x + 3) = 2x^2 + 11x + 15$$

is different from the product

$$(2x + 3)(x + 5) = 2x^2 + 13x + 15,$$

and so each different placement of the constants must be considered.

**EXAMPLE 2**    Factor $8x^2 + 14x - 15$.

$$8x^2 + 14x - 15 = (8x \quad 1)(x \quad 15) \qquad \text{wrong}$$
$$8x^2 + 14x - 15 = (8x \quad 15)(x \quad 1) \qquad \text{wrong}$$
$$8x^2 + 14x - 15 = (8x \quad 3)(x \quad 5) \qquad \text{wrong}$$
$$8x^2 + 14x - 15 = (8x \quad 5)(x \quad 3) \qquad \text{wrong}$$
$$8x^2 + 14x - 15 = (4x \quad 1)(2x \quad 15) \qquad \text{wrong}$$
$$8x^2 + 14x - 15 = (4x \quad 15)(2x \quad 1) \qquad \text{wrong}$$
$$8x^2 + 14x - 15 = (4x \quad 3)(2x \quad 5) \qquad \text{right}$$
$$8x^2 + 14x - 15 = (4x \quad 5)(2x \quad 3) \qquad \text{wrong.}$$

Inserting the proper signs gives the correct factorization.

$$8x^2 + 14x - 15 = (4x - 3)(2x + 5). \quad \square$$

Many trinomials involving *more* than one variable can be factored using this same technique.

**EXAMPLE 3**    Factor $12x^2 + xy - y^2$.

$$12x^2 + xy - y^2 = (12x \quad y)(x \quad y) \qquad \text{wrong}$$
$$12x^2 + xy - y^2 = (6x \quad y)(2x \quad y) \qquad \text{wrong}$$
$$12x^2 + xy - y^2 = (4x \quad y)(3x \quad y) \qquad \text{right.}$$

Inserting the proper signs gives the correct factorization.

$$12x^2 + xy - y^2 = (4x - y)(3x + y). \quad \square$$

**EXAMPLE 4**   Factor $30x^3 + 20x^2y - 80xy^2$.

The common factor $10x$ is factored out and the remaining trinomial is then factored.

$$30x^3 + 20x^2y - 80xy^2 = 10x(3x^2 + 2xy - 8y^2)$$
$$= 10x(3x - 4y)(x + 2y). \quad \square$$

## Problem Set 6.6

Factor each of the following polynomials.

1. $2x^2 + 7x + 3$
2. $2x^2 + 7x + 5$
3. $3x^2 + 8x + 5$
4. $3x^2 + 13x + 4$
5. $5y^2 + 4y - 1$
6. $7y^2 - 6y - 1$
7. $11a^2 - 3a - 14$
8. $6a^2 + a - 5$
9. $4a^2 + 28a + 49$
10. $9a^2 + 30a + 25$
11. $6x^2 - x - 8$
12. $4x^2 + x - 6$
13. $12x^2 - x - 1$
14. $6x^2 - x - 1$
15. $9h^2 + 6b + 1$
16. $4b^2 + 4b + 1$
17. $6x^2 - x + 11$
18. $8x^2 + 3x + 7$
19. $16x^2 - 38x - 5$
20. $16x^2 - 11x - 5$
21. $4a^2 + 23a - 6$
22. $4a^2 - 11a + 6$
23. $16x^2 - 8xy + y^2$
24. $36x^2 - 12xy + y^2$
25. $a^2 + 5ab - 14b^2$
26. $a^2 - 2ab - 35b^2$
27. $9a^2 + 9ab - 4b^2$
28. $15a^2 + 16ab + 4b^2$
29. $36r^2 + 5rs - 24s^2$
30. $36r^2 - 13rs - 40s^2$

Factor out a common factor and then factor the second-degree trinomial that remains.

31. $4x^3 - 10x^2 - 6x$
32. $18x^3 - 9x^2 - 27x$
33. $60x^2 - 70xy - 30y^2$
34. $42x^2 + 7xy - 14y^2$
35. $4x^2 - 24xy + 36y^2$
36. $5x^2 - 40xy + 80y^2$
37. $12a^2b + 15ab^2 + 3b^3$
38. $4a^3 + 10a^2b + 6ab^2$

39. If the area of a triangle is $-\frac{5}{2} + k + \frac{3}{2}k^2$ and the base is $3k + 5$, find the height.
40. If the area of a triangle is $-3 - \frac{5}{2}k + 3k^2$ and the height is $2k - 3$, find the base.

## Calculator Problems

41. If the product of two numbers is $9792y^2 + 4864y - 1225$ and one number is $72y + 49$, find the other number.
42. If the area of a triangle is $1134y^2 - 1230y + \frac{667}{2}$ and the base is $54y - 29$, find the height.

## Challenge Problems

43. Factor each polynomial.
    a) $6t^4 + 5t^2 - 25$      b) $12y^{2n} + 23y^n - 24$
44. Factor $(3x - 5)^2 - 8(3x - 5) + 12$ using two different methods.

## 6.7   SUM OR DIFFERENCE OF CUBES, GROUPING (OPTIONAL)

In Section 6.4 we observed that the *difference* of two squares $a^2 - b^2$ could easily be factored as $(a - b)(a + b)$, but that the *sum* of two squares $a^2 + b^2$ could *not* be factored using real numbers.

As it turns out, we can factor *both* a **sum of two cubes** *and* a **difference of two cubes** using the formulas below.

*memorize this* ☆

$$a^3 + b^3 = (a + b)(a^2 - ab + b^2) \quad \text{sum of two cubes}$$
$$a^3 - b^3 = (a - b)(a^2 + ab + b^2) \quad \text{difference}$$

These formulas can be verified by computing the products on the right-hand side. The student is asked to do this in Problems 45 and 46.

Notice that the first factor in the sum of two cubes formula is simply the sum of the cube *roots* of the original two terms.*

---

* The number $b$ is a **cube root** of the number $a$ if $b^3 = a$. Therefore, 2 is a cube root of 8, $x$ is a cube root of $x^3$, and $3t^2$ is a cube root of $27t^6$.

$$a^3 + b^3 = (a + b)(\qquad).$$

↑

Sum of cube
roots of $a^3$ and $b^3$.

The first factor in the difference of two cubes formula is the difference of the cube roots of $a^3$ and $b^3$.

$$a^3 - b^3 = (a - b)(\qquad).$$

↑

Difference of cube
roots of $a^3$ and $b^3$.

In both formulas, we can obtain the *second* factor from the *first* factor as follows:

1. Square the first term of the first factor to get the first term of the second factor.
2. Find the product of the two terms in the first factor and change the sign to get the second term of the second factor.
3. Square the last term of the first factor to get the last term of the second factor.

This technique is illustrated in the examples that follow.

**EXAMPLE 1** Factor $x^3 - 8$.

Using the difference of two cubes formula with $a = x$ and $b = 2$, we have

$$x^3 - 8 = x^3 - 2^3$$
$$= (x - 2)(x^2 + 2x + 4).$$

1. Square $x$ to get $x^2$.
2. Product of $x$ and $-2$ with sign change.
3. Square $-2$ to get 4. □

Notice that the second-degree trinomial $x^2 + 2x + 4$ is prime. Therefore the factorization given in Example 1 is a complete factorization.

**EXAMPLE 2**    Factor $64x^3 + y^3$.

Using the sum of two cubes formula with $a = 4x$ and $b = y$, we have

$64x^3 + y^3 = (4x)^3 + y^3$

$\qquad\qquad = (4x + y)(16x^2 - 4xy + y^2).$

1. Square $4x$ to get $16x^2$.
2. Product of $4x$ and $+y$ with sign change.
3. Square $+y$ to get $y^2$.  □

**EXAMPLE 3**    Factor $24r^3s - 81s$.

First the common factor $3s$ is factored out.

$$24r^3s - 81s = 3s(8r^3 - 27).$$

Then the difference of two cubes $8r^3 - 27$ is factored.

$\qquad\qquad = 3s((2r)^3 - 3^3)$

$\qquad\qquad = 3s(2r - 3)(4r^2 + 6r + 9).$  □

Occasionally a polynomial can be factored by **grouping.**

**EXAMPLE 4**    Factor $x^3 + 5x^2 + 3x + 15$.

The terms can be grouped as follows:

$$x^3 + 5x^2 + 3x + 15 = (x^3 + 5x^2) + (3x + 15).$$

The common factor $x^2$ is then factored out of the first group, and the common factor 3 is factored out of the second group.

$\qquad\qquad = x^2(x + 5) + 3(x + 5).$

Finally, the common factor $x + 5$ is factored out of the entire polynomial.

$\qquad\qquad = (x + 5)(x^2 + 3).$  □

**EXAMPLE 5**    Factor $rs - 7r + 2s - 14$.

$rs - 7r + 2s - 14 = (rs - 7r) + (2s - 14)$

$\qquad\qquad = r(s - 7) + 2(s - 7)$

$\qquad\qquad = (s - 7)(r + 2).$  □

**EXAMPLE 6**    Factor $a^2 + 10a + 25 - b^2$.

In this case we group the first *three* terms together.

$$a^2 + 10a + 25 - b^2 = (a^2 + 10a + 25) - b^2.$$

The perfect square trinomial in parentheses is then factored.

$$= (a + 5)^2 - b^2.$$

Finally, this last expression is factored as a difference of two squares.

$$= ((a + 5) - b)((a + 5) + b)$$
$$= (a + 5 - b)(a + 5 + b). \quad \square$$

**EXAMPLE 7**  Factor $x^2y + x^2 - 4y - 4$.

$$x^2y + x^2 - 4y - 4 = x^2(y + 1) - 4(y + 1)$$
$$= (y + 1)(x^2 - 4)$$
$$= (y + 1)(x - 2)(x + 2). \quad \square$$

## Problem Set 6.7

Factor each sum or difference of two cubes.

1. $x^3 + 8$
2. $x^3 + 27$
3. $y^3 - 64$
4. $y^3 - 125$
5. $z^3 + 1$
6. $z^3 - 1$
7. $27r^3 - 1$
8. $8r^3 + 1$
9. $125s^3 + t^3$
10. $64s^3 - t^3$
11. $27a^3 - 125b^3$
12. $125a^3 + 8b^3$
13. $p^3q^3 + 1$
14. $p^3q^3 - 1$
15. $343u^3 + 216v^3$
16. $125u^3 - 216v^3$
17. $x^6 - y^3$
18. $x^6 + y^3$

Factor each polynomial by grouping.

19. $x^3 + 7x^2 + 3x + 21$
20. $x^3 + 4x^2 + 5x + 20$
21. $ab + 13a + 2b + 26$
22. $ab + 11a + 3b + 33$
23. $rs - r + 3s - 3$
24. $rs - r + 6s - 6$
25. $uv - v - u + 1$
26. $uv + v - u - 1$
27. $s^2 + 8st^2 + 6st + 48t^3$
28. $s^3 + 9s^2t + 7st + 63t^2$
29. $x^2 + 6x + 9 - y^2$
30. $x^2 + 4x + 4 - y^2$
31. $x^2 + 2x + 1 - 4y^2$
32. $x^2 + 10x + 25 - 9y^2$
33. $a^2 - b^2 - 8b - 16$
34. $a^2 - b^2 + 8b - 16$
35. $4r^2 - 20rs + 25s^2 - 9t^2$
36. $9r^2 - 12rs + 4s^2 - 25t^2$
37. $x^2y + x^2 - y - 1$
38. $x^2y - x^2 - y + 1$

39. $p^2q^2 - 16q^2 + 9p^2 - 144$        40. $p^2q^2 - 9q^2 + 4p^2 - 36$
41. $t^4 + 5t^3 - 8t - 40$              42. $t^4 - 2t^3 + 27t - 54$
43. $t^4 + s^3t + st^3 + s^4$           44. $t^4 - s^3t - st^3 + s^4$

45. Verify that $a^3 + b^3 = (a + b)(a^2 - ab + b^2)$ by computing the product on the right-hand side.
46. Verify that $a^3 - b^3 = (a - b)(a^2 + ab + b^2)$ by computing the product on the right-hand side.

## Calculator Problems

Factor each polynomial.

47. $512x^3 + 729$        48. $2197y^3 - 4913$        49. $19rs + 1007r + 29s + 1537$

## Challenge Problems

Completely factor each polynomial.

50. $64k^6 - 1$        51. $s^{6n} - t^{3m}$        52. $x^3 + 6x^2 + 12x + 8$

## 6.8    DIVISION OF POLYNOMIALS

The operations of addition, subtraction, multiplication, and factorization of polynomials have been demonstrated. We shall now illustrate division of polynomials, beginning with division by a monomial.

**EXAMPLE 1**   Divide the monomial $20x^6$ by the monomial $4x^2$.

$$20x^6 \div 4x^2 = \frac{20x^6}{4x^2} = 5x^{6-2} = 5x^4. \quad \square$$

**EXAMPLE 2**   Divide the binomial $8x + 8y$ by the monomial 8.

Recall that addition of fractions was defined as follows:

$$\frac{a}{c} + \frac{b}{c} = \frac{a+b}{c}.$$

Reading this equation from right to left, we have

$$\frac{a+b}{c} = \frac{a}{c} + \frac{b}{c}.$$

Using this rule, we can perform our division as follows:

$$\frac{8x + 8y}{8} = \frac{8x}{8} + \frac{8y}{8} = x + y. \quad \square$$

In other words, *to divide a polynomial by a monomial we divide each term of the polynomial by the monomial.*

**EXAMPLE 3**   Perform the division $(6x^8 + 5x^7 - 14x^6)/2x^4$.

$$\frac{6x^8 + 5x^7 - 14x^6}{2x^4} = \frac{6x^8}{2x^4} + \frac{5x^7}{2x^4} - \frac{14x^6}{2x^4}$$

$$= 3x^4 + \frac{5}{2}x^3 - 7x^2. \quad \square$$

We will now see the operation of division by a monomial applied to a problem in business. If it costs a firm $6000 to produce 250 units of a particular product, then the **average cost per unit** is

$$\frac{\text{Total cost}}{\text{Number of units}} = \frac{6000}{250} = 24.$$

Again, $24 is the *average* cost per unit. It is possible that the first several units cost *more* than $24 each to produce due to initial setup costs. On the other hand, it may be that the *last* several units are the most expensive to produce due to such factors as crowded conditions and payment of overtime.

**EXAMPLE 4**   Suppose that the total cost $C$ in dollars of producing $x$ units of a product is given by $C = 0.04x^2 + 15x + 750$. Write a formula for the average cost $AC$ per unit of producing $x$ units. Then use this formula to determine the average cost per unit of producing 100 units.

Since average cost is total cost divided by number of units, we have

$$AC = \frac{C}{x} = \frac{0.04x^2 + 15x + 750}{x} = 0.04x + 15 + \frac{750}{x}.$$

When $x = 100$,

$$AC = 0.04(100) + 15 + \frac{750}{100} = 4 + 15 + 7.5 = 26.5.$$

Therefore, the average cost per unit of producing 100 units is $26.50.

□

Division by a polynomial of *two or more terms* is accomplished by a process similar to long division in arithmetic. This process is called **long division of polynomials.** We shall illustrate long division of polynomials by finding the quotient $(x^2 + 7x + 10) \div (x + 2)$.

$$
\begin{array}{r}
x \\
x + 2 \overline{)\, x^2 + 7x + 10}
\end{array}
\quad \leftarrow \text{Divide } x \text{ into } x^2.
$$

$$
\begin{array}{r}
x \\
x + 2 \overline{)\, x^2 + 7x + 10} \\
x^2 + 2x
\end{array}
\quad \leftarrow \text{Multiply } x \text{ by } x + 2.
$$

$$
\begin{array}{r}
x \\
x + 2 \overline{)\, x^2 + 7x + 10} \\
\underline{x^2 + 2x} \\
5x + 10
\end{array}
\quad \leftarrow \text{Subtract } x^2 + 2x \text{ from } x^2 + 7x + 10.
$$

$$
\begin{array}{r}
x + 5 \\
x + 2 \overline{)\, x^2 + 7x + 10} \\
\underline{x^2 + 2x} \\
5x + 10
\end{array}
\quad \leftarrow \text{Divide } x \text{ into } 5x.
$$

$$
\begin{array}{r}
x + 5 \\
x + 2 \overline{)\, x^2 + 7x + 10} \\
\underline{x^2 + 2x} \\
5x + 10 \\
5x + 10
\end{array}
\quad \leftarrow \text{Multiply } 5 \text{ by } x + 2.
$$

$$
\begin{array}{r}
x + 5 \\
x + 2 \overline{)\, x^2 + 7x + 10} \\
\underline{x^2 + 2x} \\
5x + 10 \\
\underline{5x + 10} \\
0
\end{array}
\quad \leftarrow \text{Subtract to obtain the remainder 0.}
$$

Therefore $(x^2 + 7x + 10) \div (x + 2) = x + 5$. This answer can of course be checked by finding the product of $x + 2$ and $x + 5$.

$$(x + 2)(x + 5) = x^2 + 2x + 5x + 10 = x^2 + 7x + 10.$$

This procedure will probably seem a little complicated at first, but like long division in arithmetic, once mastered it is quite simple.

**EXAMPLE 5**    Use long division of polynomials to find

$$(8x^3 - 4x + 5) \div (2x - 1).$$

Writing both polynomials in decreasing powers of $x$ and writing $0x^2$ for the missing second-degree term in the dividend, our work is arranged as follows:

*[handwritten: This term is like 1068 in polynomials like 0x² use descending powers]*

$$
\begin{array}{r}
4x^2 + 2x - 1 \\
2x - 1 \overline{\smash{)}\, 8x^3 + 0x^2 - 4x + 5} \\
\underline{-\ 8x^3 - 4x^2} \\
4x^2 - 4x + 5 \\
\underline{4x^2 - 2x} \\
-2x + 5 \\
\underline{-2x + 1} \\
4
\end{array}
$$

*[handwritten: So subtract −4x² = −−4x² so 4x²   −−2x ↖ same thing]*

*[handwritten: 4. once you get to a lower power can't divide anymore]*

Checking this result we have

Divisor · Quotient + Remainder

$$(2x - 1)(4x^2 + 2x - 1) + 4 = (8x^3 + 4x^2 - 2x - 4x^2 - 2x + 1) + 4$$
$$= 8x^3 - 4x + 5.$$

Dividend □

Recall from arithmetic that the solution to the division problem

$$
\begin{array}{r}
5 \\
3 \overline{\smash{)}\, 17} \\
\underline{15} \\
2
\end{array}
$$

can be written as

$$\frac{17}{3} = 5 + \frac{2}{3}.$$

That is,

$$\frac{\text{Dividend}}{\text{Divisor}} = \text{Quotient} + \frac{\text{Remainder}}{\text{Divisor}}.$$

So too can the solution to Example 5 be written as

$$\frac{8x^3 - 4x + 5}{2x - 1} = 4x^2 + 2x - 1 + \frac{4}{2x - 1}.$$

Notice that when both sides of this last equation are multiplied by

$2x - 1$, we obtain the equation

$$8x^3 - 4x + 5 = (2x - 1)(4x^2 + 2x - 1) + 4.$$

This is the same equation that we obtained when checking the solution to Example 5 above.

## Problem Set 6.8

Find each quotient.

1. $\dfrac{9x^{10}}{3x^5}$

2. $\dfrac{20x^8}{10x^4}$

3. $\dfrac{-4x^5}{2x}$

4. $\dfrac{-6x^3}{2x}$

5. $\dfrac{80x^7}{10x^7}$

6. $\dfrac{36x^5}{12x^5}$

7. $\dfrac{7x^{25}}{7x^{24}}$

8. $\dfrac{5x^{31}}{5x^{30}}$

9. $\dfrac{6x - 6y}{6}$

10. $\dfrac{7x + 7y}{7}$

11. $\dfrac{x^3 + x^2}{x}$

12. $\dfrac{x^5 - x^4}{x^2}$

13. $\dfrac{3x^3 + 6x^2}{3x^2}$

14. $\dfrac{4x^7 - 12x^6}{4x^4}$

15. $\dfrac{64x^3 + 3x^2 - 4x}{4x}$

16. $\dfrac{25x^3 - 3x^2 + 10x}{5x}$

17. $\dfrac{6xy^2 - 2x^2y + xy}{xy}$

18. $\dfrac{4x^2y^2 + x^2y - xy}{xy}$

19. $\dfrac{45a^5b^3 + 75a^3b^5 - 30a^2b^5}{15a^2b^3}$

20. $\dfrac{60a^5b^5 - 40a^3b^3 + 50a^3b^2}{10a^2b}$

21. $\dfrac{3x^3y^3 - 15x^2y^2 + x^2y}{5x^2y}$

22. $\dfrac{7x^3y^3 - 16x^2y^2 + xy^2}{2xy^2}$

23. $\dfrac{180x^{10} - 150x^8 + 120x^4 + 90x^2}{30x^2}$

24. $\dfrac{140x^8 - 100x^5 + 40x^3 - 60x^2}{20x^2}$

Use long division of polynomials to perform the division. Check your result.

25. $(x^2 + 8x + 12) \div (x + 2)$
26. $(x^2 + 10x + 21) \div (x + 3)$
27. $(2x^2 + 3x - 20) \div (x + 4)$
28. $(3x^2 + 13x - 10) \div (x + 5)$
29. $\dfrac{9x^2 + 6x + 8}{3x - 2}$
30. $\dfrac{6x^2 - 7x + 5}{3x + 4}$
31. $\dfrac{4x^3 - 4x^2 - x + 1}{2x - 1}$
32. $\dfrac{4x^3 - 16x^2 + 21x - 9}{2x - 3}$
33. $\dfrac{8x^3 - 4x^2 - 14x + 15}{2x + 3}$
34. $\dfrac{2x^3 + 11x^2 - 25x + 6}{2x - 3}$
35. $(3a^3 + 2a + 25) \div (a + 2)$
36. $(5a^3 + 7a^2 + 9) \div (a + 1)$
37. $(y^3 - 8y + 10) \div (y + 3)$
38. $(y^3 - 5y + 30) \div (y + 4)$
39. $\dfrac{x^3 - 1}{x - 1}$
40. $\dfrac{x^3 + 1}{x + 1}$
41. $\dfrac{8m^4 - 10m^3 - 19m - 21}{4m + 3}$
42. $\dfrac{16m^4 - 13m^2 + 23m - 15}{4m - 3}$
43. $(25x^3 + 10x^2 - 2x + \tfrac{1}{5}) \div (5x - 1)$
44. $(30x^3 + 14x^2 - 3x + \tfrac{1}{5}) \div (5x - 1)$

45. If three resistors of size $R_1$, $R_2$, and $R_3$ are connected in parallel, the reciprocal of the total resistance in the electrical circuit is given by the expression

$$\frac{R_2R_3 + R_1R_3 + R_1R_2}{R_1R_2R_3}.$$

Find this quotient.

46. If two thin lenses of focal lengths $f_1$ and $f_2$ are placed in contact, the reciprocal of the focal length of the resulting compound lens is approximately given by the expression

$$\frac{f_2 + f_1}{f_1f_2}.$$

Find this quotient.

47. Suppose that the total cost $C$ in dollars of producing $x$ units of a product is given by $C = 0.05x^2 + 25x + 1400$. Write a formula for the average cost $AC$ per unit of producing $x$ units. Then use this formula to determine the average cost per unit of producing (a) 100 units. (b) 500 units.

48. Repeat Problem 47 if $C = 4.5x + 2500$.

49. If a particle travels $7t^2 + 8t + 2t^3 + 28$ cm in $7 + 2t$ sec, find its average speed.

50. If a particle travels $5t^2 + 9t + 3t^3 + 15$ cm in $5 + 3t$ sec, find its average speed.

51. Determine the value of $k$ that makes $3x - 2$ a factor of $6x^3 + 2x^2 - 19x + k$. (*Hint:* When $6x^3 + 2x^2 - 19x + k$ is divided by $3x - 2$ the remainder must be zero.)

52. Determine the value of $k$ that makes $2x - 3$ a factor of $8x^3 - 6x^2 + x + k$. (*Hint:* When $8x^3 - 6x^2 + x + k$ is divided by $2x - 3$ the remainder must be zero.)

## Calculator Problems

53. Find the quotient $(36.162p^3q^2 - 60.3684p^2q + 70.11p)/7.38p$.

54. Perform the division and check your result.

$$\frac{32.802m^3 + 10.577m^2 - 7.255m - 8.324}{4.26m + 1.18}$$

## Challenge Problems

Perform the division and check your result.

55. $\dfrac{6x^4 + 4x^3 + 3x^2 + 10x + 9}{2x^2 + 2x - 1}$      56. $\dfrac{2x^5 + 8x^4 - x^3 + 3x^2 - x}{2x^2 + 1}$

57. Prove that the average of *any* three consecutive integers equals the middle integer.

## Chapter Review

True or false.

1. Two polynomials are multiplied by multiplying each term of one of the polynomials by each term of the other polynomial.
2. The key word FOIL is used when multiplying two trinomials.
3. A factorization can always be checked by multiplying the factors to see if the original polynomial is obtained.
4. To divide a polynomial by a monomial we divide each term of the polynomial by the monomial.

5. When one polynomial is divided by another polynomial containing two or more terms, we can use long division of polynomials to determine the quotient and remainder.
6. $t^2 + 25$ is a prime polynomial.
7. $s^2 - 12s + 36$ is a perfect square trinomial.
8. $a^3 + b^3 = (a + b)(a^2 - 2ab + b^2)$.
9. $a^3 - b^3 = (a - b)(a^2 + ab + b^2)$.
10. $(a + b)^3 = a^3 + b^3$.
11. Every polynomial can be factored using integers.
12. Every polynomial can be factored using real numbers.

Completion.

13. When a polynomial is expressed as a product, the polynomial is

said to be _____?_____.
14. A polynomial is in completely factored form when it is expressed

as a product of _____?_____ polynomials.
15. When factoring a polynomial, we should always look for

_____?_____ before attempting any other type of factorization.

16. The polynomial $x^4 + 2x^2 + 3x + 4$ is written in _____?_____
powers of $x$.

Find each product.

17. $6x^2(3x - 1)$
18. $-x^2y(x^2 - 5xy + 4y^2)$
19. $x(2x + 1)(3x - 5)$
20. $(a - 1)(a^3 - 2a^2 + a + 1)$
21. $(t - 5)^2$
22. $(4x - 7y)^2$
23. $(a + 4)^3$
24. $(8 - 3s)(6s + 11)(s + 2)$

Completely factor each polynomial.

25. $6a^2 + a$
26. $x^2 - 10x + 25$
27. $x^2 - 100$
28. $9a^4b^4 - 12a^3b^2 + 15a^2b$
29. $x^2 + 3x - 54$
30. $x^2 + 9x + 20$
31. $5m^2 - 50m - 55$
32. $16a^2 - 121b^2$
33. $x^7y^7 - x^3y^3$
34. $3s^2 + 14s - 24$
35. $24a^2b - 32ab - 32b$
36. $70x^3 - 14x^2y - 84xy^2$
37. $(a + b)^2 - 9c^2$
38. $-14c^4d - 14c^2d^3$
39. $p^3 + \frac{1}{8}$
40. $10q^3 + 10$   *sum of 2 cubes*
  *4 terms*
  *grouping*   41. $a^2b + a^2 + 4b + 4$
42. $s^2 - t^2 + 18t - 81$
43. $125wu^3 - wv^6$
44. $64r^3 - 27s^3$
45. $p^4 + 8pq^3 + 2p^3 + 16q^3$
46. $49x^2 - 28xy + 4y^2 - z^2$
47. $12t^2 + 7t - 12$
48. $(1 + r) + (1 + r)r$

Find each quotient.

49. $\dfrac{-64x^{10}}{4x^5}$         50. $\dfrac{8x + 8y}{8}$

51. $\dfrac{x^6 - x^4 + x^2}{x^2}$         52. $\dfrac{48a^4b^4 - 60a^2b^3 + 18ab^3}{12ab^3}$

Use long division of polynomials to perform the division. Check your result.

53. $(2x^3 - 5x^2 + x - 12) \div (x - 3)$
54. $(5x^4 - 9x^3 + 3x^2 - 1) \div (5x + 1)$

55. Find an expression for the area of a rectangle whose width is $\frac{1}{2}k + \frac{1}{3}$ and whose length is $\frac{4}{5}k - \frac{3}{2}$.

56. This piece of sheet metal is to be bent at right angles along the dashed lines to form a trough. Find an expression for the cross-sectional area of the trough.

57. The volume of this cylindrical shell is given by $\pi R^2 h - \pi r^2 h$. Write this expression in factored form.

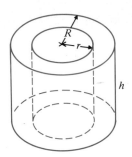

58. If a particle travels $t^4 + 16$ cm in $2 + t$ sec, find its average speed.

# Chapter
# Chapter
# Chapter
# Chapter Seven
# Seven
# Seven
# Seven

## RATIONAL EXPRESSIONS

## 7.1  REDUCING EXPRESSIONS

A rational *number* was defined previously as any number that can be written as a ratio of two integers where the divisor is not zero. We define a rational *expression* in a similar way.

**Definition**  A **rational expression** is any algebraic expression that can be written as a ratio of two polynomials where the divisor is not zero.

**EXAMPLE 1**  $\dfrac{x^2 + 3x + 1}{x - 5}$ is a rational expression since it is a quotient of the two polynomials $x^2 + 3x + 1$ and $x - 5$. Since the divisor $x - 5$ is zero when $x = 5$, however, we must have that $x \neq 5$. □

Since integers are polynomials of degree zero (except the integer zero, which has no degree), *every rational number is also a rational expression.*

**EXAMPLE 2**  The rational *number* $\frac{3}{5}$ is a ratio of the two polynomials 3 and 5 and is therefore a rational *expression* as well. □

Since a polynomial can be written with a denominator of 1, *every polynomial is also a rational expression.*

**EXAMPLE 3**  The polynomial $x^2 + 7x + 5$ is a rational expression since

*this is rational number it can be written over 1*

$$x^2 + 7x + 5 = \frac{x^2 + 7x + 5}{1}. \quad \square$$

**EXAMPLE 4**  For what value(s) is the rational expression $\dfrac{x - 6}{x^2 - 2x - 3}$ undefined?

First, we factor the denominator.

*factor out*

$$0 \neq \frac{x - 6}{x^2 - 2x - 3} = \frac{x - 6}{(x - 3)(x + 1)}. \text{ so could be 3 or -1}$$

We then note that when $x = 3$, the value of the rational expression is

$$\frac{3 - 6}{(3 - 3)(3 + 1)} = \frac{-3}{0 \cdot 4} = \frac{-3}{0}, \text{ which is undefined.}$$

Also, when $x = -1$ we have

$$\frac{-1-6}{(-1-3)(-1+1)} = \frac{-7}{(-4)\cdot 0} = \frac{-7}{0}, \text{ which is undefined.}$$

Therefore, the rational expression is undefined when $x = 3$ or when $x = -1$. □

Since rational expressions can be written as fractions, the techniques for working with them are essentially the same as the techniques developed for fractions in Section 1.3. The only difference is that now the numerator or denominator (or both) may contain variables.

For example, the fundamental law of fractions, which states that

*Factor out common factor*
$$\frac{a \cdot c}{b \cdot c} = \frac{a}{b} \quad \text{where } b, c \neq 0,$$

applies to rational expressions as well as to ordinary fractions. In other words, if both the numerator and the denominator of a rational expression are multiplied or divided by the same nonzero polynomial the resulting expression is equivalent to the original.

Thus, just as the rational number $\frac{6}{8}$ can be expressed in the reduced form $\frac{3}{4}$, some rational expressions can be expressed in simpler form. *To find the reduced form of a rational expression, we must factor both the numerator and denominator completely and then divide out the common factors.*

**EXAMPLE 5**  Find the reduced form of $14a/21a$.

First the numerator and denominator are completely factored.

$$\frac{14a}{21a} = \frac{2 \cdot 7 \cdot a}{3 \cdot 7 \cdot a}.$$

Then the common factors are divided out.

$$\frac{14a}{21a} = \frac{2 \cdot \cancel{7} \cdot \cancel{a}}{3 \cdot \cancel{7} \cdot \cancel{a}} = \frac{2}{3}. \quad \square$$

**EXAMPLE 6**  Find the reduced form of $\dfrac{3x-3}{5x-5}$.

The numerator and denominator are completely factored, and then the common factors are divided out.

$$\frac{3x - 3}{5x - 5} = \frac{3(\cancel{x-1})}{5(\cancel{x-1})} = \frac{3}{5}. \quad \square$$

**EXAMPLE 7**   Find the reduced form of $\dfrac{x^2 - 4}{x^2 + x - 6}$.

$$\frac{x^2 - 4}{x^2 + x - 6} = \frac{(\cancel{x-2})(x + 2)}{(\cancel{x-2})(x + 3)} = \frac{x + 2}{x + 3}. \quad \square \qquad x \neq -3, 2$$

The last expression $(x + 2)/(x + 3)$ *cannot* be reduced further by dividing out the $x$'s, since they are *terms*. Remember, *we cannot divide out terms, we can only divide out factors.*

**EXAMPLE 8**   Find the reduced form of $\dfrac{y - x}{x - y}$.

At first glance, there does not seem to be any way in which we can factor either the numerator or denominator. However, we can factor $-1$ out of the numerator (or the denominator if we choose) and write

$$y - x = -1(-y + x) = -1(x - y).$$

Therefore,

$$\frac{y - x}{x - y} = \frac{-1(\cancel{x-y})}{1(\cancel{x-y})} = \frac{-1}{1} = -1. \quad \square$$

The solution to Example 8 could have been obtained simply by noting that $y - x$ and $x - y$ are *negatives* of each other.

One of the most common errors made by beginning algebra students involves improperly reducing rational expressions. The next two examples present both an *incorrect* and a *correct* method for reducing the given rational expression. In each case notice that *only polynomials that are factors of the entire numerator and the entire denominator are divided out.*

**EXAMPLE 9**   Find the reduced form of $\dfrac{r^2 - s^2}{r - s}$.

*[handwritten top right:]*

$$r - s \enspace\overline{)\,r^2 + 0rs - s^2\,}^{\textstyle r+s}$$
$$\underline{r^2 - rs}$$
$$+rs - s^2$$
$$\underline{rs - s^2}$$
$$0$$

INCORRECT: $\dfrac{r^2 - s^2}{r - s} = \dfrac{\overset{r}{\cancel{r^2}} - \overset{s}{\cancel{s^2}}}{\cancel{r} - \cancel{s}} = r - s.$

CORRECT: $\dfrac{r^2 - s^2}{r - s} = \dfrac{(r + s)\cancel{(r - s)}}{\cancel{r - s}} = r + s. \quad \square$

**EXAMPLE 10**   Find the reduced form of $\dfrac{(p + 3)4 + 3}{(p + 3)5 - p}.$

*[handwritten: Terms]*

INCORRECT: $\dfrac{(p + 3)4 + 3}{(p + 3)5 - p} = \dfrac{\cancel{(p + 3)}4 + 3}{\cancel{(p + 3)}5 - p} = \dfrac{7}{5 - p}.$

*[handwritten left: Terms   those are not factors]*

CORRECT: $\dfrac{(p + 3)4 + 3}{(p + 3)5 - p} = \dfrac{4p + 12 + 3}{5p + 15 - p} = \dfrac{\cancel{4p + 15}}{\cancel{4p + 15}} = 1. \quad \square$

*[handwritten: $(a + b)c = ac + bc$]*

The next example illustrates the fact that the value of the *reduced* form of a given rational expression is the same as the value of the *original* rational expression for any value of the variable(s) at which both expressions are defined.

**EXAMPLE 11**   Find the value of $\dfrac{8a + 8b}{a^2 - b^2}$ when $a = 4$ and $b = -2$. Then find the value of the reduced form of this expression when $a = 4$ and $b = -2$ and note that the two values are the same.

Substituting $a = 4$ and $b = -2$ into the original expression, we have

$$\frac{8(4) + 8(-2)}{4^2 - (-2)^2} = \frac{32 + (-16)}{16 - 4} = \frac{16}{12} = \frac{4}{3}.$$

Reducing the original expression, we have

$$\frac{8a + 8b}{a^2 - b^2} = \frac{8(a + b)}{(a - b)(a + b)} = \frac{8}{a - b}.$$

The value of this reduced form when $a = 4$ and $b = -2$ is

$$\frac{8}{4 - (-2)} = \frac{8}{6} = \frac{4}{3},$$

which is the same as the value obtained above. $\quad \square$

## Problem Set 7.1

For what value(s) is each rational expression undefined?

1. $\dfrac{1}{5x}$    2. $\dfrac{1}{3x}$    3. $\dfrac{8}{x-2}$    4. $\dfrac{6}{x-4}$

5. $\dfrac{x-3}{x+7}$    6. $\dfrac{x-1}{x+5}$    7. $\dfrac{x^2}{x^2-25}$    8. $\dfrac{x^2}{x^2-16}$

9. $\dfrac{13}{y^2+8y}$    10. $\dfrac{17}{y^2+6y}$    11. $\dfrac{ab}{a^2-b^2}$    12. $\dfrac{ab}{a^2-4b^2}$

13. $\dfrac{r^2-9}{r^2+r-12}$    14. $\dfrac{r^2-4}{r^2+3r-10}$    15. $\dfrac{4p}{p^2+4}$    16. $\dfrac{9p}{p^2+9}$

Find the reduced form of each rational expression.

17. $\dfrac{6a}{8a}$    18. $\dfrac{10a}{15a}$    19. $\dfrac{7a^2}{28a^2}$

20. $\dfrac{9a^2}{27a^2}$    21. $\dfrac{22a}{99a^3}$    22. $\dfrac{21a}{35a^3}$

23. $\dfrac{24a^2b}{9ab}$    24. $\dfrac{16ab^3}{12ab}$    25. $\dfrac{5x+5}{7x+7}$

26. $\dfrac{3x-3}{4x-4}$    27. $\dfrac{2x-2y}{2x+2y}$    28. $\dfrac{3x+3y}{9x-9y}$

29. $\dfrac{10x}{25x^2-5x}$    30. $\dfrac{6x}{9x^2-3x}$    31. $\dfrac{x^2+x}{x^2-x}$

32. $\dfrac{x+2}{x^2+2x}$    33. $\dfrac{x-3}{x^2-9}$    34. $\dfrac{x+4}{x^2-16}$

35. $\dfrac{(x+y)^3}{(x+y)^6}$    36. $\dfrac{(x-y)^2}{(x-y)^4}$    37. $\dfrac{a^2-b^2}{a-b}$

38. $\dfrac{a-b}{a^2-b^2}$    39. $\dfrac{(x-y)^2}{x^2-y^2}$    40. $\dfrac{x^2-y^2}{(x-y)^2}$

41. $\dfrac{x^2-6x+9}{x^2-9}$    42. $\dfrac{x^2-4}{x^2-5x+6}$    43. $\dfrac{x^2-4x+3}{x^2-2x+1}$

44. $\dfrac{x^2-9x-22}{x^2-13x+22}$    45. $\dfrac{2x^2-9xy-5y^2}{x^2-25y^2}$    46. $\dfrac{3x^2+11xy-4y^2}{x^2-16y^2}$

47. $\dfrac{a+5}{5+a}$    48. $\dfrac{a+b}{b+a}$    49. $\dfrac{a-5}{5-a}$

50. $\dfrac{a-b}{b-a}$    51. $\dfrac{a^2-ab-2b^2}{a^2+ab-6b^2}$    52. $\dfrac{a^2+ab-2b^2}{a^2+5ab+6b^2}$

53. $\dfrac{a^2 + 4ab - 5b^2}{5b^2 - 4ab - a^2}$     54. $\dfrac{a^2 + 6ab - 7b^2}{7b^2 - 6ab - a^2}$     55. $\dfrac{(p - 5)p + 6}{(p - 2)p - 3}$

56. $\dfrac{(p - 7)p + 12}{(p - 2)p - 3}$     57. $\dfrac{(q + 2)3 - 6}{(q + 2)q}$     58. $\dfrac{(q + 1)5 - 5}{(q + 1)q}$

Find (a) the value of the given rational expression at the indicated value(s) of the variable(s). Then find (b) the value of the reduced form of the expression at the same value(s) of the variable(s) and note that it is the same as the value found in part (a).

59. $\dfrac{4x}{5x^3}$   at   $x = 3$         60. $\dfrac{3x}{7x^4}$   at   $x = 2$

61. $\dfrac{8x - 8}{2x - 2}$   at   $x = -2$      62. $\dfrac{6x + 6}{2x + 2}$   at   $x = -3$

63. $\dfrac{12a + 12b}{a^2 - b^2}$   at   $a = 4, b = -6$     64. $\dfrac{12a - 12b}{a^2 - b^2}$   at   $a = 4, b = -6$

65. $\dfrac{r - s}{s - r}$   at   $r = 7, s = 5$      66. $\dfrac{r - s}{s - r}$   at   $r = -8, s = 9$

67. $\dfrac{(t - 3)t - 18}{(t - 3)2 - t}$   at   $t = 14$     68. $\dfrac{(t - 5)t - 50}{(t - 5)2 - t}$   at   $t = 12$

69. According to experiments conducted by A. J. Clark, the response of a particular frog's heart to the injection of $x$ units of acetylcholine might be given by $\dfrac{100x}{15 + x}$. Find the response when $x = 22.5$ units.

70. Suppose the percentage of certain information that is remembered $t$ days after it is learned is given by $\dfrac{100}{1 + t}$. Find the percentage when $t = 4$.

71. The price of a certain item is given by $\dfrac{500 - 5x}{x + 2}$, where $x$ is the quantity demanded. Find the price when $x = 38$.

72. The concentration of a certain drug that remains in the bloodstream $t$ hours after it is injected is given by $\dfrac{t}{5t^2 + 60}$. Find the concentration when $t = 2$.

73. The focal length of a simple convex lens is given by $\dfrac{d_o d_i}{d_i + d_o}$,

where $d_o$ is the distance from the lens to the object and $d_i$ is the distance from the lens to the image. Find the focal length of a simple convex lens if the distances from the lens to the object and the image are, respectively, 15 cm and 5 cm.

74. The present value of a sum $S$ that is due $t$ years in the future is given by $\dfrac{S}{1 + rt}$, where $r$ is the simple interest rate expressed as a decimal. Find the present value of $900 due in two years if the simple interest rate is 10%.

## Calculator Problems

75. Suppose that the number of persons having a certain contagious disease $t$ days after an epidemic begins is given by $\dfrac{100,000}{t^2 - 40t + 440}$. Find the approximate number of persons having the disease when $t = 19$.

76. Find to the nearest hundredth the value of $\dfrac{x^2 - 13xy + 7y^2}{x^2 + 9xy - 19y^2}$ at $x = 3.18$ and $y = -5.91$.

## Challenge Problems

77. The sum of the *infinite geometric series* $a + ar + ar^2 + ar^3 + \cdots$ is given by $\dfrac{a}{1 - r}$ if $-1 < r < 1$. Find the sum $1 + \frac{1}{2} + \frac{1}{4} + \frac{1}{8} + \cdots$ .

78. Write the repeating decimal $0.\overline{27}$ as a ratio of two integers. (*Hint:* Note that $0.\overline{27} = 0.27 + 0.0027 + 0.000027 + \cdots$. Then use Problem 77.)

## 7.2 MULTIPLICATION AND DIVISION OF EXPRESSIONS

When multiplying two rational numbers we simply multiplied numerator by numerator and denominator by denominator. That is

$$\frac{a}{b} \cdot \frac{c}{d} = \frac{a \cdot c}{b \cdot d} \qquad \text{where } b, d \neq 0.$$

Often the work was shortened by dividing out common factors *before* multiplying the fractions. For example, to find the product $\frac{3}{8} \cdot \frac{4}{5}$ we wrote

*[handwritten: invert + multiply]*
*[handwritten: $\frac{a}{b} \div \frac{c}{d} = \frac{a}{b} \cdot \frac{d}{c}$]*

$$\frac{3}{8} \cdot \frac{4}{5} = \frac{3}{\overset{}{\underset{2}{8}}} \cdot \frac{\overset{1}{\cancel{4}}}{5} = \frac{3 \cdot 1}{2 \cdot 5} = \frac{3}{10}.$$

This same procedure is used to multiply rational expressions.

**EXAMPLE 1**   Find the product $\dfrac{16}{7a} \cdot \dfrac{15a^2}{4b}$.

*[handwritten: signs / numbers / letters]*

$$\frac{16}{7a} \cdot \frac{15a^2}{4b} = \frac{\overset{4}{\cancel{16}}}{7\cancel{a}} \cdot \frac{15\overset{a}{\cancel{a^2}}}{\cancel{4}b}$$

$$= \frac{60a}{7b}.$$

Therefore, the product of $\dfrac{16}{7a}$ and $\dfrac{15a^2}{4b}$ is $\dfrac{60a}{7b}$.   □

Before multiplying, the numerator and denominator of a rational expression should always be completely factored in order to determine whether there are any common factors that can be divided out.

**EXAMPLE 2**   Find the product $\dfrac{x^2 - 2x}{x^2 - 4} \cdot \dfrac{3}{x^2 - 5x}$.

*[handwritten: factor out]*

$$\frac{x^2 - 2x}{x^2 - 4} \cdot \frac{3}{x^2 - 5x} = \frac{\cancel{x}(\cancel{x - 2})}{(\cancel{x - 2})(x + 2)} \cdot \frac{3}{\cancel{x}(x - 5)}$$

$$= \frac{3}{(x + 2)(x - 5)}.$$   □

*[handwritten: can go to $\frac{3}{x^2 - 3x - 10}$   But leave factored]*

**EXAMPLE 3**   Find the product $\dfrac{x^2 - x - 12}{x^2 + 5x + 6} \cdot \dfrac{x^2 + 3x + 2}{x - 4}$.

$$\frac{x^2 - x - 12}{x^2 + 5x + 6} \cdot \frac{x^2 + 3x + 2}{x - 4} = \frac{(x + 3)(x - 4)}{(x + 2)(x + 3)} \cdot \frac{(x + 1)(x + 2)}{x - 4}$$

$$= \frac{x + 1}{1}$$

$$= x + 1. \;\square$$

Recall that to *divide* two rational numbers we inverted the divisor and then proceeded as in multiplication. That is

$$\frac{a}{b} \div \frac{c}{d} = \frac{a}{b} \cdot \frac{d}{c} = \frac{a \cdot d}{b \cdot c} \qquad \text{where } b, c, d \neq 0.$$

For example, to find the quotient $\frac{3}{7} \div \frac{4}{9}$ we wrote

$$\frac{3}{7} \div \frac{4}{9} = \frac{3}{7} \cdot \frac{9}{4} = \frac{27}{28}.$$

Rational expressions are divided in the same manner. <u>*Remember*</u> *that when dividing two rational expressions, the divisor must be inverted before any cancellation can be attempted.*

**EXAMPLE 4**   Find the quotient $5a^2/2b \div a^4/10b^3$.

$$\frac{5a^2}{2b} \div \frac{a^4}{10b^3} = \frac{5a^2}{2b} \cdot \frac{\overset{5}{\cancel{10}} \, b^2 \,}{\underset{a^2}{\cancel{a^4}}}$$

$$= \frac{25b^2}{a^2}.$$

Therefore, the quotient of $5a^2/2b$ divided by $a^4/10b^3$ is $25b^2/a^2$.   $\square$

**EXAMPLE 5**   Find the quotient $\dfrac{5x + 10y}{x - y} \div \dfrac{x^2 + 5xy + 6y^2}{x^2 - y^2}$.

$$\frac{5x + 10y}{x - y} \div \frac{x^2 + 5xy + 6y^2}{x^2 - y^2} = \frac{5x + 10y}{x - y} \cdot \frac{x^2 - y^2}{x^2 + 5xy + 6y^2}$$

$$= \frac{5(x + 2y)}{x - y} \cdot \frac{(x - y)(x + y)}{(x + 2y)(x + 3y)}$$

$$= \frac{5(x + y)}{x + 3y}. \;\square$$

*can multiply out Numerator* → $= \dfrac{5x + 5y}{x + 3y}$

**EXAMPLE 6** Find the quotient $\dfrac{x-2}{2} \div \dfrac{3x+12}{5x-10}$.

$$\frac{x-2}{2} \div \frac{3x+12}{5x-10} = \frac{x-2}{2} \cdot \frac{5x-10}{3x+12}$$

$$= \frac{x-2}{2} \cdot \frac{5(x-2)}{3(x+4)}$$

$$= \frac{5(x-2)^2}{6(x+4)}.$$

Note that in this case there were no common factors to be divided out.

$\square$

## Problem Set 7.2

Find each product and express your answer in reduced form.

1. $\dfrac{2a}{9} \cdot \dfrac{a}{3}$

2. $\dfrac{3a}{8} \cdot \dfrac{a}{4}$

3. $\dfrac{a}{5b} \cdot \dfrac{4a}{b}$

4. $\dfrac{11a}{b} \cdot \dfrac{a}{6b}$

5. $\dfrac{a^2}{9b} \cdot \dfrac{27}{a}$

6. $\dfrac{8}{ab} \cdot \dfrac{a^2}{24}$

7. $\dfrac{2a}{7b^2} \cdot \dfrac{3ab}{8} \cdot \dfrac{4b}{9a^3}$

8. $\dfrac{2}{15a^4} \cdot \dfrac{5a^2}{14} \cdot \dfrac{7a^3}{10b}$

9. $\dfrac{7a+14}{5} \cdot \dfrac{15a}{6a+12}$

10. $\dfrac{21a}{5a-15} \cdot \dfrac{3a-9}{7}$

11. $\dfrac{a^2-b^2}{8a} \cdot \dfrac{24a}{a+b}$

12. $\dfrac{5ab}{a^2-b^2} \cdot \dfrac{a-b}{ab}$

13. $\dfrac{x+5}{x+2} \cdot \dfrac{x^2-4}{5x^2+25x}$

14. $\dfrac{x^2-81}{x+7} \cdot \dfrac{x+7}{x^2+9x}$

15. $\dfrac{9x^2-1}{6x+2} \cdot \dfrac{2}{3x-1}$

16. $\dfrac{3}{4x-1} \cdot \dfrac{16x^2-1}{12x+3}$

17. $\dfrac{x^2+3x-10}{x^2-25} \cdot \dfrac{x^2-2x-15}{8x^2-16x}$

18. $\dfrac{x^2+6x-7}{x^2-49} \cdot \dfrac{x^2-5x-14}{9x^2-9x}$

19. $\dfrac{(x+y)^2}{x^3} \cdot \dfrac{x^4}{x^2-y^2}$

20. $\dfrac{y^3}{(x-y)^2} \cdot \dfrac{x^2-y^2}{y^2}$

Find each quotient and express your answer in reduced form.

21. $\dfrac{10a}{b} \div \dfrac{b}{3a}$

22. $\dfrac{a}{11b} \div \dfrac{4b}{a}$

23. $\dfrac{125ab}{12} \div \dfrac{5b^3}{a}$

24. $\dfrac{100a}{b} \div \dfrac{10ab}{3}$

25. $\dfrac{11a^3}{b} \div 121a^2b$

26. $\dfrac{225a^3b^2}{a^2} \div 15ab$

27. $\dfrac{4a-6}{a^2-a} \div \dfrac{6a-9}{a^2}$

28. $\dfrac{6a+18}{a^2} \div \dfrac{7a+21}{a^2+a}$

29. $\dfrac{a+1}{8} \div \dfrac{8a+16}{a+1}$

30. $\dfrac{a+3}{5a-5} \div \dfrac{5}{a+3}$

31. $\dfrac{a^2 + 13ab + 12b^2}{a + 1} \div \dfrac{a^2 - b^2}{a^2 + a}$

32. $\dfrac{a^2 + 7ab + 6b^2}{b - 1} \div \dfrac{a^2 + ab}{b^2 - b}$

33. $\dfrac{x^2 - 2x - 8}{x^2 - x - 12} \div \dfrac{x^2 - 6x + 8}{x^2 + x - 6}$

34. $\dfrac{x^2 - x - 6}{x^2 + 2x - 15} \div \dfrac{x^2 + 9x + 14}{x^2 + 2x - 35}$

35. $\dfrac{x^3 - 4x}{2x + 8} \div (x^2 + 2x)$

36. $\dfrac{x^2 + x}{x + 2} \div (x^3 - x)$

37. $\dfrac{x^4 + x^3}{y + xy} \div \dfrac{x^3}{y^2}$

38. $\dfrac{x^3 - x^2}{y - xy} \div \dfrac{x^2}{y^2}$

39. $\dfrac{c^2 + c - 6}{c^2 - 6c + 8} \div \dfrac{c^2 + 2c - 8}{c^2 - c - 12}$

40. $\dfrac{c^2 + 4c + 3}{c^2 + c - 2} \div \dfrac{c^2 + 2c + 1}{c^2 + 5c + 6}$

41. The product $\dfrac{n + r}{n} \cdot \dfrac{n + r}{n} \cdot \dfrac{n + r}{n}$ occurs in interest problems. Find this product.

42. The product $3 \cdot \dfrac{(t - 1)^2}{(t + 1)^2} \cdot \dfrac{2}{(t + 1)^2}$ occurs in calculus. Find this product.

43. The reaction to a drug of dosage size $d$ is given by $\dfrac{d^2}{2} \cdot \dfrac{3k - 2d}{3}$. Find this product.

44. **Poiseuille's law**[*] states that the velocity of blood in an artery is given by $\dfrac{p}{2kn} \cdot \dfrac{R^2 - r^2}{2}$. Find this product.

45. The average cost per unit for producing $x$ units of a particular product is given by $\dfrac{3x^2 + 26x + 40}{x + 2} \div x$. Find this quotient.

## Calculator Problems

46. Find the product $\dfrac{931r - 1007s}{8717} \cdot \dfrac{379}{2401r^2 - 2809s^2}$.

47. Evaluate $\dfrac{m^2 + 3m + 2}{m^2 + m - 2} \div \dfrac{m^2 + 2m + 1}{m^2 - 1}$ at (a) $m = 13$. (b) $m = 0.7$. Then perform the division.

[*] Named after Jean Louis Poiseuille (1799–1869).

## Challenge Problems

48. Find the product $\dfrac{(a + b)^n}{b^m} \cdot \dfrac{ab - b^2}{a^2 - b^2}$.

49. Find the quotient $\dfrac{x^{k+1} - x^k}{y^{k+1} + y} \div \dfrac{x^k}{y^k}$.

## 7.3 ADDITION AND SUBTRACTION OF EXPRESSIONS I

Recall that to add two rational numbers we use the rule

$$\frac{a}{c} + \frac{b}{c} = \frac{a + b}{c} \qquad \text{where } c \neq 0.$$

That is, to add two rational numbers having the same denominator we add their numerators and place that sum over the common denominator.

**EXAMPLE 1**    $\dfrac{4}{15} + \dfrac{7}{15} = \dfrac{11}{15}$.  □

On the other hand, to subtract two rational numbers we use the rule

$$\frac{a}{c} - \frac{b}{c} = \frac{a - b}{c} \qquad \text{where } c \neq 0.$$

These same two rules are used to add and subtract rational expressions.

**EXAMPLE 2**   Find the sum $\dfrac{1}{7x} + \dfrac{5}{7x}$.

Since the denominators are the same, we simply add the numerators.

$$\frac{1}{7x} + \frac{5}{7x} = \frac{6}{7x}. \quad \square$$

**EXAMPLE 3**   Find the sum $\dfrac{3x}{x+2} + \dfrac{6}{x+2}$.

Noting that the denominators are the same, we write

$$\frac{3x}{x+2} + \frac{6}{x+2} = \frac{3x+6}{x+2},$$

which can be reduced as follows:

$$= \frac{3\cancel{(x+2)}}{\cancel{x+2}}$$

$$= 3. \quad \square$$

**EXAMPLE 4**   Find the difference $\dfrac{a^2+b^2}{a^2-b^2} - \dfrac{2ab}{a^2-b^2}$.

$$\frac{a^2+b^2}{a^2-b^2} - \frac{2ab}{a^2-b^2} = \frac{a^2+b^2-2ab}{a^2-b^2}$$

$$= \frac{a^2-2ab+b^2}{a^2-b^2}$$

$$= \frac{(a-b)^2}{(a+b)(a-b)}$$

$$= \frac{a-b}{a+b}. \quad \square$$

If the rational expressions we are adding or subtracting do *not* have the same denominator, then we must determine the *least common denominator*.

---

**Definition**   The **least common denominator** (lcd) of a collection of rational expressions is the simplest polynomial that is a polynomial multiple of each denominator in the collection.

---

Often the lcd can be determined simply by inspection.

**EXAMPLE 5**   Determine the lcd of $\dfrac{1}{8x}$ and $\dfrac{1}{12x}$.

The simplest polynomial that is a multiple of both $8x$ and $12x$ is $24x$. Note that

$$24x = 3 \cdot 8x, \text{ and}$$
$$24x = 2 \cdot 12x.$$

Therefore, the lcd is $24x$. □

**EXAMPLE 6**  Determine the lcd of $\dfrac{5}{x^2y}$ and $\dfrac{4}{xy^2}$.

The lcd is $x^2y^2$, since

$$x^2y^2 = y \cdot x^2y, \text{ and}$$
$$x^2y^2 = x \cdot xy^2, \text{ and}$$

$x^2y^2$ is the *simplest* multiple of both $x^2y$ and $xy^2$. □

**EXAMPLE 7**  Determine the lcd of $\dfrac{1}{x}$ and $\dfrac{1}{x + 2}$.

The lcd in this case is simply the product of the two denominators. That is, the lcd is $x(x + 2)$, or $x^2 + 2x$. The lcd is *not* $x^2 + 2$. In fact, $x^2 + 2$ is neither a multiple of $x$ nor of $x + 2$. For example, if $x^2 + 2$ were a multiple of $x + 2$, then we would have

$$x^2 + 2 = (\text{some polynomial}) \cdot (x + 2).$$

But there is no polynomial that satisfies this last equation. □

**EXAMPLE 8**  Determine the lcd of $\dfrac{x}{x + 2}$ and $\dfrac{x}{x + 3}$.

The lcd is $(x + 2)(x + 3)$. □

The lcd for this last example can also be written as $x^2 + 5x + 6$. When adding or subtracting rational expressions, however, the factored form is generally the more convenient form to use.

Note that the lcd for Example 8 is *not* $x^2 + 6$. If we divide $x^2 + 6$ by $x + 2$ we obtain a remainder of 10, not zero.

$$
\require{enclose}
\begin{array}{r}
x - 2 \phantom{+6} \\
x + 2 \enclose{longdiv}{x^2 \phantom{+2x} + 6} \\
\underline{x^2 + 2x} \phantom{+6} \\
-2x + 6 \\
\underline{-2x - 4} \\
10.
\end{array}
$$

Thus, $x^2 + 6$ is *not* a multiple of $x + 2$. (Neither is $x^2 + 6$ a multiple of $x + 3$.)

**EXAMPLE 9**   Determine the lcd of $a$ and $\dfrac{3}{a - 8}$.

Since $a = a/1$, the lcd is $a - 8$. $\square$

If the denominators are at all complicated, it may be difficult to determine the lcd simply by inspection. In that case, the two-step procedure below should be used to find the lcd. Note the similarity between this procedure and the procedure that was used in Section 1.2 to find the least common multiple of a set of natural numbers.

---

**Finding the lcd**

1. Factor each denominator *completely*.
2. Take each distinct factor the *most* number of times it appears in any *single* factorization.

---

**EXAMPLE 10**   Determine the lcd of $\dfrac{r}{40r - 40}$ and $\dfrac{r + 1}{18r^2 - 18r}$.

First, we factor each denominator completely.

$$40r - 40 = 40(r - 1) = 2 \cdot 2 \cdot 2 \cdot 5 \cdot (r - 1).$$
$$18r^2 - 18r = 18r(r - 1) = 2 \cdot 3 \cdot 3 \cdot r \cdot (r - 1).$$

Then we take each distinct factor the most number of times it appears in any single factorization.

$$\text{lcd} = 2 \cdot 2 \cdot 2 \cdot 3 \cdot 3 \cdot 5 \cdot r \cdot (r - 1) = 360r(r - 1). \quad \square$$

$= \dfrac{9r^2 + 20r + 20}{360r(r-1)}$

**EXAMPLE 11**   Determine the lcd of $\dfrac{2m}{m^2 + 2m - 15}$ and $\dfrac{3}{m^2 + m - 12}$.

$$m^2 + 2m - 15 = (m + 5)(m - 3)$$
$$m^2 + m - 12 = (m + 4)(m - 3)$$
$$\text{lcd} = (m + 5)(m - 3)(m + 4). \quad \square$$

**EXAMPLE 12** Determine the lcd of $\dfrac{4}{x^2 - 4}$, $\dfrac{1}{x + 2}$, and $\dfrac{4}{5x - 10}$.

$$x^2 - 4 = (x - 2)(x + 2)$$
$$x + 2 = x + 2$$
$$5x - 10 = 5(x - 2)$$
$$\text{lcd} = 5(x - 2)(x + 2). \ \square$$

The two-step procedure outlined above could have been used to find the lcd for Examples 5 through 9 as well, but normally this procedure is not used when the lcd is easily determined by inspection.

## Problem Set 7.3

Perform the indicated operations and express your answer in reduced form.

1. $\dfrac{1}{6x} + \dfrac{1}{6x}$

2. $\dfrac{1}{8x} + \dfrac{1}{8x}$

3. $\dfrac{9}{10x} - \dfrac{7}{10x}$

4. $\dfrac{5}{12x} - \dfrac{1}{12x}$

5. $\dfrac{a - 3}{a} + \dfrac{3}{a}$

6. $\dfrac{a + 1}{a} - \dfrac{1}{a}$

7. $\dfrac{m}{m^2} - \dfrac{1}{m^2}$

8. $\dfrac{m}{m^2} + \dfrac{4}{m^2}$

9. $\dfrac{8}{15k^3} + \dfrac{7}{15k^3}$

10. $\dfrac{25}{18k^3} - \dfrac{7}{18k^3}$

11. $\dfrac{x + y}{x - y} - \dfrac{x}{x - y}$

12. $\dfrac{x - y}{x + y} + \dfrac{x - y}{x + y}$

13. $\dfrac{a^2 + b^2}{a + b} + \dfrac{2ab}{a + b}$

14. $\dfrac{a^2 + b^2}{a - b} - \dfrac{2ab}{a - b}$

15. $\dfrac{a^2}{a + b} - \dfrac{b^2}{a + b}$

16. $\dfrac{a^2}{a - b} - \dfrac{b^2}{a - b}$

17. $\dfrac{x + 3}{x(x + 3)} + \dfrac{x}{x(x + 3)}$

18. $\dfrac{x - 4}{x(x - 4)} - \dfrac{x}{x(x - 4)}$

19. $\dfrac{r^2 - r}{r - 1} + \dfrac{12}{r - 1}$

20. $\dfrac{r^2 + r}{r + 1} + \dfrac{6}{r + 1}$

21. $\dfrac{x(x + 5)}{(x - 5)(x + 5)} - \dfrac{5(x - 5)}{(x + 5)(x - 5)}$

22. $\dfrac{x(x + 6)}{(x - 6)(x + 6)} - \dfrac{6(x - 6)}{(x + 6)(x - 6)}$

23. $\dfrac{2x}{x^2 + 3x - 28} - \dfrac{8}{x^2 + 3x - 28}$

24. $\dfrac{6x}{x^2 + 5x - 24} - \dfrac{18}{x^2 + 5x - 24}$

Determine the least common denominator (lcd) for each problem.

25. $\dfrac{1}{3x}, \dfrac{1}{4x}$

26. $\dfrac{1}{3x}, \dfrac{1}{5x}$

27. $\dfrac{3}{8x^2}, \dfrac{7}{20x^2}$

28. $\dfrac{5}{8x^2}, \dfrac{7}{12x^2}$

29. $\dfrac{1}{x^3y}, \dfrac{1}{xy^2}$

30. $\dfrac{1}{x^2y^2}, \dfrac{1}{xy^3}$

31. $x, \dfrac{x}{x+5}$

32. $x, \dfrac{x}{x+3}$

33. $\dfrac{2}{x+2}, \dfrac{3}{x+3}$

34. $\dfrac{4}{x+4}, \dfrac{5}{x+5}$

35. $\dfrac{r}{5r-20}, \dfrac{r+1}{r-4}$

36. $\dfrac{r}{10r-30}, \dfrac{r+1}{r-3}$

37. $\dfrac{10}{s+1}, \dfrac{1}{s^2-1}$

38. $\dfrac{12}{s+2}, \dfrac{1}{s^2-4}$

39. $\dfrac{a+b}{4a-4b}, \dfrac{ab}{6a^2-6b^2}$

40. $\dfrac{a-b}{8a+8b}, \dfrac{ab}{6a^2-6b^2}$

41. $\dfrac{p-5}{5p^2+25p}, \dfrac{5p}{2p^2-50}$

42. $\dfrac{p+7}{7p^2-49p}, \dfrac{7p}{2p^2-98}$

43. $\dfrac{1}{x-3}, \dfrac{1}{7x+21}, \dfrac{1}{x^2-9}$

44. $\dfrac{1}{x-4}, \dfrac{1}{9x+36}, \dfrac{1}{x^2-16}$

45. $\dfrac{x}{x-9}, \dfrac{16}{x+2}, \dfrac{5}{x^2-7x-18}$

46. $\dfrac{x}{x+7}, \dfrac{15}{x-5}, \dfrac{4}{x^2+2x-35}$

47. $\dfrac{m^2}{81m+54n}, \dfrac{2mn}{80m-20n}, \dfrac{n^2}{12m^2+5mn-2n^2}$

48. $\dfrac{m^2}{80m+40n}, \dfrac{2mn}{27m-36n}, \dfrac{n^2}{6m^2-5mn-4n^2}$

49. $\dfrac{9x}{(x+1)^2}, \dfrac{3}{x^2-1}$

50. $\dfrac{6x}{(x-1)^2}, \dfrac{2}{x^2-1}$

51. $\dfrac{b-1}{a^2-ab}, \dfrac{a}{ab-b^2}$

52. $\dfrac{b+1}{a^2+ab}, \dfrac{a}{ab+b^2}$

## Calculator Problems

53. Simplify $\dfrac{69,557}{197x^3} + \dfrac{46,814}{197x^3} - \dfrac{8815}{197x^3} + \dfrac{55,363}{197x^3}.$

54. Determine the lcd of $\dfrac{1}{120k-1320}$ and $\dfrac{k}{180k^2-21,780}.$

## Challenge Problems

55. It can be shown that $\dfrac{a}{b} + \dfrac{c}{d} = \dfrac{ad + bc}{bd}$. Using this rule,

    a) do Problem 1.    b) do Problem 5.    c) do Problem 12.

56. It can be shown that $\dfrac{a}{b} - \dfrac{c}{d} = \dfrac{ad - bc}{bd}$. Using this rule,

    a) do Problem 4.    b) do Problem 6.    c) do Problem 11.

## 7.4 ADDITION AND SUBTRACTION OF EXPRESSIONS II

When adding or subtracting rational expressions that do *not* have the same denominator, we will begin by finding the least common denominator. Once the lcd has been determined, we will write each rational expression in the problem as an equivalent rational expression having that lcd. This process is called **building the fraction.**

**EXAMPLE 1**   Supply the missing numerator: $\dfrac{1}{6x} = \dfrac{?}{24x}$.

Since $24x \div 6x = 4$, the missing numerator is $1 \cdot 4 = 4$. Therefore,

$$\frac{1}{6x} = \frac{4}{24x}. \quad \square$$

**EXAMPLE 2**   Supply the missing numerator: $\dfrac{5}{xy^2} = \dfrac{?}{x^3y^3}$.

Since $x^3y^3 \div xy^2 = x^2y$, the missing numerator is $5 \cdot x^2y = 5x^2y$. Therefore,

$$\frac{5}{xy^2} = \frac{5x^2y}{x^3y^3}. \quad \square$$

**EXAMPLE 3**   Supply the missing numerator: $\dfrac{a}{a + 3} = \dfrac{?}{a(a + 3)}$.

Since $a(a + 3) \div (a + 3) = a$, the missing numerator is $a \cdot a = a^2$. Therefore,

$$\frac{a}{a + 3} = \frac{a^2}{a(a + 3)}. \quad \square$$

**EXAMPLE 4**  Supply the missing numerator:

$$\frac{m + 1}{m + 2} = \frac{?}{(m + 2)(m - 2)}.$$

Since $(m + 2)(m - 2) \div (m + 2) = m - 2$, the missing numerator is $(m + 1) \cdot (m - 2) = m^2 - m - 2$. Therefore,

$$\frac{m + 1}{m + 2} = \frac{m^2 - m - 2}{(m + 2)(m - 2)}. \quad \square$$

**EXAMPLE 5**  Supply the missing numerator:

*Use to build fractions*

$$\frac{x}{x - 4} = \frac{?}{6(x + 5)(x - 4)}. \quad 6(x+5) \; 6x \; (x+5) = 6x^2 + 30x$$

Since $6(x + 5)(x - 4) \div (x - 4) = 6(x + 5)$, the missing numerator is $x \cdot 6(x + 5) = 6x^2 + 30x$. Therefore,

$$\frac{x}{x - 4} = \frac{6x^2 + 30x}{6(x + 5)(x - 4)}. \quad \square$$

We shall now see how the process of building fractions is used to add or subtract rational expressions having different denominators.

**EXAMPLE 6**  Find the sum $\dfrac{1}{8x} + \dfrac{1}{12x}$.

First, the lcd is determined by inspection to be $24x$. Therefore, we write

$$\frac{1}{8x} + \frac{1}{12x} = \frac{?}{24x} + \frac{?}{24x}.$$

Supplying the missing numerators, we have

$$\frac{1}{8x} + \frac{1}{12x} = \frac{3}{24x} + \frac{2}{24x}$$

$$= \frac{5}{24x}. \quad \square$$

**EXAMPLE 7**  Find the sum $\dfrac{5}{x^2y} + \dfrac{4}{xy^2}$.

The lcd is $x^2y^2$. Therefore, we write

$$\frac{5}{x^2y} + \frac{4}{xy^2} = \frac{?}{x^2y^2} + \frac{?}{x^2y^2}.$$

Supplying the missing numerators, we have

$$\frac{5}{x^2y} + \frac{4}{xy^2} = \frac{5y}{x^2y^2} + \frac{4x}{x^2y^2}$$

$$= \frac{5y + 4x}{x^2y^2}. \quad \square$$

*(handwritten: $x \cdot x\, y = x^2 y^2$)*
*(handwritten: $x \cdot y \cdot y$)*

**EXAMPLE 8**  Find the sum $\dfrac{1}{x} + \dfrac{1}{x + 2}$.

The lcd is $x(x + 2)$.

$$\frac{1}{x} + \frac{1}{x + 2} = \frac{?}{x(x + 2)} + \frac{?}{x(x + 2)}$$

$$= \frac{x + 2}{x(x + 2)} + \frac{x}{x(x + 2)}$$

$$= \frac{x + 2 + x}{x(x + 2)}$$

$$= \frac{2x + 2}{x(x + 2)}. \quad \square$$

*(handwritten: $= \dfrac{2(x+1)}{x(x+2)}$)*

**EXAMPLE 9**  Find the difference $\dfrac{x}{x - 3} - \dfrac{3}{x + 3}$.

The lcd is $(x - 3)(x + 3)$.

$$\frac{x}{x - 3} - \frac{3}{x + 3} = \frac{x(x + 3)}{(x - 3)(x + 3)} - \frac{3(x - 3)}{(x - 3)(x + 3)}$$

$$= \frac{x^2 + 3x}{(x - 3)(x + 3)} - \frac{3x - 9}{(x - 3)(x + 3)}$$

$$= \frac{(x^2 + 3x) - (3x - 9)}{(x - 3)(x + 3)}$$

$$= \frac{x^2 + 3x - 3x + 9}{(x - 3)(x + 3)} \quad \leftarrow \text{(Notice that the signs of } both \text{ terms in the second numerator were changed.)}$$

$$= \frac{x^2 + 9}{(x - 3)(x + 3)}. \quad \square$$

**EXAMPLE 10**   Find the sum $a + \dfrac{3}{a + 1}$.

The lcd is $a + 1$.

$$
\begin{aligned}
a + \frac{3}{a + 1} &= \frac{a}{1} + \frac{3}{a + 1} \\[2mm]
&= \frac{a(a + 1)}{(a + 1)} + \frac{3}{a + 1} \\[2mm]
&= \frac{a^2 + a}{a + 1} + \frac{3}{a + 1} \\[2mm]
&= \frac{a^2 + a + 3}{a + 1}. \;\square
\end{aligned}
$$

**EXAMPLE 11**   Perform the operations $\dfrac{4}{x^2 - 4} + \dfrac{1}{x + 2} - \dfrac{4}{5x - 10}$.

Once the denominators are factored, the lcd can be determined.

$$
\frac{4}{x^2 - 4} + \frac{1}{x + 2} - \frac{4}{5x - 10}
$$

$$
= \frac{4}{(x - 2)(x + 2)} + \frac{1}{x + 2} - \frac{4}{5(x - 2)}.
$$

The lcd is $5(x - 2)(x + 2)$. Therefore

$$
= \frac{4 \cdot 5}{5(x - 2)(x + 2)} + \frac{1 \cdot 5(x - 2)}{5(x - 2)(x + 2)} - \frac{4 \cdot (x + 2)}{5(x - 2)(x + 2)}
$$

$$
= \frac{20}{5(x - 2)(x + 2)} + \frac{5x - 10}{5(x - 2)(x + 2)} - \frac{4x + 8}{5(x - 2)(x + 2)}
$$

*combine likes*
$$
= \frac{20 + (5x - 10) - (4x + 8)}{5(x - 2)(x + 2)}
$$

$$
= \frac{x + 2}{5(x - 2)(x + 2)},
$$

which can be simplified to

$$
= \frac{1}{5(x - 2)}. \;\square
$$

## Problem Set 7.4

Supply the missing numerator.

1. $\dfrac{1}{8x} = \dfrac{?}{24x}$

2. $\dfrac{1}{4x} = \dfrac{?}{24x}$

3. $\dfrac{2}{3x} = \dfrac{?}{12x^2}$

4. $\dfrac{4}{5x} = \dfrac{?}{15x^2}$

5. $\dfrac{8}{x^2 y} = \dfrac{?}{x^3 y^3}$

6. $\dfrac{9}{xy^2} = \dfrac{?}{x^3 y^3}$

7. $\dfrac{b}{a} = \dfrac{?}{ab^5}$

8. $\dfrac{a}{b} = \dfrac{?}{a^4 b}$

9. $\dfrac{b}{1} = \dfrac{?}{a^4 b^4}$

10. $\dfrac{a}{1} = \dfrac{?}{a^5 b^5}$

11. $\dfrac{r}{1} = \dfrac{?}{r+9}$

12. $\dfrac{r}{1} = \dfrac{?}{r-8}$

13. $\dfrac{s}{s-7} = \dfrac{?}{s(s-7)}$

14. $\dfrac{s}{s+6} = \dfrac{?}{s(s+6)}$

15. $\dfrac{s+3}{s-7} = \dfrac{?}{s(s-7)}$

16. $\dfrac{s+2}{s+6} = \dfrac{?}{s(s+6)}$

17. $\dfrac{s-1}{s} = \dfrac{?}{s(s-7)}$

18. $\dfrac{s+1}{s} = \dfrac{?}{s(s+6)}$

19. $\dfrac{14}{m+5} = \dfrac{?}{(m+5)(m-5)}$

20. $\dfrac{15}{m-4} = \dfrac{?}{(m+4)(m-4)}$

21. $\dfrac{m-6}{m+5} = \dfrac{?}{(m+5)(m-5)}$

22. $\dfrac{m+7}{m-4} = \dfrac{?}{(m+4)(m-4)}$

23. $\dfrac{2x}{x-3} = \dfrac{?}{4(x+5)(x-3)}$

24. $\dfrac{2x}{x+2} = \dfrac{?}{5(x+2)(x-6)}$

25. $\dfrac{a+1}{a+b} = \dfrac{?}{3(a+b)(a-b)}$

26. $\dfrac{a-1}{a-b} = \dfrac{?}{2(a+b)(a-b)}$

Perform the indicated operations and express your answer in reduced form.

27. $\dfrac{1}{3a} + \dfrac{1}{4a}$

28. $\dfrac{1}{5a} + \dfrac{1}{2a}$

29. $\dfrac{5}{12b} - \dfrac{1}{8b}$

30. $\dfrac{8}{15b} - \dfrac{1}{10b}$

31. $\dfrac{1}{a^2} + \dfrac{5}{a}$

32. $\dfrac{8}{a} + \dfrac{1}{a^2}$

33. $\dfrac{7}{ab^2} - \dfrac{6}{a^2 b}$

34. $\dfrac{11}{ab} - \dfrac{4}{a^2 b}$

35. $\dfrac{5}{x} + \dfrac{3}{x^2} - \dfrac{1}{x^3}$

36. $\dfrac{10}{x} - \dfrac{1}{x^2} + \dfrac{1}{x^3}$

37. $\dfrac{1}{x^2} + \dfrac{2}{y^2} - \dfrac{3}{xy}$

38. $\dfrac{1}{x^2} - \dfrac{1}{y^2} + \dfrac{5}{xy}$

39. $x + \dfrac{9}{x}$

40. $3 - \dfrac{7}{x}$

41. $x - \dfrac{10}{x+1}$

42. $x + \dfrac{1}{x + 4}$

43. $\dfrac{3}{a + 2} + \dfrac{8}{a - 4}$

44. $\dfrac{4}{a + 3} + \dfrac{2}{a - 1}$

45. $\dfrac{8}{x - 5} - \dfrac{5}{x + 5}$

46. $\dfrac{7}{x + 6} - \dfrac{3}{x - 6}$

47. $\dfrac{x}{x - 3} - \dfrac{1}{x + 2}$

48. $\dfrac{x}{x + 1} - \dfrac{1}{x - 4}$

49. $\dfrac{10}{3x + 12} + \dfrac{1}{x + 4}$

50. $\dfrac{8}{5x - 10} + \dfrac{1}{x - 2}$

51. $\dfrac{6}{x^2 - 1} + \dfrac{3}{x + 1}$

52. $\dfrac{30}{x^2 - 9} + \dfrac{5}{x + 3}$

53. $\dfrac{3}{2a + 18} + \dfrac{27}{a^2 - 81}$

54. $\dfrac{11}{2a - 4} - \dfrac{22}{a^2 - 4}$

55. $\dfrac{a + 1}{a^2 - b^2} - \dfrac{1}{3a + 3b}$

56. $\dfrac{a - 1}{a^2 - b^2} - \dfrac{1}{7a - 7b}$

57. $\dfrac{b - 1}{a^2 + ab} + \dfrac{1}{ab + b^2}$

58. $\dfrac{b + 1}{a^2 + ab} + \dfrac{1}{ab + b^2}$

59. $\dfrac{1}{x - 3} + \dfrac{2}{x + 3} - \dfrac{6}{x^2 - 9}$

60. $\dfrac{1}{x + 1} + \dfrac{1}{x - 1} + \dfrac{2}{x^2 - 1}$

61. $\dfrac{2x}{x - 6} + \dfrac{1}{x + 4} + \dfrac{10}{x^2 - 2x - 24}$

62. $\dfrac{2x}{x + 7} + \dfrac{1}{x - 5} - \dfrac{12}{x^2 + 2x - 35}$

63. $\dfrac{6r}{(r - 1)^2} - \dfrac{2}{r^2 - 1}$

64. $\dfrac{4r}{(r + 2)^2} - \dfrac{3}{r^2 - 4}$

65. $\dfrac{2}{p^2 - 3p} + \dfrac{3}{5p}$

66. $\dfrac{5}{p^2 - 4p} + \dfrac{2}{3p}$

67. $\dfrac{8}{m - n} + \dfrac{9}{n - m}$

68. $\dfrac{11}{m - n} - \dfrac{9}{n - m}$

69. $\dfrac{2}{x - 1} - x - 2$

70. $1 - x + \dfrac{2}{x + 2}$

71. $\dfrac{x}{x^2 + 6x + 9} - \dfrac{x + 1}{x^2 + 5x + 6}$

72. $\dfrac{x}{x^2 + 8x + 16} - \dfrac{x + 1}{x^2 + 7x + 12}$

73. Construct an example to show that $\dfrac{1}{x} + \dfrac{1}{y} \neq \dfrac{1}{x + y}$.

74. Construct an example to show that $\dfrac{1}{x} - \dfrac{1}{y} \neq \dfrac{1}{x - y}$.

75. Prove that $\dfrac{a}{b} + \dfrac{c}{d} = \dfrac{ad + bc}{bd}$ where $b, d \neq 0$.

76. Prove that $\dfrac{a}{b} - \dfrac{c}{d} = \dfrac{ad - bc}{bd}$ where $b, d \neq 0$.

77. If one car travels at $r$ mph and another car travels 5 mph faster, then the difference in time that it takes the two cars to travel 500 miles is given by $\dfrac{500}{r} - \dfrac{500}{r + 5}$. Simplify this expression. Then find its value when (a) $r = 20$ mph. (b) $r = 50$ mph.

78. If one plane travels 750 mi in $t$ hr and another plane travels the same distance in an hour less time, then the difference in the speeds of the two planes is given by $\dfrac{750}{t-1} - \dfrac{750}{t}$. Simplify this expression. Then find its value when (a) $t = 3$ hr. (b) $t = 5$ hr.

## Calculator Problems

79. Find the sum $\dfrac{41}{113x^3} + \dfrac{43}{127x^3} + \dfrac{47}{131x^3}$.

80. Calculate the value of $\left(1 + \dfrac{1}{n}\right) \cdot \left(1 + \dfrac{1}{n+.1}\right) \cdot \left(1 + \dfrac{1}{n+2}\right) \cdot$
$\left(1 + \dfrac{1}{n+3}\right)$ when $n = 1.25$. Then simplify this expression and perform the calculation again.

## Challenge Problems

Simplify.

81. $\left(x + \dfrac{1}{x}\right)\left(y + \dfrac{1}{y}\right) - \left(x \quad \dfrac{1}{x}\right)\left(y - \dfrac{1}{y}\right) - \dfrac{y}{x} - \dfrac{x}{y}$

82. $\dfrac{m}{m^2 + 5m + 4} - \dfrac{m-1}{m^2 + 2m + 1} - \dfrac{1}{m^2 + 4m}$

83. $1 - \dfrac{1}{a+1} - \dfrac{a}{(a+1)^2}$

## 7.5 COMPLEX FRACTIONS

One morning Jackie oversleeps, and so she drives the 20 miles to work at a speed of 60 mph. On the way home, however, she drives at a speed of only 40 mph. What was her average speed for the round trip to and from work?

The answer to the question above might surprise you! It is *not* 50 mph, which is the *arithmetic mean* of 60 mph and 40 mph. This is due to the fact that Jackie travels at a speed of 40 mph for a *longer* period of time than she travels at a speed of 60 mph. Hence her average speed is closer to 40 mph than it is to 60 mph.

To solve this problem we recall that

$$\text{time} = \frac{\text{distance}}{\text{rate}}.$$

Therefore, it took Jackie $\frac{20}{60}$ of an hour to get to work and $\frac{20}{40}$ of an hour to return home. But since

$$\text{rate} = \frac{\text{distance}}{\text{time}},$$

her *average* speed (rate) is then the *total* distance traveled divided by the *total* time it took to travel that distance. That is, her average speed is

$$\frac{\text{Distance to and from work}}{\text{Time to work} + \text{time home}} = \frac{40}{\dfrac{20}{60} + \dfrac{20}{40}} = \frac{40}{\dfrac{1}{3} + \dfrac{1}{2}}.$$

This last expression is called a *complex fraction.*

---

**Definition**    A **complex fraction** is a fraction that contains other fractions in its numerator or denominator (or both). A fraction that is not a complex fraction is called a **simple fraction.**

---

Because of its numerous fractional parts, the complex fraction above is difficult to read and interpret. It may be simplified, however, using either of two basic methods. Both of these methods are illustrated in Example 1.

**EXAMPLE 1**   Simplify the complex fraction $\dfrac{40}{\frac{1}{3} + \frac{1}{2}}$.

**METHOD I**

*Simplify numerator and denominator separately, and then divide.*

$$\frac{40}{\dfrac{1}{3} + \dfrac{1}{2}} = \frac{\dfrac{40}{1}}{\dfrac{2}{6} + \dfrac{3}{6}} = \frac{\dfrac{40}{1}}{\dfrac{5}{6}} = \frac{40}{1} \cdot \frac{6}{5} = 48.$$

**METHOD II**

*Multiply numerator and denominator by the lcd of the fractions within the numerator and denominator.*

Since the lcd of $\frac{1}{3}$ and $\frac{1}{2}$ is 6, we have

$$\frac{40}{\frac{1}{3}+\frac{1}{2}}\cdot\frac{6}{6}=\frac{40\cdot 6}{\frac{1}{3}\cdot 6+\frac{1}{2}\cdot 6}=\frac{240}{2+3}=\frac{240}{5}=48. \quad \square$$

Therefore, Jackie's average speed was 48 mph. The number 48 is called the *harmonic mean* of the numbers 60 and 40.

Note that our original complex fraction can also be written as

$$\frac{40}{\frac{20}{60}+\frac{20}{40}}=\frac{2\cdot 20}{\frac{1}{60}\cdot 20+\frac{1}{40}\cdot 20}=\frac{2}{\frac{1}{60}+\frac{1}{40}}\cdot\frac{20}{20}=\frac{2}{\frac{1}{60}+\frac{1}{40}}.$$

This last form shall be used to define the harmonic mean of two numbers.

---

**Definition**    The **harmonic mean** of the two nonzero numbers $a$ and $b$ is given by the complex fraction

$$\frac{2}{\frac{1}{a}+\frac{1}{b}}.$$

---

The harmonic mean was known in Pythagoras' time and has many applications today, particularly in the field of statistics.

**EXAMPLE 2**  Simplify $\dfrac{\frac{1}{x}+\frac{1}{y}}{\frac{1}{xy}+1}$.

The lcd of $\frac{1}{x}, \frac{1}{y},$ and $\frac{1}{xy}$ is $xy$. Therefore we write

$xy \cdot all$

$$\frac{\frac{1}{x}+\frac{1}{y}}{\frac{1}{xy}+1}=\frac{\frac{1}{x}+\frac{1}{y}}{\frac{1}{xy}+1}\cdot\frac{xy}{xy}=\frac{\frac{1}{x}\cdot xy+\frac{1}{y}\cdot xy}{\frac{1}{xy}\cdot xy+1\cdot xy}=\frac{y+x}{1+xy}. \quad \square$$

**EXAMPLE 3**    Simplify $\dfrac{2 + \dfrac{5}{a} - \dfrac{3}{a^2}}{2 - \dfrac{5}{a} + \dfrac{2}{a^2}}$.

The lcd is $a^2$.

$$\frac{2 + \dfrac{5}{a} - \dfrac{3}{a^2}}{2 - \dfrac{5}{a} + \dfrac{2}{a^2}} \cdot \frac{a^2}{a^2} = \frac{2a^2 + 5a - 3}{2a^2 - 5a + 2}$$

$$= \frac{(2a - 1)(a + 3)}{(2a - 1)(a - 2)}$$

$$= \frac{a + 3}{a - 2}. \quad \square$$

## Problem Set 7.5

Simplify each of the following complex fractions.

1. $\dfrac{1 + \frac{1}{3}}{5}$

2. $\dfrac{1 + \frac{1}{5}}{2}$

3. $\dfrac{3}{1 + \frac{1}{11}}$

4. $\dfrac{2}{4 + \frac{1}{10}}$

5. $\dfrac{\frac{3}{4} + \frac{1}{3}}{\frac{1}{3} + \frac{1}{6}}$

6. $\dfrac{\frac{4}{5} + \frac{1}{3}}{\frac{2}{15} + \frac{1}{5}}$

7. $\dfrac{2 - \dfrac{a}{b}}{2 + \dfrac{a}{b}}$

8. $\dfrac{\dfrac{a}{b} + 1}{3 + \dfrac{a}{b}}$

9. $\dfrac{\dfrac{1}{b} + a}{\dfrac{1}{a} + b}$

10. $\dfrac{a - \dfrac{1}{b}}{b - \dfrac{1}{a}}$

11. $\dfrac{1 + \dfrac{2}{x}}{\dfrac{1}{4} - \dfrac{1}{x^2}}$

12. $\dfrac{1 - \dfrac{1}{x^2}}{\dfrac{1}{5} + \dfrac{1}{5x}}$

13. $\dfrac{9 - \dfrac{1}{x^2}}{3 + \dfrac{1}{x}}$

14. $\dfrac{3 - \dfrac{x}{y}}{9 - \dfrac{x^2}{y^2}}$

15. $\dfrac{1 - \dfrac{5}{x + 2}}{1 + \dfrac{5}{2 + x}}$

16. $\dfrac{\dfrac{1}{x + 1} + 1}{1 - \dfrac{3}{1 + x}}$

17. $\dfrac{\dfrac{1}{xy} + 1}{\dfrac{1}{x} - \dfrac{y}{x^2}}$

18. $\dfrac{1 + \dfrac{x}{y^2}}{\dfrac{1}{x} + \dfrac{1}{xy}}$

19. $\dfrac{\dfrac{1}{ab} - \dfrac{1}{b}}{\dfrac{1}{b} - \dfrac{1}{ab}}$

20. $\dfrac{\dfrac{1}{a} - \dfrac{1}{ab}}{\dfrac{1}{ab} - \dfrac{1}{a}}$

21. $\dfrac{\dfrac{1}{r} + \dfrac{1}{s}}{\dfrac{1}{rs}}$

22. $\dfrac{\dfrac{1}{r} - \dfrac{1}{s}}{\dfrac{1}{rs}}$

23. $\dfrac{1 - \dfrac{1}{t}}{t^2 - 1}$

24. $\dfrac{1 + \dfrac{1}{t}}{t + 1}$

25. $\dfrac{\dfrac{1}{c^2} - \dfrac{1}{d^2}}{\dfrac{1}{c} + \dfrac{1}{d}}$

26. $\dfrac{\dfrac{1}{c} - \dfrac{1}{d}}{\dfrac{1}{c^2} - \dfrac{1}{d^2}}$

27. $\dfrac{1 - \dfrac{9}{m^2}}{1 - \dfrac{1}{m} - \dfrac{6}{m^2}}$

28. $\dfrac{1 - \dfrac{4}{m^2}}{1 - \dfrac{1}{m} - \dfrac{6}{m^2}}$

29. $\dfrac{1 - \dfrac{2}{p} - \dfrac{24}{p^2}}{1 - \dfrac{10}{p} + \dfrac{24}{p^2}}$

30. $\dfrac{10 - \dfrac{3}{p} - \dfrac{1}{p^2}}{2 + \dfrac{9}{p} - \dfrac{5}{p^2}}$

31. $x + \dfrac{x + 1}{x - \dfrac{1}{x}}$

32. $1 - \dfrac{1}{1 + \dfrac{1}{x - 1}}$

33. The expression $\dfrac{\dfrac{1}{x + h} - \dfrac{1}{x}}{h}$ appears in calculus. Simplify this complex fraction.

34. The expression $\dfrac{\dfrac{3}{t^2} - \dfrac{3}{x^2}}{t - x}$ appears in calculus. Simplify this complex fraction.

35. Find the reciprocal of the expression $\dfrac{1}{x + 1} - \dfrac{1}{x - 1}$.

36. Find the reciprocal of the expression $\dfrac{1}{x + 1} + \dfrac{1}{x - 1}$.

37. Find the harmonic mean of (a) 6 and 12. (b) $\frac{1}{2}$ and $\frac{1}{3}$.

38. Find the harmonic mean of (a) 10 and 15. (b) $\frac{1}{4}$ and $\frac{1}{5}$.

39. If you drive to work at 50 mph and drive home at 30 mph, what is your average speed?

40. A mountain climber averages 2 mph going up a mountain and 6 mph coming down. What is the climber's average speed?

41. Show that the harmonic mean of the two nonzero numbers $a$ and $b$ can also be written as $\dfrac{2ab}{a + b}$.

42. In order to determine the angle between two lines, the expression
$$\frac{\dfrac{1}{m_1} - \dfrac{1}{m_2}}{\dfrac{1}{m_1 m_2} + 1}$$
must be evaluated. Simplify this expression.

The expressions below are called **continued fractions.** Find the value of each continued fraction.

43. $1 + \dfrac{1}{1 + \dfrac{1}{1 + \dfrac{1}{1 + 1}}}$
   
44. $2 + \dfrac{1}{2 + \dfrac{1}{2 + \dfrac{1}{2 + 1}}}$

## Calculator Problems

45. Find the harmonic mean of 38.35 and 22.15 to the nearest hundredth.

46. The positive square root of 2 can be expressed as an *infinite* continued fraction as follows:
$$\sqrt{2} = 1 + \cfrac{1}{2 + \cfrac{1}{2 + \cfrac{1}{2 + \cdots}}}.$$
Show that
$$\sqrt{2} \approx 1 + \frac{1}{2},$$
$$\sqrt{2} \approx 1 + \cfrac{1}{2 + \cfrac{1}{2}},$$
$$\sqrt{2} \approx 1 + \cfrac{1}{2 + \cfrac{1}{2 + \cfrac{1}{2}}},$$
$$\sqrt{2} \approx 1 + \cfrac{1}{2 + \cfrac{1}{2 + \cfrac{1}{2 + \cfrac{1}{2}}}},$$
and note that each approximation is better than the previous one.

## Challenge Problems

47. Simplify $\dfrac{\dfrac{2}{x-1} - x - 2}{1 - x + \dfrac{2}{x+2}}$.

48. A particular triathlon consists of swimming 2 miles, cycling 2 miles, and running 2 miles. If a competitor swims at 1 mph, cycles at 20 mph, and runs at 10 mph, what is the competitor's average rate for the triathlon?

49. A car averages 30 mph over the first mile of a 2-mile oval track. What must it average over the second mile in order to have an average speed of 60 mph for the entire 2-mile lap?

## 7.6 EQUATIONS INVOLVING RATIONAL EXPRESSIONS

In Section 3.3 we noted that when solving an equation involving fractions, it is generally best to begin by multiplying both sides of the equation by the lcd of all of the fractions in the equation. The result is an equivalent equation that is free of fractions.

**EXAMPLE 1** Solve $\dfrac{x}{3} - 1 = \dfrac{2}{5}$.

We begin by multiplying both sides by the lcd 15.

$$15 \cdot \frac{x}{3} - 15 \cdot 1 = 15 \cdot \frac{2}{5}$$
$$5x - 15 = 6$$
$$5x = 21$$
$$x = \frac{21}{5}. \quad \square$$

When solving an equation involving rational expressions, the same technique is used. In this case, though, variables may appear in the denominators, and as a result the lcd itself may contain variables.

**EXAMPLE 2** Solve the equation $\dfrac{1}{4x} - \dfrac{1}{3x} = \dfrac{1}{12}$.

The lcd is $12x$. Multiplying each term by $12x$ should therefore clear the equation of fractions.

$$12x \cdot \frac{1}{4x} - 12x \cdot \frac{1}{3x} = 12x \cdot \frac{1}{12}$$
$$3 \cdot 1 - 4 \cdot 1 = x \cdot 1.$$

This equation is then easily solved.

$$\boxed{-1 = x.}$$

$$\text{CHECK:} \quad \frac{1}{4(-1)} - \frac{1}{3(-1)} \overset{?}{=} \frac{1}{12}$$

$$-\frac{1}{4} + \frac{1}{3} \overset{?}{=} \frac{1}{12}$$

$$\frac{1}{12} = \frac{1}{12}. \ \square$$

The equation of Example 2 *cannot* be written as

$$4x - 3x = 12.$$

This produces the solution $x = 12$, which is *incorrect*. When writing the equation in this way, the student *thinks* that the same operation was performed on each side. But actually, the same operation was performed on each *term*. In order to invert each *side*, we would have to write

$$\frac{1}{4x} - \frac{1}{3x} = \frac{1}{12}$$

$$\frac{3}{12x} - \frac{4}{12x} = \frac{1}{12}$$

$$-\frac{1}{12x} = \frac{1}{12}$$

$$-12x = 12$$

$$x = -1.$$

It is generally easier, however, to multiply through by the lcd.

**EXAMPLE 3** Solve $\dfrac{5x - 1}{x + 7} = 2$.

Multiplying both sides by the lcd $x + 7$, we have

$$(\cancel{x + 7}) \cdot \frac{5x - 1}{\cancel{x + 7}} = (x + 7) \cdot 2$$

$$5x - 1 = 2x + 14$$

$$5x = 2x + 15$$

$$3x = 15$$

$$x = 5.$$

CHECK: $\dfrac{5(5) - 1}{5 + 7} \overset{?}{=} 2$

$$\frac{24}{12} \overset{?}{=} 2$$

$$2 = 2. \quad \square$$

**EXAMPLE 4**  Solve $\dfrac{1}{2x + 8} = \dfrac{4}{x + 11}$.

To determine the lcd, we factor the denominator $2x + 8$.

$$\frac{1}{2(x + 4)} = \frac{4}{x + 11}.$$

We can now see that the lcd is $2(x + 4)(x + 11)$. Therefore, we write

$$M 2(x+4)(x+11) \quad \cancel{2}(\cancel{x + 4})(x + 11) \cdot \frac{1}{\cancel{2}(\cancel{x + 4})} = 2(x + 4)(\cancel{x + 11}) \cdot \frac{4}{\cancel{x + 11}}$$

$$(x + 11) \cdot 1 = 2(x + 4) \cdot 4$$

$$x + 11 = 8x + 32$$

$$x = 8x + 21$$

$$-7x = 21$$

$$x = -3.$$

CHECK: $\dfrac{1}{2(-3) + 8} \overset{?}{=} \dfrac{4}{-3 + 11}$

$$\frac{1}{-6 + 8} \overset{?}{=} \frac{4}{8}$$

$$\frac{1}{2} = \frac{1}{2}. \quad \square$$

**EXAMPLE 5**  Solve $\dfrac{x + 1}{x - 3} = \dfrac{4}{x - 3} + 6$.

The lcd is $x - 3$.

$$\cancel{(x-3)} \cdot \frac{x+1}{\cancel{x-3}} = \cancel{(x-3)} \cdot \frac{4}{\cancel{x-3}} + (x-3) \cdot 6$$

$$x + 1 = 4 + 6x - 18$$
$$x + 1 = 6x - 14$$
$$x = 6x - 15$$
$$-5x = -15$$
$$x = 3.$$

CHECK:   $\dfrac{3+1}{3-3} \stackrel{?}{=} \dfrac{4}{3-3} + 6$

$$\frac{4}{0} \stackrel{?}{=} \frac{4}{0} + 6.$$

But division by zero is undefined! Therefore the number 3 does not satisfy the equation. Since the only proposed solution does not check, the equation has *no* solution.  ☐

As this last example illustrates, when an equation contains variables in a denominator, any solution that is found *must* be checked in the *original* equation to make certain that it does not cause a denominator to equal zero.

## Problem Set 7.6

Solve each equation.

1. $\dfrac{x}{9} - 1 = \dfrac{2}{3}$

2. $\dfrac{x}{8} - 1 = \dfrac{3}{4}$

3. $\dfrac{1}{3x} + \dfrac{1}{5x} = \dfrac{1}{15}$

4. $\dfrac{1}{2x} + \dfrac{1}{3x} = \dfrac{1}{6}$

5. $1 + \dfrac{3}{x} = \dfrac{2}{x}$

6. $2 + \dfrac{6}{x} = \dfrac{4}{x}$

7. $\dfrac{4}{x} + \dfrac{2}{3} = 1$

8. $\dfrac{3}{x} + \dfrac{2}{5} = 1$

9. $\dfrac{2}{x} - \dfrac{1}{x} = 6$

10. $\dfrac{3}{x} - \dfrac{2}{x} = 5$

11. $7 - \dfrac{5}{2x} = \dfrac{3}{x} + \dfrac{3}{2}$

12. $3 - \dfrac{4}{3x} = \dfrac{2}{x} + \dfrac{7}{3}$

13. $\dfrac{5x-2}{x+4} = 0$

14. $\dfrac{4x-3}{x+5} = 0$

15. $\dfrac{2x+11}{x+6} = 3$

16. $\dfrac{2x + 4}{x + 3} = 3$

17. $\dfrac{7x - 23}{2x - 1} = 2$

18. $\dfrac{9x - 11}{3x - 1} = 2$

19. $\dfrac{6x}{x + 6} = \dfrac{12}{x + 6}$

20. $\dfrac{5x}{x + 5} = \dfrac{10}{x + 5}$

21. $\dfrac{6}{x + 2} = \dfrac{2}{x - 2}$

22. $\dfrac{5}{x + 3} = \dfrac{2}{x - 3}$

23. $\dfrac{3}{5x - 1} = \dfrac{3}{2x - 4}$

24. $\dfrac{3}{3x + 1} = \dfrac{3}{2x - 6}$

25. $\dfrac{x}{x + 4} + 1 = \dfrac{16}{x + 4}$

26. $\dfrac{x}{x + 6} + 1 = \dfrac{8}{x + 6}$

27. $\dfrac{x}{x - 5} - 6 = \dfrac{x + 6}{x - 5}$

28. $\dfrac{x}{x - 4} - 8 = \dfrac{x + 8}{x - 4}$

29. $\dfrac{x + 2}{2x + 6} + \dfrac{3}{x + 3} = \dfrac{3}{2}$

30. $\dfrac{x + 4}{2x + 10} + \dfrac{5}{x + 5} = \dfrac{3}{2}$

31. $\dfrac{x}{x - 2} + 4 = \dfrac{2}{x - 2}$

32. $\dfrac{x}{x - 2} + 5 = \dfrac{2}{x - 2}$

33. $\dfrac{5}{p} - \dfrac{2}{p + 2} = \dfrac{4}{p}$

34. $\dfrac{7}{p} - \dfrac{2}{p + 1} = \dfrac{6}{p}$

35. $\dfrac{1}{m - 3} - \dfrac{3}{m + 3} = \dfrac{11}{m^2 - 9}$

36. $\dfrac{1}{m + 2} - \dfrac{5}{m - 2} - \dfrac{-15}{m^2 - 4}$

37. $\dfrac{4r}{r^2 - r - 2} = \dfrac{7r}{r^2 + r - 6} - \dfrac{3r - 1}{r^2 + 4r + 3}$

38. $\dfrac{3r}{r^2 + 5r + 6} = \dfrac{5r}{r^2 + 2r - 3} - \dfrac{2r + 1}{r^2 + r - 2}$

## Calculator Problems

Solve each equation.

39. $\dfrac{17}{4x} + \dfrac{35.7}{3x} = 9.5$

40. $\dfrac{24.472}{1.5y} + \dfrac{122.36}{1.5y} = \dfrac{367.08}{1.5}$

## Challenge Problems

41. Solve $\dfrac{a + 3b}{x + a} - \dfrac{a}{x} = \dfrac{b}{x}$ for $x$.

42. Solve $\dfrac{1}{R} = \dfrac{1}{R_1} + \dfrac{1}{R_2}$ for $R_1$.

## 7.7    APPLIED PROBLEMS

Rational expressions appear in various types of applied problems. The formula $1/R = 1/R_1 + 1/R_2$, for example, is used to calculate the total resistance in an electrical circuit when two resistors are connected in parallel. The symbol $R$ denotes the total resistance, while $R_1$ denotes the resistance of one of the resistors and $R_2$ the resistance of the other.

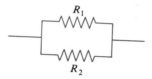

**EXAMPLE 1**    Two resistors are connected in parallel. If one has a resistance of 3 ohms and the other has a resistance of 6 ohms, find the total resistance of the circuit.

Letting $R_1 = 3$ and $R_2 = 6$ in the equation

$$\frac{1}{R} = \frac{1}{R_1} + \frac{1}{R_2},$$

we have

$$\frac{1}{R} = \frac{1}{3} + \frac{1}{6}.$$

This equation involving rational expressions can be solved by multiplying both sides by the lcd $6R$.

$$6R \cdot \frac{1}{R} = 6R \cdot \frac{1}{3} + 6R \cdot \frac{1}{6}$$
$$6 = 2R + R$$
$$6 = 3R$$
$$2 = R.$$

Therefore, the total resistance is 2 ohms.  □

**EXAMPLE 2**    Two resistors are connected in parallel. If the resistance in one branch of the circuit is 12 ohms and the total resistance of the circuit is 9 ohms, find the resistance in the other branch.

In this case we let $R_1 = 12$ and $R = 9$. This yields the equation

$$\frac{1}{9} = \frac{1}{12} + \frac{1}{R_2}.$$

The lcd is $36R_2$. Thus,

$$36R_2 \cdot \frac{1}{9} = 36R_2 \cdot \frac{1}{12} + 36R_2 \cdot \frac{1}{R_2}$$
$$4R_2 = 3R_2 + 36$$
$$R_2 = 36.$$

The resistance in the other branch is 36 ohms. $\square$

There are many other types of problems that lead to equations involving rational expressions.

**EXAMPLE 3**   The denominator of a certain fraction exceeds the numerator by 3. If 1 is added to both the numerator and the denominator, the resulting fraction equals $\frac{1}{2}$. Find the original fraction.

Let $x$ = the numerator of the original fraction.

Then $x + 3$ = the denominator of the original fraction.

That is, the original fraction is $\dfrac{x}{x + 3}$.

Now, if 1 is added to both the numerator and the denominator, the resulting fraction equals $\frac{1}{2}$. Writing this condition in equation form we have

$$\frac{x + 1}{(x + 3) + 1} = \frac{1}{2},$$

or

$$\frac{x + 1}{x + 4} = \frac{1}{2}.$$

Both sides are then multiplied by the lcd $2(x + 4)$.

$$2(x + 4) \cdot \frac{x + 1}{x + 4} = 2(x + 4) \cdot \frac{1}{2}$$
$$2(x + 1) = (x + 4) \cdot 1$$
$$2x + 2 = x + 4$$
$$x = 2,$$
$$x + 3 = 5.$$

Therefore, the original fraction is $\frac{2}{5}$. $\square$

**EXAMPLE 4**   If Mike can do a certain job in 6 hours and John can do the same job in 4 hours, how long would it take them to complete the job working together?

Let $x$ = the number of hours it takes Mike and John to do the job working together.

Since Mike can do the job in 6 hours, he can do $\frac{1}{6}$ of the job in *one* hour.

Since John can do the job in 4 hours, he can do $\frac{1}{4}$ of the job in *one* hour.

Since the two of them working together can do the job in $x$ hours, then working together they can do $1/x$ of the job in *one* hour.

$$\begin{array}{ccc} \text{The portion of the} & \text{the portion of the} & \text{the portion of the} \\ \text{job done by Mike} + & \text{job done by John} = & \text{job done by both} \\ \text{in 1 hour} & \text{in one hour} & \text{in 1 hour} \end{array}$$

$$\frac{1}{6} + \frac{1}{4} = \frac{1}{x}.$$

Multiplying each side by the lcd $12x$ we have

$$12x \cdot \frac{1}{6} + 12x \cdot \frac{1}{4} = 12x \cdot \frac{1}{x}$$

$$2x + 3x = 12$$

$$5x = 12$$

$$x = \frac{12}{5} = 2\frac{2}{5}.$$

Working together, it will take Mike and John $2\frac{2}{5}$ hours to complete the job. □

Recall that the formula which relates distance, rate, and time is $d = rt$. If we solve this formula for $t$ we have

$$t = \frac{d}{r}.$$

**EXAMPLE 5**   An express train travels 180 miles in the same time that a freight train travels 120 miles. If the express goes 20 mph faster than the freight, find the rate of each.

Let $r$ = the rate of the freight in mph.

Then $r + 20$ = the rate of the express in mph.

Then

$$\text{freight train's time} = \frac{\text{distance of freight}}{\text{rate of freight}} = \frac{120}{r},$$

$$\text{express train's time} = \frac{\text{distance of express}}{\text{rate of express}} = \frac{180}{r + 20}.$$

Freight train's time = express train's time

$$\frac{120}{r} = \frac{180}{r + 20}.$$

The lcd is $r(r + 20)$.

$$\cancel{r}(r + 20) \cdot \frac{120}{\cancel{r}} = r\cancel{(r + 20)} \cdot \frac{180}{\cancel{r + 20}}$$

$$(r + 20) \cdot 120 = r \cdot 180$$

$$120r + 2400 = 180r$$

$$2400 = 60r$$

$$40 = r,$$

$$60 = r + 20.$$

The rate of the express train is 60 mph and the rate of the freight train is 40 mph. □

Note that the original equation in Example 5 could have been simplified by dividing each side by 60. We leave it to the student to perform this simplification and solve the resulting equation.

## Problem Set 7.7

1. Two resistors are connected in parallel. If one has a resistance of 4 ohms and the other has a resistance of 12 ohms, find the total resistance of the circuit.
2. Two resistors are connected in parallel. If one has a resistance of 6 ohms and the other has a resistance of 12 ohms, find the total resistance of the circuit.
3. Find the resistance in one branch of a parallel wiring circuit if the resistance in the other branch is 60 ohms and the total resistance is 40 ohms.

4. Find the resistance in one branch of a parallel wiring circuit if the resistance in the other branch is 30 ohms and the total resistance is 20 ohms.

5. The denominator of a certain fraction exceeds the numerator by 4. If 1 is added to both the numerator and the denominator, the resulting fraction equals $\frac{1}{2}$. Find the original fraction.

6. The denominator of a certain fraction exceeds the numerator by 5. If 1 is added to both the numerator and the denominator, the resulting fraction equals $\frac{1}{2}$. Find the original fraction.

7. The denominator of a certain fraction is 5 more than the numerator. If 2 is added to the numerator and 1 is subtracted from the denominator, the resulting fraction equals $\frac{3}{4}$. Find the original fraction.

8. The denominator of a certain fraction is 7 more than the numerator. If 3 is added to the numerator and 2 is subtracted from the denominator, the resulting fraction equals $\frac{2}{3}$. Find the original fraction.

9. If Bob can mow a lawn in 3 hr and Bill can mow the same lawn in 2 hr, how long would it take them to mow the lawn working together?

10. If Jack can paint a house in 12 hr and Jim can paint the same size house in 8 hr, how long would it take them to paint a house of that size working together?

11. One pipe can fill a swimming pool in 6 hr while a second pipe takes 9 hr. How long will it take to fill the pool if both pipes are open?

12. The cold water faucet takes 8 min to fill a tub and the hot water faucet takes 10 min. How long will it take to fill the tub if both faucets are running?

13. A faucet can fill an empty utility sink in 3 min. The drain can empty a full sink in 5 min. If by mistake both are open, how long will it take to fill an empty sink?

14. Several inlet pipes can fill an empty pool in 10 hr. The drain pipe can empty a full pool in 15 hr. If by mistake all pipes are open, how long will it take to fill an empty pool?

15. A man drives 160 mi in the same time that another man drives 120 mi. If the speed of the first driver is 10 mph faster than the speed of the second driver, find the speed of each.

16. An airplane travels 600 mi in the same time that a car travels 200 mi. If the speed of the plane is 120 mph faster than the speed of the car, find the speed of each.

17. A boat can travel at a speed of 12 mph in still water. If the boat takes the same amount of time to travel 8 mi upstream as it does to travel 10 mi downstream, find the rate of the current.
18. Charlie can row 4 mph in still water. If it takes him as long to row 3 mi upstream as it does to row 6 mi downstream, find the rate of the current.
19. Find two consecutive integers such that one-half the smaller plus two-thirds the larger equals 66.
20. Find all three interior angles of a triangle if two are equal and the third is $\frac{11}{7}$ of the sum of the other two. (*Hint:* The sum of the measures of the interior angles of any triangle is 180°.)

## Calculator Problems

A planet that orbits closer to the Sun than the Earth does is called an **inferior planet.** Mercury and Venus are the only inferior planets. A planet that orbits farther from the Sun than the Earth does is called a **superior planet.** The **sidereal period** of a planet is the time required for the planet to make one complete orbit about the Sun. The **synodic period** of a planet is the time required for the planet, the Sun, and the Earth to repeat the same configuration. The synodic period of another planet can therefore be observed from the Earth, while the sidereal period cannot. The relationship between the sidereal period $I$ and the synodic period $Y$ of a planet is given by the formula

$$\frac{1}{Y} = \frac{1}{I} - \frac{1}{E} \quad \text{for an inferior planet,}$$

and by the formula

$$\frac{1}{Y} = \frac{1}{E} - \frac{1}{I} \quad \text{for a superior planet,}$$

where $E$ is the sidereal period of the Earth (approximately 365.26 days).

21. Determine the approximate sidereal period $I$ of Venus, which has an approximate synodic period $Y$ of 583.96 days.
22. Determine the approximate sidereal period $I$ of Mars, which has an approximate synodic period $Y$ of 779.87 days.

**Challenge Problems**

23. A car travels 400 mi on 18 gal of gasoline. If the car's city mileage is 20 mpg and its highway mileage is 30 mpg, how far did the car travel in the city?

24. A motorboat that travels 5 mph in still water can travel downstream to a hunting lodge in half the time it takes to make the return trip upstream. What is the rate of the current?

## 7.8  RATIO AND PROPORTION

There are several ways to compare two quantities. For example, if your boss earns $4000 monthly while you earn $1000 monthly, then your boss earns $3000 *more* than you since $4000 − $1000 = $3000. This is a comparison by *subtraction*. The two salaries can also be compared by *division*. That is $4000/$1000 = 4, which means that your boss' salary is 4 *times* your salary. We say that the *ratio* of your boss' salary to your salary is 4000 to 1000, or 4 to 1. The ratio 4 to 1 can be written as 4 : 1, or as the fraction $\frac{4}{1}$.

---

**Definition**   The **ratio** of the number $a$ to the number $b$ $(b \neq 0)$ is the quotient of $a$ divided by $b$, written $a : b$ or $a/b$.

---

**EXAMPLE 1**   Express each of the following ratios as fractions:

$$1 \text{ ft to } 7 \text{ ft} \qquad 2 \text{ cm to } 10 \text{ cm} \qquad 2 \text{ days to } 15 \text{ hrs.}$$

The ratio of 1 ft to 7 ft is written as $\dfrac{1 \text{ ft}}{7 \text{ ft}} = \dfrac{1}{7}$.

The ratio of 2 cm to 10 cm is written as $\dfrac{2 \text{ cm}}{10 \text{ cm}} = \dfrac{1}{5}$.

The ratio of 2 days to 15 hr is $\dfrac{2 \text{ days}}{15 \text{ hr}} = \dfrac{48 \text{ hr}}{15 \text{ hr}} = \dfrac{16}{5}$. □

**EXAMPLE 2**   If there are 500 boys and 400 girls in a school, what is the ratio of boys to girls? What is the ratio of girls to boys?

The ratio of boys to girls is 5 : 4, or $\frac{5}{4}$.
The ratio of girls to boys is 4 : 5, or $\frac{4}{5}$. ☐

**EXAMPLE 3**   The operator's manual of an automobile whose radiator has a capacity of 20 quarts recommends that it be filled with 10 quarts of water and 10 quarts of antifreeze. What is the ratio of water to antifreeze? What is the ratio of antifreeze to water?

The ratio is 1 : 1 in both cases. ☐

Two triangles are said to be **similar** if their corresponding angles are equal. Thus similar triangles have the same *shape* but not necessarily the same *size*. The two triangles pictured below are similar.

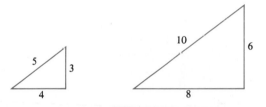

*If two triangles are similar, the ratios of their corresponding sides are equal.* Therefore, for the two similar triangles pictured we could write

$$\frac{6}{3} = \frac{8}{4},$$

which is read 6 *is to* 3 *as* 8 *is to* 4. This last equation is called a *proportion.*\*

---

**Definition**   A **proportion** is an equation that states that two ratios are equal.

---

Every proportion has several equivalent forms. For example, the proportion

$$\frac{6}{3} = \frac{8}{4}$$

---

\* This proportion can also be written as 6 : 3 :: 8 : 4; however, this notation is seldom used.

extremes

means

can also be written in any of the forms below:

$$\frac{6}{8} = \frac{3}{4}, \quad \frac{4}{3} = \frac{8}{6}, \quad \text{or} \quad \frac{4}{8} = \frac{3}{6}.$$

Note how each of these last three proportions relates to the two similar triangles pictured previously.

The proportion $a/b = c/d$ is read *a is to b as c is to d*. The terms *a* and *d* are called the **extremes** of the proportion, and the terms *b* and *c* are called the **means** of the proportion.

If each side of the proportion

$$\frac{a}{b} = \frac{c}{d}$$

is multiplied by $bd$, we have

$$(bd)\frac{a}{b} = (bd)\frac{c}{d}, \quad \text{or} \quad ad = bc.$$

Hence we have the following rule:

Law of Porportion

---

In any proportion, the product of the extremes is equal to the product of the means.

---

We may use the principle above to *solve* a proportion when one of its terms is unknown.

**EXAMPLE 4**   Solve the proportion $x/21 = 22/7$ for $x$.

Since the product of the *extremes* equals the product of the *means*, we can write

$$7x = 21 \cdot 22$$
$$x = 3 \cdot 22$$
$$x = 66. \quad \square$$

There is a great variety of problems that can be solved by setting up a proportion.

**EXAMPLE 5**   If a tree casts a shadow of 45 feet at the same time a yardstick is casting a shadow of 27 inches, find the height of the tree.

A diagram of this situation appears below.

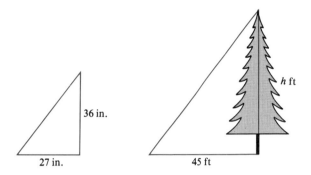

Since the two triangles are similar, their corresponding sides are proportional. Therefore, we can set up the following proportion:

$$\frac{h \text{ ft}}{45 \text{ ft}} = \frac{36 \text{ in.}}{27 \text{ in.}},$$

or

$$\frac{h}{45} = \frac{36}{27} = \frac{4}{3}$$

$$3h = 4 \cdot 45$$

$$h = 4 \cdot 15$$

$$h = 60.$$

Therefore, the height of the tree is 60 ft. □

**EXAMPLE 6**  The ratio of boys to girls in a school is $\frac{3}{5}$. If there are 1450 girls, how many boys are there?

Let $x$ = the number of boys in the school. Then we can set up the proportion

$$\frac{x}{1450} = \frac{3}{5}.$$

Solving for $x$ we have

$$5x = 3 \cdot 1450$$

$$x = 3 \cdot 290$$

$$x = 870.$$

Therefore, there are 870 boys in the school. □

## Problem Set 7.8

Express each ratio as a reduced fraction.

| | | |
|---|---|---|
| 1. 1 in. to 5 in. | 2. 1 ft to 7 ft | 3. 5 in. to 1 in. |
| 4. 7 ft to 1 ft | 5. 4 to 6 | 6. 6 to 15 |
| 7. 6 cm to 14 cm | 8. 8 cm to 12 cm | 9. 54 kg to 30 kg |
| 10. 28 kg to 20 kg | 11. 15 in. to 2 ft | 12. 4 yd to 15 ft |
| 13. 20 hr to 5 days | 14. 48 sec to 6 min | 15. $3 to 80¢ |
| 16. 60¢ to $5 | 17. 6 dimes to 5 quarters | 18. 3 quarters to 4 dimes |

19. The circumference $c$ of a circle to the diameter $d$
20. The diameter $d$ of a circle to the circumference $c$

21. If Jack runs a marathon in 2 hr 36 min and Diane runs the same marathon in 3 hr 10 min, what is the ratio of Jack's time to Diane's time?    $\frac{78}{95}$

22. In Problem 21, what is the ratio of Diane's time to Jack's time?

Express each of the following as a proportion and solve for $x$.

23. $x$ is to 16 as 3 is to 4
24. $x$ is to 9 as 2 is to 3
25. 5 is to 7 as 20 is to $x$
26. 6 is to 11 as 24 is to $x$
27. 3 is to 5 as $x$ is to 4
28. 5 is to 2 as $x$ is to 3
29. 12 is to $x$ as 8 is to 2
30. 15 is to $x$ as 9 is to 3
31. $x$ is to $x + 3$ as 42 is to 48
32. $x$ is to $x + 5$ as 36 is to 39

33. If a flagpole casts a shadow of 28 ft at the same time a yardstick is casting a shadow of 21 in., find the height of the flagpole.
34. If a tree casts a shadow of 63 ft at the same time a yardstick is casting a shadow of 54 in., find the height of the tree.
35. The ratio of girls to boys in a school is 7 : 9. If there are 910 girls, how many boys are there?
36. The ratio of boys to girls in a school is 5 : 7. If there are 630 girls, how many boys are there?
37. An architect wishes to make a scale drawing of a rectangular room measuring 24 ft by 16 ft. If his drawing is 5 in. wide, how long is it?
38. An enlargement of a 4-in. by 5-in. photograph is 10 in. wide. How long is it?
39. A light bulb manufacturer advertises that no more than 8 out of 1000 of its bulbs are defective. If that is true, what is the maximum number of defective bulbs that can be expected in a shipment of 2250 bulbs?

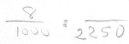

40. If you drive your new car 4300 mi during the first five months of ownership, how many miles can you expect to drive during the first year?

41. If the ratio of the width to the length of the U.S. flag must be $\frac{10}{19}$, what is the length of a U.S. flag that is 3 ft wide?

42. If the annual property tax rate in a particular township is $41.20 per $1000 on 35% of the appraised value of the property, what is the total annual tax on a property appraised at $80,000?

43. If $1\frac{1}{2}$ in. on a map represents 5 mi on the ground, approximately how many mi does $3\frac{7}{8}$ in. represent?

44. If $3\frac{1}{2}$ bags of lime will cover 3200 sq ft of lawn, approximately how much lawn will $8\frac{3}{5}$ bags cover?

45. If it takes 1 hr and 20 min to address 200 envelopes, how many envelopes can be addressed in 5 hr?

46. If it takes a secretary 1 hr and 20 min to type 12 pages, how long will it take her to type 99 pages?

47. Two persons decide to share profits in the ratio of 5 : 7. If the profits total $6120, how much will each person receive?

48. Two persons decide to share profits in the ratio of 5 : 9. If the profits total $6300, how much will each person receive?

49. A game warden tags 62 deer and then returns them to their park. Later, he catches 45 deer and finds that 6 of them are tagged. How many deer are in the park?

50. A fish warden tags 80 fish and then returns them to their pond. Later, she catches 65 fish from the pond and finds that 10 of them are tagged. How many fish are in the pond?

## Calculator Problems

51. Solve each proportion.

    a) $\dfrac{x}{541} = \dfrac{14,091}{671}$     b) $\dfrac{1.102}{x} = \dfrac{56.40}{14.10}$

52. If a bottle-capping machine caps 471 bottles in 12 min, how many bottles will it cap in an 8-hour workday?

53. The **golden ratio,** which has been used in art and architecture for centuries, is $\dfrac{1 + \sqrt{5}}{2}$. Show that the golden ratio is approximately $\frac{8}{5}$.

54. The **price-to-earnings ratio** (or $P/E$ Ratio) of a stock is given by

$$P/E \text{ Ratio} = \frac{\text{price per share}}{\text{earnings per share}}.$$

Generally speaking, the higher the $P/E$ Ratio the more speculative the stock. In 1982, Procter & Gamble reported total earnings of $777,000,000 for 82,791,000 shares. What was the $P/E$ Ratio if the price of a share of Procter & Gamble stock was $80\frac{7}{8}$?

## Challenge Problems

55. What are the dimensions of the largest picture frame that can be constructed with 60 in. of material if the ratio of the width to the length must be 5 : 7?
56. Determine the three interior angles of a triangle if they are in the ratio 2 : 3 : 4. (*Hint:* The sum of the measures of the interior angles of any triangle is 180°.)

## Chapter Review

True or false.

1. The techniques used in working with rational expressions are similar to the techniques used in working with common fractions.
2. Every polynomial is also a rational expression.
3. Every rational expression is also a polynomial.
4. To reduce a rational expression we factor its numerator and denominator completely and then divide out the factors common to the numerator and the denominator.
5. The lcd of a collection of rational expressions can be determined by factoring each denominator completely and then taking each distinct factor the least number of times it appears in any single factorization.

6. One method for simplifying a complex fraction involves multiplying both its numerator and denominator by the lcd of the fractions within its numerator and denominator.
7. When solving an equation involving rational expressions, it is generally best to begin by multiplying both sides of the equation by the lcd of all of the rational expressions appearing in the equation.
8. The ratio of $m$ to $n$ is written $n : m$, where $m \neq 0$.
9. If two triangles are similar, the ratios of their corresponding sides are equal.
10. Every proportion has several equivalent forms.
11. In any proportion, the product of the means is equal to the product of the extremes.
12. The expression $\dfrac{x + 8}{x^5 - 4x^3 + 7}$ is a rational expression.
13. The expression $\dfrac{x + 19}{x}$ is equal to 19.
14. The lcd of $\dfrac{1}{x + 5}$ and $\dfrac{1}{x - 5}$ is $x^2 + 25$.
15. The lcd of $\dfrac{1}{x - 2}$ and $\dfrac{1}{x + 3}$ is $x^2 - 6$.
16. The expression $\dfrac{5 + 2}{12 - 6}$ is a complex fraction.
17. The expression $\dfrac{5 + 2}{12 - 6}$ is a simple fraction.
18. If neither $a$ nor $b$ is zero, then $\dfrac{1}{a} + \dfrac{1}{b} = \dfrac{2}{a + b}$.
19. If $\dfrac{x + 4}{x - 3} = 0$, then $x = -4$.
20. If $3 - 2t \neq 0$, then $\dfrac{2t - 3}{3 - 2t} = -1$.

Completion.

21. An algebraic expression that can be written as a ratio of two polynomials where the divisor is not zero is called a(n)

    _____?_____ .

22. A fraction that contains other fractions in its numerator, or denominator, or both, is called a(n) _____?_____ .

23. The harmonic mean of the two nonzero numbers $x$ and $y$ is
    _____?_____.

24. An equation that states that two ratios are equal is a(n)
    _____?_____.

25. The means of the proportion $\dfrac{x}{x+1} = \dfrac{3}{4}$ are _____?_____ and

    _____?_____, while the extremes are _____?_____ and

    _____?_____.

For what value(s) is each rational expression undefined?

26. $\dfrac{x}{x-6}$    27. $\dfrac{1}{t^2+1}$    28. $\dfrac{r-5}{3r^2+r-2}$

29. Find the value of $\dfrac{(x-4)y+16}{(x-4)4-y}$ when $x = 3$ and $y = -1$.

Reduce each rational expression.

30. $\dfrac{x^2+x-6}{x^2-9}$    31. $\dfrac{5a-5b}{b-a}$    32. $\dfrac{(p+q)^2}{p^2-q^2}$    33. $\dfrac{10m^2n+15mn^2}{12m^2n+8mn^2-15n^3}$

Supply the missing numerator.

34. $\dfrac{5k}{k+13} - \dfrac{?}{k^2(k+13)}$    35. $\dfrac{c-6}{c+4} = \dfrac{?}{3(c+4)(c-2)}$

Determine the lcd for each problem.

36. $\dfrac{1}{m^3-m}, \dfrac{m}{(m-1)^2}$    37. $\dfrac{10r}{7r+21s}, \dfrac{5}{r^2-rs-12s^2}, \dfrac{s-3}{14r-56s}$

Perform the indicated operations and express your answer in reduced form.

38. $\dfrac{3}{10a} + \dfrac{3}{10a}$    39. $\dfrac{1}{y^2} + \dfrac{1}{xy} - \dfrac{1}{x^2}$

40. $\dfrac{2}{x-2} + \dfrac{1}{x+1}$    41. $\dfrac{y}{y^2-16} - \dfrac{2}{y-4}$

42. $\dfrac{15a^2}{8b} \cdot \dfrac{b^3}{9a^2} \cdot \dfrac{12a}{5b^2}$    43. $\dfrac{4x^2+8x}{x^2-2x-15} \cdot \dfrac{x^2-25}{x^2+2x}$

44. $\dfrac{6y+12}{3y+9} \div \dfrac{4y+8}{5y+15}$    45. $\dfrac{a^2-2ab+b^2}{b-1} \div \dfrac{a^2-b^2}{b^2-b}$

46. $x - \dfrac{17}{x + 17}$

47. $\dfrac{m}{m^2 + 4m + 4} - \dfrac{m + 1}{m^2 + 5m + 6}$

48. $\dfrac{k^2 + k}{k^2 + 2k - 15} - \dfrac{k + 9}{k^2 + 2k - 15}$

49. $\dfrac{5}{2y - 6} - \dfrac{15}{y^2 - 9}$

50. $\left( \dfrac{8x^2}{x^3 + 8x^2} \cdot \dfrac{5x^2 - 13x - 28}{x^2 - 16} \right) \div (10x + 14)$

51. $\dfrac{(c + d)^2}{c^2 + d^2} \cdot \left( \dfrac{-c^3 - cd^2}{c^2 - c - 2} \div \dfrac{c^2 - d^2}{c^2 + 2c + 1} \right)$

Simplify each complex fraction.

52. $\dfrac{\frac{1}{2} - \frac{1}{3}}{4 + \frac{1}{6}}$

53. $\dfrac{x - (1/y)}{y - (1/x)}$

54. $\dfrac{1 - \dfrac{25}{r^2}}{1 - \dfrac{3}{r} - \dfrac{10}{r^2}}$

55. $x - \dfrac{1}{1 + \dfrac{1}{x}}$

Solve each equation.

56. $\dfrac{5}{7x} = \dfrac{1}{2x} + \dfrac{1}{2}$

57. $\dfrac{x}{4x + 4} + \dfrac{9}{x + 1} = -1$

58. $\dfrac{7}{x + 3} = \dfrac{2}{x - 4}$

59. $\dfrac{6}{x} - 1 = \dfrac{5}{3x}$

60. $\dfrac{y}{y + 1} + 7 = \dfrac{-1}{y + 1}$

61. $\dfrac{2}{r + 6} - \dfrac{1}{r - 6} = \dfrac{13}{r^2 - 36}$

62. Find the harmonic mean of 8 and 12.
63. Express as a proportion and solve for $x$:
    a) $x$ is to 5 as 12 is to 18.
    b) $x$ is to $x + 1$ as 48 is to 64.

64. The expression $\dfrac{\dfrac{8}{x + h} - \dfrac{8}{x}}{h}$ appears in calculus. Simplify this complex fraction.

65. The concentration of a certain drug that remains in the blood-
    stream $t$ hours after it is injected is given by $\dfrac{t}{50t^2 + 200}$. Find the
    concentration that remains after 4 hours.

66. If Sue runs a 6.2-mi race in 40 min, and Dale runs the same race
    in 2 hr, what is the ratio of Sue's time to Dale's time? Of Dale's
    time to Sue's time?

67. Rick's mother drives him to school at 45 mph. After school, Rick

walks home at 5 mph. What is his average speed for the round trip to and from school?

68. Find the resistance in one branch of a parallel-wired circuit if the resistance in the other branch is 36 ohms and the total resistance is 24 ohms.

69. The denominator of a certain fraction exceeds the numerator by 6. If 2 is added to both the numerator and the denominator, the resulting fraction equals $\frac{5}{7}$. Find the original fraction.

70. One pipe can fill a tank in 6 hours while a second pipe takes 8 hours. How long will it take to fill the tank with both pipes working together?

71. The ratio of girls to boys in a school is 3 : 4. If there are 732 boys, how many girls are there?

72. Two persons decide to share profits in the ratio of 7 : 9. If the profits total $8480, how much will each person receive?

73. A power boat can travel 6 mph in still water. If the boat takes the same amount of time to travel 4 miles upstream as it does to travel 10 miles downstream, find the rate of the current.

74. If a tree casts a shadow of $58\frac{3}{4}$ ft at the same time a yardstick is casting a shadow of 30 in., find the height of the tree.

# Chapter Chapter Chapter Chapter Eight Eight Eight Eight

## GRAPHS IN
## A PLANE

## 8.1   CARTESIAN COORDINATE SYSTEM

René Descartes (1596–1650) was mentioned earlier as the first mathematician to use the shorter notation $x^3$ instead of $x \cdot x \cdot x$. Descartes' greatest achievement, however, was the invention of coordinate geometry in 1637. This clever, but simple, idea was to have an impact on mathematical thinking from that time on. It marked the birth of modern mathematics.

Using Descartes' idea, algebra and geometry were linked together for the first time. Geometric curves could be represented algebraically as equations. The algebraic techniques that had already been developed could then be applied to these equations to study the curves they represented and deduce more facts about them.

In turn, given an equation between two variables, Descartes' method enabled a geometric picture, or **graph,** of the equation to be drawn. One advantage that a graph had over an equation or a table of numbers was that it could provide information at a glance. It gave a clarity of thought to algebraic processes that helped to pave the way for, among other things, the development of the calculus by Isaac Newton (1642–1727) and Gottfried Leibniz (1646–1716) a few years later.

Descartes' idea was this: If a single point in a plane (a *geometric* notion) could somehow be represented using numbers (an *algebraic* notion), then a curve, which is simply a collection of points, could also be represented algebraically.

There are many versions of how Descartes came upon the idea of representing a point in a plane. One version has it that the idea came to him while lying in bed watching raindrops form on the window of his room. He observed that the location of any given raindrop could be indicated by specifying the distance of the raindrop from the *vertical* frame and the distance of the drop from the *horizontal* frame.

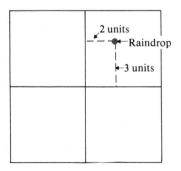

In place of the window frames, Descartes introduced two perpendicular number lines, joined at their origins, and called **axes.** Each axis served as a yardstick to measure the distance from a point to the other axis. Any point in the plane could then be represented using a pair of numbers.

To illustrate, the point $P$ in the diagram below is represented using the numbers 4 and 1, since it is 4 units to the right of the vertical axis and 1 unit above the horizontal axis. Alternatively, we may say that one reaches point $P$ by starting at the **origin** (the point of intersection of the two axes) and traveling 4 units in a horizontal direction and 1 unit in a vertical direction. The numbers 4 and 1 are called the **coordinates** of point $P$. They are generally written in parentheses as (4, 1) and referred to as an **ordered pair** of numbers. The number 4 is called the **first component** of the ordered pair (4, 1), while the number 1 is the **second component.**

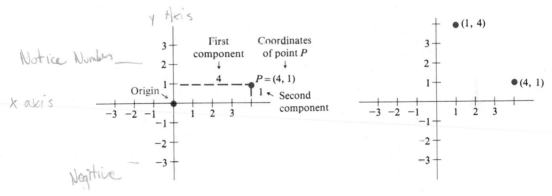

It is important to recognize that the ordered pair (1, 4) indicates a horizontal movement of 1 unit and a vertical movement of 4 units, and it therefore represents a *different* point than does the ordered pair (4, 1). That is, (1, 4) ≠ (4, 1), as we can see from the diagram above.

To distinguish points to the left of the vertical axis from those to the right, distances to the *left* are denoted using *negative* numbers. Similarly, distances *below* the horizontal axis are denoted using negative numbers. The point having coordinates (−5, −3), for example, would be located 5 units to the left of the vertical axis and 3 units below the horizontal axis (pg. 284). We can graph any ordered pair of real numbers $(x, y)$ using this method. This is also called **plotting** the point $(x, y)$.

Just as there is a one-to-one correspondence between the real numbers and the points on a number line, so is there a one-to-one correspondence between ordered pairs of real numbers and the points in a plane. That is, to each point in a plane there corresponds a unique ordered pair of

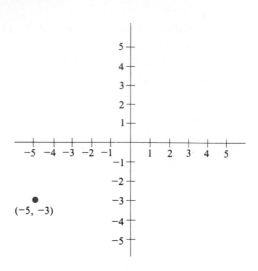

numbers, and to each ordered pair there corresponds a unique point. In honor of Descartes, this method of assigning ordered pairs of numbers to points in a plane is called a **Cartesian coordinate system.** It is also called a **rectangular coordinate system,** since the path that is followed from the origin to a point lies along the perimeter of some rectangle.

**EXAMPLE 1**   Graph (plot) each of the following points in a Cartesian coordinate system: $(5, 1)$ $(-2, 4)$ $(-3, -3)$ $(\frac{3}{2}, -\frac{5}{2})$ $(0, 4)$.

The five points are plotted below.

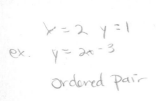

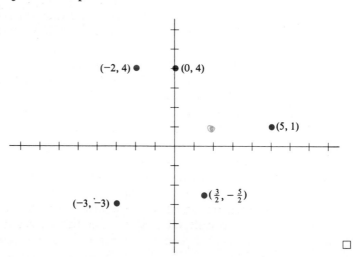

Notice that the axes divide the plane into four disjoint regions. These regions are called **quadrants.** The quadrants are numbered as shown in the figure below. *The axes themselves are not part of any quadrant.* Therefore the point (3, 2) lies in the first quadrant, the point (3, −2) lies in the fourth quadrant, and the point (3, 0) lies *between* quadrants I and IV.

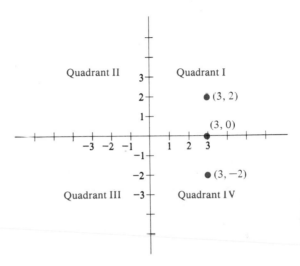

## Problem Set 8.1

1. Graph the point that is 5 units to the left of the vertical axis and 3 units above the horizontal axis. Write the coordinates of this point.
2. Graph the point that is 6 units to the right of the vertical axis and 2 units below the horizontal axis. Write the coordinates of this point.
3. Graph the point that is 4 units to the right of the vertical axis and $2\frac{1}{2}$ units above the horizontal axis. Write the coordinates of this point.
4. Graph the point that is 3 units to the left of the vertical axis and $2\frac{1}{2}$ units below the horizontal axis. Write the coordinates of this point.

5. Graph the point that is 8 units to the left of the vertical axis and on the horizontal axis. Write the coordinates of this point.
6. Graph the point that is 10 units to the right of the vertical axis and on the horizontal axis. Write the coordinates of this point.
7. Graph the point that is on the vertical axis and $\sqrt{2}$ units above the horizontal axis. Write the coordinates of this point.
8. Graph the point that is on the vertical axis and $\sqrt{3}$ units below the horizontal axis. Write the coordinates of this point.
9. List the coordinates of each point in the diagram (below left).

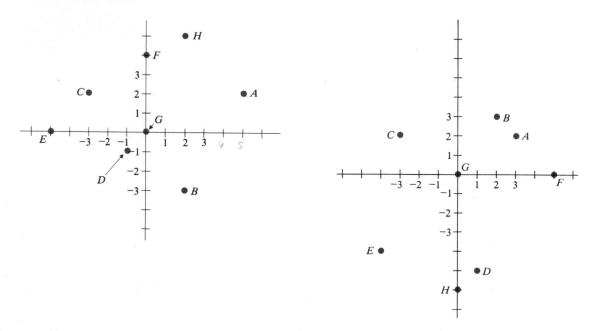

10. List the coordinates of each point in the diagram (above right).
11. In what quadrant is a point located if
    a) its first component is positive and its second component is negative?
    b) both components are negative?
    c) its first component is positive?
    d) its second component is negative?
12. Describe the coordinates of a point if
    a) it lies in quadrant I.
    b) it lies in quadrant III.

c) it lies on the horizontal axis between qudrants I and IV.
d) it lies on the vertical axis between quadrants III and IV.

Plot all of the given points on the same Cartesian coordinate system.

| | | | | |
|---|---|---|---|---|
| 13. (1, 5) | 14. (3, 4) | 15. (5, 1) | 16. (4, 3) | 17. (−4, −3) |
| 18. (2, −6) | 19. (−2, 6) | 20. (−5, −1) | 21. (2, 0) | 22. (0, 2) |
| 23. (0, −$\frac{7}{2}$) | 24. (−$\frac{5}{2}$, 0) | 25. (8, −1) | 26. (−8, 1) | |

Plot all of the given points on the same Cartesian coordinate system. Let the distance between successive hash marks on the axes represent 5 units.

| | | |
|---|---|---|
| 27. (35, 10) | 28. (25, 40) | 29. (−20, 15) |
| 30. (35, −20) | 31. (−5, 30) | 32. (30, −5) |

Plot all the given points on the same Cartesian coordinate system. Let the distance between successive hash marks on the horizontal axis represent 1 unit, and on the vertical axis 10 units.

| | | |
|---|---|---|
| 33. (3, 50) | 34. (4, 60) | 35. (5, −70) |
| 36. (−6, 50) | 37. (−4, 85) | 38. (2, 75) |

39. Consider the set of all those ordered pairs whose first and second components are equal. These points take the form $(a, a)$.

   a) Plot five of these points.
   b) How many of these points are there?
   c) If all of these points are plotted on the same Cartesian coordinate system, what would the completed graph look like?

40. Consider the set of all those ordered pairs whose second component is one more than the first component. These points take the form $(a, a + 1)$.

   a) Plot five of these points.
   b) How many of these points are there?
   c) If all of these points are plotted on the same Cartesian coordinate system, what would the completed graph look like?

41. Consider the set of all those ordered pairs whose second component is twice the first component. These points take the form $(a, 2a)$.

   a) Plot five of these points.
   b) How many of these points are there?
   c) If all of these points are plotted on the same Cartesian coordinate system, what would the completed graph look like?

42. Consider the set of all those ordered pairs whose second component is 2. These points take the form $(a, 2)$.
    a) Plot five of these points.
    b) How many of these points are there?
    c) If all of these points are plotted on the same Cartesian coordinate system, what would the completed graph look like?

## Calculator Problems

43. Plot the point $(\sqrt{827}/7, -277/\sqrt{1087})$.
44. Determine to the nearest hundredth the distance between the points $(-\sqrt{7}, 3)$ and $(\sqrt{5}, 3)$.
45. Determine to the nearest tenth the distance between the points $(6.5, 3.1)$ and $(1.8, -4.7)$. (*Hint:* Use the Pythagorean theorem.)

## Challenge Problems

46. Given that $m > 0$ and $n < 0$, in what quadrant does each point below lie?
    a) $(-m, -n)$    b) $(m, n - m)$    c) $(m/n, m - n)$
47. The Cartesian coordinate system can be used to display the collection of all possible outcomes (called the **sample space**) that can occur when two fair dice (one red and one green) are rolled. If we agree that the first component denotes the outcome of the red die and the second component denotes the outcome of the green die, then the ordered pair $(5, 2)$ would denote a roll that produced a 5 on the red die and a 2 on the green die. This, of course, is a different outcome than $(2, 5)$, which denotes a 2 on the red die and a 5 on the green die. The 36 outcomes that form the sample space are graphed here.

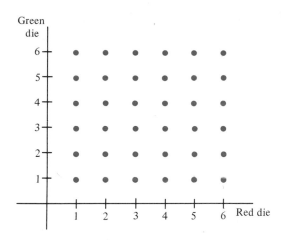

Now, the **probability** of rolling a total of $n$ is denoted $P(n)$ and is given by

$$P(n) = \frac{\text{number of ways to roll a total of } n}{36}.$$

a) What is the probability of rolling a total of 6?
b) What is the probability of rolling a total of less than 6?
c) What is the probability of rolling a total of 16?
d) What is the probability of rolling a total between 1 and 13?
e) What is the easiest total to roll?
f) What is the most difficult total to roll?
g) How many possible outcomes are there if *three* fair dice are rolled?

## 8.2  GRAPHING LINEAR EQUATIONS

We shall now consider how the Cartesian coordinate system is used to visually depict a relationship between two variables. We begin our study of graphing in this chapter with the simplest type of mathematical curve — the straight line.

Consider a laboratory experiment. Technician $A$ begins the experiment, and after several hours technician $B$ takes over. Technician $B$ notes that the temperature at the start of his observation period is 4 degrees. After observing for several hours, he further notes that the temperature is rising at a constant rate of 2 degrees per hour. He decides that an equation that completely describes the relationship between the temperature $T$ and his hour of observation $h$ is

$$T = 4 + 2h.$$

Using this equation we see that after 3 hours the temperature is 10 degrees, since upon substituting $h = 3$ we have

$$T = 4 + 2 \cdot 3$$
$$T = 4 + 6$$
$$T = 10.$$

The pair of values $h = 3$ and $T = 10$ is called a **solution** to the equation $T = 4 + 2h$. This is because the equation is a true statement when these substitutions are made. That is, $10 = 4 + 2 \cdot 3$ is a true statement.

If we agree that the first component of an ordered pair shall represent a value of the variable $h$ while the second component of the same ordered pair shall represent the corresponding value of $T$, then we can write this solution more simply as the ordered pair (3, 10). Therefore (3, 10) is a solution to $T = 4 + 2h$. The ordered pair (5, 7) is *not* a solution to $T = 4 + 2h$ since $7 \neq 4 + 2 \cdot 5$. Hence the ordered pair (3, 10) is said to *satisfy* the equation $T = 4 + 2h$, while the ordered pair (5, 7) does not.

Recall that a first-degree equation in *one* variable, such as $x + 2 = 7$, has just *one* solution (in this case the number 5). A first-degree equation in *two* variables, such as our equation $T = 4 + 2h$, has an *infinite* number of solutions. Each solution takes the form of an ordered pair that contains a value for each of the variables $h$ and $T$.

Since there are an *infinite* number of solutions to our equation, it should be an easy matter to find other solutions. In fact, it is. We simply substitute any value at random for one of the variables, and then we solve the resulting equation for the other variable. For example, suppose we choose to let $h = -1$. Then the equation becomes

$$T = 4 + 2(-1)$$
$$T = 4 + (-2)$$
$$T = 2.$$

Therefore, the ordered pair $(-1, 2)$ is also a solution to $T = 4 + 2h$. Continuing to find solutions, we have

$$\text{when } h = 0, T = 4 + 2 \cdot 0$$
$$T = 4.$$
$$\text{when } h = 1, T = 4 + 2 \cdot 1$$
$$T = 6.$$
$$\text{when } h = 2, T = 4 + 2 \cdot 2$$
$$T = 8.$$

Therefore, the ordered pairs $(0, 4)$, $(1, 6)$, and $(2, 8)$ are all solutions to $T = 4 + 2h$.

We can also substitute values for $T$ and then solve the resulting equation for $h$. For example,

$$\text{when } T = 0, 0 = 4 + 2h$$
$$-4 = 2h$$
$$-2 = h.$$

The most convenient way to collect these ordered-pair solutions is in a **table of values** like the one below.

Indepent variable

Dependent on h

| $h$ | $T$ |
| --- | --- |
| $-2$ | $0$ |
| $-1$ | $2$ |
| $0$ | $4$ |
| $1$ | $6$ |
| $2$ | $8$ |

The **graph** of a first-degree equation in two variables is simply the graph of all of its solutions. That is, the graph of the equation $T = 4 + 2h$ is the graph of all those ordered pairs that are solutions to this equation.

It would be impossible to *write* all of the solutions to the equation $T = 4 + 2h$, since there are an infinite number of them. We can, however, graph several ordered pair solutions and determine whether some sort of pattern exists. So that we do not forget that each first component represents a value of $h$ and each second component represents a value of $T$, we label the horizontal axis with the letter $h$ and call it the **h-axis,** and we label the vertical axis with the letter $T$ and call it the

***T*-axis.** Graphing the points from our table of values in a Cartesian coordinate system, we obtain the diagram below.

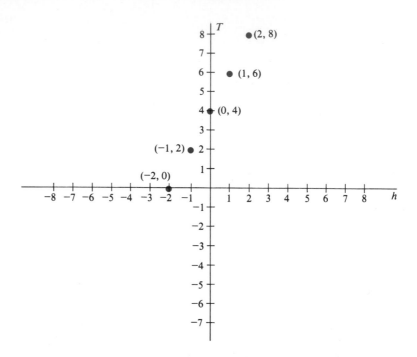

Note that all of these points lie on the same straight line. As a matter of fact, it can be shown that *every* ordered pair that is a solution to the equation $T = 4 + 2h$ will lie on this same straight line. Therefore we can complete the graph of the equation by drawing a straight line through the points that we have just plotted (see next page). A line actually goes on forever in both directions so, of course, we can only draw a portion of it.

It can be proved that the graph of *any* first-degree equation in two variables is a straight line. For this reason, such equations are generally referred to as *linear* equations in two variables. Without a doubt, the two variables that are used most often when writing linear equations in two variables are *x* and *y*. Therefore it has become common practice to denote the *horizontal axis* as the **x-axis** and the *vertical axis* as the **y-axis**. The first component of the ordered pair is then called the **x-value** and the second component the **y-value**. For example, the *x*-value of the ordered pair $(6, -5)$ is 6, while the *y*-value is $-5$.

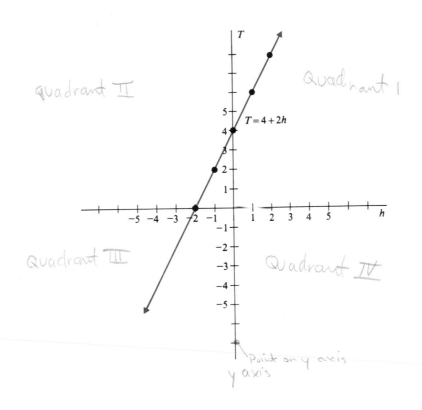

---

**Definition**   A **linear equation** in the variables $x$ and $y$ is any equation that can be written in the form

$$ax + by = c,$$

where $a$ and $b$ are not both zero. The **graph** of a linear equation in two variables is a straight line.

---

**EXAMPLE 1**   The equation $y = 4x + 3$ is a linear equation in two variables, since it can be written in the form $-4x + y = 3$. This last equation fits the definition above with $a = -4$, $b = 1$, and $c = 3$. □

**EXAMPLE 2**   The equation $y = x^2 + 6$ is *not* a linear equation in two variables. The variable $y$ is linear (since it is of the *first* degree), but the variable $x$ is *not* linear (since it is of the *second* degree). □

**EXAMPLE 3**   The equation $y = 4 - 3\sqrt{x}$ is *not* a linear equation in two variables. (We shall see in Section 10.6 that this equation is equivalent to $y = 4 - 3x^{1/2}$.) □

**EXAMPLE 4**   The equation $1/x + 1/y = 8$ is *not* a linear equation in two variables. (This equation is equivalent to $x^{-1} + y^{-1} = 8$.) □

Generally speaking, the graph of a *non*linear equation is *not* a straight line.

**EXAMPLE 5**   Graph $x + 2y = 6$.

Since this is a linear equation in two variables, we know that its graph will be a straight line. Thus we need to find only *two* ordered pairs in order to draw the graph. As a check, it might be wise to find a third ordered pair to see if it lies on the same line as the other two. Two solutions that are easy to find are those that occur when $x = 0$ and when $y = 0$.

$$\text{When } x = 0, \quad 0 + 2y = 6$$
$$y = 3.$$
$$\text{When } y = 0, \quad x + 2 \cdot 0 = 6$$
$$x = 6.$$

For our third solution we might let $x = 2$.

$$\text{When } x = 2, \quad 2 + 2y = 6$$
$$2y = 4$$
$$y = 2.$$

Hence we obtain the table of values below.

| $x$ | $y$ |
|---|---|
| 0 | 3 |
| 6 | 0 |
| 2 | 2 |

Plotting these points and drawing a line through them completes the graph (see next page).

Since this line crosses the $x$-axis at the point $(6, 0)$, we call 6 the **x-intercept** of the line. Similarly, since the line crosses the $y$-axis at $(0, 3)$, the number 3 is called the **y-intercept.** Whenever possible, we should draw enough of a line so that both intercepts are displayed.

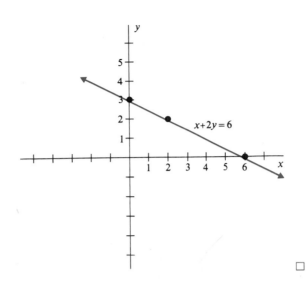

We can determine the x-intercept of a line by substituting 0 for $y$ in the equation of the line and solving for $x$. This is because the y-value of a point on the x-axis is 0. Also, since the x-value of a point on the y-axis is 0, we can determine the y-intercept by setting $x = 0$ in the equation and solving for $y$.

---

**Finding the Intercepts of a Line**

To find the x-intercept, set $y = 0$.
To find the y-intercept, set $x = 0$.

---

**EXAMPLE 6**   Determine the x- and y-intercepts of the line $3x + 5y = 15$, and then graph the line.

The x-intercept is found by setting $y = 0$ and solving for $x$.

$$3x + 5 \cdot 0 = 15$$
$$3x = 15$$
$$x = 5.$$

*(handwritten annotations in the left margin:)*

$(0 = x)$ ~~cancels~~ $\overline{y \text{ inter}}$   $3x + 5y = 15$

$(0 = y)$ $\overline{x \text{ inter}}$   $3x + 5y = 15$

y intercept $(0, 3)$

x intercept $(5, 0)$

The $x$-intercept is 5.

The $y$-intercept is found by setting $x = 0$ and solving for $y$.

$$3 \cdot 0 + 5y = 15$$
$$5y = 15$$
$$y = 3.$$

The $y$-intercept is 3.

A third point can be found to check the other two. When $x = 4$,

$$3 \cdot 4 + 5y = 15$$
$$12 + 5y = 15$$
$$5y = 3$$
$$y = \tfrac{3}{5}.$$

Therefore, our table of values contains the two points at which the line intersects the axes, and a third point not on an axis.

| $x$ | $y$ |
|-----|-----|
| 5 | 0 |
| 0 | 3 |
| 4 | $\frac{3}{5}$ |

To graph the equation $3x + 5y = 15$, we plot these three points and join them with a straight line.

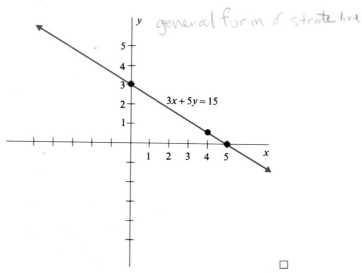

**EXAMPLE 7**    Graph $y = \frac{1}{2}x$.

First we construct a table of values.

| $x$ | $y$ |
|---|---|
| 0 | 0 — *won't work* |
| 2 | 1 |
| 4 | 2 |

Then we plot these points and join them with a straight line.

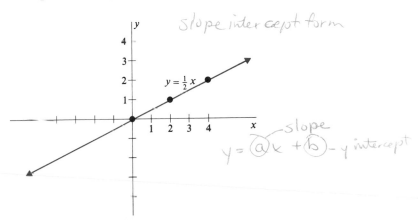

In this case *both* the x-intercept and the y-intercept are 0.  □

Even though we may substitute *any* value for a variable when constructing our table of values, we try to choose numbers that make our calculations as simple as possible. In general, we try to avoid fractional values and values that are large.

We will now give an example of how a linear equation can be used to illustrate the depreciation of a business property. Suppose that you purchase a twinplex for $70,000 ($60,000 for the building and $10,000 for the lot), and then you rent out both units. The $60,000 building can then be depreciated (land cannot be depreciated), since it is being used for business purposes. One of the methods for calculating the amount of depreciation that can be taken each year is the *straight-line method*. In the **straight-line method,** a property whose useful life is determined to be $n$ years will depreciate by $1/n$ of its original value each year. For example, if the useful life of the twinplex above is determined to be 30 years, then the twinplex will depreciate by $\frac{1}{30}$th of its original value, or

$2000, each year. This amount can then be subtracted from your taxable income each year before computing your tax liability for that year.

**EXAMPLE 8**   Write an equation that gives the undepreciated balance $B$ of the twinplex described above after $t$ years. Then graph this equation.

The desired equation is $B = 60{,}000 - 2000t$.
The table of values and the graph for this equation lie below. Note that the equation has meaning only for $t$-values such that $0 \leqslant t \leqslant 30$.

| $t$ | $B$ |
|-----|-----|
| 0 | 60,000 |
| 10 | 40,000 |
| 30 | 0 |

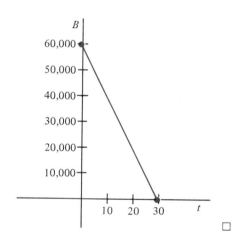

## Problem Set 8.2

1. Which of the equations below are linear equations in two variables?

   a) $y = 5x - \frac{3}{2}$     b) $y^2 = x + 4$     c) $\sqrt{x} + \sqrt{y} = 6$
   d) $x + y = \sqrt{6}$     e) $y = 1/x$

2. Which of the equations below are linear equations in two variables?

    a) $y = 4x + \frac{1}{2}$    b) $y = x^2 + 10$    c) $\sqrt{x} - \sqrt{y} = 9$
    d) $x + y = \sqrt{3}$    e) $y = 5/x$

3. Which of the ordered pairs below are solutions of (satisfy) the linear equation $x + y = 6$?

    a) $(3, 3)$    b) $(2, 3)$    c) $(0, 6)$    d) $(6, 0)$    e) $(-2, 8)$

4. Which of the ordered pairs below are solutions of (satisfy) the linear equation $x + y = 8$?

    a) $(4, 4)$    b) $(2, 4)$    c) $(0, 8)$    d) $(8, 0)$    e) $(10, -2)$

5. Which of the ordered pairs below satisfy the linear equation $y = 2x + 1$?

    a) $(0, 1)$    b) $(3, 7)$    c) $(2, 4)$    d) $(-4, -7)$    e) $(-1, -1)$

6. Which of the ordered pairs below satisfy the linear equation $y = 3x + 1$?

    a) $(0, 1)$    b) $(2, 7)$    c) $(1, 3)$    d) $(-3, -8)$    e) $(-1, -2)$

7. Which of the ordered pairs below are solutions of the linear equation $y - 5x = 8$?

    a) $(0, 8)$    b) $(4, 25)$    c) $(\frac{1}{5}, 9)$    d) $(-\frac{8}{5}, 16)$    e) $(-2, -2)$

8. Which of the ordered pairs below are solutions of the linear equation $y - 3x = 5$?

    a) $(0, 5)$    b) $(5, 21)$    c) $(\frac{2}{3}, 7)$    d) $(-\frac{5}{3}, -10)$    e) $(-2, -1)$

9. Consider the equation $y = 5x + 1$. Find the $y$-value corresponding to each of the $x$-values below. Express your answer as an ordered pair.

    a) $x = 0$    b) $x = 1$    c) $x = 3$    d) $x = -2$    e) $x = \frac{1}{5}$

10. Consider the equation $y = 4x + 1$. Find the $y$-value corresponding to each of the $x$-values below. Express your answer as an ordered pair.

    a) $x = 0$    b) $x = 1$    c) $x = 2$    d) $x = -3$    e) $x = \frac{1}{4}$

11. Consider the equation $y - 2x = 10$. Find the $y$-value corresponding to each of the $x$-values below. Express your answer as an ordered pair.

    a) $x = 0$    b) $x = 1$    c) $x = 4$    d) $x = -5$    e) $x = \frac{1}{2}$

12. Consider the equation $y - 3x = 12$. Find the $y$-value

corresponding to each of the $x$-values below. Express your answer as an ordered pair.

a) $x = 0$   b) $x = 1$   c) $x = 2$   d) $x = -4$   e) $x = \frac{1}{3}$

13. Consider the equation $3x + y = 0$. Find the $x$-value corresponding to each of the $y$-values below. Express your answer as an ordered pair.

a) $y = 0$   b) $y = 6$   c) $y = -12$   d) $y = -1$   e) $y = 2$

14. Consider the equation $2x + y = 0$. Find the $x$-value corresponding to each of the $y$-values below. Express your answer as an ordered pair.

a) $y = 0$   b) $y = 4$   c) $y = -10$   d) $y = -1$   e) $y = 3$

Determine at least two ordered pairs that satisfy each of the following linear equations. Then graph the equation by plotting these points and joining them with a straight line. Identify the $x$- and the $y$-intercept of each line.

15. $y = x + 1$   16. $y = x + 2$   17. $y = 3x - 2$   18. $y = 2x - 1$
19. $x + y = 4$   20. $x + y = 5$   21. $x - y = 6$   22. $x - y = 3$
23. $2x + y = 6$   24. $3x + y = 6$   25. $y = -x$   26. $y = x$
27. $x - 4y = 0$   28. $x + 5y = 0$   29. $y = 3 - \frac{1}{3}x$   30. $y = 4 - \frac{1}{4}x$
31. $2x + 5y = 10$   32. $3x + 4y = 12$   33. $2x - 3y = 1$   34. $4x - 3y = 1$
35. $x = 3y$   36. $x = 2y$

37. Neglecting air resistance, the velocity $v$ of an object in ft/sec $t$ seconds after it is dropped is given by the equation $v = 32t$. Graph this equation for $t \geqslant 0$.

38. According to *Hooke's law*, the force $F$ required to stretch a certain spring a distance of $d$ units is given by the equation $F = \frac{1}{12}d$. Graph this equation for $d \geqslant 0$.

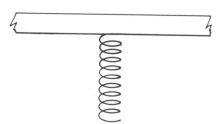

39. The *price-demand* equation for a certain item is $p = 125 - 0.25x$. Graph this equation for $0 \leqslant x \leqslant 500$.

40. Scientists have shown that the Fahrenheit temperature $F$ and the number of chirps per minute of a house cricket $n$ are related by the equation $F = 40 + 0.25n$. Graph this equation for $0 \leq n \leq 160$.

41. The cost per day of running a certain small business is $2 per manufactured unit plus a daily overhead of $20. If $C$ represents the total daily cost and $x$ the number of units manufactured, write an equation relating $C$ and $x$. Then graph this equation.

42. The daily profit that a certain small company makes is $5 per unit sold minus a daily overhead of $25. If $P$ represents the profit and $x$ the number of units sold, write an equation relating $P$ and $x$. Then graph this equation.

43. A landscaper is going to spend $600 to buy trees for her nursery. Pin oak trees cost $20 apiece and variegated-leaf maple trees cost $30 apiece. If $x$ is the number of oak trees and $y$ the number of maple trees that she can buy, write an equation relating $x$ and $y$. Then graph this equation.

44. A man is going to spend $1000 on new tools. Brand $A$ costs $20 per tool and brand $B$ costs $50 per tool. If $x$ is the number of brand $A$ and $y$ the number of brand $B$ that he can buy, write an equation relating $x$ and $y$. Then graph this equation.

See if you can write an equation that describes each graph below.

45.

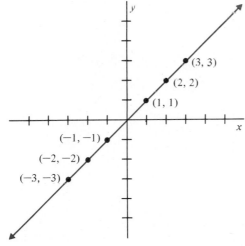

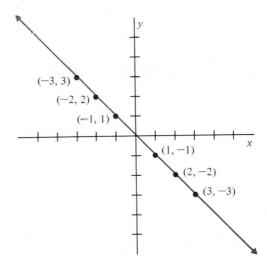

47.

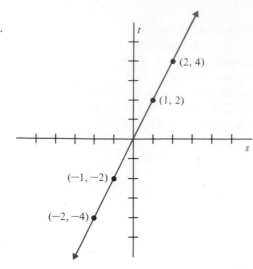

48.

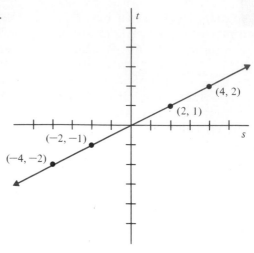

## Calculator Problems

49. Is the ordered pair (7.7, 1.05) a solution to $13x - 4y = 95.9$?
50. Determine the intercepts of the line $6.1x + 3.05y = 10.37$.
51. The equation $F = \frac{9}{5}C + 32$ relates Fahrenheit temperature $F$ and Celsius temperature $C$. Graph this equation for $C \geqslant -273.15°$ (*absolute zero*).*

## Challenge Problems

52. Graph $y = |x|$.
53. Two cars start at the same point at the same time and travel along the same route, one at 55 mph and the other at 40 mph. Given that $d$ is the distance in miles between the two cars after $t$ hours, write an equation relating $d$ and $t$. Then graph this equation.

---

* Although there is no *upper* limit on temperature, there is a natural *lower* limit called **absolute zero.** Temperatures within a few millionths of a degree of absolute zero have been obtained in laboratory experiments.

## 8.3 HORIZONTAL AND VERTICAL LINES

Suppose that a technician begins to observe a laboratory experiment and notes that the temperature remains constant at 3°. If $T$ denotes temperature and $h$ her hour of observation, then the graph depicting the relationship between $T$ and $h$ would be a *horizontal line* 3 units above the $h$-axis.

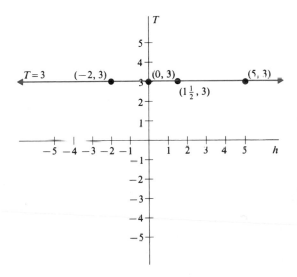

This horizontal line consists of all those ordered pairs whose second component, or $T$-value, is 3. The ordered pair $(1\frac{1}{2}, 3)$ indicates a temperature of 3 degrees $1\frac{1}{2}$ hours *after* the technician began her observation. The ordered pair $(-2, 3)$ indicates a temperature of 3 degrees 2 hours *before* the technician began her observation. The infinite collection of ordered pairs that form this line can be described using the equation $T = 3$.

In order to look further at the relationship between an equation of this type and its graph, consider the equation $y = 5$. We may think of this equation as a linear equation in two variables in which the coefficient of $x$ is 0. Writing the equation with this in mind, we have

$$y = 5$$
$$y = 0 + 5$$
$$y = 0 \cdot x + 5.$$

Now, if any value is substituted for $x$ in this last equation, the resulting

$y$-value is 5. For example,

$$\text{when } x = 4, \quad y = 0 \cdot 4 + 5$$
$$y = 0 + 5$$
$$y = 5.$$
$$\text{When } x = -3, \quad y = 0 \cdot (-3) + 5$$
$$y = 0 + 5$$
$$y = 5.$$

Therefore, to graph the equation $y = 5$ we simply graph all those ordered pairs having a $y$-value of 5. There are an infinite number of these ordered pairs and they are all of the form $(x, 5)$, where $x$ can be any real number. Some of these ordered pairs are

$$(0, 5) \quad (2, 5) \quad (4, 5) \quad (5, 5) \quad (-3, 5).$$

If these points are plotted, we see that they all lie on the same horizontal line. This horizontal line is the graph of the equation $y = 5$.

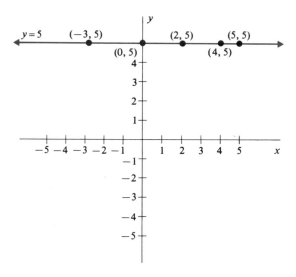

The discussion above leads us to the following rule:

**Horizontal Lines**

The graph of the linear equation $y = c$ in the plane is a horizontal line through the point $(0, c)$.

**EXAMPLE 1**   Graph $2y + 4 = 0$.

This equation can be written as

$$2y + 4 = 0$$
$$2y = -4$$
$$y = -2.$$

The graph is a horizontal line through the point $(0, -2)$.

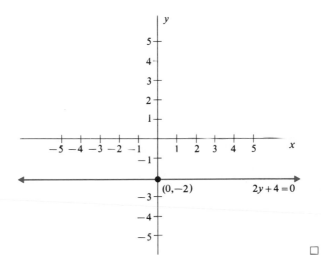

Now consider the equation $x = 2$. There are an infinite number of ordered pairs that satisfy this equation, and they are all of the form $(2, y)$, where $y$ can be any real number. Some of these ordered pairs are

$$(2, 0) \quad (2, 1) \quad (2, 3) \quad (2, 5) \quad (2, -4).$$

If these points are plotted, we see that they all lie on the same *vertical line*. This vertical line is the graph of the equation $x = 2$ (see next page).

Generalizing on this last discussion, we have the following rule:

---

**Vertical Lines**

The graph of the linear equation $x = c$ in the plane is a vertical line passing through the point $(c, 0)$.

---

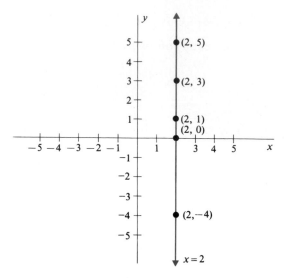

**EXAMPLE 2**    Graph $2x + 7 = 0$.

This equation can be written as

$$2x + 7 = 0$$
$$2x = -7$$
$$x = -\frac{7}{2}.$$

The graph is a vertical line through the point $\left(-\frac{7}{2}, 0\right)$.

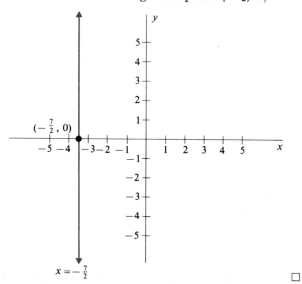

## Problem Set 8.3

1. Consider all of those ordered pairs $(x, y)$ such that $y = 4$.

   a) List five of these ordered pairs.
   b) How many of these ordered pairs are there?
   c) Graph all such ordered pairs.

2. Consider all of those ordered pairs $(x, y)$ such that $y = -3$.

   a) List five of these ordered pairs.
   b) How many of these ordered pairs are there?
   c) Graph all such ordered pairs.

3. Consider all of those ordered pairs $(x, y)$ such that $x = -2$.

   a) List five of these ordered pairs.
   b) How many of these ordered pairs are there?
   c) Graph all such ordered pairs.

4. Consider all of those ordered pairs $(x, y)$ such that $x = 1$.

   a) List five of these ordered pairs.
   b) How many of these ordered pairs are there?
   c) Graph all such ordered pairs.

5. Consider all of those ordered pairs $(x, y)$ such that $y = 0$.

   a) List five of these ordered pairs.
   b) How many of these ordered pairs are there?
   c) Graph all such ordered pairs.

6. Consider all of those ordered pairs $(x, y)$ such that $x = 0$.

   a) List five of these ordered pairs.
   b) How many of these ordered pairs are there?
   c) Graph all such ordered pairs.

Graph each of the following linear equations in two variables.

| | | | |
|---|---|---|---|
| 7. $x = 3$ | 8. $y = 2$ | 9. $y = -1$ | 10. $x = -5$ |
| 11. $x + 4 = 0$ | 12. $y - 1 = 0$ | 13. $y - \frac{3}{2} = 0$ | 14. $x + \frac{5}{2} = 0$ |
| 15. $x = 0$ | 16. $y = 0$ | 17. $2y + 11 = 0$ | 18. $2x - 9 = 0$ |
| 19. $\frac{1}{2}y = 0$ | 20. $\frac{1}{3}x = 0$ | 21. $x - \sqrt{2} = 0$ | 22. $y + \sqrt{3} = 0$ |

Write an equation that describes each graph below.

23.

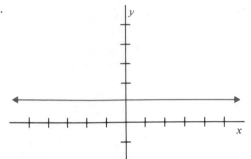

24.

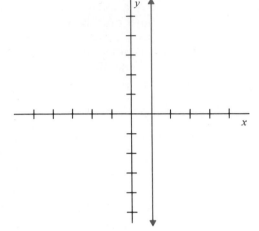

25.

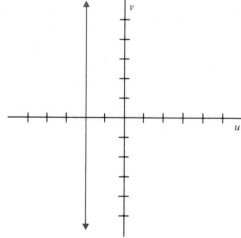

26.

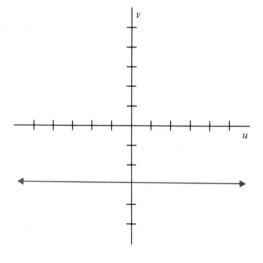

27. State the intersection point of the lines $x = 4$ and $y = -3$.
28. State the intersection point of the lines $x = -2$ and $y = 5$.
29. A commodity will generally have *inelastic demand* when there is no known alternative for that commodity. Insulin is a good example of a commodity having inelastic demand. In that case, a change in the price $p$ of the commodity has little effect on the

quantity demanded $q$. That is, the quantity demanded remains relatively constant. Label the vertical axis $p$ and the horizontal axis $q$, and then graph the equation $q = 75$ for $p \geq 0$.

30. The *acceleration* $a$ on a falling body due to the gravitational attraction of the earth is a constant 32 ft/sec$^2$ at any time $t$. Label the vertical axis $a$ and the horizontal axis $t$, and then graph the equation $a = 32$ for $t \geq 0$.

## Calculator Problems

Graph each equation in a Cartesian coordinate system.

31. $953x + 2099 = 0$        32. $y = 0.26\sqrt{607}$

## Challenge Problems

33. Graph all those ordered pairs $(x, y)$ such that $x \geq 2$.
34. In 1983, the cost of sending a letter first-class was 20¢ for the first ounce (or part of an ounce) and 17¢ for each ounce (or part of an ounce) after the first ounce (up to and including 12 ounces). If $C$ denotes the cost of sending a first-class letter weighing $x$ ounces, write a relationship between $C$ and $x$. Then graph this relationship.

## 8.4    GRAPHING LINEAR INEQUALITIES

In earlier sections of this chapter we learned that the graph of a linear equation in two variables such as $x = 2$, or $y = 3$, or $x + y = 2$ was a straight line. In this section we shall be concerned with graphing **linear inequalities** in two variables such as $x > 2$, or $y < 3$, or $x + y < 2$. The graph of such a linear inequality is a *half-plane*. To see this, let us begin with an example.

Consider all of those ordered pairs $(x, y)$ such that $x > 2$. These ordered pairs represent all points in the plane whose $x$-value is greater than 2. There are an infinite number of such points, and they are all found to the *right* of the vertical line $x = 2$. Therefore we graph these ordered pairs by shading the region to the right of the line $x = 2$.

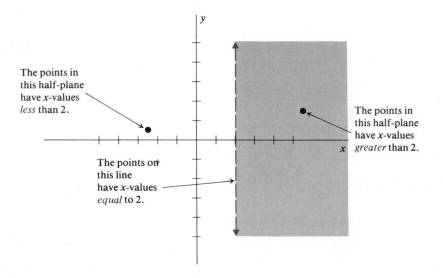

The points in this half-plane have $x$-values *less* than 2.

The points in this half-plane have $x$-values *greater* than 2.

The points on this line have $x$-values *equal* to 2.

The line $x = 2$ is shown as a *broken* line since it is *not* included as part of the graph.

Thus, just as a cut across a piece of paper divides the paper into two pieces, so each line in a plane divides the plane into two pieces, called **half-planes.** In our case, the vertical line $x = 2$ divided the plane into the two half-planes represented by the inequalities $x > 2$ and $x < 2$. A half-plane that *includes* its boundary line is called a **closed half-plane.** A half-plane that does *not* include its boundary line is an **open half-plane.**

**EXAMPLE 1** Graph $y < 3$.

The graph of $y < 3$ is the *open* half-plane that lies below the horizontal line $y = 3$.

Starting point deal with it as an equality =
then use a check number

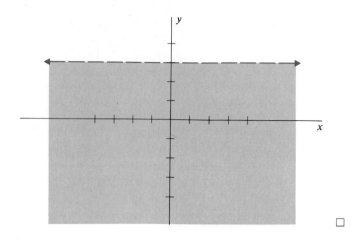

**EXAMPLE 2**   Graph $x + y < 2$.

First we graph the line $x + y = 2$.

| $x$ | $y$ |
|-----|-----|
| 0   | 2   |
| 1   | 1   |
| 2   | 0   |

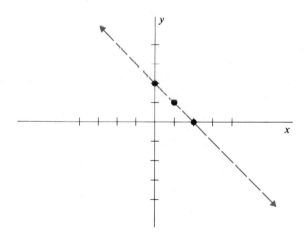

This line divides the plane into the two half-planes represented by

$$x + y < 2 \quad \text{and} \quad x + y > 2.$$

One of these half-planes lies *above* the line $x + y = 2$ and the other lies *below*. We must now determine which half-plane corresponds to *our* inequality $x + y < 2$. This is done by first choosing a **test point** that does not lie *on* the line $x + y = 2$ itself. If this point causes the inequality $x + y < 2$ to be a *true* statement, then the half-plane that *contains* the test point is the desired one. If the test point causes $x + y < 2$ to be a *false* statement, then the desired half-plane is the one that does *not* contain the test point. To make the test an easy one, we decide to choose the point (0, 0) as our test point. Substituting this point into the inequality $x + y < 2$, we have

$$0 + 0 < 2,$$

which is a true statement. Therefore, the desired half-plane is the one that contains the test point (0, 0).

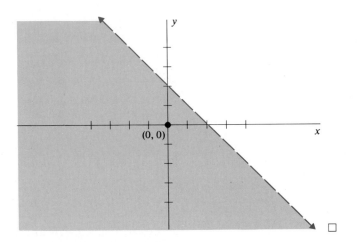

**EXAMPLE 3**   Graph $y \geqslant 2x$.

First, we graph the line $y = 2x$.

| x | y |
|---|---|
| 0 | 0 |
| 1 | 2 |
| 2 | 4 |

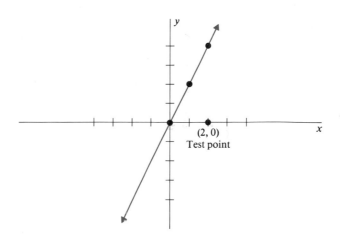

Next, we pick a test point *not* on the line. In this case we *cannot* choose the origin, since it lies *on* the line $y = 2x$. We decide to choose $(2, 0)$. Substituting $(2, 0)$ into $y \geq 2x$, we have

$$0 \geq 2 \cdot 2,$$

which is a *false* statement. Hence the desired half-plane is the one that does *not* contain the test point $(2, 0)$.

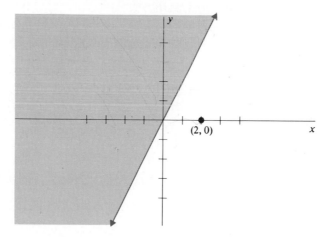

In this case the boundary line $y = 2x$ is *solid* (not broken), since it is part of the graph. This is due to the fact that the original inequality was $y \geq 2x$ and *not* $y > 2x$. Therefore the graph is a *closed* half-plane.  □

## Problem Set 8.4

1. Consider all of those ordered pairs $(x, y)$ such that $x > 3$.
   a) List five of these ordered pairs.
   b) Graph all such ordered pairs.
2. Consider all of those ordered pairs $(x, y)$ such that $x < 4$.
   a) List five of these ordered pairs.
   b) Graph all such ordered pairs.
3. Consider all of those ordered pairs $(x, y)$ such that $y < -1$.
   a) List five of these ordered pairs.
   b) Graph all such ordered pairs.
4. Consider all of those ordered pairs $(x, y)$ such that $y > -2$.
   a) List five of these ordered pairs.
   b) Graph all such ordered pairs.
5. Consider all of those ordered pairs $(x, y)$ such that $x + y < 3$.
   a) List five of these ordered pairs.
   b) Graph all such ordered pairs.
6. Consider all of those ordered pairs $(x, y)$ such that $x + y > 1$.
   a) List five of these ordered pairs.
   b) Graph all such ordered pairs.

In each of the problems below, the required boundary line has been graphed. Complete each graph by shading the appropriate half-plane.

7. $x < 5$

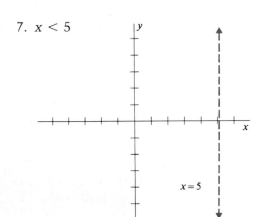

8. $y > 2$

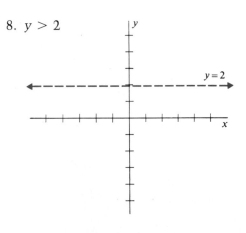

9. $x + y < 4$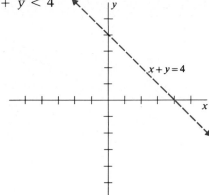

10. $x + y < 3$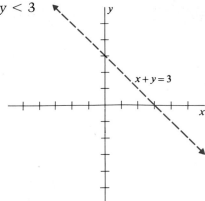

11. $x + y > 4$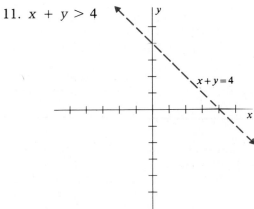

12. $x + y > 3$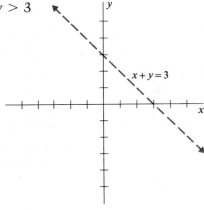

13. $4x - 5y \le 20$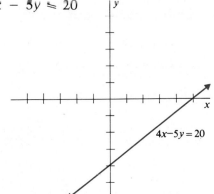

14. $3x - 4y > 12$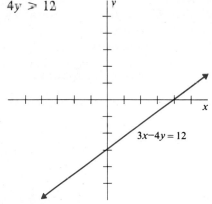

15. $y \geq 2x$

16. $y \leq \frac{1}{2}x$

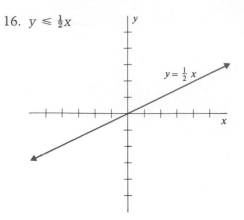

Graph each of the following linear inequalities in two variables.

17. $x < 4$
18. $y > 1$     $y = 2x + 1$
19. $y + 1 > 0$
20. $x + 2 < 0$
21. $y < 2x + 1$     $1 = 20 + 1$
22. $y < 3x + 2$
23. $y < 3x - 2$
24. $y < 2x - 1$     $0 = \frac{2}{7} \cdot -\frac{1}{2} + 1$
25. $x + y < 5$
26. $x + y > 5$
27. $y \geq 3x$
28. $y \leq \frac{1}{3}x$
29. $2x - 3y \leq 6$
30. $2x - 5y \geq 10$
31. $3x + 7y > 21$
32. $3x + 5y < 15$
33. $y \leq -\frac{1}{2}x$
34. $y \geq -2x$

35. Describe algebraically all those points that lie to the right of the y-axis.
36. Describe algebraically all those points that lie above the x-axis.
37. Graph all $(x, y)$ such that $x \geq 2$ *and* $y \geq 1$.
38. Graph all $(x, y)$ such that $x \leq 2$ *and* $y \leq -1$.
39. A hospital patient is to consume at least 12 g of protein at break-fast. Each ounce of food A contains 4 g of protein and each ounce of food B contains 5 g of protein. If $x$ denotes the number of ounces of food A consumed and $y$ the number of ounces of food B consumed, write an inequality relating $x$ and $y$. Then graph this inequality.
40. Do Problem 39 if the patient is to consume at *most* 12 gm of protein at breakfast each day.

## Calculator Problems

Graph each linear inequality in two variables.

41. $x \leq 233/\sqrt{701}$
42. $18.45x - 6.15y \leq 51.66$

## Challenge Problems

Graph all $(x, y)$ satisfying the given conditions.

43. $-1 \leqslant x < 2$     44. $xy \geqslant 0$     45. $|y| \leqslant 3$     46. $y > |x|$

## Chapter Review

True or false.

1. The two coordinate axes in a Cartesian coordinate system are perpendicular to one another.
2. To each point in the plane there corresponds a unique ordered pair of real numbers.
3. To each ordered pair of real numbers there corresponds a unique point in the plane.
4. An equation that can be written in the form $ax + by = c$, where $a$ and $b$ are not both zero, is called a linear equation in the variables $x$ and $y$.
5. A solution to a linear equation in two variables can be represented by an ordered pair of real numbers.
6. A linear equation in two variables has an infinite number of ordered pair solutions.
7. The graph of a linear equation in two variables is a straight line.
8. The $x$-intercept of a line is found by setting $x = 0$.
9. The $x$-intercept of $y = x + 3$ is 3.
10. The graph of $y = c$ in the plane is a horizontal line through $(0, c)$.
11. The graph of $x = c$ in the plane is a vertical line through $(c, 0)$.
12. The graph of a linear inequality in two variables is either an open half-plane or a closed half-plane.
13. The equation $y = 6x - 4$ is a linear equation.
14. The equation $y = x^2 + 3$ is a linear equation.
15. The equation $y = 1/x + 4$ is a linear equation.
16. The point $(a, 0)$ lies on the $x$-axis.
17. The point $(3, 5)$ lies on the line $y = 3$.
18. The point $(-\frac{1}{2}, -2)$ satisfies the equation $y = 4x$.

watch

19. The line $y = 5$ has no $x$-intercept.
20. If $a < 0$ and $b > 0$, then $(-a, -b)$ lies in quadrant IV.
21. If $a \cdot b > 0$, then $(a, b)$ lies in quadrant I or III.

Reversed

22. The lines $y = -12$ and $x = 14$ intersect at the point $(-12, 14)$.
23. The graph of $y \geqslant x$ is a closed half-plane.

Completion.

24. The point of intersection of the coordinate axes is called the

      _____?_____ .

25. The coordinate axes divide the plane into four disjoint regions

      called _____?_____ .

26. If the ordered pair $(6, -8)$ corresponds to the point $P$ in the plane,

      then the numbers 6 and $-8$ are called the _____?_____ of
      point $P$.

27. Give the coordinates of the points $A$, $B$, and $C$ in the diagram
      below.

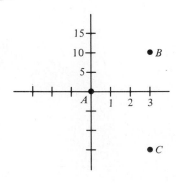

Graph each linear equation in two variables. Identify the $x$- and the
$y$-intercept of each line.

28. $y = x + 3$      29. $x + y = 2$      30. $x - 2y = 5$      31. $y = -\frac{1}{3}x + 1$
32. $5x = 0$      33. $y - 2x = 0$      34. $2x - 3y = 12$      35. $3y + 4 = -2$
36. $3y - 12 = 0$      37. $x = \pi$

In each problem below, the required boundary line has been graphed.
Complete each graph by shading the appropriate half-plane.

38. $x \geqslant 4$

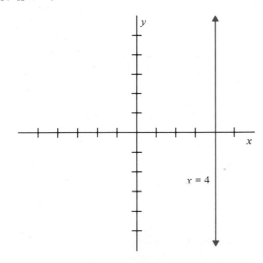

39. $2x + 3y < 6$

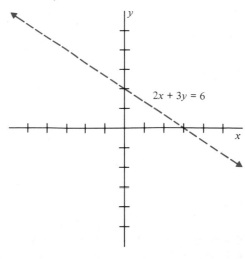

Graph each linear inequality in two variables.

40. $x \leqslant 3$

41. $-2y - 6 > 1$

42. $x - y < 4$

43. $y \geqslant \frac{1}{5}x$

Write an equation that describes each graph below.

44.

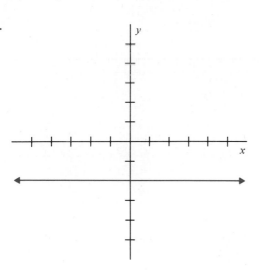

45.

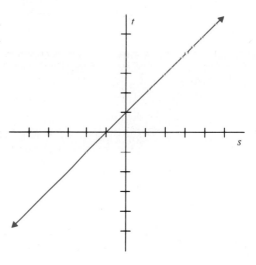

46. The perimeter $P$ of a square is related to the length $s$ of a side by the equation $P = 4s$. Graph this equation for $s \geq 0$.

47. The *Intelligence Quotient, I.Q.*, of an individual remains fairly constant with age $a$. Label the vertical axis I.Q. and the horizontal axis $a$. Now, if Melissa's I.Q. was measured to be 110 when she was 12 years old, then we can write the equation I.Q. = 110. Graph this equation for $a \geq 0$.

48. A dieter is to consume no more than 300 calories at breakfast. Suppose that one cooked egg contains 100 calories and one piece of toast (with butter and jelly) contains 150 calories. If $x$ denotes the number of eggs consumed and $y$ the number of pieces of toast consumed, write an inequality relating $x$ and $y$. Then graph this inequality.

49. A firm can produce their product for a cost of 50¢ per unit plus a daily overhead of $10. If $C$ represents the total daily cost of producing $x$ units, write an equation relating $C$ and $x$. Then graph this equation.

50. Graph the collection of all those ordered pairs of the form $(a, -a)$.

Graph all $(x, y)$ that satisfy the given conditions.

51. $x > 0$ *and* $y \leq 2$        52. $xy \leq 0$

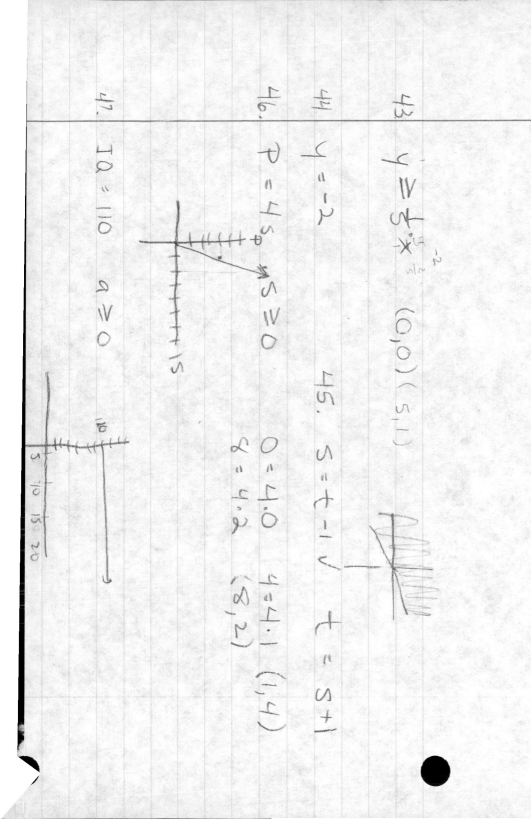

43. $y = 5 \cdot \frac{1}{x}^{-2}$   (0,0) (5,1)

44. $y = -2$   45. $S = t - 1$ ✓   $t = S+1$

46. $P = 45p$   $S \geq 0$   $0 = 4 \cdot 0$   $4 = 4 \cdot 1$   $(1,4)$

$8 = 4 \cdot 2$   $(2,8)$

47. $IQ = 110$   $a \geq 0$

# Chapter 8 extra practice

302 51.

302 53.

## Review

| 1. T | 2. T | 3. T | 4. T | 5. T | 6. T | 7. T | 8. F |
|------|------|------|------|------|------|------|------|
| 9. F | 10. T | 11. T | 12. T | 13. T | 14. F | 15. F | 16. T |
| 17. F | 18. T | 19. T | 20. F | 21. T | 22. T | 23. T | |

24. Origin; Point

25. Quadrants

26. Coordinates

27. a. 0,0   b. (3,10)   c. (3,-3)/15

28. $y = x + 3$   (3,0)  (-3,0)

30. $x + 2y = 5$   $(5,0)$ $(1,2)$

31. $y = -3x + 1$   $(0,1)$ $(3,0)$

32. $5x = 0$   $(0,0)$ $(0,0)$

33. $y - 2x = 0$   $(0,0)$ $(1,2)$

34. $2x - 3y = 12$   $(0,-4)$ $(6,0)$

35. $3y + 4 = -2$   $(0,-2)$

36. $3y - 12 = 0$   $(0,4)$

37. $x = 11$   $11 = 11$

38. $x \geq 4$   $0 \cdot 0 \neq 4$

39. $2x + 3y < 6$

40. $x \leq 3$

41. $-2y - 6 \geq 1$   $(0,-4)$

42. $x - y < 4$   $(4,-4)$ $6 - 2 = 4$ $0 - 0 < 4$

48. $x \cdot 100 + 150y \leq 300$
$0 \cdot 100 + 150 \cdot 2 = 300$   $(0, 2)$
$3 \cdot 100 + 150 \cdot 0 \leq 300$   $(3, 0)$

49. $C = .50x + 10$    $(0, 10)$
               $(1, 10.50)$

50. $(a, -a)$

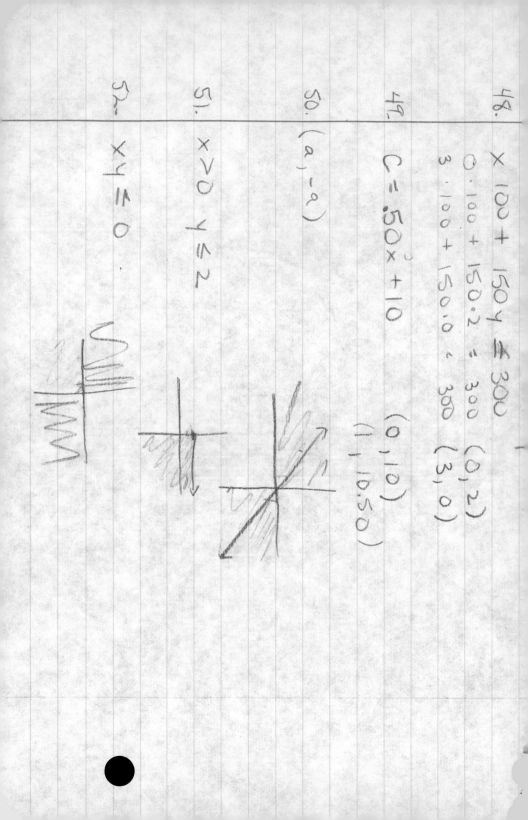

51. $x > 0 \quad y \leq 2$

52. $xy = 0$

# Chapter
# Chapter
# Chapter
# Chapter Nine
# Nine
# Nine
# Nine

**SYSTEMS OF
EQUATIONS
AND
INEQUALITIES**

## 9.1   GRAPHICAL METHOD

A paper boy has $11 extra in Christmas tips to divide between his two helpers, Mary and Ray. Since Mary has helped more often than Ray, he decides that Mary should receive $3 more than Ray. How much should each helper receive?

This particular problem is easy to do simply by trial and error. Many problems of this type, however, are too difficult to be solved using a trial-and-error approach. Our intent here is to develop a *systematic* approach to solving problems of this type. Once developed, this method will prove useful in many different situations in mathematics.

We shall let $x$ represent the number of dollars Mary is to receive and $y$ the number of dollars Ray is to receive. We can then write the two equations

$$x + y = 11$$

and

$$x - y = 3.$$

These two equations taken together are called a **system of equations.** [*] To *solve* the system means to find a pair of values $x$ and $y$ that satisfies the conditions of *both* equations. For example, the ordered pair (8, 3) is a solution to the *first* equation, since $8 + 3 = 11$; but it is *not* a solution to the *second* equation, since $8 - 3 \neq 3$.

From Chapter 8 we know that all solutions to the first equation $x + y = 11$ lie on a straight line. Also, all solutions to the second equation $x - y = 3$ lie on some other straight line. If the two equations are graphed using the same coordinate axes, we obtain the two *intersecting lines* shown on the following page.

From our graph, the **intersection point** of the two lines *appears* to be (7, 4). Since the point (7, 4) is the *only* point that lies on *both* lines, it is the only point that is a *solution* to *both* equations. The point (7, 4) is therefore called the **solution** of the system

$$x + y = 11$$
$$x - y = 3.$$

Another way of writing the solution of the system above is to say that $x = 7$ *and* $y = 4$.

---

[*] Since the two equations are to be true at the same time, they are also referred to as **simultaneous equations.**

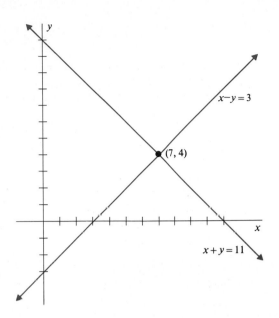

To check our solution we must substitute (7, 4) in *both* equations. If the ordered pair (7, 4) fails to satisfy *either* equation, then it is *not* a solution to the system.

CHECK:    $7 + 4 \stackrel{?}{=} 11$    and    $7 - 4 \stackrel{?}{=} 3$
                $11 = 11$                    $3 = 3.$

Therefore, Mary should receive $7 and Ray $4.

This method of solving a system of equations is called the **graphical method.**

EXAMPLE 1   Solve the system below using the graphical method.

$$x - y = 4$$
$$2x + y = 5$$

We begin by graphing both equations.

$$x - y = 4 \qquad 2x + y = 5$$

| x | y | x | y |
|---|---|---|---|
| 0 | −4 | 0 | 5 |
| 2 | −2 | 2 | 1 |
| 4 | 0 | 4 | −3 |

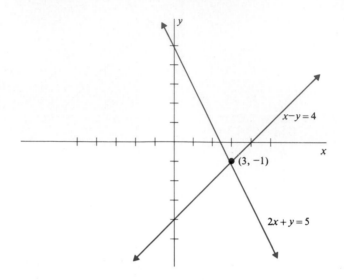

Since the lines intersect at the point $(3, -1)$, the point $(3, -1)$ is the solution to the system.

CHECK:   $3 - (-1) \overset{?}{=} 4$    $2(3) + (-1) \overset{?}{=} 5$

$3 + 1 \overset{?}{=} 4$     $6 + (-1) \overset{?}{=} 5$

$4 = 4$      $5 = 5.$ □

If the two linear equations that form a system represent two *distinct* lines, then the system is said to be **independent.** If the system has at least one solution, it is said to be **consistent.** Therefore, the system of Example 1 is independent and consistent, which we usually shorten to just *independent.*

**EXAMPLE 2**   Solve the system below using the graphical method.

$$x + 2y = 0$$
$$x = 4$$

Graphing the two equations, we obtain two intersecting lines.

$$x + 2y = 0 \qquad x = 4$$

| $x$ | $y$ | $x$ | $y$ |
|-----|-----|-----|-----|
| 0 | 0 | 4 | 0 |
| 2 | $-1$ | 4 | 1 |
| 4 | $-2$ | 4 | 2 |

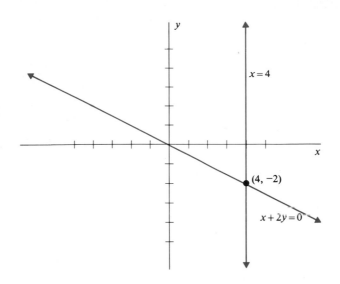

The solution is $(4, -2)$.

$$\text{CHECK:} \quad 4 + 2(-2) \overset{?}{=} 0 \qquad 4 = 4$$
$$4 - 4 \overset{?}{=} 0$$
$$0 = 0. \quad \square$$

**EXAMPLE 3**   Solve the system below using the graphical method.

$$x + y = 2$$
$$x + y - 4$$

Graphing both equations, we see that the two lines are *parallel* (see next page).

$$x + y = 2 \qquad x + y = 4$$

| x | y | x | y |
|---|---|---|---|
| 0 | 2 | 0 | 4 |
| 1 | 1 | 2 | 2 |
| 2 | 0 | 4 | 0 |

Since the lines do *not* intersect, there is *no* solution to the system. $\square$

The conclusion in Example 3 becomes obvious if we study the two equations closely. Note that it would be impossible to find a pair of numbers $x$ and $y$ whose sum is *both 2 and 4*.

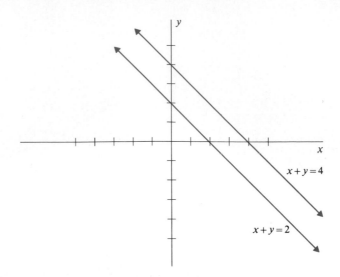

When the two lines of a system are parallel, as those of Example 3 were, the system is said to be independent and inconsistent, which we usually shorten to just *inconsistent*.

**EXAMPLE 4**    Solve the system below using the graphical method.

$$x + y = 1$$
$$3x + 3y = 3$$

Graphing both equations, we see that the two lines actually *coincide* (see next page).

$$x + y = 1 \qquad 3x + 3y = 3$$

| x | y | x | y |
|---|---|---|---|
| 0 | 1 | 0 | 1 |
| 1 | 0 | 1 | 0 |
| 2 | −1 | 2 | −1 |

The solution in this case consists of *all* points on this line. □

Again, if we study the two equations of Example 4, we observe that the second equation can be *obtained* from the first equation by multiplication of both sides by 3. Hence the two equations are actually equivalent.

When the two lines of a system coincide, as those of Example 4 did, the system is said to be dependent and consistent, which we usually shorten to just *dependent*.

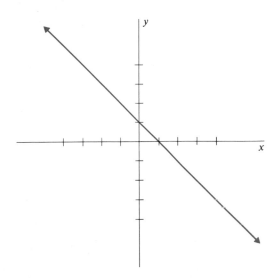

Given a system of *two linear equations in two variables,* exactly *one* of three situations must occur. Either the system has *one solution, no solution,* or *infinitely many solutions.* These three possibilities are illustrated below.

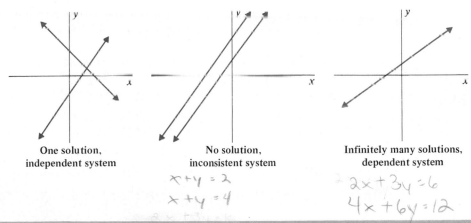

One solution,
independent system

No solution,
inconsistent system

Infinitely many solutions,
dependent system

$x + y = 2$
$x + y = 4$

$2x + 3y = 6$
$4x + 6y = 12$

## Problem Set 9.1

Solve each system using the *graphical method* and check your solution. Classify each system as independent, inconsistent, or dependent.

1. $x + y = 4$
   $x - y = 2$

2. $x + y = 5$
   $x - y = 3$

3. $x + y = 3$
   $x + y = 5$

4. $x + y = 1$
   $x + y = 3$

5. $x + y = 2$
  $2x + 2y = 4$

6. $x - y = 1$
  $3x - 3y = 3$

7. $y = 5x$
  $y = -x$

8. $y = 4x$
  $y = -x$

9. $x + 3y = 6$
  $2x - 3y = -6$

10. $2x + 3y = 12$
  $x - 2y = -1$

11. $x - 2y = 4$
  $3x - 6y = 12$

12. $3x + y = 3$
  $6x + 2y = 6$

13. $y = 2x + 1$
  $y = 2x + 3$

14. $y = 3x + 2$
  $y = 3x + 4$

15. $y = x$
  $y = -x - 3$

16. $y = -x$
  $y = x + 3$

17. $x - y = 3$
  $x = 4$

18. $x + y = 7$
  $y = 2$

19. $y = \frac{1}{3}x$
  $y = 2$

20. $y = \frac{1}{2}x$
  $x = 4$

A **demand equation** for a product gives the quantity $x$ demanded at price $p$. A **supply equation** gives the quantity $x$ that a firm is willing to supply at price $p$. The point at which the graphs of the two equations intersect is called the **equilibrium point,** and the price at that point (where supply equals demand) is called the **equilibrium price.** Determine the equilibrium point for each pair of supply and demand equations below.

21. $x = 21 - 2p$   (demand)
   $x = \frac{3}{2}p$       (supply)

22. $x = 16 - 2p$   (demand)
   $x = \frac{2}{3}p$       (supply)

## Calculator Problems

Substitute the given ordered pair into the given system to determine if it is a solution to the system.

23. $(4.4, 6.5)$
   $84.6x - 75.1y = -115.91$
   $7.15x + 9.72y = 94.64$

24. $(137, -968)$
   $814x + 77y = 36,982$
   $999x + 142y = -594$

## Challenge Problems

Graphically determine whether the given system is consistent or inconsistent.

25. $x + y = 4$
   $y = x$
   $x = 2$

26. $y = x + 2$
   $y = -x$
   $y = 2$

## 9.2   SUBSTITUTION METHOD

While solving the problems of the previous section, you probably discovered that the graphical method for solving a system is not always an *accurate* method. The results depend upon how accurately the graphs are constructed. The solution is even more difficult to obtain when fractions are involved.

Thus, the graphical method gives us a clear picture of what is happening in the solving process, but in order to be assured of obtaining an *exact* solution to a system, we must use an algebraic method. A completely systematic method for solving systems of equations was developed by the German mathematician Carl Friedrich Gauss (1777–1855), one of the greatest mathematicians who ever lived. His method is closely related to the addition method of solving a system of equations. We will discuss this method in Section 9.3.

First, however, we will discuss a different method, called the *substitution method*. The **substitution method** involves solving *one* of the equations for one of its variables (we usually choose the easiest variable to solve for) and then *substituting* that expression into the *other* equation. The resulting equation then contains only one variable.

**EXAMPLE 1**   Solve the system below using the substitution method.

$$x - 2y = 6$$
$$x + 2y = 10$$

We decide to solve the first equation for $x$. Adding $2y$ to both sides gives

$$x = 6 + 2y.$$

Substituting the expression $6 + 2y$ for $x$ in the *second* equation, we have

$$(6 + 2y) + 2y = 10.$$

This is a first-degree equation in *one* variable, and it is easily solved.

$$6 + 2y + 2y = 10$$
$$6 + 4y = 10$$
$$4y = 4$$
$$y = 1.$$

Finally, we substitute 1 for $y$ in the equation $x = 6 + 2y$ (actually this substitution could also be made in *either* of the *original* equations).

$$x = 6 + 2 \cdot 1$$
$$x = 8.$$

Therefore the solution is (8, 1). ☐

**EXAMPLE 2**    Solve the system below using the substitution method.

$$x - 2y = 8$$
$$3x + y = 3$$

Solving the second equation for $y$ gives

$$y = 3 - 3x.$$

Then substituting $3 - 3x$ for $y$ in the first equation, we have

$$x - 2(3 - 3x) = 8$$
$$x - 6 + 6x = 8$$
$$-6 + 7x = 8$$
$$7x = 14$$
$$x = 2.$$

Finally, we substitute 2 for $x$ in the equation $y = 3 - 3x$.

$$y = 3 - 3 \cdot 2$$
$$y = 3 - 6$$
$$y = -3.$$

Therefore the solution is (2, −3). ☐

**EXAMPLE 3**    Solve the system below using the substitution method.

$$2x + 6y = 5$$
$$4x - 3y = 0$$

We solve the first equation for $x$.

$$2x = 5 - 6y$$
$$x = \frac{5}{2} - 3y.$$

Substituting the expression $\frac{5}{2} - 3y$ for $x$ in the second equation gives

$$4\left(\frac{5}{2} - 3y\right) - 3y = 0$$
$$10 - 12y - 3y = 0$$
$$10 - 15y = 0$$
$$-15y = -10$$
$$y = \frac{-10}{-15} = \frac{2}{3}.$$

Substituting $\frac{2}{3}$ for $y$ in $x = \frac{5}{2} - 3y$, we have

$$x = \frac{5}{2} - 3\left(\frac{2}{3}\right)$$
$$x = \frac{5}{2} - 2 \qquad \frac{2}{1} \cdot \frac{3}{2} = \frac{4}{2}$$
$$x = \frac{1}{2}.$$

Therefore the solution is $(\frac{1}{2}, \frac{2}{3})$. $\square$

## Problem Set 9.2

Solve each system using the *substitution method*.

1. $x - 2y = 3$
   $x + y = 3$
2. $x - y = 1$
   $x + 3y = 5$
3. $2x + y = 9$
   $x - y = 3$
4. $2x - y = 2$
   $x + y = 7$
5. $4x + y = 1$
   $2x - 3y = 11$
6. $5x + y = 4$
   $5x - 3y = 8$
7. $2x + 3y = 1$
   $y = x + 2$
8. $4x + 2y = -4$
   $y = x + 1$
9. $x = y + 5$
   $3x + 2y = 25$
10. $x = 5 - 2y$
    $3x + 2y = 19$
11. $5x + 2y = 10$
    $3x - 4y = 6$
12. $4x - 5y = 3$
    $2x + 3y = 7$
13. $x - 2y = 4$
    $2x + y = 2$
14. $5x + 2y = 1$
    $3x - y = 2$
15. $2x + 4y = 3$
    $2x - 8y = -3$
16. $4x - 9y = -1$
    $2x + 3y = 2$
17. $2x + y = 0$
    $y = 6$
18. $x + 3y = 0$
    $x = 3$
19. $x = \frac{1}{2}$
    $4x - y = 10$
20. $y = \frac{1}{3}$
    $x - 6y = 9$
21. $11x - y = 1$
    $y = 4x$

22. $13x + y = 5$
      $y = 7x$

23. $x - 8y = 0$
      $x - y = 0$

24. $x + 6y = 0$
      $x - y = 0$

Clear each equation of fractions by multiplying both sides by the lcd, and then solve the system using the *substitution method.*

25. $\dfrac{a}{3} + b = \dfrac{2}{3}$

$\dfrac{a}{3} - \dfrac{3b}{4} = -\dfrac{1}{2}$

26. $\dfrac{a}{6} - b = -\dfrac{3}{2}$

$\dfrac{a}{2} + \dfrac{b}{4} = 2$

27. $\dfrac{m+4}{6} - \dfrac{n-1}{4} = -\dfrac{1}{3}$

$\dfrac{2m-3}{5} + n = \dfrac{3}{5}$

28. $\dfrac{m-2}{4} - \dfrac{n+3}{2} = \dfrac{1}{4}$

$m + \dfrac{n-4}{7} = -\dfrac{5}{7}$

29. The sum of two numbers $p$ and $q$ is 112. When $p$ is subtracted from $q$, the difference is 34. Find $p$ and $q$.
30. The sum of two numbers $p$ and $q$ is 131. When $p$ is subtracted from $q$, the difference is 37. Find $p$ and $q$.

## Calculator Problems

Solve each system using the *substitution method.*

31. $10.95x + 8.50y = 7761.30$
      $x + y = 739$

32. $141x - 47y = 126.9$
      $-104x + 34y = -96$

## Challenge Problems

Solve each system using the *substitution method.*

33. $\dfrac{2x}{5} - \dfrac{y}{2} = \dfrac{4}{5}$

$x = 2 + \dfrac{5y}{4}$

34. $\dfrac{r}{2} = \dfrac{2s}{3} - 1$

$\dfrac{r+1}{2} - \dfrac{2s}{3} = 1$

35. $c - d = 5$

$\dfrac{2}{c+d} = \dfrac{5}{c-d}$

36. $x = 3$
      $x + y = 7$
      $z + y = 5$

## 9.3 ADDITION METHOD

Recall that the *addition axiom for equality* states:

$$\text{If } a = b, \text{ then } a + c = b + c.$$

In other words, the *same* quantity when added to equals produces equals. This axiom can be *extended* to state:

---
$$\text{If } a = b \text{ and } c = d, \text{ then } a + c = b + d.$$
---

In other words, *equal* quantities when added to equals produce equals. Using this property, we can add the corresponding sides of two given equations in two variables to produce *one* equation in *one* variable. This method for solving a system of equations is called the **addition method**.

**EXAMPLE 1**   Solve the system below using the addition method.

$$x + y = 6$$
$$x - y = 4$$

Adding the corresponding sides of the two equations, we see that the variable $y$ drops out.

$$x + y = 6$$
$$\underline{x - y = 4}$$
$$2x + 0 = 10.$$

Solving this last equation, we have

$$2x = 10$$
$$x = 5.$$

Finally, we substitute 5 for $x$ in *either* of the original equations and solve for $y$. For example, using the *first* equation we have

$$5 + y = 6$$
$$y = 1.$$

We note that using the *second* equation gives the same value for $y$. That is,

$$5 - y = 4$$
$$-y = -1$$
$$y = 1.$$

Therefore the solution is $(5, 1)$.   □

**EXAMPLE 2**   Solve the system below using the addition method.

$$2x + 3y = 2$$
$$4x + 9y = 9$$

In this case, adding the two equations will not eliminate *either* of the variables. Therefore, we begin by multiplying both sides of the first equation by $-2$. This will cause the coefficients of $x$ in the two equations to be *equal in absolute value but opposite in sign*. The system then becomes

$$-4x - 6y = -4$$
$$+4x + 9y = 9.$$

If the equations are now added, the variable $x$ will drop out, and we get

$$3y = 5.$$

Solving this equation gives

$$y = \frac{5}{3}.$$

Substituting $y = \frac{5}{3}$ back in the first equation, we have

$$2x + 3\left(\frac{5}{3}\right) = 2$$
$$2x + 5 = 2$$
$$2x = -3$$
$$x = -\frac{3}{2}.$$

Therefore the solution is $\left(-\frac{3}{2}, \frac{5}{3}\right)$. □

**EXAMPLE 3**   Solve the system below using the addition method.

$$4x + 5y = 3$$
$$3x - 2y = 8$$

In this case, *both* equations must be multiplied by a suitable number in order to force either the variable $x$ *or* the variable $y$ to drop out. We decide to multiply the first equation by 2 and the second by 5, thereby eliminating the variable $y$ when the equations are added. The resulting system is then

$$8x + 10y = 6$$
$$15x - 10y = 40.$$

Adding, we have

$$23x = 46$$
$$x = 2.$$

Substituting $x = 2$ in the first equation, we have

$$4 \cdot 2 + 5y = 3$$
$$8 + 5y = 3$$
$$5y = -5$$
$$y = -1.$$

Therefore the solution is $(2, -1)$. □

Notice that we could have eliminated the variable $x$ in Example 3 by multiplying the first equation by $-3$ and the second equation by 4, and then adding. There are generally a variety of ways in which the variable of our choice may be eliminated.

In all of the examples thus far, the terms involving like variables have been lined up on the left-hand side of the equation, and the constants have been lined up on the right-hand side. When a system of equations is so arranged, it is said to be in **standard form**.

---

**System in Standard Form**

$$2x + 3y = 2$$
$$4x + 9y = 9$$

**System not in Standard Form**

$$2x = 2 - 3y$$
$$4x + 9y - 9 = 0$$

---

*When solving a system using the addition method, it is generally convenient to write the system in standard form before proceeding with the solution.*

**EXAMPLE 4**   Solve the system below using the addition method.

$$3x = 2y$$
$$7x = 3y + 5$$

$3x = 2y$
$7x = 3y + 5$

Writing the system in standard form, we have

$7 = 5 + 2 = ?$
$7 - 2 = 5$

$$3x - 2y = 0$$
$$7x - 3y = 5.$$

In order to eliminate the variable $y$, we multiply the first equation by $-3$ and the second equation by 2.

$$-9x + 6y = 0$$
$$14x - 6y = 10.$$

Adding the two equations yields

$$5x = 10$$
$$x = 2.$$

Substituting $x = 2$ in the first equation, we have

$$3 \cdot 2 = 2y$$
$$6 = 2y$$
$$3 = y.$$

Therefore the solution is (2, 3). □

## Problem Set 9.3

Solve each system using the *addition method*.

1. $x + y = 4$
   $x - y = 2$

2. $x + y = 5$
   $x - y = 3$

3. $x - y = 1$
   $x + y = 5$

4. $x - y = 4$
   $x + y = 10$

5. $2x + y = 7$
   $2x - y = 13$

6. $3x + y = 11$
   $3x - y = 19$

7. $a + b = 4$
   $-a + b = 8$

8. $a + b = 3$
   $-a + b = 7$

9. $3x - 2y = 11$
   $3x + 2y = 19$

10. $10x + 7y = -13$
    $-2x - 7y = -3$

11. $-3x + 5y = 16$
    $3x + 5y = 14$

12. $-6x - 4y = -3$
    $6x + 9y = -17$

13. $2x - y = -7$
    $x + 3y = 0$

14. $2x - y = 0$
    $x + 2y = -5$

15. $4x - 9y = -1$
    $2x + 3y = 2$

16. $8x - 10y = 1$
    $2x + 2y = 1$

17. $2x + 3y = 1$
    $2x + 8y = 11$

18. $3x - 4y = 1$
    $3x - 6y = -1$

19. $7x + 8y = -31$
    $-4x + 8y = 35$

20. $9x + 7y = -35$
    $-4x + 7y = 30$

21. $5x - 2y = 10$
    $15x + 10y = 38$

22. $7x - 3y = 9$
    $21x + 11y = 37$

23. $3a + 4b = -12$
    $a + 2b = -4$

24. $5a + 6b = -10$
    $2a + 3b = -4$

25. $7x = 3y + 4$
    $5x + 2y = 7$

26. $2x = 3y + 5$
    $5x + 4y = 1$

27. $\dfrac{x}{2} + \dfrac{y}{3} = \dfrac{2}{3}$

    $\dfrac{x}{3} + \dfrac{y}{5} = \dfrac{1}{3}$

28. $\dfrac{x}{2} + \dfrac{y}{5} = -\dfrac{1}{2}$

    $\dfrac{x}{3} + \dfrac{y}{4} = \dfrac{1}{4}$

29. $3x + 2y = 11$
    $5x + 7y + 11 = 0$

30. $3x + 4y = 10$
    $4x + 5y - 14 = 0$

31. $\dfrac{y}{2} - x = \dfrac{1}{2}$

    $\dfrac{y}{7} = -\dfrac{x}{7} + \dfrac{1}{7}$

32. $\dfrac{y}{8} + \dfrac{x}{8} = \dfrac{1}{8}$

    $\dfrac{y}{3} = x + \dfrac{1}{3}$

33. $0.2s + 0.3t = -1.2$
    $0.5s - 0.7t = -3$

34. $0.2s + 0.9t = 1.6$
    $0.5s - 0.6t = 4$

35. $\dfrac{m + 2}{2} - \dfrac{n - 1}{3} = \dfrac{11}{6}$

    $\dfrac{m}{4} + \dfrac{n}{4} = \dfrac{13}{2}$

36. $\dfrac{m + 3}{4} - \dfrac{3n - 4}{6} = \dfrac{43}{6}$

    $\dfrac{m}{2} + \dfrac{n}{3} = -\dfrac{1}{2}$

37. The sum of two numbers $x$ and $y$ is 42. The number $y$ is 3 more than one-half $x$. Find $x$ and $y$.

38. The sum of two numbers $x$ and $y$ is 41. The number $y$ is 5 more than one-half $x$. Find $x$ and $y$.

## Calculator Problems

Solve each system using the *addition method*. Give the value of each variable to the nearest hundredth.

39. $6.4x + 3.7y = 1.75$
    $4.1x - 3.4y = -0.61$

40. $401p + 607q = 233$
    $757p - 311q = 1381$

## Challenge Problems

Solve each system using the *addition method*.

41. $1.8x + 1.2y = 1$
    $\dfrac{x}{2} = -\dfrac{y}{3}$

42. $\dfrac{3y}{4} - \dfrac{4x - 1}{3} = 1$
    $y = \dfrac{16x + 8}{9}$

43. $\dfrac{1}{x} + \dfrac{1}{y} = 2$
    $\dfrac{2}{x} - \dfrac{1}{y} = 2$

44. Solve for the variables $x$ and $y$ in terms of the constants $a$ and $b$.
    $x + 2y = a$
    $x - \ y = b$

## 9.4    APPLIED PROBLEMS

Many practical problems are easier to translate into mathematical equations if *two* variables are used instead of just one. However, if two variables are related by a *single* linear equation, there are infinitely many ordered pairs that are solutions to that equation. Therefore, another *different* linear equation relating the same two variables must be written using the information given in the problem. The two equations together then form a *system* of equations. This system is then solved to produce a single ordered-pair solution to the original problem.

**EXAMPLE 1**   Two consecutive even integers have a sum of 74. Find the integers.

Let $x$ = the smaller even integer
and $y$ = the larger even integer.

Then we can write the system

$y = x + 2 \leftarrow$ (since $x$ and $y$ are consecutive *even* integers)

$x + y = 74.$

Solving this system using the substitution method, we have

$x + (x + 2) = 74$

$2x + 2 = 74$

$2x = 72$

$x = 36.$

Hence
$$y = 36 + 2$$
$$y = 38.$$

Therefore, the integers are 36 and 38.

CHECK:    36 and 38 are consecutive even integers and their sum is 74. □

**EXAMPLE 2**    Chris saves nickels and dimes in a piggy bank. Before leaving for school one day, he asked his mother to shake out all of the coins and count the amount of money he had. When he returned, his mother told him that the bank contained 60 coins worth $4.85. When Chris asked how many of each kind there were, his mother said she did not keep track, but she was sure Chris could figure it out without removing all of the coins again. How many of each kind of coin were in the bank?

Let $n$ = the number of nickels

and $d$ = the number of dimes.

Then $5n$ = the *value* of the nickels in cents

and $10d$ = the *value* of the dimes in cents.

Therefore, we can write the system
$$n + d = 60$$
$$5n + 10d = 485.$$

To solve by addition, we multiply the first equation by $-5$. The system then becomes
$$-5n - 5d = -300$$
$$5n + 10d = 485.$$

Adding the two equations, we have
$$5d = 185$$
$$d = 37.$$

Hence
$$n + 37 = 60$$
$$n = 23.$$

Therefore, the bank contained 23 nickels and 37 dimes.

CHECK:    23 nickels + 37 dimes = 60 coins in all. Also, 23 nickels are worth $23 \cdot 5¢$ = 115 cents and 37 dimes are worth $37 \cdot 10¢$ = 370 cents, making a total amount of 115¢ + 370¢ = 485 cents. □

**EXAMPLE 3**    A pharmacist needs 100 gallons of 50% alcohol solution. She has on hand 20% alcohol solution and 70% alcohol solution. How many gallons of each should she use to make the 100 gallons of 50% alcohol solution?

Let $x$ = the number of gallons of 20% solution needed

and $y$ = the number of gallons of 70% solution needed.

Since a total of 100 gallons of final solution is needed, we can write

$$x + y = 100.$$

Also, since no alcohol is lost during the mixing process, we must have

$$\begin{matrix} \text{no. of} & & \text{no. of} & & \text{no. of} \\ \text{gal of alcohol} & + & \text{gal of alcohol} & = & \text{gal of alcohol} \\ \text{in 20\% solution} & & \text{in 70\% solution} & & \text{in 50\% solution.} \end{matrix}$$

In other words,

$$(20\% \text{ of } x) + (70\% \text{ of } y) = 50\% \text{ of } 100$$
$$.20x + .70y = (.50)(100)$$
$$.2x + .7y = 50.$$

Multiplying both sides by 10 to remove the decimal, we have

$$2x + 7y = 500.$$

Combining this equation with the first equation produces the system

$$x + y = 100$$
$$2x + 7y = 500.$$

To solve by the addition method, we multiply the first equation by $-2$.

$$-2x - 2y = -200$$
$$2x + 7y = 500.$$

Adding gives

$$5y = 300$$
$$y = 60.$$

Hence

$$x + 60 = 100$$
$$x = 40.$$

Therefore, 40 gallons of 20% solution and 60 gallons of 70% solution are needed to make 100 gallons of 50% solution.

CHECK:  40 gal + 60 gal = 100 gal. Also, 20% of 40 gal = 8 gal, and 70% of 60 gal = 42 gal. The total is 8 gal + 42 gal = 50 gal, which is the number of gallons of alcohol in 100 gallons of 50% solution. □

**EXAMPLE 4**  An enemy missile is sighted by radar to be 5500 miles from a friendly missile base and approaching the base at 7000 mph. Immediately, an anti-missile missile whose speed is 8400 mph is launched from the base. How far does each missile travel before they meet?

Let $f$ = the distance traveled by the friendly missile and $e$ = the distance traveled by the enemy missile.

Then one of the equations is

$$f + e = 5500.$$

Also, since the time each missile travels after the radar sighting is the same, and since $t = d/r$, we can write

$$\frac{\text{Distance of friendly missile}}{\text{Rate of friendly missile}} = \frac{\text{distance of enemy missile}}{\text{rate of enemy missile}}$$

$$\frac{f}{8400} = \frac{e}{7000}.$$

Solving this last equation for $f$, we have

$$7000f = 8400e$$
$$f = 1.2e.$$

Substituting $f = 1.2e$ into the first equation gives

$$1.2e + e = 5500$$
$$2.2e = 5500$$
$$e = 2500.$$

Hence

$$f = 1.2(2500) = 3000.$$

Therefore, the enemy missile travels 2500 miles and the friendly missile travels 3000 miles.

CHECK:  2500 mi + 3000 mi = 5500 mi. Also, the friendly missile travels for $\dfrac{3000 \text{ mi}}{8400 \text{ mi/hr}} = \dfrac{5}{14}$ hr, and the enemy missile travels for $\dfrac{2500 \text{ mi}}{7000 \text{ mi/hr}} = \dfrac{5}{14}$ hr. □

## Problem Set 9.4

1. The sum of two numbers is 63 and their difference is 19. Find the numbers.
2. The sum of two numbers is 87 and their difference is 39. Find the numbers.
3. Two consecutive even integers have a sum of 54. Find the integers.
4. Two consecutive even integers have a sum of 166. Find the integers.
5. Two consecutive odd integers have a sum of 148. Find the integers.
6. Two consecutive odd integers have a sum of 64. Find the integers.
7. The difference of two natural numbers is 44. One number is 10 less than one-third of the other number. Find the numbers.
8. The difference of two natural numbers is 38. One number is 10 less than one-third of the other number. Find the numbers.
9. Each ounce of food A contains 3 grams of protein and 5 grams of fat, while each ounce of food B contains 7 grams of protein and 1 gram of fat. How many ounces of each food should be used to prepare a lunch containing 36 grams of protein and 28 grams of fat?
10. Each ounce of food A contains 2 grams of protein and 3 grams of fat, while each ounce of food B contains 4 grams of protein and 1 gram of fat. How many ounces of each food should be used to prepare a dinner containing 28 grams of protein and 27 grams of fat?
11. A house and lot together sold for $35,000. If the house was valued at $19,000 more than the lot, what was the value of the house?
12. A boat and its trailer sold for $18,000. If the boat was valued at $14,500 more than the trailer, what was the value of the boat?
13. A company wanted to grant a bonus of $4000 to two employees, with the senior of the two receiving $1300 more than the junior. How much should each employee receive?
14. An athletic committee is to be formed consisting of 33 students with the stipulation that there be 9 more boys than girls on the committee. How many of each should be appointed to the committee?

15. A 24-ft board is cut into two parts so that one part is 6 ft longer than the other. Find the length of each part.
16. A 42-ft piece of metal pipe is cut into two parts so that one part is 8 ft longer than the other. Find the length of each part.
17. A collection of 28 nickels and dimes is worth $1.95. How many of each kind of coin are in the collection?
18. A collection of 24 nickels and dimes is worth $1.75. How many of each kind of coin are in the collection?
19. In a collection of dimes and quarters there are 21 more dimes than quarters. If the total value of the collection is $4.90, how many of each kind of coin are there?
20. In a collection of dimes and quarters there are 19 more dimes than quarters. If the total value of the collection is $4.35, how many of each kind of coin are there?
21. A grocer wishes to mix nuts worth $.85 a pound with nuts worth $1.35 a pound to produce 20 pounds of nuts worth $1.00 a pound. How many pounds of each type should she use?
22. A grocer wishes to mix nuts worth $.75 a pound with nuts worth $1.15 a pound to produce 40 pounds of nuts worth $1.00 a pound. How many pounds of each type should he use?
23. One solution contains 20% alcohol and a second solution contains 60% alcohol. How many gallons of each solution are needed to make 100 gallons of 50% alcohol solution?
24. A pharmacist needs 100 gallons of 50% alcohol solution. He has on hand 30% alcohol solution and 80% alcohol solution. How many gallons of each solution should he use to make 100 gallons of 50% alcohol solution?
25. On an investment of $25,000, part yields 5% interest and part yields 7% interest. How much is invested at each rate if the total yearly interest is $1390?
26. A total of $100,000 is to be invested, part at a low-risk 7% interest rate and part at a higher-risk 12% interest rate. How much should be invested at each rate so that the total yearly income on both investments is $10,000?
27. Two runners, Alberto and Rosie, who live 7 miles apart, leave their respective homes simultaneously and run toward each other. If Alberto runs at a speed of 9 mph and Rosie at a speed of 12 mph, how far does each run before they meet?
28. Two cars start 330 miles apart and travel toward each other, one at 50 mph and the other at 60 mph. How far does each travel before they meet?

29. Two cars start 198 miles apart and travel toward each other, one car traveling 15 mph faster than the other. If they meet in 2 hr, find the speed of each car.
30. Two ships start 147 miles apart and travel toward each other, one ship traveling 5 mph faster than the other. If they meet in 3 hr, find the speed of each ship.

## Calculator Problems

31. Each ounce of food A contains 2.9 grams of protein and 4.3 grams of fat, while each ounce of food B contains 3.5 grams of protein and 3.2 grams of fat. Approximately how many ounces of each food should be used to prepare a dinner containing 41 grams of protein and 52 grams of fat?
32. An investor purchased 725 ounces of silver and gold for $73,078.80. If the silver sold for $10.35 per ounce and the gold for $489 per ounce, how many ounces of each did the investor buy?

## Challenge Problems

33. The sum of the digits of a two-digit number is 11. If the digits are reversed, this new number is 45 less than the original number. Find the original number. (*Hint:* If the original number has a tens digit of $t$ and a units digit of $u$, then it can be written as $10t + u$.)
34. If the area of the triangle is 104 and the area of the rectangle is 247, find $x$ and $y$.

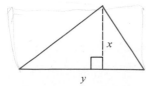 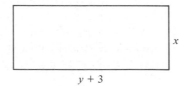

# 9.5 SYSTEMS OF LINEAR INEQUALITIES (OPTIONAL)

It was noted earlier in this chapter that the graphical method is the *least* efficient method for solving a system of linear *equations*. The graphical method is, however, the *best* method for displaying the solution to a system of linear *inequalities* in two variables. This is because the solution to each inequality is a half-plane, and therefore the solution to a system of *two* inequalities is the *intersection* of two half-planes. Generally, the best method for describing this type of region is by graphing it.

To graph a system of two linear inequalities, we use the methods of Section 8.4 to graph each inequality in turn on the same coordinate axes. The solution to the system then is that region which is in common to the two regions just graphed.

**EXAMPLE 1**   Graph the system of inequalities below.

$$x > 2$$
$$y < 3$$

Each inequality is graphed in turn on the same coordinate axes.

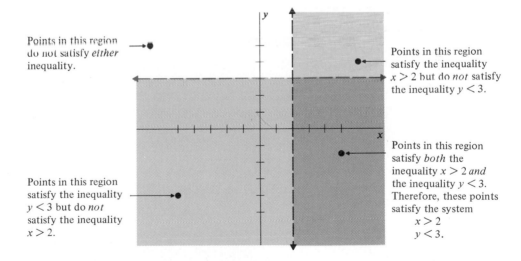

Points in this region do not satisfy *either* inequality.

Points in this region satisfy the inequality $x > 2$ but do *not* satisfy the inequality $y < 3$.

Points in this region satisfy the inequality $y < 3$ but do *not* satisfy the inequality $x > 2$.

Points in this region satisfy *both* the inequality $x > 2$ *and* the inequality $y < 3$. Therefore, these points satisfy the system
$$x > 2$$
$$y < 3.$$

The solution appears in the graph as the doubly-shaded region. The boundary lines are broken to indicate that they are not part of the solution.  □

**EXAMPLE 2**  Graph the system of inequalities below.

$$x + y > 2$$
$$y \leqslant x + 2$$

First, the inequality $x + y > 2$ is graphed.

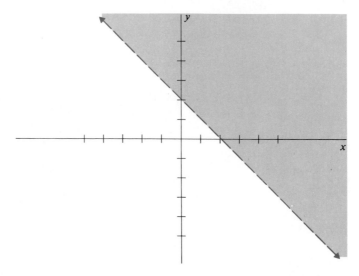

Then the inequality $y \leqslant x + 2$ is graphed on the same coordinate axes.

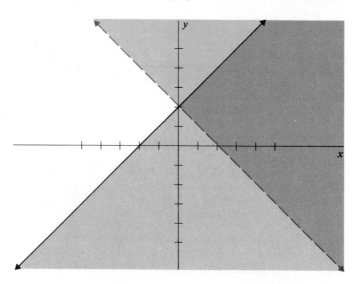

The graph of the system is then the doubly-shaded region that lies *above* the line $x + y = 2$ and *below or on* the line $y = x + 2$. □

A system may contain any number of inequalities. The next example illustrates the graphical method of solving a system of *three* linear inequalities.

**EXAMPLE 3**   Graph the system of inequalities below.

$$x + y \leqslant 4$$
$$x \geqslant 0$$
$$y \geqslant 0$$

First, the inequality $x + y \leqslant 4$ is graphed.

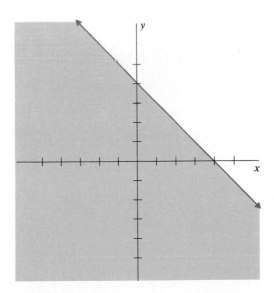

Next, the inequality $x \geqslant 0$ is graphed on the same coordinate axes.

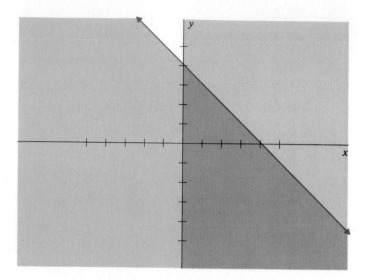

Finally, the inequality $y \geq 0$ is graphed on the same coordinate axes as the other two inequalities.

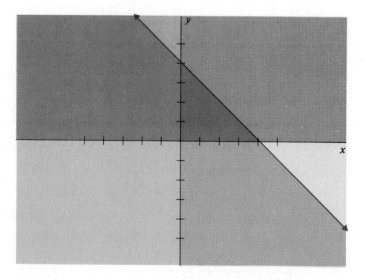

The intersection of these three regions is the triply-shaded triangular region shown above. This region is therefore the graph of the system.

□

Often, in order to make the graph easier to read, another graph is drawn indicating the solution region only. For the example above, such a graph would appear as below.

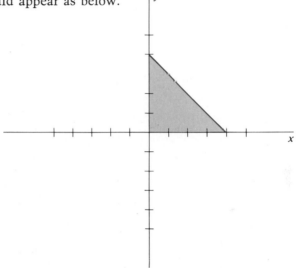

## Problem Set 9.5

Graph each system of inequalities.

1. $x < 2$
   $y > 1$

2. $x > 3$
   $y < -1$

3. $x \geq -4$
   $y \leq -3$

4. $x \leq -2$
   $y \geq 5$

5. $x + y \leq 5$
   $x \leq 3$

6. $x + y \leq 4$
   $x \leq 2$

7. $x - y > 5$
   $y > -5$

8. $x - y > 3$
   $y > -3$

9. $x + y \geq 2$
   $x - y \geq 3$

10. $x + y \leq 6$
    $x - y \leq 1$

11. $x + y \geq 1$
    $y \leq x + 1$

12. $x + y \leq 3$
    $y \leq x + 3$

13. $3x + y \geq 6$
    $x - 2y > 2$

14. $2x + y \leq 6$
    $3x - y < -3$

15. $x + y < 4$
    $2x - y \geq -4$

16. $x - y > 5$
    $2x + y \leq 4$

17. $x + 2y < 8$
    $x - y > -1$

18. $x - 2y > 8$
    $2x + y > 4$

19. $5x + y \leq 10$
    $y \geq x$

20. $3x + y \leq 9$
    $y \geq x$

21. $y \leq \frac{1}{2}x$
    $y \geq -\frac{1}{2}x$

22. $y \leq \frac{1}{3}x$
    $y \geq -\frac{1}{3}x$

23. $x + y \leq 6$
    $x \geq 0$
    $y \geq 0$

24. $x + y \leq 5$
    $x \geq 0$
    $y \geq 0$

25. $y - x \geqslant 1$
$x \geqslant 2$
$y \leqslant 5$

26. $y - x \geqslant 2$
$x \geqslant 1$
$y \leqslant 5$

27. $4x + 3y \leqslant 48$
$y - 4x \leqslant 0$
$y > 1$

28. $4x + 3y \leqslant 48$
$y - 4x \leqslant 0$
$y > 2$

29. $\dfrac{x}{4} + \dfrac{y}{4} \leqslant 0.625$
$y \geqslant -x$

30. $\dfrac{x}{2} - \dfrac{y}{2} \geqslant -2.25$
$y \geqslant x$

31. $y \leqslant x$
$x - y \leqslant -1$

32. $y \leqslant -x$
$x + y \geqslant 1$

Write a system of inequalities to describe each graph below.

33.

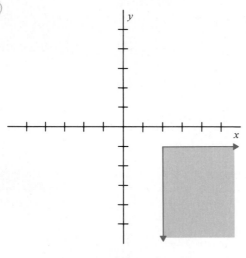

34.

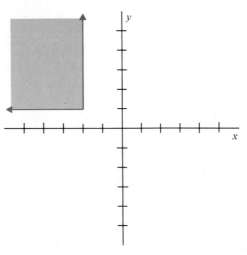

35.

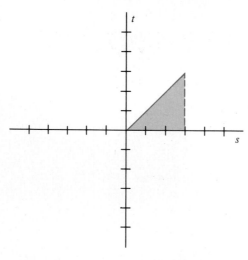

36.

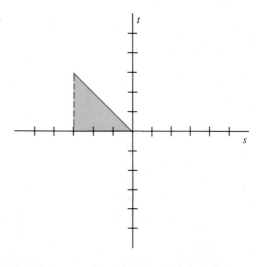

An area of mathematics that is receiving a great deal of attention lately is *linear programming*. Each system below might be part of a linear programming problem. Graph each system.

37.  $x + y \leq 8$

    $x + 3y \leq 12$

      $x \geq 3$

      $y \geq 1$

38.  $x + y \leq 10$

      $x \geq 0$

    $0 \leq y \leq 6$

39. A theater owner wants to be able to admit a family of three (one child and two adults) for less than 8 dollars. Also, he wants the price of a child to be less than $\frac{2}{3}$ the price of an adult. If $x$ is the price of a child's ticket and $y$ is the price of an adult's ticket, write a system of inequalities that describes these conditions. Then graph the system to illustrate the price choices the owner has.

40. A shoe-store owner wants to order shoes to be kept in her storeroom. The storeroom will hold at most 300 pairs of shoes and she wants to order at least twice as many women's shoes as men's shoes. If $x$ is the number of pairs of women's shoes and $y$ is the number of pairs of men's shoes she can order, write a system of inequalities that describes these conditions. Then graph the system to illustrate the possible orders the owner can make.

## Calculator Problems

41. Determine if the ordered pair $(-0.069, 0.213)$ is a solution to the system

    $8873x + 2971y < 22$

    $1.59x - 1.79y > -0.50.$

42. Graph the system

    $2417x + 1229y \leq 10{,}802$

    $x \geq \dfrac{\sqrt{1823}}{19.3}$

## Challenge Problems

Graph each system of inequalities.

43. $y < x + 2$
    $y > x - 2$
    $xy \leq 0$

44. $|x| \leq 2$
    $|y| \leq 1$

45. $y \geq x$
    $3y \leq 2x + 3$
    $y + x > 0$

46. $x + y \geq 2$
    $3x \geq y$
    $y + 2x \leq 0$

## Chapter Review

True or false.

1. A system of two linear equations in two variables has either one solution, no solution, or infinitely many solutions.
2. A disadvantage of the graphical method for solving a system of equations is that it may yield only an approximate solution.
3. If the ordered pair $(a, b)$ is a solution to a system of two linear equations, then $(a, b)$ will satisfy one equation or the other but not both.
4. The graph of a system of two linear inequalities in two variables consists of a region that is in common to two half-planes.
5. An independent system has infinitely many solutions.
6. A dependent system has no solutions.
7. An inconsistent system has one solution.
8. The system below is in standard form.

    $5x - 2y = 7$
    $3x + 6y = 4$

Each graph below illustrates a system of two linear equations in two variables. Identify each system as independent, inconsistent, or dependent.

9.

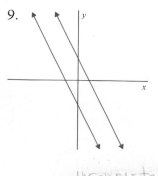

inconsistent

10.

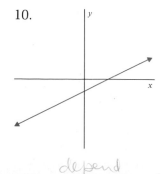

depend

11.

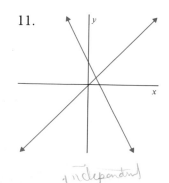

independent

Solve each system using the graphical method and check your solution.

12. $y = x - 3$
    $y = -x - 3$

13. $x + y = 6$
    $y = 2x$

Solve each system using the substitution method.

14. $x + 3y = 13$
    $2x + y = 1$

15. $7x - 4y = -11$
    $x + 2y = 10$

Solve each system using the addition method.

16. $2x - 3y = 5$
    $7x + 5y = 2$

17. $2x + y - 5 = 0$
    $4x + 2y - 11 = 0$

Solve each system. Choose the method that seems easiest to you.

18. $\dfrac{c}{5} + d = -\dfrac{1}{5}$
    $-\dfrac{c}{6} - \dfrac{d}{4} = \dfrac{5}{2}$

19. $\dfrac{m - 1}{6} + \dfrac{n + 1}{12} = \dfrac{11}{8}$
    $\dfrac{m}{4} - \dfrac{2n - 1}{2} = 7$

20. $4.5p - 2.8q = 8.5$
    $p = 0.6q$

Graph each system of inequalities.

21. $x \geq -1$
    $y \leq 1$

22. $\dfrac{x}{4} + \dfrac{y}{2} \geq 1$
    $3x - 5y > 15$

23. $x + y < 2$
    $-x + y < 2$

24. $x + y \geq 0$
    $y \leq -x + 4$

25. Given the supply and demand equations below, determine the equilibrium point.

$x = \dfrac{1}{4}p$   (supply)

$x = 18 - 2p$   (demand)

26. Two consecutive odd integers have a sum of 76. Find the integers.

27. The sum of two numbers is 134. One number is 6 more than one-third of the other number. Find the numbers.

28. One solution contains 25% alcohol and a second solution contains 75% alcohol. How many gallons of each are needed to make 50 gallons of 35% alcohol solution?

29. Each ounce of food A contains 2 g of protein and 4 g of fat, while each ounce of food B contains 5 g of protein and no fat. How many ounces of each food should a nutritionist use to prepare a dinner containing 30 g of protein and 20 g of fat?

30. Suppose that in Problem 29 the nutritionist must prepare the dinner so that it contains no *more* than 30 g of protein and no *more* than 20 g of fat. If $x$ denotes the number of ounces of food A and $y$ the number of ounces of food B in the dinner, write a system of inequalities that describes all of the possible food choices that the nutritionist can make. Then graph this system.

31. Two trains on parallel tracks start 400 mi apart and travel toward each other, one train traveling 20 mph faster than the other. If the trains meet in 4 hr, find the speed of each.

32. Write a system of inequalities that describes the shaded region in the graph below.

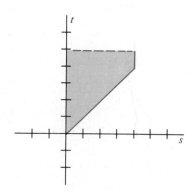

# Chapter
# Chapter
# Chapter
# Chapter Ten
# Ten
# Ten
# Ten

## ROOTS AND RADICALS

## 10.1    ROOTS

In this chapter we shall extend the notion of a *square* root of a number to an *n*th root of a number. We shall then look at methods of simplifying such expressions and performing operations on them.

If $b^2 = a$, the number $b$ is called a **square root** of the number $a$. Thus 5 is a square root of 25, since $5^2 = 25$. *Also,* $-5$ is a square root of 25 since $(-5)^2 = 25$. While each *positive* number has *two* square roots, the number 0 has just *one* square root, namely 0 itself. *Negative* numbers have *no real* number square roots. For example, if you were to try to find a real square root of the number $-4$, you would have to find a real number $b$ such that $b^2 = -4$. But this is not possible since $b^2$ cannot be a negative number! Note that $(+2)^2 = +4$, *and* $(-2)^2 = +4$. A square root of a negative number is called an *imaginary number.* We shall leave the topic of imaginary numbers to a more advanced course.

If $b^3 = a$, the number $b$ is called a **cube root** of the number $a$. Unlike square roots, each positive number has only *one* real number cube root. The number 2 is a cube root of 8 since $2^3 = 8$. The number $-2$ is *not* a cube root of 8 since $(-2)^3 \neq 8$. Also, unlike square roots, it is possible to find cube roots of *negative* numbers. For example, $-4$ is a cube root of $-64$ since $(-4)^3 = -64$.

The number $b$ is called a **fourth root** of the number $a$ if $b^4 = a$. For example, both of the numbers 3 and $-3$ are fourth roots of 81 since $3^4 = 81$ and $(-3)^4 = 81$.

We are now ready to define an **nth root** of a number.

---

**Definition**    Let $n$ be a natural number greater than 1. The number $b$ is called an **nth root** of the number $a$ if $b^n = a$.

---

In Chapter 1, the symbol $\sqrt{\phantom{x}}$ was used to denote the *nonnegative* square root of a number. Therefore, while 25 has the *two* square roots 5 and $-5$, the symbol $\sqrt{25}$ denotes only the nonnegative square root 5. This is sometimes called the **principal square root** of 25. To indicate the *negative* square root $-5$, we would write $-\sqrt{25}$. To indicate *both* roots, we write $\pm\sqrt{25}$.

To denote the **principal nth root** of the number $a$, we write $\sqrt[n]{a}$. As before, the symbol $\sqrt{\phantom{x}}$ is called a **radical sign** and $a$ is called the

**radicand.** The number $n$ is called the **index.** The index 2 is usually omitted, and we simply write $\sqrt{a}$ for the principal *square* root of $a$. The features of the principal $n$th root are summarized below:

---

**Principal $n$th Root**

*Case I:* The index $n$ is *even.*

a) If $a > 0$, then $\sqrt[n]{a}$ is positive. For example, $\sqrt[4]{16} = 2$.
b) If $a < 0$, then $\sqrt[n]{a}$ is not a real number. For example, $\sqrt[4]{-16}$ is not a real number.

*Case II:* The index $n$ is *odd.*

a) If $a > 0$, then $\sqrt[n]{a}$ is positive. For example, $\sqrt[3]{27} = 3$.
b) If $a < 0$, then $\sqrt[n]{a}$ is negative. For example, $\sqrt[3]{-27} = -3$.
Finally, if $a = 0$, then $\sqrt[n]{a} = \sqrt[n]{0} = 0$ whether $n$ is even *or* odd.

---

**EXAMPLE 1**   The square roots of 225 are $+15$ and $-15$, *but* $\sqrt{225} = +15$. $\sqcap$

**EXAMPLE 2**   Find $\sqrt{10{,}000}$.
$$\sqrt{10{,}000} = 100. \ \square$$

**EXAMPLE 3**   Find $-\sqrt{10{,}000}$.
$$-\sqrt{10{,}000} = -100. \ \square$$

*$\sqrt{10{,}000}$ not possible*

**EXAMPLE 4**   Find $\sqrt[3]{216}$.
$$\sqrt[3]{216} = 6, \text{ since } 6^3 = 216. \ \square$$

*$\sqrt[3]{-216} = -6$*

**EXAMPLE 5**   Find $-\sqrt[3]{216}$.

*ok if odd*

$$-\sqrt[3]{216} = -6. \ \square$$

*$-\sqrt[3]{-216} = 6$*

**EXAMPLE 6**   Find $\sqrt[5]{-32}$.
$$\sqrt[5]{-32} = -2, \text{ since } (-2)^5 = -32. \ \square$$

**EXAMPLE 7**   Find $\sqrt[4]{16/81}$.

$$\sqrt[4]{\frac{16}{81}} = \frac{2}{3}, \text{ since } \left(\frac{2}{3}\right)^4 = \frac{16}{81}. \quad \square$$

**EXAMPLE 8**   Find $\sqrt{4^2}$, $\sqrt{(-4)^2}$, $\pm\sqrt{29^2}$, and $\sqrt[3]{17^3}$.

$$\sqrt{4^2} = 4,$$
$$\sqrt{(-4)^2} = \sqrt{4^2} = 4,$$
$$\pm\sqrt{29^2} = \pm 29,$$
$$\sqrt[3]{17^3} = 17. \quad \square$$

$\sqrt{(\pm 29)^2} = 29$

Often, we cannot express a root as an integer or as a ratio of integers as we were able to do in the examples above. For example, $\sqrt{2}$, $\sqrt[3]{9}$, $\sqrt[4]{20}$, and $\sqrt[5]{\frac{8}{11}}$ cannot be expressed as integers or as ratios of integers. These roots are examples of *irrational* numbers.

A certain amount of care must be exercised when finding *even* roots of expressions that contain *variables*. This is due to the fact that we often don't know whether these variables represent *positive* numbers or *negative* numbers. For example,

$$\text{if } a = 3, \text{ then } \sqrt{a^2} = \sqrt{3^2} = \sqrt{9} = 3 = a.$$

However,

$$\text{if } a = -3, \text{ then } \sqrt{a^2} = \sqrt{(-3)^2} = \sqrt{9} = 3 = -a!$$

Generalizing on the discussion above, we can write

$|a| = \begin{cases} a \text{ if } a \text{ is } \geq 0 \\ -a \text{ if } a \text{ is } < 0 \end{cases}$
$$\sqrt{a^2} = \begin{cases} a, & \text{if } a \geq 0 \\ -a, & \text{if } a < 0. \end{cases} \quad = \text{to absolute value}$$
*opposite of a*

In other words, $\sqrt{a^2} = |a|$!

The same type of situation actually occurs with any *even* principal root. That is,

$$\boxed{\sqrt[n]{a^n} = |a| \quad \text{if } n \text{ is even.}}$$

This problem does *not* occur when the index $n$ is *odd*.

To avoid having to use absolute value signs when finding even roots of variable expressions, *we shall assume throughout this chapter that all variables are positive unless stated otherwise.*

**EXAMPLE 9**  Find $\sqrt[3]{x^{15}}$.

$$\sqrt[3]{x^{15}} = x^5, \quad \text{since } (x^5)^3 = x^{15}. \quad \square$$

Note that the power of the answer to Example 9 could have been obtained by dividing the index 3 into the exponent 15.

**EXAMPLE 10**  Find $\sqrt{9x^2y^4}$.  *root of number then do x + y*

$$\sqrt{9x^2y^4} = 3xy^2, \quad \text{since } (3xy^2)^2 = 9x^2y^4. \quad \square$$

**EXAMPLE 11**  The radius $r$ of a circle of area $A$ is given by the formula $r = \sqrt{A/\pi}$. What should the radius of a circular air vent be if its area is required by a local building code to be $121\pi$ square centimeters?

Substituting $A = 121\pi$ in the formula above, we have

*D $\pi$ $\dfrac{A}{\pi}$ = $r^2$*

*$r = \sqrt{\dfrac{A}{\pi}}$*

$$r = \sqrt{\frac{121\pi}{\pi}} = \sqrt{121} = 11.$$

The radius of the vent should be 11 cm.  $\square$

## Problem Set 10.1

Find each root.

1. $\sqrt{36}$            2. $\sqrt{49}$            3. $-\sqrt{81}$            4. $-\sqrt{100}$

5. $\pm\sqrt{64}$        6. $\pm\sqrt{121}$        7. $\sqrt{1}$            8. $-\sqrt{1}$

9. $-\sqrt{144}$        10. $\sqrt{256}$        11. $\sqrt{\frac{4}{121}}$        12. $\sqrt{\frac{9}{64}}$

13. $\sqrt{\frac{9}{16}}$        14. $\sqrt{\frac{4}{25}}$        15. $\sqrt{.01}$        16. $\sqrt{.81}$

17. $\sqrt{.0036}$        18. $\sqrt{.0001}$        19. $\sqrt{1.69}$        20. $\sqrt{1.96}$

21. $\sqrt{-100}$        22. $\sqrt{-81}$        23. $\sqrt{5^2}$        24. $\sqrt{3^2}$

25. $\sqrt{7^2}$        26. $\sqrt{8^2}$        27. $\pm\sqrt[3]{125}$        28. $\pm\sqrt[3]{216}$

29. $\sqrt[3]{-8}$        30. $\sqrt[3]{-64}$        31. $-\sqrt[3]{-8}$        32. $-\sqrt[3]{-64}$

33. $\sqrt[4]{-81}$        34. $\sqrt[4]{-16}$        35. $\sqrt[4]{.0001}$        36. $\sqrt[4]{.0081}$

37. $\sqrt[5]{-1024}$        38. $\sqrt[5]{-243}$        39. $\sqrt[7]{8^7}$        40. $\sqrt[7]{5^7}$

41. $\sqrt[10]{1024}$        42. $\sqrt[8]{6561}$        43. $\sqrt{(-5)^2}$        44. $\sqrt[4]{(-2)^4}$

45. $\sqrt{x^2}$            46. $-\sqrt{y^2}$            47. $-\sqrt[4]{x^4}$            48. $\sqrt[8]{y^8}$

49. $\sqrt{x^4}$

50. $\sqrt{y^8}$

51. $\sqrt{4x^6}$

52. $\sqrt{9y^4}$

53. $\sqrt{25x^2y^8}$

54. $\sqrt{16x^6y^2}$

55. $\sqrt[5]{s^{10}t^{10}}$

56. $\sqrt[6]{s^{12}t^{12}}$

57. $\sqrt[3]{27a^{12}b^3}$

58. $\sqrt[3]{8a^3b^{15}}$

59. $\sqrt{(x + y)^2}$

60. $\sqrt{(a + b)^4}$

61. $\sqrt{y^2 + 4y + 4}$

62. $\sqrt{x^2 + 2x + 1}$

Write each pair of radical expressions as integers and compare the results. What conclusion can you make?

63. $\sqrt{16} + \sqrt{9}$  and  $\sqrt{16 + 9}$

64. $\sqrt{64} + \sqrt{36}$  and  $\sqrt{64 + 36}$

65. $\sqrt{289} - \sqrt{225}$  and  $\sqrt{289 - 225}$

66. $\sqrt{625} - \sqrt{576}$  and  $\sqrt{625 - 576}$

67. Neglecting air resistance, the time $t$ in seconds that it takes an object to hit the ground if it is dropped from a height of $h$ feet is given by the formula $t = \sqrt{h}/4$. How long would it take a marble to hit the ground if it is dropped from a height of (a) 4 ft, (b) 16 ft, (c) 100 ft?

68. The radius $r$ of a sphere of volume $V$ is given by the formula $r = \sqrt[3]{3V/4\pi}$. What should the radius of a spherical hot-air balloon be if its volume is to be $288\pi$ cubic feet?

69. The time $t$ in seconds that it takes a pendulum $\ell$ ft long to complete a cycle is given by the formula $t = 2\pi\sqrt{\ell/32}$. How long does it take a pendulum that is 2 ft long to complete a cycle?

70. To estimate the speed $s_a$ of a car that was involved in an accident, a policeman drives a car (the same car if possible) under similar conditions at some test speed $s_t$ and then skids to a stop. Then $s_a$ is given by the formula $s_a = s_t\sqrt{\ell_a/\ell_t}$, where $\ell_a$ and $\ell_t$ are the lengths of the skid marks from the accident and the test, respectively. Determine $s_a$ if $s_t = 40$ mph, $\ell_a = 90$ ft, and $\ell_t = 40$ ft.

## Calculator Problems

Find each root to the nearest thousandth.

71. $\sqrt{21,736}$    72. $\sqrt[3]{\pi}$    73. $\sqrt[5]{1747}$    74. $\sqrt{2 + \sqrt{2 + \sqrt{2}}}$

75. One of the results of Einstein's *theory of relativity* is that time on a moving object will appear to an observer on a stationary object to run at a slower rate than time on the stationary object.

The relationship between elapsed time $t_m$ on the moving object and the corresponding elapsed time $t_s$ on the stationary object is given by the formula $t_m = t_s\sqrt{1 - (v/c)^2}$, where $v$ is the velocity of the moving object in mi/sec and $c$ is the velocity of light (approximately 186,000 mi/sec). Using this formula, determine the elapsed time on each of the following.

a) A train traveling at 60 mph, if the elapsed time on a stationary object is 5 hr.

b) A rocketship traveling at 148,800 mi/sec, if the elapsed time on a stationary object is 7 yr.

## *Challenge Problems*

Find each root.

76. $\sqrt{x^{2n}y^{6m}}$    77. $\sqrt{r^{2k+2}}$    78. $\sqrt{a^2b^{2n} + 10a^2b^n + 25a^2}$

## 10.2    FIRST LAW OF RADICALS

Consider the expression $\sqrt{4 \cdot 9}$. We know that $\sqrt{4 \cdot 9} = \sqrt{36} = 6$. Also, $\sqrt{4} \cdot \sqrt{9} = 2 \cdot 3 = 6$. Therefore we can write

$$\sqrt{4 \cdot 9} = \sqrt{4} \cdot \sqrt{9}.$$

This example illustrates an important property of radicals. The property states that a *radical sign may be distributed over a product provided that each factor is positive*, and it is true for *every* index $n$.

---

**First Law of Radicals**

$$\sqrt[n]{ab} = \sqrt[n]{a} \cdot \sqrt[n]{b}$$

for all positive numbers $a$ and $b$.

---

The first law of radicals can be proved as follows:

Let $x = \sqrt[n]{a}$ and $y = \sqrt[n]{b}$. Then $x$ is an $n$th root of $a$ and $y$ is an $n$th root of $b$. By the definition of an $n$th root we can write that $x^n = a$ and $y^n = b$. Therefore, we have

$$\sqrt[n]{a} \cdot \sqrt[n]{b} = x \cdot y = \sqrt[n]{(xy)^n} = \sqrt[n]{x^n y^n} = \sqrt[n]{ab},$$

which is the desired result.

We may use the first law of radicals to *simplify* certain types of radical expressions. For example, to simplify $\sqrt{75}$ we find the largest factor of 75 which is a perfect square and then apply the first law of radicals. Our work looks like this:

*factor*

$$\sqrt{75} = \sqrt{25 \cdot 3} = \sqrt{25} \cdot \sqrt{3} = 5\sqrt{3}.$$

Notice that $5 \cdot \sqrt{3}$ is usually just written as $5\sqrt{3}$.

**EXAMPLE 1**   Simplify $\sqrt{700}$.

$$\sqrt{700} = \sqrt{100 \cdot 7} = \sqrt{100} \cdot \sqrt{7} = 10\sqrt{7}. \quad \square$$

$\sqrt{700} = \sqrt{100} \cdot \sqrt{7}$
$= 10\sqrt{7}$

Using this last form it is an easy matter to approximate $\sqrt{700}$. The number 700 is too large to be found in our table of square roots, so we find the square root of 7 and multiply by 10.

$$\sqrt{700} = 10\sqrt{7} \approx 10(2.646) = 26.46.$$

**EXAMPLE 2**   Simplify $5\sqrt{18}$.

$$5\sqrt{18} = 5\sqrt{9 \cdot 2}$$
$$= 5\sqrt{9} \cdot \sqrt{2}$$
$$= 5 \cdot 3 \cdot \sqrt{2}$$
$$= 15\sqrt{2}. \quad \square$$

**EXAMPLE 3**   Simplify $\sqrt[3]{250}$.

In this case we look for the largest perfect *cube* that is a factor of 250. Recall from Section 1.2 the procedure that was used to factor large integers. This procedure is illustrated below.

$$
\begin{array}{r|l}
2 & 250 \\ \hline
5 & 125 \\ \hline
5 & 25 \\ \hline
  & 5
\end{array}
$$

$\sqrt[3]{250} = \sqrt[3]{2 \cdot 5 \cdot 5 \cdot 5}$
$= \sqrt[3]{2} \sqrt[3]{5 \cdot 5 \cdot 5}$
$= 5\sqrt[3]{2}$

Therefore,

$$\sqrt[3]{250} = \sqrt[3]{2 \cdot 5^3}$$
$$= \sqrt[3]{2} \cdot \sqrt[3]{5^3}$$
$$= 5\sqrt[3]{2}. \quad \square$$

*[handwritten:]* $\sqrt[3]{2 \cdot 125}$
$\sqrt[3]{2} \cdot \sqrt[3]{125}$
$= 5 \sqrt[3]{2}$

The same techniques apply when the radicand involves variables.

**EXAMPLE 4**  Simplify $\sqrt{288x^5}$.

*[handwritten left margin:]* $\times$ add up
$\sqrt{x^4} = x^2$
$\sqrt{x^6} = x^3 = 12x^2 \sqrt{2x}$
$\sqrt{2(12 \cdot 12) \times (x4)}$

$$\sqrt{288x^5} = \sqrt{2^4 \cdot 2 \cdot 3^2 \cdot x^4 \cdot x}$$
$$= \sqrt{2^4 \cdot 3^2 \cdot x^4} \cdot \sqrt{2 \cdot x}$$
$$= 2^2 \cdot 3 \cdot x^2 \cdot \sqrt{2 \cdot x}$$
$$= 12x^2 \sqrt{2x}.$$

*[handwritten:]* = Square root of $288x^5$
not actually $288x^5$

*[handwritten division:]*
2 | 288
2 | 144
2 | 72
2 | 36
2 | 18
3 | 9
3    $\square$

**EXAMPLE 5**  Simplify $\sqrt[3]{x^6 y^{11}}$.

$$\sqrt[3]{x^6 y^{11}} = \sqrt[3]{x^6 y^9 \cdot y^2}$$
$$= \sqrt[3]{x^6 y^9} \cdot \sqrt[3]{y^2}$$
$$= x^2 y^3 \sqrt[3]{y^2}. \quad \square$$

Note that we could have obtained the solution to Example 5 by dividing the index 3 into each *exponent* in the radicand. Dividing 3 into 6 produces 2 (thus $x^2$ is written *outside* the radical). Dividing 3 into 11 produces 3 (thus $y^3$ is written *outside* the radical), with a remainder of 2 (thus $y^2$ is kept *inside* the radical).

The first law of radicals is also used to *multiply* radicals having the same index.

**EXAMPLE 6**  Find the product $\sqrt{15} \cdot \sqrt{12}$ and simplify.

$$\sqrt{15} \cdot \sqrt{12} = \sqrt{15 \cdot 12}$$
*[handwritten:]* $\sqrt{5 \cdot 3 \cdot 2 \cdot 2 \cdot 3}$
$$= \sqrt{(3 \cdot 5)(2^2 \cdot 3)}$$
$$= \sqrt{2^2 \cdot 3^2 \cdot 5}$$
$$= \sqrt{2^2 \cdot 3^2} \cdot \sqrt{5}$$
$$= 2 \cdot 3 \cdot \sqrt{5}$$
$$= 6\sqrt{5}. \quad \square$$

**EXAMPLE 7**   Find the product $\sqrt[4]{10} \cdot \sqrt[4]{24}$ and simplify.

$$
\begin{aligned}
\sqrt[4]{10} \cdot \sqrt[4]{24} &= \sqrt[4]{(2 \cdot 5)(2^3 \cdot 3)} \\
&= \sqrt[4]{2^4 \cdot 5 \cdot 3} \\
&= \sqrt[4]{2^4} \cdot \sqrt[4]{5 \cdot 3} \\
&= 2\sqrt[4]{15}. \quad \square
\end{aligned}
$$

*(handwritten: $\sqrt[4]{2 \cdot 5 \cdot 2 \cdot 2 \cdot 3}$   $= 2\sqrt[4]{15}$)*

**EXAMPLE 8**   Find the product $\sqrt{a^5} \cdot \sqrt{7a}$ and simplify.

*(handwritten: $a^6 = a^3$    $\sqrt{a^5 \cdot 7a} = \sqrt{7a^6}$)*

$$\sqrt{a^5} \cdot \sqrt{7a} = \sqrt{7a^6} = \sqrt{7} \cdot \sqrt{a^6} = a^3\sqrt{7}. \quad \square$$

**EXAMPLE 9**   The voltage $V$ required to operate an electrical appliance is given by $V = \sqrt{WR}$, where $W$ is the wattage of the appliance and $R$ the resistance of the appliance in ohms. Determine the voltage needed to operate a toaster that uses 1100 watts of power and has a resistance of 12 ohms.

Substituting $W = 1100$ and $R = 12$ in the formula above, we have

$$
\begin{aligned}
V &= \sqrt{1100 \cdot 12} \\
&= \sqrt{(2^2 \cdot 5^2 \cdot 11)(2^2 \cdot 3)} \\
&= \sqrt{2^4 \cdot 5^2 \cdot 11 \cdot 3} \\
&= \sqrt{2^4 \cdot 5^2} \cdot \sqrt{11 \cdot 3} \\
&= 2^2 \cdot 5 \cdot \sqrt{33} \\
&= 20\sqrt{33}.
\end{aligned}
$$

| 2 | 1100 |
|---|------|
| 2 | 550 |
| 5 | 275 |
| 5 | 55 |
|   | 11 |

| 2 | 12 |
|---|-----|
| 2 | 6 |
|   | 3 |

The voltage needed is $20\sqrt{33}$ volts. $\square$

## Problem Set 10.2

Express each radical in simplest form.

1. $\sqrt{12}$
2. $\sqrt{50}$
3. $\sqrt{45}$
4. $\sqrt{27}$
5. $5\sqrt{32}$
6. $3\sqrt{72}$
7. $-\sqrt{200}$
8. $-\sqrt{500}$
9. $\pm\sqrt{160}$
10. $\pm\sqrt{250}$
11. $\sqrt{112x^4}/2$
12. $\sqrt{162x^2}/3$
13. $2\sqrt{540x^2y}$
14. $7\sqrt{252x^4y}$
15. $\sqrt[3]{48}$

16. $\sqrt[3]{54}$

17. $\sqrt[3]{375x^3}/5$

18. $\sqrt[3]{648x^3}/9$

19. $\sqrt[4]{405}$

20. $\sqrt[5]{160}$

21. $-\sqrt{720}$

22. $-\sqrt{882}$

23. $10\sqrt{1080}$

24. $5\sqrt{1125}$

25. $\sqrt{75a^5}$

26. $\sqrt{20a^7}$

27. $\sqrt[3]{x^5y^9}$

28. $\sqrt[3]{x^6y^5}$

29. $\sqrt{108a^8b^3}$

30. $\sqrt{288a^{10}b^5}$

31. $\sqrt{(a+8)^3}$

32. $\sqrt{(b-1)^3}$

33. $10x^4y\sqrt{81x^5y^4}$

34. $15x^3y\sqrt{64x^2y^5}$

35. $\sqrt{s^2t-s^3}$

36. $\sqrt{s^4t+s^5}$

Find the product and simplify.

37. $\sqrt{11}\cdot\sqrt{11}$

38. $\sqrt{7}\cdot\sqrt{7}$

39. $\sqrt{30}\cdot\sqrt{15}$

40. $\sqrt{14}\cdot\sqrt{7}$

41. $(\sqrt{5})^2$

42. $(\sqrt{3})^2$

43. $\sqrt{6}\cdot\sqrt{10}$

44. $\sqrt{21}\cdot\sqrt{15}$

45. $\sqrt{77}\cdot\sqrt{22}$

46. $\sqrt{27}\cdot\sqrt{45}$

47. $(\sqrt{5})^3$

48. $(\sqrt{7})^3$

49. $(\sqrt{3x+1})^2$

50. $(\sqrt{2x-1})^2$

51. $\sqrt{30}\cdot\sqrt{6}\cdot\sqrt{60}$

52. $\sqrt{10}\cdot\sqrt{35}\cdot\sqrt{42}$

53. $\sqrt[3]{20}\cdot\sqrt[3]{10}$

54. $\sqrt[3]{6}\cdot\sqrt[3]{18}$

55. $\sqrt[4]{12}\cdot\sqrt[4]{20}$

56. $\sqrt[4]{18}\cdot\sqrt[4]{45}$

57. $\sqrt{5a}\sqrt{a^2}\sqrt{a^3}$

58. $\sqrt{11a}\sqrt{a^4}\sqrt{a^5}$

59. $(3x^4y\sqrt{14y})(2y\sqrt{7x})$

60. $(5x^3y\sqrt{15x})(2x\sqrt{5y})$

61. $\sqrt[3]{t^3r+t^3s}\,\sqrt[3]{(r+s)^2}$

62. $\sqrt[3]{r^2+2rs+s^2}\,\sqrt[3]{(r+s)^4}$

Find a decimal approximation for each of the following by first simplifying each radical and then referring to the table of square roots on the inside front cover.

63. $\sqrt{600}$

64. $\sqrt{500}$

65. $\sqrt{130,000}$

66. $\sqrt{170,000}$

67. $\sqrt{1750}$

68. $\sqrt{750}$

69. $\sqrt{4800}$

70. $\sqrt{640}$

71. $\sqrt{1188}$

72. $\sqrt{1925}$

73. The length $d$ of a diagonal of a rectangle of width $w$ and length $\ell$ is given by $d = \sqrt{w^2 + \ell^2}$. Find the diagonal of a rectangle of width 6 cm and length 10 cm.

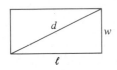

74. The length $d$ of a main diagonal of a rectangular room of width $w$, length $\ell$, and height $h$ is given by $d = \sqrt{w^2 + \ell^2 + h^2}$. Find the main diagonal of a rectangular room of width 14 ft, length 16 ft, and height 8 ft.

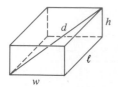

75. Determine the voltage needed to operate a hair dryer that uses 800 watts of power and has a resistance of 16 ohms.
76. Determine the voltage needed to operate a heater that uses 1500 watts of power and has a resistance of 10 ohms.

## Calculator Problems

77. Verify that $\sqrt{ab} = \sqrt{a}\sqrt{b}$ for $a = 1369$ and $b = 2209$.
78. Verify that $\sqrt[3]{ab} = \sqrt[3]{a}\sqrt[3]{b}$ for $a = 6859$ and $b = 4913$.

## Challenge Problems

79. Simplify $\sqrt{x^{2k+3}}$.
80. Find the incorrect step in the "proof" below.
$$1 = \sqrt{1} = \sqrt{(-1)\cdot(-1)} = \sqrt{-1}\cdot\sqrt{-1} = -1 \ ?!?$$

81. **Heron's formula** gives the area $A$ of a triangle in terms of the lengths of its sides $a$, $b$, and $c$ as
$$A = \sqrt{s(s - a)(s - b)(s - c)},$$

    where $s$ is one-half the perimeter. Show that for an *equilateral* triangle (a triangle with all sides equal) Heron's formula reduces to $A = (x^2/4)\sqrt{3}$, where $x$ is the length of each side.

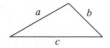

## 10.3 | SECOND LAW OF RADICALS

Consider the expression $\sqrt{\frac{4}{9}}$. We know that $\sqrt{\frac{4}{9}} = \frac{2}{3}$. Also, $\sqrt{4}/\sqrt{9} = \frac{2}{3}$. Therefore we can write

$$\sqrt{\frac{4}{9}} = \frac{\sqrt{4}}{\sqrt{9}}.$$

*(handwritten: $\frac{\sqrt{4}}{\sqrt{9}} = \frac{2}{3}$)*

This example illustrates another property of radicals. This property states that *a radical sign may be distributed over a quotient provided that the numerator and the denominator are positive.* Like the first law of radicals, it is also true for *every* index n.

---

**Second Law of Radicals**

$$\sqrt[n]{\frac{a}{b}} = \frac{\sqrt[n]{a}}{\sqrt[n]{b}}$$

for all positive numbers $a$ and $b$.

---

The second law of radicals can be proved as follows:

Let $x = \sqrt[n]{a}$ and $y = \sqrt[n]{b}$. Then $x$ is an $n$th root of $a$ and $y$ is an $n$th root of $b$. By the definition of an $n$th root we can write that $x^n = a$ and $y^n = b$. Therefore, we have

$$\frac{\sqrt[n]{a}}{\sqrt[n]{b}} = \frac{x}{y} = \sqrt[n]{\left(\frac{x}{y}\right)^n} = \sqrt[n]{\frac{x^n}{y^n}} = \sqrt[n]{\frac{a}{b}},$$

which is the desired result.

The following examples illustrate how the second law of radicals can be used to simplify certain types of radical expressions.

**EXAMPLE 1**  Simplify $\sqrt{\frac{49}{9}}$.

$$\sqrt{\frac{49}{9}} = \frac{\sqrt{49}}{\sqrt{9}} = \frac{7}{3}. \quad \square$$

**EXAMPLE 2**  Simplify $\sqrt[3]{\frac{8}{125}}$.

*(handwritten: not simplified  $\sqrt{\frac{3}{4}}$ or $\frac{2}{\sqrt{3}}$)*

$$\sqrt[3]{\frac{8}{125}} = \frac{\sqrt[3]{8}}{\sqrt[3]{125}} = \frac{2}{5}. \quad \square$$

**EXAMPLE 3**   Simplify $\sqrt{\frac{3}{4}}$.

$$\sqrt{\frac{3}{4}} = \frac{\sqrt{3}}{\sqrt{4}} = \frac{\sqrt{3}}{2}. \quad \square$$

**EXAMPLE 4**   Simplify $\sqrt{\frac{50}{121}}$.

$$\sqrt{\frac{50}{121}} = \frac{\sqrt{50}}{\sqrt{121}} = \frac{\sqrt{25 \cdot 2}}{11} = \frac{5\sqrt{2}}{11}. \quad \square$$

**EXAMPLE 5**   Simplify $\sqrt{7a^2b^3/144}$.

$$\sqrt{\frac{7a^2b^3}{144}} = \frac{\sqrt{7a^2b^3}}{\sqrt{144}} = \frac{\sqrt{a^2b^2 \cdot 7b}}{12} = \frac{ab\sqrt{7b}}{12}. \quad \square$$

Sometimes a quotient of *two* radicals that have the same index can be simplified by first expressing it as *one* radical.

**EXAMPLE 6**   Simplify $\sqrt{32}/\sqrt{2}$.

$$\frac{\sqrt{32}}{\sqrt{2}} = \sqrt{\frac{32}{2}} = \sqrt{16} = 4. \quad \square$$

**EXAMPLE 7**   Simplify $\sqrt{15}/\sqrt{5}$.

$$\frac{\sqrt{15}}{\sqrt{5}} = \sqrt{\frac{15}{5}} = \sqrt{3}. \quad \square$$

**EXAMPLE 8**   Simplify $\dfrac{\sqrt[3]{54x^8y^2}}{\sqrt[3]{2x^4y^2}}$.

$$\frac{\sqrt[3]{54x^8y^2}}{\sqrt[3]{2x^4y^2}} = \sqrt[3]{\frac{54x^8y^2}{2x^4y^2}} = \sqrt[3]{27x^4} = \sqrt[3]{27x^3 \cdot x} = 3x\sqrt[3]{x}. \quad \square$$

**EXAMPLE 9**   Simplify $\sqrt{6}/\sqrt{12}$.

$$\frac{\sqrt{6}}{\sqrt{12}} = \sqrt{\frac{6}{12}} = \sqrt{\frac{1}{2}} = \frac{\sqrt{1}}{\sqrt{2}} = \frac{1}{\sqrt{2}}. \quad \square$$

Note that the answer to this last example has a radical in the denominator. While the form $1/\sqrt{2}$ is perfectly acceptable, another equivalent form is more convenient if we want to approximate this number with a decimal. The equivalent form can be obtained by multiplying numerator and denominator by $\sqrt{2}$.

$$\frac{1}{\sqrt{2}} = \frac{1}{\sqrt{2}} \cdot \frac{\sqrt{2}}{\sqrt{2}} = \frac{1 \cdot \sqrt{2}}{\sqrt{2} \cdot \sqrt{2}} = \frac{\sqrt{2}}{2}.$$

This procedure is called **rationalizing the denominator,** since the denominator is converted from the *irrational* number $\sqrt{2}$ to the *rational* number 2 in the process. Note that $\sqrt{2}/2$ is easily approximated using the table of square roots on the inside front cover as

$$\frac{\sqrt{2}}{2} \approx \frac{1.414}{2} = 0.707,$$

while $1/\sqrt{2} \approx 1/1.414$ requires a more involved division.

**EXAMPLE 10**   Rationalize the denominator of $3/\sqrt{3}$.

In this case we multiply numerator and denominator by $\sqrt{3}$.

$$\frac{3}{\sqrt{3}} = \frac{3}{\sqrt{3}} \cdot \frac{\sqrt{3}}{\sqrt{3}} = \frac{3\sqrt{3}}{3} = \sqrt{3}. \quad \square$$

**EXAMPLE 11**   Find a decimal approximation to $\sqrt{2}/\sqrt{5}$.

If we approach this problem directly we have

$$\frac{\sqrt{2}}{\sqrt{5}} \approx \frac{1.414}{2.236},$$

which involves a complicated division. Instead, let's first rationalize the denominator.

$$\frac{\sqrt{2}}{\sqrt{5}} = \frac{\sqrt{2}}{\sqrt{5}} \cdot \frac{\sqrt{5}}{\sqrt{5}} = \frac{\sqrt{10}}{5}.$$

This last expression is easily approximated as

$$\frac{\sqrt{10}}{5} \approx \frac{3.162}{5} \approx 0.632. \quad \square$$

**EXAMPLE 12**   The current $A$ in amperes of an electrical appliance is given by $A = \sqrt{W/R}$, where $W$ is the wattage of the appliance and $R$ the resistance of the appliance in ohms. Determine the current in an electric hair dryer that uses 1100 watts of power and has a resistance of 18 ohms.

Substituting $W = 1100$ and $R = 18$ in the formula above, we have

$$A = \sqrt{\frac{1100}{18}} = \sqrt{\frac{550}{9}} = \frac{\sqrt{550}}{\sqrt{9}} = \frac{\sqrt{2 \cdot 5^2 \cdot 11}}{3} = \frac{5\sqrt{22}}{3}.$$

The current is $5\sqrt{22}/3$ amps. $\square$

## Problem Set 10.3

Express each radical in simplest form.

1. $\sqrt{\frac{1}{9}}$
2. $\sqrt{\frac{1}{25}}$
3. $\sqrt{\frac{4}{25}}$
4. $\sqrt{\frac{9}{16}}$
5. $\pm\sqrt{\frac{121}{36}}$
6. $\pm\sqrt{\frac{100}{81}}$
7. $\sqrt{\frac{5}{16}}$
8. $\sqrt{\frac{3}{25}}$
9. $\sqrt{\frac{3}{49}}$
10. $\sqrt{\frac{7}{9}}$
11. $\sqrt[3]{\frac{1}{64}}$
12. $\sqrt[3]{\frac{1}{27}}$
13. $\sqrt[3]{\frac{8}{27}}$
14. $\sqrt[3]{\frac{64}{125}}$
15. $\sqrt{3x^2y^5/25}$
16. $\sqrt{5x^2y^5/16}$
17. $\sqrt{\frac{12}{25}}$
18. $\sqrt{\frac{18}{49}}$
19. $\sqrt{\frac{50}{9}}$
20. $\sqrt{\frac{75}{16}}$
21. $\sqrt[3]{32y^4/125}$
22. $\sqrt[3]{81y^4/8}$
23. $3\sqrt{\frac{28}{81}}$
24. $4\sqrt{\frac{45}{64}}$
25. $\pm\sqrt{\frac{32}{225}}$
26. $\pm\sqrt{\frac{72}{625}}$
27. $\sqrt{r^3/s^2t^6}$
28. $\sqrt{r^5/s^2t^2}$

Find the quotient and simplify.

29. $\sqrt{40}/\sqrt{10}$
30. $\sqrt{75}/\sqrt{3}$
31. $\sqrt{288}/\sqrt{2}$
32. $\sqrt{500}/\sqrt{5}$
33. $\sqrt{300}/\sqrt{3}$
34. $\sqrt{242}/\sqrt{2}$
35. $\sqrt{21x}/\sqrt{7x}$
36. $\sqrt{50x}/\sqrt{10x}$
37. $25\sqrt{50}/5\sqrt{5}$
38. $36\sqrt{60}/6\sqrt{6}$
39. $26\sqrt{10}/13\sqrt{5}$
40. $51\sqrt{30}/17\sqrt{10}$
41. $\sqrt{338x^5y^5}/\sqrt{2xy}$
42. $\sqrt{588x^5y^5}/\sqrt{3xy}$
43. $\sqrt[3]{32}/\sqrt[3]{4}$
44. $\sqrt[3]{54}/\sqrt[3]{2}$
45. $\sqrt[3]{15x^6}/\sqrt[3]{3x^3}$
46. $\sqrt[3]{35x^6}/\sqrt[3]{5x^3}$
47. $\sqrt{18a^3}/\sqrt{2a^2b^2}$
48. $\sqrt{27b^5}/\sqrt{3a^2b^4}$

Rationalize the denominator and then use the table of square roots on the inside front cover to find a decimal approximation.

49. $1/\sqrt{3}$
50. $1/\sqrt{5}$
51. $2/\sqrt{7}$
52. $3/\sqrt{2}$
53. $10/\sqrt{2}$
54. $14/\sqrt{7}$
55. $\sqrt{5}/\sqrt{2}$
56. $\sqrt{3}/\sqrt{2}$
57. $\sqrt{2}/\sqrt{3}$
58. $\sqrt{5}/\sqrt{3}$
59. $\sqrt{\frac{1}{10}}$
60. $\sqrt{\frac{9}{10}}$

61. The time $t$ in seconds that it takes a pendulum $\ell$ ft long to complete a cycle is given by the formula $t = 2\pi\sqrt{\ell/32}$. How long does it take a pendulum 6 ft long to complete a cycle?
62. The radius $r$ of a sphere of volume $V$ is given by the formula $r = \sqrt[3]{3V/4\pi}$. Determine the radius of a sphere whose volume is $(45/2)\pi$ cubic feet.

63. Determine the current in a contact lens disinfecting unit that uses 27 watts of power and has a resistance of 564 ohms.
64. Determine the current in a toaster oven that uses 1350 watts of power and has a resistance of 12 ohms.

## Calculator Problems

65. Verify that $\sqrt{a/b} = \sqrt{a}/\sqrt{b}$ for $a = 7056$ and $b = 3136$.
66. Verify that $\sqrt[3]{a/b} = \sqrt[3]{a}/\sqrt[3]{b}$ for $a = 46{,}656$ and $b = 1728$.

## Challenge Problems

67. Simplify $\sqrt{\dfrac{yx^{2n+3}}{xy^{2n+1}}}$.

68. Rationalize the denominator of $10/\sqrt[3]{4}$ and simplify.
69. Show that the theory of relativity formula given in Problem 75 of Section 10.1 can also be written as $t_m = t_0\sqrt{c^2 - v^2}/c$.

## 10.4    SUMS AND DIFFERENCES OF RADICALS

An expression consisting of a sum or difference of two radicals having *both* the same index *and* the same radicand can be simplified by combining the terms. For example, in the expression

$$5\sqrt{3} + 7\sqrt{3},$$

the index of each radical is 2 *and* the radicand of each radical is 3. Therefore, we can apply the *distributive axiom* and write

$$5\sqrt{3} + 7\sqrt{3} = (5 + 7) \cdot \sqrt{3}$$
$$= 12\sqrt{3}.$$

Thus, we may add the radical expressions $5\sqrt{3}$ and $7\sqrt{3}$ by adding the *coefficients* 5 and 7, just as we add the *like terms* $5x$ and $7x$ by adding the coefficients 5 and 7. In general, radical expressions may be added in this way provided the radicals involved are *identical*.

If the radicals *differ*, then we can only *indicate* addition. Such is the case with an expression like

$$5\sqrt{3} + 7\sqrt{2}.$$

This expression cannot be simplified any further, just as $5x + 7y$ cannot be simplified any further.

**EXAMPLE 1**    Simplify $\sqrt{3} + 6\sqrt{3}$.

Since no coefficient is written in front of $\sqrt{3}$, the coefficient is taken as 1.

$$\begin{aligned}
\sqrt{3} + 6\sqrt{3} &= 1\sqrt{3} + 6\sqrt{3} \\
&= (1 + 6)\sqrt{3} \\
&= 7\sqrt{3}. \;\square
\end{aligned}$$

**EXAMPLE 2**    Simplify $7\sqrt{5} + 6\sqrt{2} - 2\sqrt{5} + \sqrt{2}$.

Grouping the terms that have identical radicals, we write

$$\begin{aligned}
7\sqrt{5} + 6\sqrt{2} - 2\sqrt{5} + \sqrt{2} &= 7\sqrt{5} - 2\sqrt{5} + 6\sqrt{2} + 1\sqrt{2} \\
&= (7 - 2)\sqrt{5} + (6 + 1)\sqrt{2} \\
&= 5\sqrt{5} + 7\sqrt{2}. \;\square
\end{aligned}$$

**EXAMPLE 3**    Simplify $6\sqrt{13} - 11\sqrt{13}$.

$$\begin{aligned}
6\sqrt{13} - 11\sqrt{13} &= (6 - 11)\sqrt{13} \\
&= -5\sqrt{13}. \;\square
\end{aligned}$$

**EXAMPLE 4**    Simplify $10\sqrt[5]{7} + 3\sqrt[5]{7}$.

$$\begin{aligned}
10\sqrt[5]{7} + 3\sqrt[5]{7} &= (10 + 3)\sqrt[5]{7} \\
&= 13\sqrt[5]{7}. \;\square
\end{aligned}$$

**EXAMPLE 5**    Simplify $9\sqrt{x} + y + 2\sqrt{x} + y$.

$$\begin{aligned}
9\sqrt{x} + y + 2\sqrt{x} + y &= (9\sqrt{x} + 2\sqrt{x}) + (y + y) \\
&= 11\sqrt{x} + 2y. \;\square
\end{aligned}$$

Sometimes the terms of a radical expression must be simplified before they can be combined.

**EXAMPLE 6**   Simplify $\sqrt{12} + 5\sqrt{27}$.

$$\begin{aligned}
\sqrt{12} + 5\sqrt{27} &= \sqrt{4 \cdot 3} + 5\sqrt{9 \cdot 3} \\
&= \sqrt{4} \cdot \sqrt{3} + 5\sqrt{9} \cdot \sqrt{3} \\
&= 2\sqrt{3} + 15\sqrt{3} \\
&= 17\sqrt{3}. \quad \square
\end{aligned}$$

**EXAMPLE 7**   Simplify $2\sqrt[3]{16} - \sqrt[3]{54} + \sqrt[3]{2}$.

$$\begin{aligned}
2\sqrt[3]{16} - \sqrt[3]{54} + \sqrt[3]{2} &= 2\sqrt[3]{8 \cdot 2} - \sqrt[3]{27 \cdot 2} + \sqrt[3]{2} \\
&= 2\sqrt[3]{8} \cdot \sqrt[3]{2} - \sqrt[3]{27} \cdot \sqrt[3]{2} + \sqrt[3]{2} \\
&= 4\sqrt[3]{2} - 3\sqrt[3]{2} + \sqrt[3]{2} \\
&= 2\sqrt[3]{2}. \quad \square
\end{aligned}$$

**EXAMPLE 8**   Simplify $\sqrt{12r} + 5\sqrt{27r} - 3\sqrt{3r}$.

$$\begin{aligned}
\sqrt{12r} + 5\sqrt{27r} - 3\sqrt{3r} &= \sqrt{4 \cdot 3r} + 5\sqrt{9 \cdot 3r} - 3\sqrt{3r} \\
&= 2\sqrt{3r} + 15\sqrt{3r} - 3\sqrt{3r} \\
&= 14\sqrt{3r}. \quad \square
\end{aligned}$$

**EXAMPLE 9**   Simplify $\sqrt{48} + \sqrt{\tfrac{1}{3}}$.

$$\begin{aligned}
\sqrt{48} + \sqrt{\frac{1}{3}} &= \sqrt{16 \cdot 3} + \frac{\sqrt{1}}{\sqrt{3}} \\
&= 4\sqrt{3} + \frac{1}{\sqrt{3}} \cdot \frac{\sqrt{3}}{\sqrt{3}} \\
&= 4\sqrt{3} + \frac{\sqrt{3}}{3} \\
&= \frac{12\sqrt{3}}{3} + \frac{\sqrt{3}}{3} \\
&= \frac{13\sqrt{3}}{3}. \quad \square
\end{aligned}$$

The distributive axiom allows us to multiply radical expressions in much the same way that we multiplied polynomial expressions.

**EXAMPLE 10**   Find the product $\sqrt{2}(11\sqrt{3} - \sqrt{2})$.

$$\begin{aligned}
\sqrt{2}(11\sqrt{3} - \sqrt{2}) &= 11\sqrt{3} \cdot \sqrt{2} - \sqrt{2} \cdot \sqrt{2} \\
&= 11\sqrt{6} - 2. \quad \square
\end{aligned}$$

**EXAMPLE 11** Find the product and simplify $(\sqrt{5} + \sqrt{3})(\sqrt{5} - \sqrt{3})$.

This product is handled in the same way as a product of two binomials.

$$(\sqrt{5} + \sqrt{3})(\sqrt{5} - \sqrt{3}) = \sqrt{5}\sqrt{5} - \sqrt{5}\sqrt{3} + \sqrt{3}\sqrt{5} - \sqrt{3}\sqrt{3}$$
$$= 5 - \sqrt{15} + \sqrt{15} - 3$$
$$= 2. \quad \square$$

The methods of this section can be used to rationalize the denominator of a radical expression whose denominator contains *two* terms instead of just one.

**EXAMPLE 12** Rationalize the denominator of $1/(3 - \sqrt{5})$.

This can be accomplished by multiplying numerator and denominator by the *conjugate** of $3 - \sqrt{5}$, namely $3 + \sqrt{5}$.

$$\frac{1}{3 - \sqrt{5}} = \frac{1}{3 - \sqrt{5}} \cdot \frac{3 + \sqrt{5}}{3 + \sqrt{5}} = \frac{3 + \sqrt{5}}{9 - 5}$$
$$= \frac{3 + \sqrt{5}}{4}, \text{ or } \frac{3}{4} + \frac{\sqrt{5}}{4}. \quad \square$$

**EXAMPLE 13** Determine the total voltage needed to operate two laboratory devices that are connected in series if one uses 845 watts and has a resistance of 36 ohms, while the other uses 605 watts and has a resistance of 25 ohms.

Since the current in the two devices is essentially the same, the total voltage needed to operate the two devices is the sum of the voltages needed to operate each device separately. Therefore, using the formula $V = \sqrt{WR}$ from Example 9 in Section 10.2, we have

$$\text{Total voltage} = \sqrt{845 \cdot 36} + \sqrt{605 \cdot 25}$$
$$= \sqrt{5 \cdot 13^2 \cdot 6^2} + \sqrt{5 \cdot 11^2 \cdot 5^2}$$
$$= 13 \cdot 6\sqrt{5} + 11 \cdot 5\sqrt{5}$$
$$= 78\sqrt{5} + 55\sqrt{5}$$
$$= 133\sqrt{5}.$$

The total voltage needed is $133\sqrt{5}$ volts. $\square$

* The expressions $A + B$ and $A - B$ are called **conjugates** of each other.

## Problem Set 10.4

Simplify each of the following.

1. $3\sqrt{5} + 4\sqrt{5}$

2. $5\sqrt{7} + 3\sqrt{7}$

3. $11\sqrt{2} + \sqrt{2}$

4. $6\sqrt{3} + \sqrt{3}$

5. $10\sqrt{19} - 5\sqrt{19}$

6. $10\sqrt{17} - 6\sqrt{17}$

7. $14\sqrt{3} - \sqrt{3}$

8. $12\sqrt{2} - \sqrt{2}$

9. $\sqrt{2} + \sqrt{7}$

10. $\sqrt{3} + \sqrt{13}$

11. $5\sqrt{2} - 8\sqrt{2} + \sqrt{2}$

12. $4\sqrt{5} - 10\sqrt{5} + \sqrt{5}$

13. $3\sqrt{2} - 4\sqrt{3} + 2\sqrt{2}$

14. $5\sqrt{3} - 2\sqrt{5} + 2\sqrt{3}$

15. $7\sqrt{5} + \sqrt{7}$

16. $5\sqrt{3} + \sqrt{5}$

17. $5\sqrt{13x} - 2\sqrt{13x} + 3\sqrt{13x}$

18. $8\sqrt{11x} - 3\sqrt{11x} + 4\sqrt{11x}$

19. $4\sqrt[3]{9y} + 8\sqrt[3]{9y}$

20. $5\sqrt[4]{10y} + 6\sqrt[4]{10y}$

21. $\sqrt{17}/2 + \sqrt{17}/4$

22. $\sqrt{19}/3 - \sqrt{19}/9$

23. $6\sqrt{x} + y - 2\sqrt{x} + y$

24. $8\sqrt{xy} + y - 3\sqrt{xy} + y$

Simplify each radical and then simplify the complete expression.

25. $\sqrt{8} + \sqrt{32}$

26. $\sqrt{8} + \sqrt{18}$

27. $\sqrt{72} - \sqrt{2}$

28. $\sqrt{48} - \sqrt{3}$

29. $\sqrt{75y} + \sqrt{27y}$

30. $\sqrt{28y} + \sqrt{63y}$

31. $5\sqrt{20} - 3\sqrt{5}$

32. $4\sqrt{45} - 2\sqrt{5}$

33. $2\sqrt{7r} - \sqrt{28r} + \sqrt{63r}$

34. $3\sqrt{6r} - \sqrt{54r} + \sqrt{24r}$

35. $5\sqrt[3]{3} - \sqrt[3]{24} + 5\sqrt[3]{192}$

36. $3\sqrt[3]{5} + 7\sqrt[3]{40} - \sqrt[3]{135}$

37. $\sqrt{\frac{8}{9}} + \sqrt{\frac{50}{9}}$

38. $\sqrt{\frac{27}{25}} + \sqrt{\frac{48}{25}}$

39. $3\sqrt{45a^3b} - 4a\sqrt{5ab}$

40. $5\sqrt{28ab^3} - 3b\sqrt{7ab}$

41. $\sqrt{25s/4} - \sqrt{s/4} + \sqrt{49s}$

42. $\sqrt{16s/9} - \sqrt{s/9} + \sqrt{64s}$

43. $\sqrt{20} + \sqrt{\frac{1}{5}}$

44. $\sqrt{72} + \sqrt{\frac{1}{2}}$

45. $\sqrt{24} + \sqrt{\frac{2}{3}}$

46. $\sqrt{40} + \sqrt{\frac{2}{5}}$

Find each product and express the result in simplest form.

47. $4(\sqrt{3} + 1)$

48. $6(\sqrt{2} + 1)$

49. $10(2\sqrt{5} - 1)$

50. $9(3\sqrt{5} - 1)$

51. $7(3\sqrt{11} + \sqrt{15})$

52. $5(4\sqrt{13} + \sqrt{19})$

53. $\sqrt{2}(\sqrt{3} + \sqrt{2})$

54. $\sqrt{3}(\sqrt{2} + \sqrt{3})$

55. $\sqrt{5}(2\sqrt{2} - 10\sqrt{5})$

56. $\sqrt{10}(2\sqrt{7} - 4\sqrt{10})$

57. $\sqrt{x}(\sqrt{x} + \sqrt{xy})$

58. $\sqrt{x}(\sqrt{x} - \sqrt{xy})$

59. $(t - \sqrt{5})(t + \sqrt{5})$

60. $(t + \sqrt{2})(t - \sqrt{2})$

61. $(\sqrt{3} + \sqrt{2})^2$

62. $(\sqrt{5} - \sqrt{2})^2$

63. $(3\sqrt{5} - \sqrt{2})(\sqrt{5} + \sqrt{2})$

64. $(4\sqrt{5} - \sqrt{2})(\sqrt{5} + \sqrt{2})$

65. $(\sqrt{10c} + 3\sqrt{5})^2$

66. $(\sqrt{10c} + 2\sqrt{5})^2$

67. $\sqrt[3]{4}(\sqrt[3]{2} + \sqrt[3]{3})$

68. $\sqrt[3]{9}(\sqrt[3]{3} + \sqrt[3]{2})$

Rationalize the denominator.

69. $\dfrac{1}{2 - \sqrt{3}}$

70. $\dfrac{1}{3 - \sqrt{8}}$

71. $\dfrac{1}{\sqrt{7} + 2}$

72. $\dfrac{1}{\sqrt{5} + 1}$

73. $\dfrac{1}{\sqrt{x} - \sqrt{y}}$

74. $\dfrac{1}{\sqrt{x} + \sqrt{y}}$

Simplify.

75. $\dfrac{3 + 3\sqrt{5}}{3}$

76. $\dfrac{4 + 4\sqrt{3}}{4}$

77. $\dfrac{2 + \sqrt{12}}{2}$

78. $\dfrac{2 + \sqrt{20}}{2}$

79. $\dfrac{\sqrt{5} + \sqrt{3}}{\sqrt{5} - \sqrt{3}}$

80. $\dfrac{\sqrt{7} + \sqrt{5}}{\sqrt{7} - \sqrt{5}}$

81. The expression $(\sqrt{t} - 2)/(t - 4)$ appears in calculus. Rationalize the *numerator* and simplify.

82. The expression $(\sqrt{t} - 3)/(t - 9)$ appears in calculus. Rationalize the *numerator* and simplify.

In Chapter 11 we will show that the two solutions to the *second-degree equation* $ax^2 + bx + c = 0$ are of the form $(-b \pm \sqrt{b^2 - 4ac})/2a$. Evaluate this expression for the following values of $a$, $b$, and $c$.

83. $a = 1, b = 5, c = 2$

84. $a = 3, b = 1, c = -1$

85. $a = 2, b = -6, c = -3$

86. $a = 1, b = -4, c = 2$

87. $a = 1, b = 4, c = 5$

88. $a = 5, b = 4, c = 1$

## Calculator Problems

89. Calculate the value of $1/(\sqrt{7} + 2)$. Then rationalize the denominator and calculate the value of the new expression.

90. Calculate the value of $(\sqrt{7} + \sqrt{5})/(\sqrt{7} - \sqrt{5})$. Then rationalize the denominator and calculate the value of the new expression.

## Challenge Problems

91. Find the product $(\sqrt[3]{x} - \sqrt[3]{y})(\sqrt[3]{x^2} + \sqrt[3]{xy} + \sqrt[3]{y^2})$.
92. The expression $(\sqrt{x + h} - \sqrt{x})/h$ appears in calculus. Rationalize the *numerator* and simplify.

## 10.5 EQUATIONS INVOLVING RADICALS (OPTIONAL)

The *multiplication axiom for equality* can be *extended* to state:

$$\text{If } a = b, \text{ then } a^2 = b^2.$$

In other words, *if two quantities are equal then their squares are equal.*
    This property is often used to solve an equation that involves a radical. This is done by first isolating the radical on one side of the equation, and then squaring both sides to remove the radical.

**EXAMPLE 1**   Solve $\sqrt{5x - 6} = 3$.

Since the radical is already isolated on one side, we simply square both sides and get

$$(\sqrt{5x - 6})^2 = 3^2$$
$$5x - 6 = 9.$$

This is a first-degree equation and is easily solved.

$$5x = 15$$
$$x = 3.$$
$$\text{CHECK:}\quad \sqrt{5 \cdot 3 - 6} \stackrel{?}{=} 3$$
$$\sqrt{9} \stackrel{?}{=} 3$$
$$3 = 3. \quad \square$$

While we never *lose* a solution when we square both sides of an equation, sometimes we do *gain* a solution. For example, the equation $x = 5$ has only the *one* solution 5, but the equation $x^2 = 25$ has the *two* solutions 5 *and* $-5$. The number $-5$ in this case is called an **extraneous solution** to the original equation $x = 5$, since it is not a solution to this equation but rather was introduced when both sides were squared. *Whenever both sides of an equation are raised to an* **even** *power, the solutions must be checked to determine whether any are extraneous.* Raising both sides of an equation to an *odd* power will not introduce extraneous solutions.

**EXAMPLE 2**   Solve $\sqrt{5x - 6} = -3$.

Squaring both sides, we have

$$(\sqrt{5x - 6})^2 = (-3)^2$$
$$5x - 6 = 9$$
$$5x = 15$$
$$x = 3.$$
$$\text{CHECK:}\quad \sqrt{5 \cdot 3 - 6} \overset{?}{=} -3$$
$$\sqrt{9} \overset{?}{=} -3$$
$$3 \neq -3.$$

Since 3 did not check, it is an extraneous solution and must be thrown out. Therefore, the equation $\sqrt{5x - 6} = -3$ has *no* solution. □

**EXAMPLE 3**   Solve $2\sqrt{x} + 10 = 30$.

First we isolate the radical on one side.

$$2\sqrt{x} + 10 = 30$$
$$2\sqrt{x} = 20$$
$$\sqrt{x} = 10.$$

Then we square both sides.

$$(\sqrt{x})^2 = 10^2$$
$$x = 100.$$
$$\text{CHECK:}\quad 2\sqrt{100} + 10 \overset{?}{=} 30$$
$$2 \cdot 10 + 10 \overset{?}{=} 30$$
$$30 = 30. \quad □$$

A common *error* that is made when solving a radical equation is to square each *term* rather than each *side*. For Example 3, squaring each term would have produced

$$(2\sqrt{x})^2 + 10^2 = 30^2$$
$$4x + 100 = 900$$
$$4x = 800$$
$$x = 200,$$

which is **incorrect!**

If a radical appears in two different terms, we begin by splitting the radicals, placing one on each side of the equation.

**EXAMPLE 4**    Solve $\sqrt{3m - 7} - \sqrt{m + 8} = 0$.

First, we split the radicals by adding $\sqrt{m + 8}$ to each side.

$$\sqrt{3m - 7} - \sqrt{m + 8} = 0$$
$$\sqrt{3m - 7} = \sqrt{m + 8}.$$

Then we square both sides and solve.

$$(\sqrt{3m - 7})^2 = (\sqrt{m + 8})^2$$
$$3m - 7 = m + 8$$
$$2m = 15$$
$$m = \frac{15}{2}.$$

CHECK:  $\sqrt{3 \cdot \dfrac{15}{2} - 7} - \sqrt{\dfrac{15}{2} + 8} \overset{?}{=} 0$

$\sqrt{\dfrac{45}{2} - \dfrac{14}{2}} - \sqrt{\dfrac{15}{2} + \dfrac{16}{2}} \overset{?}{=} 0$

$\sqrt{\dfrac{31}{2}} - \sqrt{\dfrac{31}{2}} \overset{?}{=} 0$

$0 = 0.$  □

**EXAMPLE 5**    The time $t$ in seconds that it takes a pendulum $\ell$ feet long to complete a cycle is called the **period** of the pendulum and is given by the formula $t = 2\pi\sqrt{\ell/32}$. What length should a pendulum have if it is to take 4 seconds to complete a cycle?

Letting $t = 4$ in the formula above, we have

$$4 = 2\pi\sqrt{\frac{\ell}{32}}.$$

Dividing each side by $2\pi$ gives

$$\frac{4}{2\pi} = \sqrt{\frac{\ell}{32}}$$

$$\frac{2}{\pi} = \sqrt{\frac{\ell}{32}}.$$

Squaring each side and solving, we have

$$\left(\frac{2}{\pi}\right)^2 = \left(\sqrt{\frac{\ell}{32}}\right)^2$$

$$\frac{4}{\pi^2} = \frac{\ell}{32}$$

$$\ell = \frac{128}{\pi^2}.$$

The pendulum should be $128/\pi^2$ (approximately 13) ft long.   □

## Problem Set 10.5

Solve each equation.

1. $\sqrt{x} = 4$

2. $\sqrt{x} = 6$

3. $\sqrt{2x - 1} = 3$

4. $\sqrt{3x - 8} = 2$

5. $\sqrt{5x + 6} = 6$

6. $\sqrt{4x + 5} = 5$

7. $\sqrt{x - 3} = -2$

8. $\sqrt{x - 2} = -3$

9. $\sqrt{y + 4} - 1 = 0$

10. $\sqrt{y + 3} - 1 = 0$

11. $\sqrt{3m - 1} + 10 = 0$

12. $\sqrt{2m - 1} + 11 = 0$

13. $\sqrt{4p + 9} + 10 = 25$

14. $\sqrt{5p + 4} + 11 = 23$

15. $6\sqrt{r} = 8$

16. $10\sqrt{r} = 15$

17. $2\sqrt{6q + 1} - 16 = -2$

18. $3\sqrt{6q + 1} - 18 = -3$

19. $9 - 3\sqrt{2s} = 12$

20. $6 - 2\sqrt{3s} = 8$

21. $\sqrt{x - 7} = \sqrt{7 - x}$

22. $\sqrt{x - 8} = \sqrt{8 - x}$

23. $\sqrt{8y} - \sqrt{y + 2} = 0$

24. $\sqrt{7y} - \sqrt{y + 1} = 0$

25. $-\sqrt{u + 15} + \sqrt{1 - 3u} = 0$

26. $-\sqrt{2u + 11} + \sqrt{1 - 2u} = 0$

27. $10\sqrt{v + 5} - 20\sqrt{v + 1} = 0$

28. $4\sqrt{v + 13} - 12\sqrt{v + 1} = 0$

29. $\sqrt{2} - 3\sqrt{c + 1} = 0$

30. $\sqrt{3} - 2\sqrt{c + 2} = 0$

31. $5/\sqrt{9u - 2} = 1$

32. $5/\sqrt{4a + 1} = 1$

33. $\sqrt{4 + 3\sqrt{x}} - 5 = 0$

34. $\sqrt{7 + 2\sqrt{x}} - 5 = 0$

35. $\sqrt{x^2 + 1} = x + 3$

36. $\sqrt{x^2 + 3} = x + 2$

37. What length should a pendulum have if it is to take 2 sec to complete a cycle?

38. What length should a pendulum have if it is to take 6 sec to complete a cycle?

39. The voltage $V$ of an electrical circuit is given by $V = \sqrt{WR}$, where $W$ is the wattage and $R$ is the resistance in ohms. Find $W$ if $V = 600$ volts and $R = 20$ ohms.

40. The current $A$ in an electrical circuit is given by $A = \sqrt{W/R}$, where $W$ is the wattage and $R$ is the resistance in ohms. Find $W$ if $A = 5$ amps and $R = 200$ ohms.

41. The square root of the sum of twice a certain number and 5 is 9. Find the number.

42. Three times the square root of a certain number equals the square root of the sum of 6 and the number. Find the number.

43. Solve $r = \sqrt{A/\pi}$ for $A$.

44. Solve $t = \sqrt{h}/4$ for $h$.

## Calculator Problems

45. Solve $1.57\sqrt{7.39x + 0.121} - 8.58 = 0$. Write your answer to the nearest hundredth.

46. Due to the curvature of the earth's surface, the distance $d$ in miles between an object at an altitude of $h$ ft and the horizon as

viewed from the object is given by $d = \sqrt{1.5h}$. At approximately what altitude in miles should an airplane fly so that its horizon is 178 mi away?

## Challenge Problems

47. Solve $2\sqrt[3]{4x + 1} + 1 = 7$.
48. Solve $r = \sqrt[3]{3V/4\pi}$ for $V$.
49. On a Hawaiian vacation you are given a room on the third floor of a hotel overlooking the Pacific Ocean. To what floor should you request to be moved in order to double your distance to the horizon? (See Problem 46.)

## 10.6    FRACTIONAL EXPONENTS (OPTIONAL)

In Section 5.1 we learned the meaning of *natural number* exponents. That is, we learned that

$$a^1 = a$$
$$a^2 = a \cdot a$$
$$a^3 = a \cdot a \cdot a, \text{ and so on.}$$

Later, in Section 5.3, we expanded our knowledge of exponents to include *zero* and *negative integer* exponents. That is, we learned that

$$a^0 = 1,$$

and also that

$$a^{-1} = \frac{1}{a}$$

$$a^{-2} = \frac{1}{a^2}$$

$$a^{-3} = \frac{1}{a^3}, \text{ and so on.}$$

Let's consider for a moment a base of 9. We know that

$$9^2 = 81,$$

and that

$$9^0 = 1,$$

and also that

$$9^{-2} = \frac{1}{9^2} = \frac{1}{81}.$$

But what is the result if the exponent is $\frac{1}{2}$? That is, what is the value of $9^{1/2}$?

Just as the English mathematician John Wallis (1616–1703) was the first to define zero and negative exponents with any degree of completeness, he was also the first to fully explain the meaning of *fractional* exponents. His definition was made in such a way that the laws of exponents hold for these fractional exponents as well as for the integer exponents previously defined. For example, if the third law of exponents is to hold for the fractional exponent $1/n$, then we must have

$$(a^{1/n})^n = a^{(1/n)n} = a^1 = a.$$

But if raising $a^{1/n}$ to the $n$th power produces $a$, then $a^{1/n}$ must be an $n$th root of $a$. Hence the following definition is made:

---

**Definition**    Let $a$ be any real number and $n$ any positive integer. Then

$$a^{1/n} = \sqrt[n]{a},$$

assuming that $\sqrt[n]{a}$ exists.

---

We are now in a position to determine the value of $9^{1/2}$.

**EXAMPLE 1**    Find $9^{1/2}$.

Applying the definition above with $a = 9$ and $n = 2$, we have

$$9^{1/2} = \sqrt[2]{9} = 3. \quad \square$$

Note that when the fractional exponent in a power is $1/n$, the problem simply involves finding the principal $n$th root of the base. That is,

$$a^{1/2} = \sqrt{a}$$
$$a^{1/3} = \sqrt[3]{a}$$
$$a^{1/4} = \sqrt[4]{a}, \text{ and so on.}$$

Suppose now that the fractional exponent is $m/n$. Again, if the third law of exponents is to hold, then we must have

$$a^{m/n} = a^{(1/n)\cdot m} = (a^{1/n})^m = (\sqrt[n]{a})^m.$$

Also, we must have

$$a^{m/n} = a^{m\cdot(1/n)} = (a^m)^{1/n} = \sqrt[n]{a^m}.$$

Hence the following definition is made:

---

**Definition**    Let $a$ be any real number, $m$ any integer, and $n$ any positive integer. Then if $m/n$ is in lowest terms*

$$a^{m/n} = (\sqrt[n]{a})^m = \sqrt[n]{a^m},$$

assuming that $\sqrt[n]{a}$ exists.

---

Notice that if $m = 1$ in the definition above, then $a^{m/n} = a^{1/n} = (\sqrt[n]{a})^1 = \sqrt[n]{a}$, which agrees with the definition of $a^{1/n}$ given previously.

**EXAMPLE 2**   Determine the value of $8^{2/3}$.

Applying the definition above with $a = 8$, $m = 2$, and $n = 3$, we first find the *third* root of 8 and then raise that number to the *second* power.

$$8^{2/3} = (\sqrt[3]{8})^2 = (2)^2 = 4.$$

We would obtain the same value by reversing the order of operations above; that is, by first raising 8 to the second power and then finding the third root of that number.

$$8^{2/3} = \sqrt[3]{8^2} = \sqrt[3]{64} = 4. \quad \square$$

**EXAMPLE 3**   Determine the value of $4^{5/2}$.

$$4^{5/2} = (\sqrt{4})^5 = (2)^5 = 32. \quad \square$$

**EXAMPLE 4**   Determine the value of $(-243)^{4/5}$.

$$(-243)^{4/5} = (\sqrt[5]{-243})^4 = (-3)^4 = 81. \quad \square$$

---

* If $m/n$ is not in lowest terms, we simply reduce it until it is.

The definition of negative *integer* exponents can be naturally extended to include negative *fractional* exponents as well.

**EXAMPLE 5**   Determine the value of $100^{-1/2}$.

First, using the condition that $a^{-n} = 1/a^n$, we write

$$100^{-1/2} = \frac{1}{100^{1/2}}.$$

Then, using the definition of fractional exponents, we have

$$100^{-1/2} = \frac{1}{100^{1/2}} = \frac{1}{\sqrt{100}} = \frac{1}{10}. \quad \square$$

The solution to Example 5 could also have been obtained by using either of the techniques below.

a) $100^{-1/2} = \sqrt{100^{-1}} = \sqrt{\frac{1}{100}} = \frac{1}{10}.$

b) $100^{-1/2} = (\sqrt{100})^{-1} = 10^{-1} = \frac{1}{10}.$

**EXAMPLE 6**   Determine the value of $16^{-3/4}$.

$$16^{-3/4} = \frac{1}{16^{3/4}} = \frac{1}{(\sqrt[4]{16})^3} = \frac{1}{2^3} = \frac{1}{8}. \quad \square$$

The student should now be able to convert an expression involving fractional exponents to radical notation and vice versa.

**EXAMPLE 7**   Express $(x^2 + 5)^{2/3}$ in radical notation.

$$(x^2 + 5)^{2/3} = \sqrt[3]{(x^2 + 5)^2}. \quad \square$$

**EXAMPLE 8**   Express $(2x - 1)^{-1/2}$ in radical notation.

$$(2x - 1)^{-1/2} = \frac{1}{(2x - 1)^{1/2}} = \frac{1}{\sqrt{2x - 1}}. \quad \square$$

**EXAMPLE 9**   Express $\sqrt[3]{7 - r}$ using a fractional exponent.

$$\sqrt[3]{7 - r} = (7 - r)^{1/3}. \quad \square$$

The application that follows utilizes a formula that involves a fractional exponent.

All plants and animals absorb and maintain a constant amount of a radioactive isotope known as *carbon-14*. When such an organism dies, however, the absorption ceases and the carbon-14 it contains will slowly decay. Thus by comparing the carbon-14 content of a dead organism with that of a similar live organism, we can, within limits, determine the age of the dead organism. This process is called **radioactive-carbon dating,** and it has been used to determine the age of a variety of archaeological specimens ranging from animal bones to the *Dead Sea Scrolls.*

Since it takes approximately 5700 years for a given quantity of carbon-14 to decay to half of its original quantity, we say that the **half-life** of carbon-14 is 5700 years. Using this fact, it can be shown that the quantity $Q$ of carbon-14 that remains after $t$ years is given by the formula

$$Q = Q_0 2^{-t/5700},$$

where $Q_0$ was the original quantity of carbon-14.

**EXAMPLE 10**  If 100 grams of carbon-14 are allowed to decay, how much will remain after 2850 years?

Substituting $Q_0 = 100$ and $t = 2850$ in the formula above, we have

$$Q = 100 \cdot 2^{-2850/5700} = 100 \cdot 2^{-1/2} = \frac{100}{2^{1/2}} = \frac{100}{\sqrt{2}} = \frac{100\sqrt{2}}{2} = 50\sqrt{2}.$$

The amount of carbon-14 that will remain is $50\sqrt{2}$ (approximately 71) g.  □

## Problem Set 10.6

Determine the value of each of the following.

1. $27^{2/3}$
2. $125^{2/3}$
3. $9^{3/2}$
4. $4^{3/2}$
5. $81^{3/4}$
6. $16^{3/4}$
7. $100^{1/2}$
8. $49^{1/2}$
9. $8^{1/3}$
10. $27^{1/3}$
11. $(-8)^{1/3}$
12. $(-27)^{1/3}$
13. $16^{1/4}$
14. $81^{1/4}$
15. $16^{5/2}$
16. $81^{5/4}$
17. $(-32)^{1/5}$
18. $(-243)^{1/5}$
19. $(-25)^{1/2}$
20. $(-36)^{1/2}$
21. $1^{5/4}$
22. $4^{5/2}$
23. $125^{4/3}$
24. $64^{4/3}$
25. $(-64)^{2/3}$
26. $(-8)^{2/3}$
27. $(-1)^{3/5}$
28. $(-1)^{5/3}$
29. $(x^2)^{1/2}$
30. $(x^4)^{1/4}$
31. $(12a^2b^4)^{1/2}$
32. $(75a^2b^6)^{1/2}$

First apply the condition that $a^{-n} = 1/a^n$, and then determine the value of each of the following.

33. $64^{-1/2}$     34. $81^{-1/2}$     35. $25^{-1/2}$     36. $4^{-1/2}$
37. $27^{-1/3}$     38. $8^{-1/3}$      39. $9^{-5/2}$      40. $4^{-5/2}$
41. $81^{-3/4}$     42. $16^{-3/4}$     43. $(-8)^{-1/3}$   44. $(-27)^{-1/3}$
45. $(-125)^{-2/3}$ 46. $(-125)^{-5/3}$ 47. $(x^4)^{-1/4}$  48. $(x^2)^{-1/2}$
49. $2^{-1/2}$      50. $3^{-1/2}$      51. $5^{-3/2}$      52. $7^{-3/2}$
53. $45^{-1/2}$     54. $32^{-1/2}$     55. $(9a^4b^8)^{-1/2}$   56. $(4a^{10}b^4)^{-1/2}$
57. $4^{1/2} + 16^{-1/2}$   58. $9^{1/2} + 81^{-1/2}$   59. $4^{-1/2} + 25^{-1/2}$   60. $9^{-1/2} + 16^{-1/2}$

Express each of the following in radical notation.

61. $x^{2/3}$         62. $x^{3/4}$          63. $(x^2 + 1)^{1/2}$     64. $(x^3 - 1)^{1/3}$
65. $(5p - 3)^{-3/5}$ 66. $(4p + 7)^{-2/5}$  67. $(3pq^2)^{1/3}$       68. $(5pq)^{1/2}$

Express each of the following using a fractional exponent.

69. $\sqrt[4]{x}$       70. $\sqrt[3]{x}$       71. $\sqrt{y^3}$           72. $\sqrt[4]{y^5}$
73. $\sqrt{a - 4}$      74. $\sqrt{u + 9}$      75. $\sqrt[3]{13ab^2}$     76. $\sqrt{11ab^3}$

77. If 200 g of carbon-14 are allowed to decay, how much will remain after (a) 2850 yr, (b) 5700 yr, (c) 8550 yr?
78. If 400 g of carbon-14 are allowed to decay, how much will remain after (a) 2850 yr, (b) 5700 yr, (c) 14,250 yr?
79. Suppose that the rate of consumption $R$ of a particular natural re source is declining and is given by $R = 2700/(t + 9)^{3/2}$ at any given time $t$. Calculate the rate $R$ when (a) $t = 0$, (b) $t = 16$.
80. Repeat Problem 79 if $R = 800/(t + 1)^{3/2}$ and (a) $t = 0$, (b) $t = 15$.

## Calculator Problems

81. Compute to the nearest hundredth.
   a) $100^{3/8}$        b) $7^{-2.25}$

82. **Kepler's third law** * of planetary motion states that the number of years $T$ that it takes a planet to revolve about the Sun is given by $T = d^{3/2}$, where $d$ is the average distance in astronomical units

* Named after the German mathematician and astronomer Johann Kepler (1571–1630).

between the planet and the Sun. How many years does Saturn take to revolve about the Sun if its average distance from the Sun is 9.534 astronomical units?

## Challenge Problems

83. Write $\dfrac{1}{\sqrt[4]{x + \sqrt[3]{x + \sqrt{x}}}}$ using fractional exponents.

84. Write $2^{-3/2} + 3^{-3/2}$ as a single fraction in radical notation.

85. If 100 g of carbon-14 are allowed to decay, how much will remain after 1900 yr?

## 10.7 OPERATIONS WITH FRACTIONAL POWERS (OPTIONAL)

Since fractional exponents were defined with the five laws of exponents in mind, these laws can often be used to simplify expressions that involve fractional exponents.

**EXAMPLE 1**   Find the product $x^{1/2} \cdot x^{1/3}$.

Using the *first law of exponents*, we have

$$x^{1/2} \cdot x^{1/3} = x^{1/2+1/3} = x^{5/6}. \quad \square$$

**EXAMPLE 2**   Find the quotient $x^{7/3}/x^{1/3}$.

Using the *second law of exponents*, we have

$$\frac{x^{7/3}}{x^{1/3}} = x^{7/3-1/3} = x^{6/3} = x^2. \quad \square$$

**EXAMPLE 3**   Simplify the expression $9^{1/4}$.

First, we observe that 9 can be written as $3^2$. Then, using the *third law of exponents*, we have

$$9^{1/4} = (3^2)^{1/4} = 3^{2(1/4)} = 3^{1/2} = \sqrt{3}. \quad \square$$

Very often it will be necessary to use a combination of the laws of exponents in the same problem.

**EXAMPLE 4** Simplify the expression $(x^{-1/2}y^{1/3}/z^{1/6})^{12}$.

$$\left(\frac{x^{-1/2}y^{1/3}}{z^{1/6}}\right)^{12} = \frac{(x^{-1/2})^{12}(y^{1/3})^{12}}{(z^{1/6})^{12}}$$

$$= \frac{x^{-6}y^4}{z^2}$$

$$= \frac{x^{-6}}{1} \cdot \frac{y^4}{z^2}$$

$$- \frac{1}{x^6} \cdot \frac{y^4}{z^2}$$

$$= \frac{y^4}{x^6 z^2}. \quad \square$$

**EXAMPLE 5** Simplify $(a^{3/4}b^{-3/2})^4(a^{-1/2}b^3)^{-1}$.

$$(a^{3/4}b^{-3/2})^4(a^{-1/2}b^3)^{-1} = (a^{3/4})^4(b^{-3/2})^4(a^{-1/2})^{-1}(b^3)^{-1}$$

$$= a^3 b^{-6} a^{1/2} b^{-3}$$

$$= a^{7/2} b^{-9}$$

$$- \frac{a^{7/2}}{b^9}. \quad \square$$

A formula that gives the number of units $P$ that can be produced using $x$ units of labor and $y$ units of capital (raw materials, buildings, machinery, etc.) is called a **production function.** A particular production function that often applies is a *Cobb-Douglas* production function.

**EXAMPLE 6** Suppose that a Cobb-Douglas production function for widgets is

$$P = 48x^{1/3}y^{2/3}.$$

How many widgets can be produced using 20 units of labor and 20 units of capital?

Substituting $x = 20$ and $y = 20$ in the production function above, we have

$$P = 48 \cdot 20^{1/3} \cdot 20^{2/3} = 48 \cdot 20^{3/3} = 48 \cdot 20 = 960.$$

Therefore 960 widgets can be produced. $\square$

## Problem Set 10.7

Use the first law of exponents to find each product.

1. $x^{1/2} \cdot x^{1/2}$
2. $x^{1/4} \cdot x^{3/4}$
3. $x^{1/3} \cdot x^{5/3}$
4. $x^{1/2} \cdot x^{3/2}$
5. $x^{1/3} \cdot x^{1/4}$
6. $x^{2/3} \cdot x^{1/4}$
7. $x^{17/5} \cdot x^{-2/5}$
8. $x^{23/7} \cdot x^{-2/7}$
9. $x^{1/2} \cdot x^{-1/2}$
10. $x^{1/3} \cdot x^{-1/3}$
11. $(r - 7)^{1/2}(r - 7)^{2/3}$
12. $(r + 5)^{1/3}(r + 5)^{3/4}$

Use the second law of exponents to find each quotient.

13. $x^{3/2}/x^{1/2}$
14. $x^{4/3}/x^{1/3}$
15. $x^{2/3}/x^{1/6}$
16. $x^{3/5}/x^{1/10}$
17. $(x + 2)^{7/3}/(x + 2)^{1/3}$
18. $(x - 1)^{5/2}/(x - 1)^{1/2}$

Use the third law of exponents to simplify each of the following.

19. $(a^{1/2})^6$
20. $(a^{1/3})^6$
21. $(a^{12})^{2/3}$
22. $(a^{15})^{2/5}$
23. $(a^{1/3})^{1/2}$
24. $(a^{1/2})^{1/4}$
25. $25^{1/4}$
26. $4^{1/4}$
27. $49^{1/4}$
28. $100^{1/4}$
29. $(-64p^6)^{1/3}$
30. $(-27p^9)^{1/3}$

Use the fourth law of exponents to simplify each of the following.

31. $(a^{1/2}b^{1/3})^6$
32. $(a^{1/2}b^{1/3})^{12}$
33. $(9a^2b^2)^{1/2}$
34. $(8a^3b^3)^{1/3}$

Use the fifth law of exponents to simplify each of the following.

35. $\left(\dfrac{a^{1/5}}{b^{2/5}}\right)^5$
36. $\left(\dfrac{a^{1/4}}{b^{3/4}}\right)^4$
37. $\left(\dfrac{a^4}{b^6}\right)^{3/2}$
38. $\left(\dfrac{a^3}{b^6}\right)^{2/3}$

Simplify each of the following.

39. $(x^{2/3} \cdot y^2 \cdot z^6 \cdot x^{-2/3})^{1/2}$
40. $(x^3 \cdot y^{3/4} \cdot z^9 \cdot y^{-3/4})^{1/3}$
41. $\left(\dfrac{x^{1/3} \cdot y^{1/2}}{z^{1/6}}\right)^{12}$
42. $\left(\dfrac{x^{2/3} \cdot y^{1/6}}{z^{1/2}}\right)^6$
43. $\left(\dfrac{x^{-1/5} \cdot y^{1/2}}{z^{3/10}}\right)^{10}$
44. $\left(\dfrac{x^{-1/4} \cdot y^{1/2}}{z^{3/8}}\right)^8$
45. $\left(\dfrac{p^{3/4}q^{-3/8}}{r^{1/8}}\right)^8$
46. $\left(\dfrac{p^{3/5}q^{-3/10}}{r^{1/5}}\right)^{10}$
47. $m^{3/2}(8m^{1/2})^{1/3}$
48. $m^{3/2}(9m^{1/4})^{1/2}$
49. $(a^{-5/2}b^{1/3})^6(a^{-2}b^{1/2})^{-1}$
50. $(a^{7/4}b^{-5/2})^4(a^{-3/2}b^4)^{-1}$

51. The enharmonic tetrachord of ancient Greek music can be represented by the expression $X^{1/4} \cdot X^{1/4} \cdot X^2$, where X is the value of a tone. Simplify this expression.

52. One type of chromatic tetrachord of ancient Greek music can be represented by the expression $X^{1/2} \cdot X^{1/2} \cdot X^{3/2}$, where X is the value of a tone. Simplify this expression.

53. According to the production function of Example 6, how many widgets can be produced using (a) 10 units of labor and 10 units of capital? (b) 100 units of labor and 10 units of capital?
54. According to the production function of Example 6, how many widgets can be produced using (a) 30 units of labor and 30 units of capital? (b) 25 units of labor and 5 units of capital?

## Calculator Problems

Simplify.

55. $(p^{37/47}q^{-19/53})^{2491}$

56. $r^{0.6897}s^{-0.4172}(r^{0.8714}s^{0.7158})^{8.5}$

## Challenge Problems

57. Write $\sqrt{x\sqrt[3]{x}}$ as $x$ to a fractional power.
58. Write $\dfrac{(x^2 + 1)^2}{\sqrt{x^2 + 1}}$ in simplest form using a single positive exponent.
59. Find the product $\sqrt{a} \cdot \sqrt[3]{a}$.

## Chapter Review

True or false.

1. If $a$ and $b$ are positive numbers, then $\sqrt{ab} = \sqrt{a} \cdot \sqrt{b}$.
2. If $a$ and $b$ are positive numbers, then $\sqrt{a/b} = \sqrt{a}/\sqrt{b}$.
3. If $a$ and $b$ are positive numbers, then $\sqrt{a + b} = \sqrt{a} + \sqrt{b}$.
4. If $a = b$, then $a^2 = b^2$.
5. If $a^2 = b^2$, then $a = b$.
6. If $\sqrt{x} + 3 = 5$, then $x + 9 = 25$.

7. Raising both sides of an equation to an even power sometimes introduces extraneous solutions.

8. The five laws of exponents that were stated in Section 5.2 apply to fractional exponents as well.

9. If $m$ is an integer and $n$ is a positive integer and $m/n$ is in lowest terms, then $a^{m/n} = (\sqrt[n]{a})^m = \sqrt[n]{a^m}$, assuming that $\sqrt[n]{a}$ exists.

10. The number $-4$ is a solution to $\sqrt{x + 5} + 3 = 4$.

11. If $a$ is positive, then $(\sqrt{a})^2 = \sqrt{a^2} = a$.

12. $\sqrt{13}/13 = 1/\sqrt{13}$.

13. $\sqrt[3]{-1}$ is a real number.

14. $\sqrt{-81}$ is a real number.

15. $\sqrt[3]{12}$ is an irrational number.

Completion.

16. If $n$ is a natural number greater than 1, then $b$ is an $n$th root of $a$ if ___$b^n = a$___?___. The expression $\sqrt[n]{a}$ is read the _principal_?_____ $n$th root of $a$. The number $n$ is called the _index_?_____, the number $a$ is called the _radicand_?_____, and the symbol $\sqrt{\phantom{x}}$ is called a(n) _radical sign_?_____.

17. The expressions $5 + \sqrt{x}$ and $5 - \sqrt{x}$ are called ____?____ of each other.

Determine each root.

18. $\pm\sqrt{1.21}$

19. $\sqrt[6]{729}$

20. $-\sqrt[3]{-125}$

21. $\sqrt{2001^2}$

22. $\sqrt{(-9)^2}$

23. $\sqrt[3]{x^{18}}$

24. $\sqrt{16x^4y^6}$

25. $\sqrt[5]{32s^{10}t^{15}}$

26. $\sqrt{a^2 + 6a + 9}$

Express in simplest form.

27. $2\sqrt{180}$

28. $\sqrt[3]{81x}$

29. $-\sqrt{800x^3y^2}$

30. $\sqrt{(p + q)^5}$

31. $18s^3t\sqrt{9s^3t^7}$

32. $\sqrt{a^6b - a^7}$

Find the product and simplify.

33. $(\sqrt{2})^5$

34. $\sqrt{60} \cdot \sqrt{105} \cdot \sqrt{42}$

35. $\sqrt{r^3} \cdot \sqrt{15r^5}$

36. $(\sqrt{4x + 10})^2$

37. $\sqrt[3]{6} \cdot \sqrt[3]{180}$

Express in simplest form.

38. $\pm\sqrt{\frac{13}{81}}$
39. $\sqrt{675}/5$
40. $-3\sqrt{\frac{12}{49}}$
41. $\sqrt{75a^4b^3}/196$

Find the quotient and simplify.

42. $\sqrt{1008x^3y}/\sqrt{7xy}$
43. $21\sqrt[4]{240}/3\sqrt[4]{5}$
44. $\sqrt[3]{81s^5t^7}/\sqrt[3]{3st}$

Simplify.

45. $4\sqrt{5} + 6\sqrt{5} - 3\sqrt{5}$
46. $\sqrt{18} - 2\sqrt{5} - \sqrt{20} + \sqrt{50}$
47. $\sqrt[3]{40r} + \sqrt[3]{135r} - \sqrt[3]{5r}$
48. $\sqrt{11}/2 - \sqrt{11}/6$
49. $\sqrt{9s/64} - \sqrt{s/64} + \sqrt{4s}$

Find each product and express your answer in simplest form.

50. $\sqrt{11}(\sqrt{11} - 3\sqrt{5})$
51. $\sqrt[3]{5}(\sqrt[3]{4} - \sqrt[3]{25})$
52. $(1 + \sqrt{y})^2$

Rationalize the denominator and express your answer in simplest form.

53. $\sqrt{7}/\sqrt{5}$
54. $\sqrt{4/13}$
55. $6/(3 + \sqrt{5})$
56. $\sqrt{x}/(\sqrt{x} - \sqrt{y})$

Determine the value in each case.

57. $4^{1/2}$
58. $64^{3/2}$
59. $(-27)^{2/3}$
60. $16^{-5/4}$
61. $(-1)^{-1/5}$
62. $6^{-3/2}$
63. $4^{-1/2} + 9^{-1/2}$

Express in radical notation.

64. $x^{4/3}$
65. $(2p - q)^{-1/3}$

Express using a fractional exponent.

66. $\sqrt[4]{y^3}$
67. $\sqrt[3]{q^2 + 1}$

Write each expression in simplest form.

68. $(-2 + 2\sqrt{5})/2$
69. $(\sqrt[4]{81} + 8^{2/3})/28$
70. $x^{1/4} \cdot x^{-1/4}$
71. $x/x^{2/3}$
72. $(x - 3)^{4/3}/(x - 3)^{1/3}$
73. $(-64p^3)^{2/3}$
74. $(3a^{3/4}b^{1/2}a^{1/4})^2$
75. $(x^{2/3}y^{-1/2}/z^{1/6})^6$
76. $(16p^8q^{12})^{1/4}$
77. $(20a^2b^4)^{1/2}$
78. $(m^{1/4}n^{-1/2})^4(m^3n^{-2/3})^{-1}$

Simplify each radical expression and then use the table of square roots on the inside front cover to find a decimal approximation.

79. $\sqrt{2300}$                     80. $6/\sqrt{3}$

Solve each equation.

81. $\sqrt{4x - 9} = 1$                82. $\sqrt{3c + 10} + \sqrt{15 - 2c} = 0$

83. $\sqrt{t} + \sqrt{t + 5} = 5$      84. $\sqrt{s^2 + 9} = s + 1$

85. Evaluate the expression $(-b \pm \sqrt{b^2 - 4ac})/2a$ for $a = 8$, $b = -6$, and $c = \frac{1}{2}$.

86. The radius $r$ of a sphere of volume $V$ is given by the formula $r = \sqrt[3]{3V/4\pi}$. Determine the radius of a spherical balloon that holds $343\pi/6$ cubic meters of hot air.

87. The radius $r$ of a sphere of surface area $S$ is given by the formula $r = \frac{1}{2}\sqrt{S/\pi}$. Given that 14 gal of paint were used to paint a spherical water tank and the label on each gal can specified that the contents would cover 200 sq ft, determine the diameter of the tank.

88. Determine the voltage needed to operate a crockpot that uses 225 watts of power and has a resistance of 72 ohms.

89. Neglecting air resistance, the time $t$ in seconds that it takes an object to fall $h$ feet is given by the formula $t = \sqrt{h}/4$. If a coin is dropped into a well and 2.5 seconds later the splash occurs, how deep is the well?

90. What length should a pendulum have if it is to take 3 sec to complete a cycle?

91. If 500 g of carbon-14 are allowed to decay, how much will remain after (a) 1900 yr, (b) 2850 yr, (c) 5700 yr, (d) 8550 yr?

92. According to the Cobb-Douglas production function of Example 6 in Section 10.7, how many widgets can be produced using (a) 15 units of labor and 15 units of capital? (b) 16 units of labor and 4 units of capital?

# Chapter Chapter Chapter Chapter Eleven Eleven Eleven Eleven

*SECOND-DEGREE EQUATIONS*

## 11.1   SOLUTION BY FACTORING

First-degree equations in one variable and their solution were studied in Chapter 3. In this chapter we shall learn to solve *second*-degree equations in one variable. We begin with a definition.

---

**Definition**   A **second-degree equation,** or **quadratic equation,** in the one variable $x$ is any equation that can be expressed in the form

$$ax^2 + bx + c = 0,$$

where $a \neq 0$.

---

The name *quadratic* equation probably stems from the fact that such an equation contains a squared term (a square being the simplest *four*-sided figure) as its highest-degree term. A procedure for solving quadratic equations was known by the Babylonians as early as 2000 B.C.

Note that if $a = 0$, then the equation above becomes

$$0 \cdot x^2 + bx + c = 0,$$

or simply

$$bx + c = 0,$$

which is a *first*-degree equation (assuming $b \neq 0$ also).

**EXAMPLE 1**   The equation $x^2 + 5x + 6 = 0$ is a quadratic equation with

$$a = 1, b = 5, c = 6. \quad \square$$

When a quadratic equation is written in the form $ax^2 + bx + c = 0$, it is said to be in **standard form**.

**EXAMPLE 2**   Write the equation $x(7x + 1) + 1 = 4x^2 + 11$ in standard form and identify $a$, $b$, and $c$.

$$x(7x + 1) + 1 = 4x^2 + 11$$
$$7x^2 + x + 1 = 4x^2 + 11$$
$$3x^2 + x - 10 = 0.$$

Therefore $a = 3$, $b = 1$, and $c = -10$. $\quad \square$

**EXAMPLE 3** Write the equation $2x^2 + 5x - 9 = x^2 + 5x$ in standard form and identify $a$, $b$, and $c$.

$$2x^2 + 5x - 9 = x^2 + 5x$$
$$x^2 - 9 = 0.$$

Therefore $a = 1$, $b = 0$, and $c = -9$. □

The easiest method for solving a second-degree equation is to first write the equation in standard form and then *factor* the left-hand side. For example, to solve the equation

$$x^2 - 5x = -6,$$

we first write the equation as

$$x^2 - 5x + 6 = 0$$

and then factor the left-hand side to get

$$(x - 2) \cdot (x - 3) = 0.$$

When written in this form, a quadratic equation may be solved using the following property of the real number system:

---

**Zero Factor Property**

$a \cdot b = 0$ if and only if $a = 0$ or $b = 0$.

---

In our case, the statement

$$(x - 2) \cdot (x - 3) = 0$$

will be a true statement if and only if

$$x - 2 = 0 \quad \text{or} \quad x - 3 = 0;$$

that is, if

$$x = 2 \quad \text{or} \quad x = 3.$$

Therefore, the solutions to the equation $x^2 - 5x = -6$ are 2 and 3.

Note that the equation $x^2 - 5x = -6$ has *two* solutions, each a value of $x$ that satisfies the original equation. The solution is *not* an ordered pair and should not be regarded as such. Remember that an ordered pair is a solution to an equation in *two* variables, and the numbers in an ordered pair represent values of two *different* variables.

We can check each of our solutions by substituting it into the original equation $x^2 - 5x = -6$.

$$\text{CHECK:} \quad 2^2 - 5 \cdot 2 \stackrel{?}{=} -6 \qquad 3^2 - 5 \cdot 3 \stackrel{?}{=} -6$$
$$4 - 10 \stackrel{?}{=} -6 \qquad 9 - 15 \stackrel{?}{=} -6$$
$$-6 = -6 \qquad\qquad -6 = -6.$$

The method that was used to solve the quadratic equation above is called the **factoring method**.

Since the quadratic equation $x^2 - 5x = -6$ had two solutions, one might be tempted to ask if *every* quadratic equation has two real number solutions. The answer is *no*! The equation $x^2 = 0$ has only the *one* solution $x = 0$, and the equation $x^2 = -4$ has *no* real number solution. Thus *a quadratic equation may have two, one, or no real solutions.*

**EXAMPLE 4**   Solve $3x^2 + x - 10 = 0$.

In this case the equation is already in standard form. Therefore we simply factor the left-hand side.

$$3x^2 + x - 10 = 0$$
$$(3x - 5)(x + 2) = 0.$$

Then each of the factors is set equal to 0.

$$3x - 5 = 0 \quad \text{or} \quad x + 2 = 0.$$

Finally, each of these *first*-degree equations is solved.

$$3x = 5 \qquad x = -2.$$
$$x = \frac{5}{3}$$

The solutions are $\frac{5}{3}$ and $-2$.

$$\text{CHECK:} \quad 3\left(\frac{5}{3}\right)^2 + \frac{5}{3} - 10 \stackrel{?}{=} 0 \qquad 3(-2)^2 + (-2) - 10 \stackrel{?}{=} 0$$
$$3\left(\frac{25}{9}\right) + \frac{5}{3} - 10 \stackrel{?}{=} 0 \qquad\qquad 3 \cdot 4 - 2 - 10 \stackrel{?}{=} 0$$
$$\frac{25}{3} + \frac{5}{3} - \frac{30}{3} \stackrel{?}{=} 0 \qquad\qquad 12 - 2 - 10 \stackrel{?}{=} 0$$
$$0 = 0 \qquad\qquad\qquad 0 = 0. \quad \square$$

**EXAMPLE 5**   Solve $x^2 + 25 = 10x$.

$$x^2 + 25 = 10x$$
$$x^2 - 10x + 25 = 0$$
$$(x - 5)(x - 5) = 0$$
$$x - 5 = 0 \quad \text{or} \quad x - 5 = 0$$
$$x = 5 \qquad\qquad x = 5.$$

The solution is 5.

$$\text{CHECK:} \quad 5^2 + 25 \stackrel{?}{=} 10 \cdot 5$$
$$25 + 25 \stackrel{?}{=} 50$$
$$50 = 50. \quad \square$$

**EXAMPLE 6**   Solve $2x^2 + 4x = 0$.

$$2x^2 + 4x = 0$$
$$2x(x + 2) = 0$$
$$2x = 0 \quad \text{or} \quad x + 2 = 0$$
$$x = 0 \qquad\qquad x = -2.$$

The solutions are 0 and $-2$.

$$\text{CHECK:} \quad 2 \cdot 0^2 + 4 \cdot 0 \stackrel{?}{=} 0 \qquad 2(-2)^2 + 4(-2) \stackrel{?}{=} 0$$
$$2 \cdot 0 + 0 \stackrel{?}{=} 0 \qquad\qquad 2 \cdot 4 - 8 \stackrel{?}{=} 0$$
$$0 = 0 \qquad\qquad\qquad 0 = 0. \quad \square$$

**EXAMPLE 7**   Solve $x^2 - 49 = 0$.

$$x^2 - 49 = 0$$
$$(x - 7)(x + 7) = 0$$
$$x - 7 = 0 \quad \text{or} \quad x + 7 = 0$$
$$x = 7 \qquad\qquad x = -7.$$

The solutions are 7 and $-7$.

$$\text{CHECK:} \quad 7^2 - 49 \stackrel{?}{=} 0 \qquad (-7)^2 - 49 \stackrel{?}{=} 0$$
$$49 - 49 \stackrel{?}{=} 0 \qquad 49 - 49 \stackrel{?}{=} 0$$
$$0 = 0 \qquad\qquad 0 = 0. \quad \square$$

The technique of factoring can be applied to solve certain special types of *higher-order* equations.

**EXAMPLE 8**    Solve the *cubic* equation $10x^3 - 30x^2 + 20x = 0$.

We begin by factoring out the common factor $10x$ from the left-hand side of the equation.

$$10x^3 - 30x^2 + 20x = 0$$
$$10x(x^2 - 3x + 2) = 0.$$

The remaining second-degree trinomial is then factored.

$$10x(x - 1)(x - 2) = 0.$$

Finally, each of the three factors is set equal to 0, since the product on the left-hand side is zero if *any* of the three factors is zero. The resulting three first-degree equations are then solved.

$$10x = 0 \quad \text{or} \quad x - 1 = 0 \quad \text{or} \quad x - 2 = 0$$
$$x = 0 \qquad\qquad x = 1 \qquad\qquad x = 2.$$

The solutions are 0, 1, and 2.

$$\text{CHECK:} \quad 10 \cdot 0^3 - 30 \cdot 0^2 + 20 \cdot 0 \stackrel{?}{=} 0$$
$$0 - 0 + 0 \stackrel{?}{=} 0$$
$$0 = 0$$
$$10 \cdot 1^3 - 30 \cdot 1^2 + 20 \cdot 1 \stackrel{?}{=} 0$$
$$10 - 30 + 20 \stackrel{?}{=} 0$$
$$0 = 0$$
$$10 \cdot 2^3 - 30 \cdot 2^2 + 20 \cdot 2 \stackrel{?}{=} 0$$
$$80 - 120 + 40 \stackrel{?}{=} 0$$
$$0 = 0. \quad \square$$

It should be pointed out that not all higher-order equations can be solved by factoring. For example, we are presently not able to solve the equation

$$x^3 + 6x^2 + 11x + 6 = 0,$$

because at this point we do not possess the skills that would enable us to factor the left-hand side.

Recall from Section 5.5 that when an object with little air resistance is projected vertically upward from an initial height of $s$ feet and with an initial velocity of $r$ feet per second, its height $h$ in feet after $t$ seconds is given by the formula

$$h = -16t^2 + rt + s.$$

**EXAMPLE 9** Suppose a ball is thrown upward from a height of 48 feet with an initial velocity of 32 feet per second. How much time will elapse before the ball strikes the ground?

Substituting $s = 48$ and $r = 32$ into the formula above, we have that the height of the ball after $t$ seconds is

$$h = -16t^2 + 32t + 48.$$

Since we want to know the value of $t$ when $h = 0$, we write

$$0 = -16t^2 + 32t + 48.$$

Writing this quadratic equation in standard form and then dividing both sides by 16, we have

$$t^2 - 2t - 3 = 0$$
$$(t - 3)(t + 1) = 0$$
$$t = 3 \quad \text{or} \quad t = -1 \quad \text{(we reject the negative answer because in this problem it does not apply).}$$

The ball strikes the ground at $t = 3$ scconds. □

## Problem Set 11.1

Write each quadratic equation in standard form and identify $a$, $b$, and $c$.

1. $2x^2 + 9x = -4$
2. $3x^2 + 7x = -2$
3. $x^2 + 4 = 4x$
4. $x^2 + 9 = 6x$
5. $x^2 = x$
6. $x^2 = 1$
7. $9(x^2 + x) - 25 = 9x$
8. $4(x^2 - x) + 5 = 5(1 - x)$
9. $4x^2 = 1$
10. $9x^2 = x$
11. $2(x^2 + 1) - x = 4x - 3 + x^2$
12. $4(x^2 + x) - 6 = 3x^2 + 4(x + 1)$

Solve each of the following quadratic equations using the factoring method.

13. $x^2 - 4x + 3 = 0$
14. $x^2 - 3x + 2 = 0$
15. $x^2 + 5x + 6 = 0$
16. $x^2 + 3x + 2 = 0$
17. $x^2 - 6x = -8$
18. $x^2 - 7x = -12$
19. $x^2 + 4x - 12 = 0$
20. $x^2 + 6x - 16 = 0$

21. $x^2 - 4x + 4 = 0$
22. $x^2 - 6x + 9 = 0$
23. $2x^2 + x - 21 = 0$
24. $10x^2 + x - 2 = 0$
25. $6x^2 + x = 1$
26. $3x^2 + 8x = -4$
27. $4x^2 + 20x = -25$
28. $9x^2 + 24x = -16$
29. $x^2 + 5x = 0$
30. $x^2 + 7x = 0$
31. $2x^2 = 16x$
32. $3x^2 = 9x$
33. $x^2 - 16 = 0$
34. $x^2 - 25 = 0$
35. $x^2 - 9 = 0$
36. $x^2 - 4 = 0$
37. $4x^2 - 25 = 0$
38. $9x^2 - 16 = 0$
39. $6x^2 = 7x + 5$
40. $2x^2 = -3x + 20$
41. $x^2 - 3x - 54 = 0$
42. $x^2 - 13x - 48 = 0$
43. $36x^2 - 13x = 40$
44. $36x^2 + 5x = 24$

Solve each of the following higher-order equations by first factoring out a common factor, then factoring the polynomial that remains, and finally setting each factor equal to 0.

45. $x^3 - 3x^2 + 2x = 0$
46. $x^3 + 3x^2 + 2x = 0$
47. $3x^3 + 15x^2 + 18x = 0$
48. $5x^3 - 25x^2 + 30x = 0$
49. $20x^3 + 90x^2 - 50x = 0$
50. $30x^3 + 100x^2 - 80x = 0$
51. $4x^3 - x = 0$
52. $9x^3 - x = 0$
53. $x^4 - 7x^3 + 12x^2 = 0$
54. $x^4 - 8x^3 + 15x^2 = 0$
55. $x^4 - 100x^2 = 0$
56. $x^4 - 81x^2 = 0$

57. The equation $R^2 - 3R + 2 = 0$ may arise when working with electrical circuits. Solve this equation.
58. The equation $D^2 + 7D + 6 = 0$ may arise when working with springs. Solve this equation.
59. A stone is thrown upward from a height of 64 ft with an initial velocity of 48 ft per second. How much time will elapse before the stone strikes the ground?
60. An arrow is shot upward from the top of a cliff which is 288 ft high. If the initial velocity of the arrow is 112 ft per second, how long will it be before it strikes the ground below?
61. The square of a number $q$ is equal to five times the number $q$ itself. Find $q$.
62. The square of a number $q$ is equal to seven times the number $q$ itself. Find $q$.
63. Solve $(x - 3)^2 = x^2 - 6x$.
64. Solve $16x^2 + 8x - 17 = (4x + 1)^2 - 18$.
65. Solve $5x^2 - 10ax = 0$   for   $x$.
66. Solve $6x^2 + 7bx = 5b^2$   for   $x$.

## Calculator Problems

Solve each quadratic equation by factoring.

67. $257x^2 = 219{,}221x$          68. $6241x^2 - 3481 = 0$

## Challenge Problems

Solve each equation involving radicals.

69. $\sqrt{x - 1} = 3 - x$          70. $\sqrt{3x + 4} - \sqrt{x} = 2$

71. Solve $(x - 2)(x - 3)^2 + (x - 2)^2(x - 3) = 0$ by factoring.

72. Find a simple value for $x$ if $x = \sqrt{2 + \sqrt{2 + \sqrt{2 + \cdots}}}$.
    (*Hint:* Begin by squaring both sides.)

## 11.2  MORE QUADRATIC EQUATIONS

Remember from Chapter 3 that when an equation involves fractions, it is generally best to begin the solving process by multiplying both sides of the equation by the lcd. This procedure clears the equation of fractions.

**EXAMPLE 1**   Solve $y^2 - \frac{9}{10}y + \frac{1}{5} = 0$.

Both sides are multiplied by the lcd 10.

$$10\left(y^2 - \frac{9}{10}y + \frac{1}{5}\right) = 10 \cdot 0$$

$$10 \cdot y^2 - 10 \cdot \frac{9}{10}y + 10 \cdot \frac{1}{5} = 0$$

$$10y^2 - 9y + 2 = 0.$$

The equation is now cleared of fractions, and the solution is determined using the method of factoring.

$$(5y - 2)(2y - 1) = 0$$

$$5y - 2 = 0 \quad \text{or} \quad 2y - 1 = 0$$

$$5y = 2 \qquad\qquad 2y = 1$$

$$y = \frac{2}{5} \qquad\qquad y = \frac{1}{2}.$$

The solutions are $\frac{2}{5}$ and $\frac{1}{2}$.  □

**EXAMPLE 2**   Solve $3x^2/5 - 6x = 0$.

Multiplying each term in the equation by the lcd 5 clears the equation of fractions.

$$5 \cdot \frac{3x^2}{5} - 5 \cdot 6x = 5 \cdot 0$$

$$3x^2 - 30x = 0.$$

The resulting equation is then solved by factoring.

$$3x(x - 10) = 0$$

$$3x = 0 \quad \text{or} \quad x - 10 = 0$$

$$x = 0 \qquad\qquad x = 10.$$

The solutions are 0 and 10.  □

When a quadratic equation has no first-degree term, it can be solved using either of two methods, the factoring method or the **extraction of roots** method.

**EXAMPLE 3**   Solve $4x^2 - 9 = 0$.

**FACTORING METHOD**

$$4x^2 - 9 = 0$$

$$(2x - 3)(2x + 3) = 0$$

$$2x - 3 = 0 \quad \text{or} \quad 2x + 3 = 0$$

$$2x = 3 \qquad\qquad 2x = -3$$

$$x = \frac{3}{2} \qquad\qquad x = -\frac{3}{2}.$$

The solutions are $\frac{3}{2}$ and $-\frac{3}{2}$.

**EXTRACTION OF ROOTS METHOD**

$$4x^2 - 9 = 0$$
$$4x^2 = 9$$
$$x^2 = \frac{9}{4}$$
$$x = \pm\frac{3}{2}.$$

The solutions are $\frac{3}{2}$ and $-\frac{3}{2}$. □

When using the extraction of roots method, make certain that both the positive *and* the negative square root are included as solutions.

**EXAMPLE 4**   Solve $x^2 - 3 = 0$.

Since the first-degree term is missing, we may use the *extraction of roots* method.

$$x^2 - 3 = 0$$
$$x^2 = 3$$
$$x = \pm\sqrt{3}.$$

If the *factoring* method is used to solve this equation, each factor will contain the irrational number $\sqrt{3}$.

$$x^2 - 3 = 0$$
$$(x - \sqrt{3})(x + \sqrt{3}) = 0$$
$$x - \sqrt{3} = 0 \quad \text{or} \quad x + \sqrt{3} = 0$$
$$x = \sqrt{3} \qquad\qquad x = -\sqrt{3}.$$

In either case, the solutions are $\sqrt{3}$ and $-\sqrt{3}$. □

Some quadratic equations that *do* possess a first-degree term can still be solved by the extraction of roots method due to their special form.

**EXAMPLE 5**   Solve $(x - 3)^2 = 5$.

This equation is of the form $X^2 = A$, where $X = x - 3$ and $A = 5$. Therefore it can be solved by extraction of roots. Taking the square root of each side, we have

$$(x - 3)^2 = 5$$
$$x - 3 = \pm\sqrt{5}.$$

Finally, to solve for $x$ we add 3 to each side and get

$$x = 3 \pm \sqrt{5}.$$

The solutions are $3 + \sqrt{5}$ and $3 - \sqrt{5}$. □

Both of the solutions to Example 5 are *irrational* numbers. They can be approximated if we so desire as follows:

$$x = 3 + \sqrt{5} \qquad x = 3 - \sqrt{5}$$
$$x \approx 3 + 2.236 \qquad x \approx 3 - 2.236$$
$$x \approx 5.236 \qquad x \approx 0.764.$$

Normally, however, we shall leave the solutions in their *exact* form $3 + \sqrt{5}$ and $3 - \sqrt{5}$.

Recall from Section 5.4 that the value $V$ of an account after $t$ years is given by the formula

$$V = P(1 + r)^t,$$

where $P$ is the original principal and $r$ is the annual interest rate (compounded annually) *expressed as a decimal.*

**EXAMPLE 6**   Determine the annual interest rate $r$ (compounded annually) that is needed if \$1000 is to amount to \$1440 in two years.

Setting $V = 1440$, $P = 1000$, and $t = 2$ in the formula above, we have

$$1440 = 1000(1 + r)^2.$$

We divide each side by 1000, and then solve for $r$ by extraction of roots.

$$(1 + r)^2 = 1.44$$
$$1 + r = \pm 1.2$$
$$r = -1 \pm 1.2$$
$$r = -1 + 1.2 \quad \text{or} \quad r = -1 - 1.2$$
$$r = 0.2, \text{ or } 20\% \qquad \cancel{r = -2.2} \quad \text{(the negative answer does not apply).}$$

A 20% interest rate is needed. □

## Problem Set 11.2

Solve each of the following quadratic equations by first multiplying both sides by the lcd.

1. $\frac{1}{6}x^2 + \frac{1}{6}x - 1 = 0$
2. $\frac{1}{12}x^2 + \frac{1}{12}x - 1 = 0$
3. $\frac{1}{5}x^2 + x + \frac{6}{5} = 0$
4. $\frac{1}{5}x^2 - x + \frac{6}{5} = 0$
5. $x^2/10 - x + 5/2 = 0$
6. $x^2/12 + x + 3 = 0$
7. $a^2 - a/6 - 1/3 = 0$
8. $a^2/6 - a/2 + 1/3 = 0$
9. $a^2/12 - a/12 - 1 = 0$
10. $a^2/5 - a/10 - 1 = 0$
11. $5a^2 + 4a + \frac{4}{5} = 0$
12. $3a^2 + 4a + \frac{4}{3} = 0$
13. $y^2/8 + 3y/4 + 1 = 0$
14. $y^2/8 - 3y/4 + 1 = 0$
15. $y^2/8 - y = 0$
16. $y^2/9 - y = 0$
17. $3m^2/7 + m/21 = 0$
18. $5m^2/6 + m/30 = 0$
19. $r^2/9 - 9 = 0$
20. $r^2/10 - 10 = 0$
21. $6s^2 - \frac{1}{6} = 0$
22. $5s^2 - \frac{1}{5} = 0$
23. $t^2/8 - t/12 = 0$
24. $t^2/10 - t/15 = 0$
25. $0.2p^2 - 0.1p = 0.6$
26. $0.3p^2 - 0.1p = 0.2$

Solve each of the following equations using (a) the factoring method, and then (b) the extraction of roots method.

27. $x^2 - 64 = 0$
28. $x^2 - 25 = 0$
29. $x^2 - 121 = 0$
30. $x^2 - 144 = 0$
31. $9x^2 - 1 = 0$
32. $4x^2 - 1 = 0$
33. $25x^2 - 4 = 0$
34. $16x^2 - 9 = 0$
35. $81x^2 - 100 = 0$
36. $49x^2 - 121 = 0$
37. $x^2 - 7 = 0$
38. $x^2 - 5 = 0$
39. $x^2 - 11 = 0$
40. $x^2 - 13 = 0$
41. $4x^2 - 3 = 0$
42. $9x^2 - 11 = 0$
43. $t^2 - 12 = 0$
44. $t^2 - 45 = 0$
45. $q^2 + 9 = 0$
46. $q^2 + 25 = 0$

Solve each equation for $x$ by extraction of roots.

47. $(x + 1)^2 = 16$
48. $(x + 1)^2 = 36$
49. $(x + 1)^2 = 3$
50. $(x + 1)^2 = 5$
51. $(x - 3)^2 = 25$
52. $(x - 3)^2 = 9$
53. $(x - 3)^2 = 11$
54. $(x - 3)^2 = 13$
55. $(x - 2)^2 - 50 = 0$
56. $(x - 2)^2 - 32 = 0$
57. $(x + 5)^2 + 1 = 0$
58. $(x + 5)^2 + 4 = 0$
59. $(x - a)^2 - b = 0$
60. $(x + a)^2 - b = 0$

61. The speed of the current in a stream can be determined by placing an open-ended, L-shaped tube into the stream (see diagram below). The current speed $s$ in ft per sec is given by **Torricelli's law**, $s^2 = 64h$, where $h$ is in ft. Determine the current speed $s$ if $h = 3$ in.

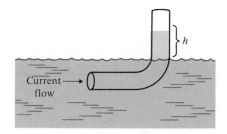

62. If the L-shaped tube of Problem 61 is used as a speedometer for a boat traveling on a still lake, find the speed of the boat if $h = 6\frac{3}{4}$ in.

63. Determine the annual interest rate $r$ (compounded annually) that is needed if $1000 is to amount to $1210 in two years.

64. Determine the annual interest rate $r$ (compounded annually) that is needed if $1000 is to amount to $1690 in two years.

65. The number of diagonals $d$ for *polygons** having $n$ sides is given by the formula $d = \frac{1}{2}n(n - 3)$. For example, a polygon with 6 sides has $d = \frac{1}{2} \cdot 6(6 - 3) = 9$ diagonals. How many *sides* does a polygon with 35 *diagonals* have?

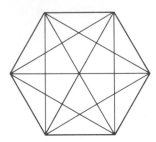

66. The sum of the first $n$ positive integers is given by the formula $1 + 2 + 3 + \cdots + n = \frac{1}{2}n(n + 1)$. For example, the sum of the first five positive integers is given by $1 + 2 + 3 + 4 + 5 = \frac{1}{2} \cdot 5(5 + 1) = 15$. If the sum of the first $n$ positive integers is 66, find $n$.

67. A piece of concrete falls from a bridge 256 ft high. How long does it take to hit the ground below? (See Example 9 of Section 11.1.)

68. A plant falls from a window ledge. How long does it take to hit the street 144 ft below? (See Example 9 of Section 11.1.)

69. The sum of a number $r$ and its reciprocal $1/r$ is 10/3. Find $r$.

70. The sum of a number $r$ and its reciprocal $1/r$ is 50/7. Find $r$.

71. The area of a circle is given by $A = \pi r^2$. Solve this equation for $r$.

72. The relationship between energy and matter is given by $E = mc^2$. Solve this equation for $c$.

73. *Kinetic energy* is given by $K = \frac{1}{2}mv^2$. Solve for $v$.

74. The volume of a cone is given by $V = \frac{1}{3}\pi r^2 h$. Solve for $r$.

75. Solve $c^2 = a^2 + b^2$    for    $a$.

76. Solve $c^2 = a^2 + b^2$    for    $b$.

* By **polygons** we mean triangles, rectangles, pentagons, and so on.

## Calculator Problems

77. The surface area $S$ of a sphere of radius $r$ is given by $S = 4\pi r^2$. Determine the approximate radius of a sphere whose surface area is 2137 sq m.
78. Determine the annual interest rate $r$ (compounded annually) that is needed if \$987 is to amount to \$1134 in two years.
79 Approximately how long would it take a rock dropped from the top of the *Leaning Tower of Pisa* to hit the ground 179 ft below? (See Example 9 of Section 11.1.)

## Challenge Problems

80. Determine the annual interest rate $r$ (compounded annually) that is needed if \$1000 is to amount to \$1728 in three years.
81. Solve Newton's *universal law of gravitation*
$$F = km_1 m_2 / d^2 \quad \text{for} \quad d.$$

Solve each equation.

82. $12 + \dfrac{5}{x^2} = \dfrac{19}{x}$

83. $\dfrac{1}{x} + \dfrac{1}{x-1} = \dfrac{7}{12}$

Solve each equation of *quadratic form*. (*Hint:* Let $x = t^2$ and then note that $x^2 = t^4$.)

84. $t^4 - 13t^2 + 36 = 0$

85. $t^4 - 5t^2 - 36 = 0$

---

## 11.3 | COMPLETING THE SQUARE

Factoring provides us with an easy method for solving many quadratic equations. Unfortunately, as we have already seen in Chapter 6, not all polynomials are factorable using integers only. For example, the left-hand side of the quadratic equation

$$x^2 - 6x + 4 = 0$$

cannot be factored using integers only.

We can solve the equation above, however, using a method called **completing the square.** The basic idea of this method is to put one side of the equation in the form $(x + d)^2$. This side of the equation is then said to be a *perfect square.*

In order to put the equation in this form, we first observe that

$$(x + d)^2 = x^2 + 2dx + d^2.$$

Now, note that *the term $d^2$ is the square of one-half the coefficient of $x$.* That is, the coefficient of $x$ is $2d$, and one-half of $2d$ squared is $(2d/2)^2 = d^2$.

We shall now return to the original equation and solve it by completing the square.

$$x^2 - 6x + 4 = 0.$$

We begin by subtracting 4 from each side.

$$x^2 - 6x = -4. \quad \left(-\frac{6}{2}\right)^2$$

We then *complete the square* on the left-hand side by adding the square of one-half the coefficient of $x$ to the left-hand side. That is, we add $(-6/2)^2 = 9$ to the left-hand side. Of course, if we add 9 to the left-hand side we must also add 9 to the right-hand side. Doing that, our equation becomes

$$x^2 - 6x + 9 = -4 + 9.$$

The left-hand side is now the perfect square $(x - 3)^2$. The equation can therefore be written as

$$(x - 3)^2 = 5.$$

Solving this last equation by extraction of roots, we have

$$x - 3 = \pm\sqrt{5}$$
$$x = 3 \pm \sqrt{5}.$$

Therefore the solutions are $3 + \sqrt{5}$ and $3 - \sqrt{5}$.

These irrational solutions may be checked in the same manner as other solutions, but the calculations are usually more involved.

CHECK: $(3 + \sqrt{5})^2 - 6(3 + \sqrt{5}) + 4 \stackrel{?}{=} 0$

$9 + 6\sqrt{5} + 5 - 18 - 6\sqrt{5} + 4 \stackrel{?}{=} 0$

$0 = 0$

$(3 - \sqrt{5})^2 - 6(3 - \sqrt{5}) + 4 \stackrel{?}{=} 0$

$9 - 6\sqrt{5} + 5 - 18 + 6\sqrt{5} + 4 \stackrel{?}{=} 0$

$0 - 0.$

While the factoring method and the extraction of roots method have the advantage of simplicity, one advantage of the completing the square method is that it can be used to solve *any* quadratic equation.

**EXAMPLE 1**   Solve $x^2 + 4x - 7 = 0$.

We begin by adding 7 to each side.

$$x^2 + 4x - 7 = 0$$
$$x^2 + 4x - 7.$$

We now complete the square by adding $(\frac{4}{2})^2 = 4$ to each side.

$$x^2 + 4x + 4 = 7 + 4$$

The left-hand side is now the perfect square $(x + 2)^2$.

$$(x + 2)^2 = 11.$$

Taking the square root of each side, we have

$$x + 2 = \pm\sqrt{11}.$$

Finally, subtracting 2 from each side gives the two solutions

$$x = -2 \pm \sqrt{11}.$$

The solutions are $-2 + \sqrt{11}$ and $-2 - \sqrt{11}$. □

**EXAMPLE 2**   Solve $4x^2 - 8x - 3 = 0$.

$$4x^2 - 8x - 3 = 0$$
$$4x^2 - 8x = 3.$$

Since the coefficient of $x^2$ is not 1, we divide both sides of the equation by 4.

$$x^2 - 2x = \frac{3}{4}.$$

$x^2 + 3x = -2$

$x^2 + 3x + \left(\frac{3}{2}\right)^2 = -2 + \frac{9}{4}$

$\left(x + \frac{3}{2}\right)^2$

$= \frac{1}{4}$

$\left(\frac{3}{2}\right)^2 = \frac{9}{4}$

$x + \frac{3}{2} = \pm\frac{1}{2}$

$x = -\frac{3}{2} \pm \frac{1}{2} = -1$ or $-2$

Completing the square by adding $(-2/2)^2 = 1$ to each side, we have

$$x^2 - 2x + 1 = \frac{3}{4} + 1$$

$$(x - 1)^2 = \frac{7}{4}$$

$$x - 1 = \pm\frac{\sqrt{7}}{2}$$

$$x = 1 \pm \frac{\sqrt{7}}{2}, \quad \text{or}$$

$$x = \frac{2 \pm \sqrt{7}}{2}.$$

The solutions are $\dfrac{2 + \sqrt{7}}{2}$ and $\dfrac{2 - \sqrt{7}}{2}$. $\square$

We shall now use the completing the square method to solve an applied problem. To set up the problem, let us first consider the three rectangles below.

Which rectangle do you think is the most pleasing to the eye? Early Greeks were so impressed with the visually pleasing characteristics of the center rectangle, called the *golden rectangle,* that they used it in much of their architecture. The *Parthenon* at Athens, built between 447 B.C. and 432 B.C., is a good example. The golden rectangle can also be found in the works of Renaissance artists such as Leonardo da Vinci (1452–1519), as well as in more modern artists like Mondrian (1872–1944). Interestingly, the golden rectangle also appears in a variety of natural forms from seashells to flowers.

The center rectangle above was constructed so that it was composed of a square and a smaller rectangle that is *similar* to the original rectangle. That is,

Since the ratios of the corresponding sides of the two similar rectangles above are equal, we can write

$$\frac{y}{x} = \frac{x}{y - x}.$$

Cross-multiplying, we have

$$y^2 - xy = x^2.$$

Dividing through by $x^2$ gives

$$\frac{y^2}{x^2} - \frac{xy}{x^2} = \frac{x^2}{x^2}$$

$$\left(\frac{y}{x}\right)^2 - \left(\frac{y}{x}\right) = 1.$$

Now $y/x$ is the ratio of the length of the original rectangle to its width. This ratio is called the **golden ratio.** If we denote the golden ratio by $G$, the last equation becomes

$$G^2 - G = 1.$$

**EXAMPLE 3** Find the golden ratio $G$ by solving the equation $G^2 - G = 1$.

We complete the square by adding $\left(-\frac{1}{2}\right)^2 = \frac{1}{4}$ to each side.

$$G^2 - G + \frac{1}{4} = 1 + \frac{1}{4}$$

$$\left(G - \frac{1}{2}\right)^2 = \frac{5}{4}$$

$$G - \frac{1}{2} = \pm\frac{\sqrt{5}}{2}$$

$$G = \frac{1}{2} + \frac{\sqrt{5}}{2} \quad \text{or} \quad G = \frac{1}{2} - \frac{\sqrt{5}}{2} \quad \begin{array}{l}\text{(the negative answer}\\\text{does not apply).}\end{array}$$

Therefore the golden ratio is $\frac{1}{2} + \frac{1}{2}\sqrt{5}$, or $(1 + \sqrt{5})/2$. □

## Problem Set 11.3

Complete the square on each expression. Then factor the resulting expression.

1. $x^2 + 4x$       2. $x^2 + 6x$       3. $y^2 - 10y$       4. $y^2 - 8y$
5. $t^2 + 14t$      6. $t^2 + 12t$      7. $s^2 - 3s$        8. $s^2 - 5s$
9. $r^2 + r$        10. $r^2 - r$       11. $4m^2$           12. $9m^2$

Solve each of the following quadratic equations by completing the square.

13. $x^2 - 4x + 1 = 0$       14. $x^2 - 6x + 7 = 0$       15. $x^2 - 2x - 6 = 0$
16. $x^2 - 8x - 1 = 0$       17. $x^2 + 10x + 14 = 0$     18. $x^2 + 14x + 42 = 0$
19. $x^2 - 8x + 13 = 0$      20. $x^2 - 4x - 15 = 0$      21. $x^2 + x - 1 = 0$
22. $x^2 + x - 3 = 0$        23. $x^2 + 3x - 9 = 0$       24. $x^2 - 3x - 9 = 0$
25. $4x^2 + 4x - 3 = 0$      26. $4x^2 - 4x - 3 = 0$      27. $2x^2 - 20x + 26 = 0$
28. $2x^2 - 20x + 14 = 0$    29. $4x^2 - 24x + 5 = 0$     30. $9x^2 - 18x - 2 = 0$
31. $3x^2 - 2x = 2$          32. $3x^2 - 10x = 2$         33. $5m^2 + 10m = -25$
34. $7m^2 + 28m = -35$

35. A pellet is projected vertically upward from ground level by a slingshot that gives it an initial velocity of 96 ft per second. When will the pellet be at a height of 64 ft? (See Example 9 of Section 11.1.)
36. When will the pellet of Problem 35 be at a height of 112 ft?
37. The square of a number $s$ equals the sum of the number $s$ and 3. Find $s$.
38. The square of a number $s$ equals the sum of the number $s$ and 5. Find $s$.

## Calculator Problems

39. Complete the square on the expression $x^2 + 5798x$. Then factor the resulting expression.
40. In Example 2 we showed that the solutions to the equation $4x^2 - 8x - 3 = 0$ were $\dfrac{2 + \sqrt{7}}{2}$ and $\dfrac{2 - \sqrt{7}}{2}$. Approximate these

irrational solutions as four-place decimals, and then check these approximate decimal solutions in the original equation.

## Challenge Problems

Given two numbers, say 3 and $-5$, we can write a quadratic equation having these numbers as solutions as follows:

$$x = 3 \quad \text{or} \quad x = -5$$
$$x - 3 = 0 \quad x + 5 = 0$$
$$(x - 3) \cdot (x + 5) = 0$$
$$x^2 + 2x - 15 = 0.$$

Use this technique to write a quadratic equation with *integer coefficients* having the given solutions.

41. 2 and $-6$    42. $\frac{1}{3}$ and $\frac{2}{5}$    43. 4 and 0    44. $1 + \sqrt{3}$ and $1 - \sqrt{3}$

## 11.4 THE QUADRATIC FORMULA

The method of completing the square can be used to develop a *formula* that enables us to solve any quadratic equation. Consider the **general quadratic equation** $ax^2 + bx + c = 0$ $(a \neq 0)$. By applying the method of completing the square, we can obtain the solutions in terms of the coefficients $a$, $b$, and $c$.

$$ax^2 + bx + c = 0$$
$$x^2 + \frac{b}{a}x + \frac{c}{a} = 0$$
$$x^2 + \frac{b}{a}x = -\frac{c}{a}.$$

Since the coefficient of $x$ is $b/a$, the square of one-half the coefficient of $x$ is $(b/2a)^2$. Thus, we complete the square by adding $(b/2a)^2$ to each side.

$$x^2 + \frac{b}{a}x + \left(\frac{b}{2a}\right)^2 = -\frac{c}{a} + \left(\frac{b}{2a}\right)^2$$

$$\left(x + \frac{b}{2a}\right)^2 = -\frac{4ac}{4a^2} + \frac{b^2}{4a^2}$$

$$\left(x + \frac{b}{2a}\right)^2 = \frac{b^2 - 4ac}{4a^2}$$

$$x + \frac{b}{2a} = \pm\sqrt{\frac{b^2 - 4ac}{4a^2}}$$

$$x + \frac{b}{2a} = \pm\frac{\sqrt{b^2 - 4ac}}{2a}$$

$$x = -\frac{b}{2a} \pm \frac{\sqrt{b^2 - 4ac}}{2a}$$

$$x = \frac{-b \pm \sqrt{b^2 - 4ac}}{2a}.$$

We now have a formula for solving any quadratic equation. It is usually stated as follows:

---

**The Quadratic Formula**

The solutions of the quadratic equation

$$ax^2 + bx + c = 0 \quad (a \neq 0)$$

are given by

$$x = \frac{-b \pm \sqrt{b^2 - 4ac}}{2a}.$$

---

**EXAMPLE 1** Solve $3x^2 - 4x = -1$ using the quadratic formula.

We first put the equation in standard form in order to identify $a$, $b$, and $c$.

$$3x^2 - 4x = -1$$
$$3x^2 - 4x + 1 = 0.$$

$a = 3$, $b = -4$, $c = 1$.

Substituting these values for $a$, $b$, and $c$ into the quadratic formula, we have

$$x = \frac{-(-4) \pm \sqrt{(-4)^2 - 4(3)(1)}}{2(3)}$$

$$x = \frac{4 \pm \sqrt{16 - 12}}{6}$$

$$x = \frac{4 \pm \sqrt{4}}{6}$$

$$x = \frac{4 \pm 2}{6}.$$

Therefore,

$$x = \frac{4 + 2}{6} = 1 \quad \text{or} \quad x = \frac{4 - 2}{6} = \frac{1}{3}.$$

The solutions are 1 and $\frac{1}{3}$. □

**EXAMPLE 2**   Solve $x^2 + x - 1 = 0$ using the quadratic formula.

$$x^2 + x - 1 = 0.$$

$a = 1, b = 1, c - -1.$

$$x - \frac{-1 \pm \sqrt{(1)^2 - 4(1)(-1)}}{2(1)}$$

$$x = \frac{-1 \pm \sqrt{1 + 4}}{2}$$

$$x = \frac{-1 \pm \sqrt{5}}{2}$$

The solutions are $\dfrac{-1 + \sqrt{5}}{2}$ and $\dfrac{-1 - \sqrt{5}}{2}$. □

**EXAMPLE 3**   Solve $x^2/6 + x/3 - 1/3 = 0$ using the quadratic formula.

We first simplify the equation by multiplying both sides by the lcd 6.

$$\frac{x^2}{6} + \frac{x}{3} - \frac{1}{3} = 0$$

$$6\left(\frac{x^2}{6} + \frac{x}{3} - \frac{1}{3}\right) = 6 \cdot 0$$

$$x^2 + 2x - 2 = 0.$$

$a = 1, b = 2, c = -2.$

$$x = \frac{-2 \pm \sqrt{(2)^2 - 4(1)(-2)}}{2(1)}$$

$$x = \frac{-2 \pm \sqrt{12}}{2}$$

$$x = \frac{-2 \pm 2\sqrt{3}}{2}.$$

Dividing the denominator 2 into *both* terms in the numerator simplifies the solution to

$$x = \frac{-2}{2} \pm \frac{2\sqrt{3}}{2}$$

$$x = -1 \pm \sqrt{3}.$$

The solutions are $-1 + \sqrt{3}$ and $-1 - \sqrt{3}$. □

**EXAMPLE 4**   Solve $x^2 - 7x = 0$ using the quadratic formula.

$$x^2 - 7x = 0.$$

$a = 1, b = -7, c = 0.$

$$x = \frac{-(-7) \pm \sqrt{(-7)^2 - 4(1)(0)}}{2(1)}$$

$$x = \frac{7 \pm \sqrt{49 - 0}}{2}$$

$$x = \frac{7 \pm 7}{2}$$

$$x = \frac{7 + 7}{2} \quad \text{or} \quad x = \frac{7 - 7}{2}$$

$$x = \frac{14}{2} \qquad\qquad x = \frac{0}{2}$$

$$x = 7 \qquad\qquad x = 0.$$

The solutions are 7 and 0. □

**EXAMPLE 5**   Solve $x^2 + 2x + 5 = 0$ using the quadratic formula.

$$x^2 + 2x + 5 = 0.$$

$a = 1, b = 2, c = 5.$

$$x = \frac{-2 \pm \sqrt{(2)^2 - 4(1)(5)}}{2(1)}$$

$$x = \frac{-2 \pm \sqrt{4 - 20}}{2}$$

$$x = \frac{-2 \pm \sqrt{-16}}{2}.$$

But $\sqrt{-16}$ is not a real number! Therefore this quadratic equation has *no* real number solution. □

The method of solving a quadratic equation by completing the square can be rather tedious, and for that reason it is seldom used to solve a quadratic equation. The operation of completing the square does, however, have a variety of other applications in algebra. Our primary purpose in introducing it in this chapter was to allow us to derive the quadratic formula. Therefore, when confronted with a quadratic equation to solve, you should first try to solve it by *factoring* or *extraction of roots*. If that fails, then go immediately to the *quadratic formula*.

## Problem Set 11.4

Solve each of the following quadratic equations (a) by factoring, and then (b) using the quadratic formula.

1. $x^2 + 4x + 3 = 0$
2. $x^2 + 5x + 4 = 0$
3. $x^2 + x - 2 = 0$
4. $x^2 + 2x - 3 = 0$
5. $3x^2 + 8x = 3$
6. $2x^2 + 9x = 5$
7. $x^2 - 10x + 25 = 0$
8. $x^2 - 12x + 36 = 0$
9. $x^2 - 5x = 0$
10. $x^2 - 3x = 0$
11. $9x^2 - x = 0$
12. $8x^2 - x = 0$
13. $4x^2 - 25 = 0$
14. $4x^2 - 9 = 0$

Solve each of the following quadratic equations using the quadratic formula.

15. $x^2 + x - 3 = 0$
16. $x^2 + x - 4 = 0$
17. $x^2 - 3x + 1 = 0$
18. $x^2 - 5x + 5 = 0$
19. $2x^2 + 3x - 1 = 0$
20. $2x^2 + x - 2 = 0$
21. $x^2 - 2x = 1$
22. $x^2 - 2x = 2$
23. $3x^2 + 6x + 2 = 0$
24. $3x^2 + 6x + 1 = 0$
25. $x^2/6 - x/3 - 1 = 0$
26. $x^2/12 - x/3 + 1/12 = 0$
27. $x^2 + 25 = 12x$
28. $x^2 + 23 = 10x$
29. $x^2 + 2x + 2 = 0$
30. $x^2 - 2x + 2 = 0$
31. $x^2 - 2x + 5 = 0$
32. $x^2 + 2x + 5 = 0$
33. $x^2 - 4x - 1 = 0$
34. $x^2 + 4x - 1 = 0$
35. $\frac{1}{4}x^2 + \frac{1}{3}x - \frac{1}{12} = 0$

36. $\frac{1}{4}x^2 - \frac{1}{3}x - \frac{1}{12} = 0$      37. $x^2 = -5x - 8$           38. $x^2 = 5x - 8$
39. $\frac{3}{2}x^2 - x = \frac{1}{3}$                      40. $\frac{2}{3}x^2 - \frac{4}{9}x = \frac{1}{3}$   41. $2x^2 + \sqrt{3}x - 3 = 0$
42. $3x^2 - \sqrt{2}x - 1 = 0$

43. When will the ball of Example 9 in Section 11.1 be at a height of
    (a) 52 ft, (b) 80 ft?
44. When will the ball of Example 9 in Section 11.1 be at a height of
    (a) 56 ft, (b) 96 ft?
45. The sum of a number $p$ and its reciprocal $1/p$ is 5. Find $p$.
46. The sum of a number $p$ and its reciprocal $1/p$ is 7. Find $p$.

## Calculator Problems

Solve to the nearest tenth using the quadratic formula.

47. $2.5x^2 - 3.25x - 4.2 = 0$        48. $43x^2 + 797x + 229 = 0$

## Challenge Problems

49. Find a simple value for $x$ if $x = 1 + \dfrac{1}{1 + \dfrac{1}{1 + \cdots}}$.

    (*Hint:* What can the denominator on the right-hand side of the
    equation be replaced by?)
50. Given that $x = 1$ is a solution to $3x^3 - 8x^2 + 6x - 1 = 0$, find
    the other two solutions. (*Hint:* If $x = 1$ is a solution, then $x - 1$
    must be a factor of the left-hand side. Find the other factor.)

## 11.5   APPLIED PROBLEMS

Quadratic equations can be used to solve a wide variety of practical
problems. The *steps* for solving the word problems in this section are
the same steps that were given in Section 3.5. The only *difference* appears

in Steps 3 and 4, where the equation that must be written and solved will be a *second*-degree equation, rather than a *first*-degree equation. These steps are repeated below for review.

---

**Steps in Solving Word Problems**

1. Choose a variable, say $x$, and use it to represent one of the unknown quantities in the problem.
2. If there are other unknown quantities in the problem, represent each of them in terms of $x$.
3. Translate a statement in the problem into an equation involving $x$. A diagram is sometimes helpful here.
4. Solve the equation.
5. Check your solution.

---

Note how the steps above are used to solve the examples that follow.

**EXAMPLE 1**   The sum of two numbers is 16 and their product is 63. Find the numbers.

$$\text{Let } x = \text{one number.}$$
$$\text{Then } 16 - x = \text{the other number.}$$

Product of the numbers $= 63$

$$x \cdot (16 - x) = 63$$
$$16x - x^2 = 63$$
$$-x^2 + 16x - 63 = 0.$$

We multiply both sides by $-1$ to make factoring the left-hand side easier.

$$(-1)(-x^2 + 16x - 63) = (-1) \cdot 0$$
$$x^2 - 16x + 63 = 0$$
$$(x - 7)(x - 9) = 0$$

$$x - 7 = 0 \quad \text{or} \quad x - 9 = 0$$
$$x = 7, \qquad\qquad x = 9,$$
$$16 - x = 9 \qquad\quad 16 - x = 7.$$

The numbers are 7 and 9. □

422    Chapter 11   Second-Degree Equations

EXAMPLE 2   A square piece of sheet metal is to be made into a pan by cutting 2-in. squares from the corners and then turning up the sides. If the volume of the pan is to be 128 cubic in., what size piece of sheet metal is needed?

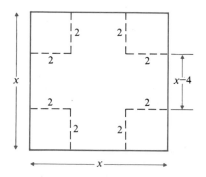

Let $x$ = the length of a side
in inches.

$$\text{Volume of pan} = 128$$
$$\ell \cdot w \cdot h = 128$$
$$(x - 4) \cdot (x - 4) \cdot 2 = 128$$
$$(x - 4)(x - 4) = 64$$
$$(x - 4)^2 = 64$$
$$x - 4 = 8 \quad \text{or} \quad x - 4 = -8$$
$$x = 12 \qquad \cancel{x = -4}.$$

The piece of metal should be 12 in. by 12 in. □

EXAMPLE 3   One computer can process a payroll in 2 hr less time than it takes another computer. If both computers working together take 3 hr, how long would it take each computer working alone?

Let $t$ = the time it takes the slower computer.
Then $t - 2$ = the time it takes the faster computer.

| The portion of the job done by the slower computer in 1 hr | + | the portion of the job done by the faster computer in 1 hr | = | the portion of the job done by both together in 1 hr |
|---|---|---|---|---|
| $\dfrac{1}{t}$ | + | $\dfrac{1}{t - 2}$ | = | $\dfrac{1}{3}$. |

We begin by multiplying both sides by the lcd $3t(t - 2)$.

$$3t(t - 2) \cdot \frac{1}{t} + 3t(t - 2) \cdot \frac{1}{t - 2} = 3t(t - 2) \cdot \frac{1}{3}$$

$$3(t - 2) + 3t = t(t - 2)$$

$$3t - 6 + 3t = t^2 - 2t$$

$$-t^2 + 8t - 6 = 0$$

$$t^2 - 8t + 6 = 0.$$

Since this last equation is not factorable, we use the quadratic formula with $a = 1$, $b = -8$, and $c = 6$.

$$t = \frac{-(-8) \pm \sqrt{(-8)^2 - 4(1)(6)}}{2(1)}$$

$$t = \frac{8 \pm \sqrt{64 - 24}}{2}$$

$$t = \frac{8 \pm \sqrt{40}}{2}$$

$$t = \frac{8 \pm 2\sqrt{10}}{2}$$

$$t = 4 + \sqrt{10}$$

$$t = 4 + \sqrt{10}, \quad \text{or} \qquad \qquad t = 4 - \sqrt{10}$$

$$t - 2 = 2 + \sqrt{10} \qquad \qquad \qquad t - 2 = 2 - \sqrt{10}.$$

The slower computer would take $4 + \sqrt{10} \approx 7.16$ hr while the faster computer would take $2 + \sqrt{10} \approx 5.16$ hr. □

**EXAMPLE 4**  A riverboat that travels 12 mph in still water makes a pleasure trip to a city upstream and back in 3 hr. If the city is 10 miles away, what is the rate of the current?

Let $r =$ the rate of the current.

| Time upstream | + | time downstream | = 3 |
|---|---|---|---|
| $\dfrac{\text{distance upstream}}{\text{rate upstream}}$ | + | $\dfrac{\text{distance downstream}}{\text{rate downstream}}$ | = 3 |
| $\dfrac{10}{12 - r}$ | + | $\dfrac{10}{12 + r}$ | = 3. |

The lcd is $(12 - r)(12 + r)$. Multiplying each side by this lcd gives

$$10(12 + r) + 10(12 - r) = 3(12 - r)(12 + r)$$
$$120 + 10r + 120 - 10r = 3(144 - r^2)$$
$$240 = 3(144 - r^2)$$
$$80 = 144 - r^2$$
$$r^2 = 64$$
$$r = 8 \quad \text{or} \quad r \cancel{=} -8.$$

The rate of the current is 8 mph. □

## Problem Set 11.5

1. The sum of two numbers is 12 and their product is 35. Find the numbers.
2. The sum of two numbers is 16 and their product is 55. Find the numbers.
3. Two consecutive positive numbers have a product of 132. Find the numbers.
4. Two consecutive positive numbers have a product of 72. Find the numbers.
5. Two consecutive odd whole numbers have a product of 143. Find the numbers.
6. Two consecutive even whole numbers have a product of 168. Find the numbers.
7. The sum of the squares of two consecutive positive integers is 221. Find the integers.
8. The sum of the squares of two consecutive positive integers is 145. Find the integers.
9. The length of a rectangle is 5 in. more than the width. If the area is 66 sq in., find the dimensions of the rectangle.
10. The length of a rectangle is 3 in. more than the width. If the area is 70 sq in., find the dimensions of the rectangle.
11. The length of a rectangle is 6 m more than twice the width. If the area is 260 sq m, find the dimensions of the rectangle.
12. The length of a rectangle is 4 m more than twice the width. If the area is 240 sq m, find the dimensions of the rectangle.

13. An artist wants to put a frame of uniform width around a 4-ft by 6-ft painting. If he wants the area of the frame to equal the area of the painting, how wide should he make the frame?

14. A rectangular garden that is 8 ft by 12 ft is surrounded by a path of uniform width. If the area of the path equals the area of the garden, find the width of the path.

15. A square piece of sheet metal is to be made into a pan by cutting 3-in. squares from the corners and turning up the sides. If the volume of the pan is to be 192 cubic in., what size piece of sheet metal is needed?

16. An open box is to be made from a square piece of cardboard by cutting a 4-in. square from each corner and turning up the sides. What size piece of cardboard is needed if the volume of the box is to be 400 cubic in.?

17. The piece of metal below is to be made into a trough with a rectangular cross-section by folding it along the dashed lines. What should the height $x$ of the trough be if it is to have a cross-sectional area of 8 sq in.?

18. Do Problem 17 if the cross-sectional area is to be 6 sq in.

19. One computer can perform a job in 1 hr less time than it takes another computer. If both computers working together can perform the job in 2 hr, find the time it takes each computer working alone.

20. One pipe can fill a tank in 2 hr less time than it takes another pipe. If both pipes are open it takes 4 hr to fill the tank. How long would it take each pipe to fill the tank on its own?

21. A private plane flew to a city 100 miles away with a tail wind, and then returned against the same wind. If the speed of the plane in still air is 150 mph and the total flying time was $1\frac{1}{2}$ hr, what was the speed of the wind?

22. A riverboat that travels 10 mph in still water makes a pleasure trip to a city downstream and back in $2\frac{1}{2}$ hr. If the city is 12 miles away, what is the rate of the current?

Determine the *equilibrium point* for each pair of supply and demand equations below. (See the discussion preceding Problems 21 and 22 in Section 9.1.)

23. $x = 15/p$         (demand)
    $x = 24p + 2$  (supply)

24. $x = 10/p$         (demand)
    $x = 36p + 2$  (supply)

## Calculator Problems

25. The sum of two numbers is 9.59 and their product is 14.319. Find the numbers.
26. The length of a rectangle is 11 cm less than twice the width. If the diagonal is 53 cm, find the dimensions of the rectangle. (*Hint:* Use the Pythagorean theorem.)

## Challenge Problems

27. What should be the radius $r$ of the circular cut shown below if it is to divide a 12-in. pie into two sections of equal area?

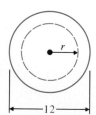

28. A couple can make the 240-mile trip to their vacation cabin in 1 hr less time if they increase their normal speed by 8 mph. What is their normal speed?

## 11.6 | GRAPHING PARABOLAS

In Chapter 8 we graphed *linear* equations in two variables, such as $y = 3x + 5$. We observed that such an equation, where both $x$ and $y$ appear to the first power only, always graphs into a straight line.

In this section we will consider equations of the form $y = ax^2 + bx + c$ $(a \neq 0)$. Note that in this equation the variable $x$ appears to the *second* power. An equation of this form does *not* graph into a straight line, but rather into a ∪-shaped or a ∩-shaped curve called a **parabola.**

The parabola is a curve that has many interesting and useful applications in a variety of fields from mathematics, science, and engineering, to astronomy, business, and architecture. It was written about in great detail by Apollonius of Alexandria in the third century B.C. The path of a projectile is essentially a parabola; the reflectors in spotlights and telescopes have parabolic cross sections, and solar furnaces use parabolas as an integral part of their design.

Neglecting air resistance, the path of this cannonball is a portion of a parabola.

When a light is placed at point $F$ (called the *focus*), the parabolic reflector of the spotlight will direct the beams into parallel rays.

We can graph parabolas in much the same way as we graphed straight lines. That is, we can construct a table of values by selecting values for $x$ and then finding the corresponding $y$-values. However, since the graph will be either a ∪-shaped or a ∩-shaped curve rather than a straight line, it will be necessary to include more than just *two* points in our table of values. Also, since the graph will contain either a *low point* or a *high point*, we shall want to choose $x$-values so that this feature is displayed. The ability to determine the proper choices for $x$ and the number of points necessary to make an accurate graph is acquired through experience.

**EXAMPLE 1**  Graph $y = x^2 - 2x - 3$.

We begin by constructing a table of values. We choose $-2, -1, 0, 1, 2, 3$, and 4 as $x$-values, and then we determine the corresponding $y$-values.

When $x = -2$,
$$y = (-2)^2 - 2(-2) - 3$$
$$= 4 + 4 - 3$$
$$= 5.$$

When $x = -1$,
$$y = (-1)^2 - 2(-1) - 3$$
$$= 1 + 2 - 3$$
$$= 0.$$

When $x = 0$,
$$y = (0)^2 - 2(0) - 3$$
$$= 0 - 0 - 3$$
$$= -3.$$

When $x = 1$,
$$y = (1)^2 - 2(1) - 3$$
$$= 1 - 2 - 3$$
$$= -4.$$

Continuing in this fashion, we arrive at the following table of values:

| $x$ | $y$ |
|---|---|
| $-2$ | $5$ |
| $-1$ | $0$ |
| $0$ | $-3$ |
| $1$ | $-4$ |
| $2$ | $-3$ |
| $3$ | $0$ |
| $4$ | $5$ |

Plotting these points and joining them with a *smooth* curve, we obtain the parabola shown on the next page. □

In the example above, the vertical line $x = 1$ is called the **axis of symmetry** of the parabola, since if we fold the page on which the parabola is drawn along this line, the two halves of the parabola will coincide.

The point at which the axis of symmetry intersects the parabola is called the **vertex** of the parabola. The vertex of the parabola on the next page is the point $(1, -4)$, and it is the *low* point of the graph.

Note that the $y$-value of each point where the graph crosses the $x$-axis is 0. Therefore the $x$-values of these points are the solutions to

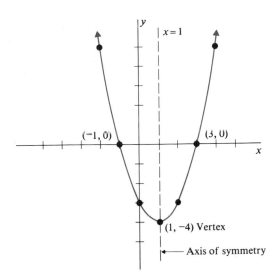

the equation $x^2 - 2x - 3 = 0$. This illustrates a *graphical method* for solving quadratic equations. Namely, the solutions to the quadratic equation $ax^2 + bx + c = 0$ are the $x$-intercepts of the parabola $y = ax^2 + bx + c$. Since the parabola will intersect the $x$-axis at two points, one point, or at no point at all, the corresponding equation will have two, one, or no real solutions. These three possibilities are illustrated below.

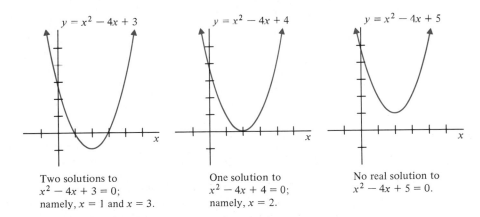

Two solutions to
$x^2 - 4x + 3 = 0$;
namely, $x = 1$ and $x = 3$.

One solution to
$x^2 - 4x + 4 = 0$;
namely, $x = 2$.

No real solution to
$x^2 - 4x + 5 = 0$.

As you continue your study of mathematics, you will find that sometimes it is advantageous to use a graphical method to solve a higher-order equation.

**EXAMPLE 2**   Graph $y = -x^2 + 2$.

First we construct a table of values.

| $x$ | $y$ |
|---|---|
| $-3$ | $-7$ |
| $-2$ | $-2$ |
| $-1$ | $1$ |
| $0$ | $2$ |
| $1$ | $1$ |
| $2$ | $-2$ |
| $3$ | $-7$ |

These points are then plotted and joined with a smooth curve.

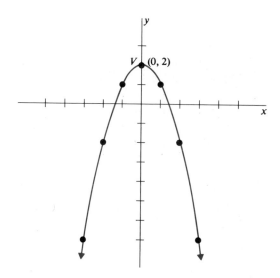

In this case the *vertex* is the point $(0, 2)$, and it is the *high* point of the graph. The *axis of symmetry* is the $y$-axis. The $x$-intercepts are the solutions to the equation $-x^2 + 2 = 0$, namely, $x = \sqrt{2}$ and $x = -\sqrt{2}$. □

Sometimes it is difficult to obtain the *exact* coordinates of the vertex of a parabola from a table of values. This is particularly true when these coordinates are not integers. In the next chapter we shall develop a *formula* that will enable us to determine the exact coordinates of the vertex. Then we will see how this information can be put to use in solving certain types of applied problems.

Also in the next chapter, we shall prove that when the coefficient $a$ in the equation $y = ax^2 + bx + c$ is *positive*, the corresponding parabola will open *upward;* and when the coefficient $a$ is *negative*, the corresponding parabola will open *downward*. These results are illustrated in the diagrams below.

Graph of $y = ax^2 + bx + c$

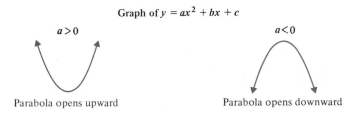

$a > 0$                              $a < 0$

Parabola opens upward         Parabola opens downward

## Problem Set 11.6

Graph each of the following equations. Observe that when $a > 0$ the parabola opens upward, and when $a < 0$ the parabola opens downward.

1. $y = x^2 - 4$
2. $y = x^2 - 9$
3. $y = -x^2 + 4$
4. $y = -x^2 + 9$
5. $y = x^2 + 3$
6. $y = x^2 + 2$
7. $y = -x^2 + 3$
8. $y = -x^2 + 2$
9. $y = x^2 + 2x$
10. $y = x^2 - 2x$
11. $y = x^2 - 2x + 1$
12. $y = x^2 - 4x + 4$
13. $y = -x^2 + 4x - 3$
14. $y = -x^2 + 6x - 5$
15. $y = 3x^2 - 2x - 1$
16. $y = 3x^2 + 2x - 1$
17. $y = \frac{1}{2}x^2 + x + 1$
18. $y = \frac{1}{2}x^2 - x + 1$
19. $y = (x + 3)^2$
20. $y = (x + 2)^2$
21. $y = (x + 3)^2 - 4$
22. $y = (x + 2)^2 + 1$

23. Graph $y = 2x^2$ and $y = \frac{1}{2}x^2$ using the same coordinate axes.
24. Graph $y = x^2$ and $y = -x^2$ using the same coordinate axes.
25. Graph $y = x^2 + 1$ and $y = x^2 - 1$ using the same coordinate axes.
26. Graph $y = (x + 1)^2$ and $y = (x - 1)^2$ using the same coordinate axes.
27. A particular frog leap follows a path given by the equation $y = 2x - \frac{1}{4}x^2$, where $x$ and $y$ are in feet and $0 \leq x \leq 8$. Graph this path.

28. A particular football punt follows a path given by the equation $y = 2x - \frac{1}{30}x^2$, where $x$ and $y$ are in yards and $0 \leqslant x \leqslant 60$. Graph this path.
29. Write an equation that relates the area $A$ of a square and the length $s$ of one side. Then graph this equation.
30. The length of a rectangle is one unit longer than the width. Write an equation that relates the area $A$ of the rectangle and its width $w$. Then graph this equation.

## Calculator Problems

31. Graph $y = 7x^2 - 2.8x + 1.1$ for $0 \leqslant x \leqslant 0.5$ by first completing the table below.

| $x$ | $y$ |
|-----|-----|
| 0 | ? |
| 0.1 | ? |
| 0.2 | ? |
| 0.3 | ? |
| 0.4 | ? |
| 0.5 | ? |

32. Write an equation that relates the volume $V$ of a cone of height $h = 2$ and its radius $r$. Then graph this equation.

## Challenge Problems

33. Suppose that the parabola $y = ax^2 + bx + c$ has two $x$-intercepts. Then the $x$-value of the vertex lies midway between these two $x$-intercepts. Show that the $x$-value of the vertex must then be given by the formula $x = -b/2a$. (*Hint:* Average the solutions to $ax^2 + bx + c = 0$ as given by the quadratic formula.)
34. Find a formula for the $y$-value of the vertex of the parabola in Problem 33.

## Chapter Review

True or false.

1. The equation $x^2 - 1 = 0$ is a quadratic equation.
2. The solutions to the equation $ax^2 + bx + c = 0$ $(a \neq 0)$ are given by the formula $x = -b + (\sqrt{b^2 - 4ac})/2a$.
3. The quadratic formula can be used to solve any quadratic equation.

Completion.

4. An equation of the form $ax^2 + bx + c = 0$ $(a \neq 0)$ is called a(n) _____?_____ equation or a(n) _____?_____ equation. When written in this form, the equation is said to be in _____?_____ form.

5. The zero factor property states that $a \cdot b = 0$ if and only if _____?_____ or _____?_____.

6. A quadratic equation has at most _____?_____ (how many) solutions.

7. Four methods that might be used to solve a quadratic equation are _____?_____, _____?_____, _____?_____, and _____?_____.

8. The graph of $y = ax^2 + bx + c$ $(a \neq 0)$ is called a(n) _____?_____. If $a > 0$, this graph opens _____?_____ (up, down). If $a < 0$, this graph opens _____?_____ (up, down). If the graph opens up, the low point of the graph is called the _____?_____. If the graph opens down, the high point of the graph is called the _____?_____. The vertical line through the low point (if the graph opens up) or the high point (if the graph opens down) is called the _____?_____.

Write each equation in standard form and identify $a$, $b$, and $c$.

9. $x(5x - 1) + 8 = 3x^2 - 4$     10. $3x^2 - 6 = 14$

Complete the square on each expression and then factor the resulting expression.

11. $y^2 - 16y$                12. $t^2 + 5t$

Solve by factoring.

13. $x^2 + 10x = -25$          14. $5x^2 + 19x - 4 = 0$
15. $9r^2 - 49 = 0$              16. $s^2/5 = s$

Solve by extraction of roots.

17. $x^2 = 100$                18. $x^2 - 18 = 0$
19. $3.6p^2 + 2.5 = 0$         20. $(q + 8)^2 - 144 = 0$

Solve by completing the square.

21. $x^2 - 6x + 3 = 0$         22. $2x^2 + 2x - 1 = 0$

Solve by the quadratic formula.

23. $x^2 + 3x = 1$             24. $x^2/8 - x/2 - 1/2 = 0$
25. $2h^2 + \sqrt{3}h - \frac{3}{4} = 0$

Solve each equation. Use the method that seems easiest to you.

26. $m^4 - 16m^2 = 0$         27. $180z^3 + 25z^2 = 120z$
28. $10x^3 - 20x^2 - 5x = 0$

Graph each equation.

29. $y = x^2$                  30. $y = x^2 - 3x$
31. $y = -\frac{1}{2}x^2 + 2$         32. $y = -x^2 + 4x - 5$

33. Given the supply and demand equations below, determine the equilibrium point.

$$x = \frac{12}{p} \quad \text{(demand)}$$

$$x = 16p + 4 \quad \text{(supply)}$$

34. Solve $4x^2 + 7ax - 15a^2 = 0$ for $x$.
35. Given the graph of $y = ax^2 + bx + c$ on the next page, determine the number of real solutions to the equation $ax^2 + bx + c = 0$.

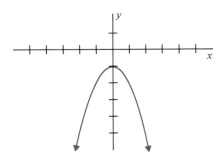

36. The surface area of a sphere is given by the formula $S = 4\pi r^2$. Solve this formula for $r$.

37. Determine the annual interest rate $i$ (compounded annually) that is needed if $5000 is to amount to $6050 in two years.

38. The square of a number is four less than five times the number itself. Find the number.

39. Computer A can process the payroll in 2 hr less time than can computer B. If both computers work together, it takes 6 hr to process the payroll. How long does it take each computer working alone?

40. A plane flew to an airfield 120 miles away with a tail wind, and then returned against the same wind. If the speed of the plane in still air is 80 mph and the total flying time was 4 hr, what was the speed of the wind?

41. A projectile is launched vertically upward from the top of a 160-ft tall tower with an initial velocity of 48 ft/sec. (a) How long will it be before the projectile strikes the ground? (b) When will the projectile be at a height of 208 ft?

42. Lightning strikes a dead tree and causes it to crack at a point on the trunk 21 ft high. The upper portion of the tree remains attached to the lower, but it falls so that the top of the tree comes to rest at a point on the ground whose distance from the base is one-half the original height of the tree. Find the original height of the tree.

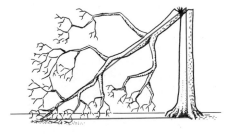

# Chapter Twelve

## FUNCTIONS AND THEIR GRAPHS (OPTIONAL)

## 12.1    DEFINITION OF A FUNCTION

A central theme that pervades many areas of mathematics is the notion of a *function*. We have all heard the expression *price is a function of quantity demanded.* That expression means that the price of an item is determined by the quantity demanded.

In mathematics we are concerned with precisely stating those rules that relate two variable quantities. Usually the rule will take the form of an equation. For example, we could say that the area $A$ of a square is a function of the length $s$ of one of its sides. As the length of a side takes on different values, the area takes on different values, and each value of $A$ depends entirely upon the value assumed by $s$. It is not enough, however, to say that $A$ is a function of $s$. We should state a rule that tells *precisely* how $A$ and $s$ are related. This rule, stated as an equation, would be

$$A = s^2.$$

The rule itself, then, is called a *function.*

It is now clear exactly how $A$ and $s$ are related. Given a value of $s$, it is easy to compute the corresponding value of $A$.

$$\text{When } s = 5, \quad A = 5^2 = 25.$$
$$\text{When } s = 10, \quad A = 10^2 = 100.$$
$$\text{When } s = \sqrt{3}, \quad A = (\sqrt{3})^2 = 3.$$

Having a relationship between two variable quantities expressed precisely in equation form allows us to examine that relationship in a manner that would otherwise not be possible.

In the equation

$$A = s^2,$$

the variable $s$, to which values are assigned at will, is called the **independent variable.** The variable $A$, whose values depend upon those of $s$, is called the **dependent variable.** Very often the letters $x$ and $y$ are used to denote the variable quantities involved in a function. Had we let $x$ denote the length of the side of a square and $y$ its area, the equation above would have been written

$$y = x^2.$$

In this case $x$ is the independent variable and $y$ the dependent variable. When $x$ and $y$ are used as variables, it is generally $x$ that is chosen as the independent variable and $y$ the dependent variable.

Not every equation involving $x$ and $y$ defines $y$ as a function of $x$, however. In order for $y$ to be a function of $x$ the two variables must be related so that whenever a permissible value is assigned to $x$, there is only *one* corresponding value assigned to $y$. For example, the equation

$$y = x + 1$$

defines $y$ as a function of $x$. This is because for each value of $x$ there is only *one* corresponding value for $y$, namely the number that is one larger than the number assigned to $x$. On the other hand,

$$y = \pm\sqrt{x}$$

does *not* define $y$ as a function of $x$. For each positive value assigned to $x$, there corresponds *two* values for $y$. For example, when $x$ equals 9, $y$ takes on the *two* values $+3$ and $-3$.

**EXAMPLE 1**   The equation $y = x + 5$ defines $y$ as a function of $x$, since for each value of $x$ there is only one corresponding value for $y$. The equation itself is called a function. □

**EXAMPLE 2**   The equation $x^2 + y^2 = 25$ does *not* define $y$ as a function of $x$. For example, when $x$ takes the value 3, $y$ assumes the two values 4 and $-4$. □

Sometimes we must be careful about the values we choose for $x$. For example, given the function

$$y = \frac{1}{x},$$

we may *not* assign a value of 0 to $x$, since division by zero is undefined. We can, however, substitute any real number *except* zero for $x$. For each such substitution, we will obtain exactly one corresponding value for $y$, namely the reciprocal of $x$. For example,

$$\text{when } x = 7, \qquad y = \frac{1}{7}.$$

$$\text{When } x = -10, \quad y = \frac{1}{-10} = -\frac{1}{10}.$$

$$\text{When } x = \frac{1}{3}, \qquad y = \frac{1}{\frac{1}{3}} = 3.$$

$$\text{When } x = \sqrt{2}, \qquad y = \frac{1}{\sqrt{2}} = \frac{\sqrt{2}}{2}.$$

---

***Definition***    If $y$ is a function of $x$, the set of all permissible values that $x$ may assume is called the **domain** of the function.

---

**EXAMPLE 3**   Determine the domain of the function $y = 1/(x - 4)$.

The domain of this function consists of all real numbers except 4. This is because if $x = 4$, then the denominator $x - 4$ is zero.

We shall describe the domain by writing $x \neq 4$. □

**EXAMPLE 4**   Determine the domain of the function $y = 1/(x^2 - 9)$.

First, $y = 1/(x^2 - 9)$ can be written as

$$y = \frac{1}{(x - 3)(x + 3)}.$$

Therefore the domain of this function is $x \neq 3, -3$. □

**EXAMPLE 5**   Determine the domain of the function $y = \sqrt{3x - 21}$.

Since an even root of a *negative* number is not a real number, we must avoid assigning a value to $x$ that will yield a negative number under the radical sign. Therefore, to determine the domain we set the radicand greater than or equal to zero and solve.

$$3x - 21 \geqslant 0$$
$$3x \geqslant 21$$
$$x \geqslant 7.$$

The domain of this function is $x \geqslant 7$. □

---

***Definition***    If $y$ is a function of $x$, the set of all values taken on by $y$ is called the **range** of the function.

---

**EXAMPLE 6**   Determine the range of the function $y = x^2$.

Since $x^2$ is always a nonnegative number, we conclude that the range of this function is $y \geqslant 0$. □

**EXAMPLE 7**   Determine the range of the function $y = x^2 + 1$.

Since $x^2 \geqslant 0$, the range of this function must be $y \geqslant 1$. □

The student should observe that a function is actually a rule that takes elements from one set and one by one assigns each of them to an element from another set. The two sets involved are not necessarily distinct; they may be the same set. In the functions discussed thus far, the set involved was the set of real numbers. The function $y = x^2$, for example, took elements from the set of real numbers and one by one assigned each of them to another element from the set of real numbers, namely its square. This assignment of elements can be represented pictorially as in the diagram below.

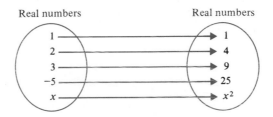

Of course, only a few of the elements that are involved in the function have been shown in the diagram.

A function may actually be a rule between *any* two sets. For example, the rule that assigns to each student in a class the age of that student can be thought of as a function. It is a function from *people* to *numbers*. A pictorial representation of this function is given below.

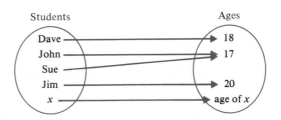

Note that it is perfectly acceptable for two elements in the domain to correspond to the *same* element in the range. What must *not* occur in a function is for an element in the domain to correspond with *more* than one element in the range. The diagram below, for example, does *not* represent a function from set $A$ to set $B$. This is because the element 2 in set $A$ corresponds with *both* $b$ and $c$ in set $B$.

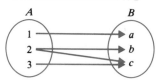

*Not* a function from $A$ to $B$

Having discussed the notion of a function, we are now prepared to state a formal definition.

---

**Definition**    A **function** from set $A$ to set $B$ is a rule that assigns to each element $x$ in set $A$ a *unique* element $y$ in set $B$.

---

This definition was originally formulated by Lejeune Dirichlet (1805–1859).

The variety of fields from which functions can be drawn is illustrated by the next three examples.

**EXAMPLE 8**   The *maximum* pulse rate $r$ that a healthy person aged 18 to 55 should attain when exercising is a function of that person's age $a$. It is determined by subtracting the person's age from 220. Write $r$ as a function of $a$.

$$r = 220 - a, \quad \text{for } 18 \leqslant a \leqslant 55. \quad \square$$

**EXAMPLE 9**   Price $p$ is a function of quantity demanded $x$. For a particular item the price-demand function is $p = 500 - 0.02x$. Of course, we must have $x \geqslant 0$ (quantity won't be negative), *and* $x \leqslant 25{,}000$ (price won't be negative). Therefore, the function along with its domain is

$$p = 500 - 0.02x, \quad \text{for } 0 \leqslant x \leqslant 25{,}000. \quad \square$$

**EXAMPLE 10**   A cubic foot of water weighs 62.4 lb. Therefore, the water pressure $P$ in lb/ft$^2$ that is exerted on a submarine is a function of the depth $d$ in feet at which the submarine lies. Specifically,

$$P = 62.4d, \quad \text{for } d \geqslant 0.$$

In Example 10, note that the pressure $P$ is *not* a function of the *surface area* of the body of water. That is, a submarine at a depth of 100 ft in a small sea would experience the same pressure as a submarine at a depth of 100 ft in a large ocean.

## Problem Set 12.1

Which of the equations below define $y$ as a function of $x$?

1. $y = x + 5$
2. $y = x + 1$
3. $y = x - 4$
4. $y = x - 3$
5. $y = 2x + 1$
6. $y = 3x + 5$
7. $y = \pm\sqrt{x}$
8. $y = \pm\sqrt{2x}$
9. $x^2 + y^2 = 100$
10. $x^2 + y^2 = 25$
11. $y = 1/(x + 1)$
12. $y = 1/(x + 5)$
13. $y = x^2 + 3$
14. $y = x^2 + 8$
15. $y^2 = x$
16. $y^2 = x + 1$
17. $x + y = 6$
18. $x + y = 10$
19. $x^2 + y^2 = 1$
20. $x^2 + y^2 = 9$
21. $y = \sqrt{2x}$
22. $y = \sqrt{x}$
23. $y = \sqrt{x - 6}$
24. $y = \sqrt{x - 2}$
25. $y = 3/(x + 4)$
26. $y = 6/(x + 3)$
27. $y^4 = x$
28. $y^6 = x$
29. $x = |y| - 2$
30. $x = |y| + 3$

Determine the domain of each of the functions below.

31. $y = x + 4$
32. $y = x + 9$
33. $y = 3x - 1$
34. $y = 5x - 2$
35. $y = \frac{1}{3}x$
36. $y = \frac{1}{2}x$

37. $y = 1/(x - 2)$

38. $y = 1/(x - 5)$

39. $y = \dfrac{1}{(x - 5)(x + 5)}$

40. $y = \dfrac{1}{(x - 3)(x + 3)}$

41. $y = 10/(x^2 - 64)$

42. $y = 11/(x^2 - 49)$

43. $y = 8/(x^2 - 5x + 6)$

44. $y = 7/(x^2 - 7x + 12)$

45. $y = (x + 1)/(x^2 - 7x)$

46. $y = (x - 1)/(x^2 + 4x)$

47. $y = \sqrt{x}$

48. $y = \sqrt{-x}$

49. $y = \sqrt{x - 6}$

50. $y = \sqrt{x - 2}$

51. $y = \sqrt{3x - 12}$

52. $y = \sqrt{6x - 12}$

53. $y = \sqrt{7x + 21}$

54. $y = \sqrt{6x + 54}$

55. $y = \sqrt{5x - 13}$

56. $y = \sqrt{3x - 11}$

57. $y = x/\sqrt{3 - 2x}$

58. $y = -x/\sqrt{5 - 3x}$

Determine the range of each of the functions below.

59. $y = x + 1$

60. $y = x + 2$

61. $y = x^2$

62. $y = \sqrt{x}$

63. $y = |x| + 1$

64. $y = x^2 + 2$

65. $y = 10x$

66. $y = 5x$

67. $y = -x^2 + 10$

68. $y = -x^2 + 20$

69. $y = 5x - 9$

70. $y = 7x - 4$

71. $y = x^4 + 100$

72. $y = x^4 + 50$

Which of the diagrams below illustrate a function from set $A$ to set $B$?

73.
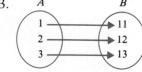

74.
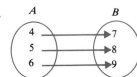

75.
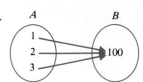

76.
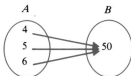

77.
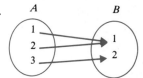

78.
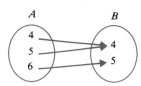

79.
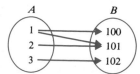

80.
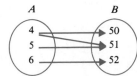

81.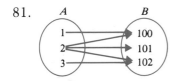

82.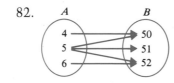

83. Write the volume $V$ of a sphere as a function of its radius $r$.
84. Write the surface area $S$ of a sphere as a function of its radius $r$.
85. Neglecting air resistance, the distance $d$ in feet that an object falls in $t$ seconds is the product of 16 and the square of $t$. Write $d$ as a function of $t$.
86. Neglecting air resistance, the velocity $v$ in ft/sec attained by an object $t$ seconds after it is dropped is the product of 32 and $t$. Write $v$ as a function of $t$.
87. A sales representative earns \$100 per week plus a commission of 15% on his sales. If $E$ denotes his weekly earnings in dollars and $s$ his weekly sales in dollars, write an equation representing $E$ as a function of $s$.
88. A sales representative earns \$150 per week plus a commission of 5% on her sales. If $E$ denotes her weekly earnings in dollars and $s$ her weekly sales in dollars, write an equation representing $E$ as a function of $s$.

## Calculator Problems

89. Determine the domain of the function $y = \sqrt{1.550x - 99.014}$.
90. Record-setting dives of over 400 ft have been made using only scuba (self-contained underwater breathing apparatus) gear. Use the function of Example 10 to determine the pressure on a scuba diver at a depth of 287 ft.

## Challenge Problems

91. Determine the domain of $y = \sqrt{9 - x^2}$.
92. Write the area $A$ of the shaded region below as a function of $s$. (The arcs are quarter-circles.)

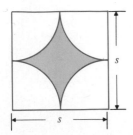

93. The amount of water that a pipe can carry is determined by the area of a circular cross section.
    a) Write the area $A$ of a circular cross section as a function of its radius $r$.
    b) What affect does doubling the radius have on the amount of water the pipe can carry?

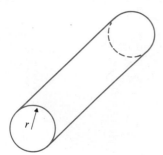

## 12.2 FUNCTION NOTATION

To denote that $y$ is a function of $x$, we often write $y = f(x)$. The expression $f(x)$ is read *function of* $x$ or simply $f$ *of* $x$, and it represents the **value of the function** $f$ **at** $x$. The symbol $f(x)$ does *not* mean $f$ *multiplied* by $x$.

Since $y$ and $f(x)$ are equal, we often, as a notational convenience, write $f(x)$ instead of $y$. Using this notation, the function

$$y = x^2$$

becomes

$$f(x) = x^2.$$

The student should be careful to note that there is a difference between the symbol $f$ and the symbol $f(x)$. We use $f$ as the *name* of the function $y = x^2$, while we use $f(x)$ as a replacement for the variable $y$.

The notation $f(x)$ is convenient because, by replacing $x$ with a specific value $b$ in the *domain* of the function, the symbol $f(b)$ then denotes the corresponding value in the *range*. For example, instead of writing

$$\text{when } x = 3, \quad y = 3^2 = 9,$$

we can simply write

$$f(3) = 3^2 = 9.$$

The equation $f(3) = 9$ means that when $x = 3$, the value of the function $f$ is 9. This procedure is called *evaluating the function at $x = 3$*.

To evaluate a function $y = f(x)$ at a particular value, the variable $x$ is simply replaced by that value throughout the function. For example, to find the value of the function

$$f(x) = 3x^2 - 5x + 8$$

at $x = 7$, we simply replace $x$ with 7 throughout the function.

$$\begin{aligned}
f(7) &= 3(7)^2 - 5(7) + 8 \\
&= 3(49) - 5(7) + 8 \\
&= 147 - 35 + 8 \\
&= 120.
\end{aligned}$$

Therefore the value of the function $f$ at $x = 7$ is 120.

In general, to evaluate the function above at a particular value of $x$, we fill in the parentheses in the equation

$$f(\ \ ) = 3 \cdot (\ \ )^2 - 5 \cdot (\ \ ) + 8$$

with that particular value of $x$.

**EXAMPLE 1**   Given $f(x) = 3x^2 + 1$, find $f(0)$, $f(5)$, $f(-10)$, $f(\sqrt{2})$, $f(a)$, $f(a + 1)$, $f(a + b)$, and $f(x + h)$.

Since $f(x) = 3x^2 + 1$, we have that

$$\begin{aligned}
f(0) &= 3 \cdot 0^2 + 1 = 0 + 1 = 1, \\
f(5) &= 3 \cdot 5^2 + 1 = 3 \cdot 25 + 1 = 75 + 1 = 76, \\
f(-10) &= 3(-10)^2 + 1 = 3 \cdot 100 + 1 = 300 + 1 = 301, \\
f(\sqrt{2}) &= 3(\sqrt{2})^2 + 1 = 3 \cdot 2 + 1 = 6 + 1 = 7, \\
f(a) &= 3a^2 + 1,
\end{aligned}$$

$$f(a + 1) = 3(a + 1)^2 + 1 = 3(a^2 + 2a + 1) + 1 = 3a^2 + 6a + 4,$$
$$f(a + b) = 3(a + b)^2 + 1 = 3(a^2 + 2ab + b^2) + 1 = 3a^2 + 6ab + 3b^2 + 1,$$
$$f(x + h) = 3(x + h)^2 + 1 = 3(x^2 + 2xh + h^2) + 1 = 3x^2 + 6xh + 3h^2 + 1. \quad \square$$

The letter $f$ is frequently used to name a particular function, but *any* letter (actually any symbol at all) can be used. Hence the functions

$$g(x) = x^2,$$
$$h(x) = x^2,$$
$$P(t) = t^2,$$

are really the same function as

$$f(x) = x^2,$$

since they all have the same range value $a^2$ when given the same domain value $a$. Each of the four functions above, for example, has a range value of 25 when the domain value is 5.

Another way to picture a function is as a "machine." The domain of the function (the set of all values of the independent variable) is the *input* for the machine, and the range of the function (the set of all values of the dependent variable) is the *output* for the machine.

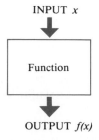

INPUT $x$

Function

OUTPUT $f(x)$

When a domain element is thrown into the machine, the function operates on that element to produce the corresponding range element. For example, the function

$$f(x) = x^2 + 1$$

will square each domain element and then add one to produce the corresponding range element.

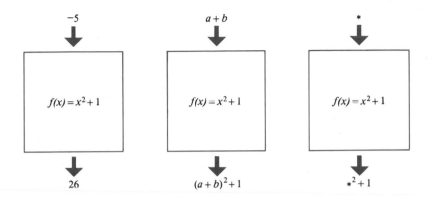

Remember that a function does not have to be a correspondence between *numbers*. It may be a correspondence between *any* two sets. The correspondence might, for instance, associate to each member of a basketball team the player's height in inches. Consider the starting roster for a certain basketball team.

| Player's name | Player's height in inches |
|---|---|
| John | 72 |
| Mike | 74 |
| Jim | 69 |
| Charlie | 72 |
| Bob | 78 |

Let $f$ be the name of the function that associates to each player the player's height in inches. That is,

$$f(x) = \text{height of } x \text{ in inches.}$$

The domain of $f$ consists of John, Mike, Jim, Charlie, and Bob.
The range of $f$ is 72, 74, 69, and 78.
Evaluating the function $f$ at $x$ = Bob, we write

$$f(\text{Bob}) = 78.$$

Note that *different* elements in the domain set may correspond to the *same* element in the range set. In this function, $f(\text{John}) = f(\text{Charlie})$ even though John and Charlie are not the same person. We could diagram this function as follows.

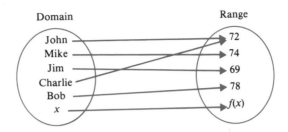

**EXAMPLE 2**   The expression $\dfrac{f(t) - f(x)}{t - x}$ is important in the study of calculus. Find this expression for the function $f(x) = x^2 + 3$, and then simplify.

$$\frac{f(t) - f(x)}{t - x} = \frac{(t^2 + 3) - (x^2 + 3)}{t - x}$$

$$= \frac{t^2 - x^2}{t - x}$$

$$= \frac{(t + x)(t - x)}{t - x}$$

$$= t + x. \ \square$$

**EXAMPLE 3**   The daily overhead involved in manufacturing a certain item is $250. In addition, there is a manufacturing cost of $7 per unit. Denote the total daily cost of manufacturing $x$ units per day by $C(x)$. Then, using this notation, write a cost function for these items.

$$\begin{pmatrix} \text{Total daily cost} \\ \text{of manufacturing} \\ x \text{ units per day} \end{pmatrix} = \begin{pmatrix} \text{cost per} \\ \text{unit} \end{pmatrix} \cdot \begin{pmatrix} \text{no. of units} \\ \text{per day} \end{pmatrix} + \begin{pmatrix} \text{daily} \\ \text{overhead} \end{pmatrix}$$

$$C(x) = 7x + 250. \ \square$$

**EXAMPLE 4**   Using the cost function of Example 3, determine the total daily cost of manufacturing 140 units per day.

The total daily cost of manufacturing $x$ units per day is

$$C(x) = 7x + 250.$$

Therefore, the total daily cost of manufacturing 140 units per day is

$$C(140) = 7(140) + 250$$
$$= 980 + 250$$
$$= 1230.$$

The total daily cost of manufacturing 140 units per day is $1230.   $\square$

## Problem Set 12.2

Given $f(x) = x^2$, determine each of the following.

1. $f(0)$
2. $f(1)$
3. $f(4)$
4. $f(6)$
5. $f(-4)$
6. $f(-6)$
7. $f(\frac{1}{2})$
8. $f(\frac{1}{3})$
9. $f(\sqrt{5})$
10. $f(\sqrt{10})$
11. $f(a)$
12. $f(b)$
13. $f(a + 1)$
14. $f(b + 1)$
15. $f(a + b)$
16. $f(a - b)$

Given $g(x) = 5x^2 - x + 1$, determine each of the following.

17. $g(0)$
18. $g(1)$
19. $g(4)$
20. $g(6)$
21. $g(-4)$
22. $g(-6)$
23. $g(\frac{1}{2})$
24. $g(\frac{1}{3})$
25. $g(\sqrt{5})$
26. $g(\sqrt{10})$
27. $g(a)$
28. $g(b)$
29. $g(a + 1)$
30. $g(b + 1)$
31. $g(x + h)$
32. $g(x - h)$

Given $h(x) = 1/x$, determine each of the following.

33. $h(0)$
34. $h(1)$
35. $h(4)$
36. $h(6)$
37. $h(-4)$
38. $h(-6)$
39. $h(\frac{1}{2})$
40. $h(\frac{1}{3})$
41. $h(\sqrt{5})$
42. $h(\sqrt{10})$
43. $h(a)$
44. $h(b)$
45. $h(a + 1)$
46. $h(b + 1)$
47. $h(x - h)$
48. $h(x + h)$

Given the diagram of function $F$ below, determine each of the following.

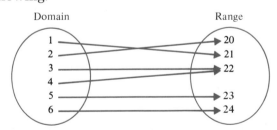

49. $F(3)$
50. $F(6)$
51. $F(2 + 4)$
52. $F(2 + 3)$
53. $F(2) + F(4)$
54. $F(2) + F(3)$
55. $F(3 - 1)$
56. $F(5 - 1)$
57. $F(3) - F(1)$
58. $F(5) - F(1)$
59. $F(7)$
60. $F(0)$

Consider the team roster below.

| Player | Height in Inches | Weight in Pounds | Age in years |
| --- | --- | --- | --- |
| Dave | 70 | 160 | 18 |
| Bill | 73 | 180 | 18 |
| Chris | 68 | 165 | 18 |
| Dan | 75 | 200 | 19 |
| Sean | 73 | 195 | 19 |

If $f$ is the function that assigns to each player his height (in inches), $g$ the function that assigns to each player his weight (in pounds), and $h$ the function that assigns to each player his age (in years), determine each of the following.

61. $g(\text{Dan})$         62. $h(\text{Bill})$         63. $f(\text{Sean})$         64. $f(\text{Dave})$
65. $h(\text{Chris})$      66. $g(\text{Chris})$     67. $f(\text{Bill})$          68. $f(\text{Dan})$

Find $\dfrac{f(t) - f(x)}{t - x}$ for each function below, and then simplify.

69. $f(x) = 2x - 5$      70. $f(x) = 3x + 8$      71. $f(x) = x^2 + 4$    72. $f(x) = x^2 - 1$

73. The velocity of sound through air is a function of the temperature of that air. If $V(C)$ denotes the velocity in ft/sec of sound through air having a Celsius temperature of $C$, then under normal atmospheric conditions we can write the function

$$V(C) = 1087 + 2C.$$

Find and interpret $V(0)$ and $V(25)$.

74. The value that \$2500 would grow to in two years if placed in an interest-bearing account is a function of the rate of interest paid by that account. If $V(r)$ denotes that value for an annual interest rate of $r$ compounded annually and expressed as a decimal, then we can write the function

$$V(r) = 2500(1 + r)^2.$$

Find and interpret $V(0.05)$ and $V(0.15)$.

75. Let $h(t)$ denote the height in feet of an arrow $t$ seconds after it is projected vertically upward from ground level. If the initial velocity of the arrow is 132 ft/sec, write the function $h$. Then find and interpret $h(2)$ and $h(5)$. (See Example 9 of Section 11.1.)

76. Do Problem 75 if the initial velocity is 160 ft/sec and the arrow is projected from the top of a building 74 ft high.

77. A manufacturer can produce small electric motors at a cost of \$8 per motor plus a daily overhead of \$350. If $C(x)$ denotes the total daily cost of producing $x$ motors per day, write a cost function for these motors. Then find and interpret $C(0)$ and $C(125)$.

78. A manufacturer can produce bearings at a cost of \$4 per bearing plus a daily overhead of \$275. If $C(x)$ denotes the total daily cost of producing $x$ bearings per day, write a cost function for these bearings. Then find and interpret $C(0)$ and $C(235)$.

## Calculator Problems

79. Given $f(x) = 2.4x^2 - 8.6x + 5$, find
    a) $f(1.2)$.     b) $f(235)$.     c) $f(\pi)$.
80. Using the function of Problem 74, find and interpret $V(0.1275)$.

## Challenge Problems

81. Given $f(x) = 5x - 2$ and $g(x) = x^2 + 1$, find
    a) $f(-a)$.     b) $g(a^7)$.     c) $f(g(3))$.
82. If $f(x) = x^2$, under what conditions does $f(a + b) = f(a) + f(b)$?
83. If $x$ is a real number, then the symbol $[x]$ denotes the greatest integer that is less than or equal to $x$. The function $f(x) = [x]$ is called the **greatest integer function.** Determine
    a) $f(7.1)$.     b) $f(0)$.     c) $f(\pi)$.     d) $f(-2.5)$.
84. If $f(x) = x^2 + 2kx + 3$ and $f(2) = 13$, find $k$.

## 12.3   CONSTANT FUNCTIONS, VERTICAL LINE TEST

The collection of all functions is so large that there is little that can be said that is true of every function. For this reason, the collection of functions is divided into "smaller" collections, or *classes.* A class of functions that has long been of interest to mathematicians because of its many applications is the class of *polynomial functions.* The word polynomial has already been defined in Chapter 5, and we will use that definition to define a polynomial function.

---

**Definition**    A **polynomial function in x** is any function of the form

$$f(x) = \text{a polynomial in } x.$$

The **degree** of the polynomial function coincides with the degree of the polynomial on the right-hand side of the equation above.

---

**EXAMPLE 1**   $f(x) = 2x + 8$ is a polynomial function of the first degree. □

**EXAMPLE 2**   $f(x) = x^2 - 3x - 5$ is a polynomial function of the second degree. □

**EXAMPLE 3**   The profit $P(x)$ derived from $x$ units of a certain product is given by the third-degree polynomial function $P(x) = -0.01x^3 - 0.48x^2 + 2100x - 1200$.

Find and interpret $P(20)$.

$$
\begin{aligned}
P(20) &= -0.01(20)^3 - 0.48(20)^2 + 2100(20) - 1200 \\
&= -0.01(8000) - 0.48(400) + 42{,}000 - 1200 \\
&= -80 - 192 + 42{,}000 - 1200 \\
&= 40{,}528.
\end{aligned}
$$

The profit derived from 20 units is 40,528. □

The simplest of all polynomial functions is the *constant function*, so called because its value is always constant no matter what the value of its domain element.

---

***Definition***    A **constant function** is any function of the form

$$f(x) = a,$$

where $a$ is a constant.

---

Again, there is nothing special about the choice of the letter $f$ to name the function, and other symbols can just as easily be used.

**EXAMPLE 4**   All three functions below are constant functions.

$$f(x) = 5$$
$$g(x) = -\frac{1}{2}$$
$$h(x) = \sqrt{10}. \;\; □$$

Since there are an infinite number of different constants $a$, there are an infinite number of constant functions $f(x) = a$.

**EXAMPLE 5**   Given the constant function $f(x) = 5$, find $f(0)$, $f(-3)$, $f(5)$, $f(\sqrt{2})$, and $f(b)$.

Since $f(x) = 5$,

$$f(0) = 5,$$
$$f(-3) = 5,$$
$$f(5) = 5,$$
$$f(\sqrt{2}) = 5,$$
$$f(b) = 5. \quad \Box$$

Note that the value of the constant function above is unchanged, despite the value of the domain variable $x$. In essence, no matter what domain value is given to the constant function $f(x) = 5$, the range value is always the same, namely 5.

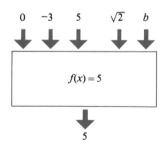

If we view the function as a machine, we see that only one element is ever ejected by the machine.

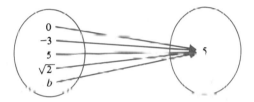

The domain of this function $f$ consists of all real numbers, while the range of $f$ is simply 5.

The **graph** of a function $f$ consists of all those points $(x, y)$ in the plane that satisfy the equation $y = f(x)$. Hence if $f(x) = 4$, the graph of the function $f$ consists of all those points $(x, y)$ in the plane that satisfy the equation $y = 4$.

**EXAMPLE 6**   Graph the constant function $f(x) = 4$.

This function can also be written as $y = 4$. Equations of this type were graphed in Section 8.3. The points in the plane that satisfy this equation can be found on a horizontal line four units above the *x*-axis.

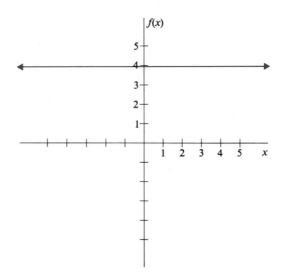

The vertical axis for this graph may be labeled *either* as *y* or as *f*(*x*).  □

**EXAMPLE 7**   Graph the constant function $g(x) = -\frac{5}{2}$.

The graph is a horizontal line lying $2\frac{1}{2}$ units below the *x*-axis.

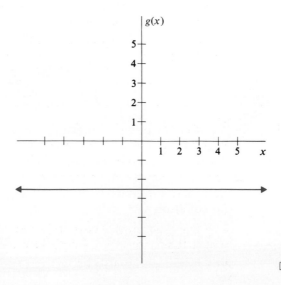

Before investigating the graphs of other types of functions, let us see if we can say something about the graphs of functions in general. Consider the two graphs below.

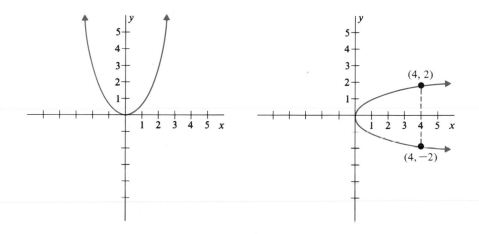

The graph on the left represents $y$ as a function of $x$. The graph on the right does not. Do you know why? It is because to each positive $x$-value in the graph on the right there corresponds *two* $y$-values. For example, to the $x$-value 4 there corresponds the two $y$-values $+2$ and $-2$. But if $y$ is a function of $x$, then to each $x$-value in the domain of the function there can correspond only *one* $y$-value. This leads us to the following rule.

---

**Vertical Line Test**

A graph in the $xy$-plane represents $y$ as a function of $x$ if and only if *no* vertical line intersects the graph at *more* than one point.

---

The graph on the left *passes* the vertical line test and therefore represents $y$ as a function of $x$. Obviously the graph on the right *fails* the vertical line test.

## Problem Set 12.3

1. Which of the functions below are polynomial functions? State the degree of each polynomial function.
   a) $f(x) = x^2 - 8x + 15$     b) $f(x) = 2x^3 - x^2 + x + 5$
   c) $g(x) = 16$               d) $g(x) = 1/(x - 2)$
   e) $h(x) = \sqrt{x} + 5$     f) $h(x) = x^5$

2. Which of the functions below are polynomial functions? State the degree of each polynomial function.
   a) $f(x) = x^2 + 9x + 18$    b) $f(x) = 4x^3 + x^2 - x + 1$
   c) $g(x) = 25$               d) $g(x) = 1/(x + 3)$
   e) $h(x) = \sqrt{x} - 9$     f) $h(x) = x^4$

3. The cost $C(x)$ of producing $x$ units of a certain product is given by the polynomial function $C(x) = 0.02x^3 - 3x^2 + 175x + 500$. Find and interpret $C(30)$.

4. The cost $C(x)$ of producing $x$ units of a certain product is given by the polynomial function $C(x) = 0.01x^3 - 2x^2 + 300x + 1200$. Find and interpret $C(20)$.

5. Given the constant function $f(x) = 7$, find $f(3)$, $f(0)$, $f(7)$, $f(-1)$, $f(\sqrt{2})$, $f(\pi)$, $f(a)$, $f(a^2)$, $f(a + 1)$, and $f(x + h)$.

6. Repeat Problem 5 for the constant function $f(x) = -1$.

7. Given that $g(x) = 6$, show that $g(a + b) \neq g(a) + g(b)$.

8. Given that $g(x) = 6$, show that $g(3a) \neq 3g(a)$.

Graph each constant function.

   9. $f(x) = 3$      10. $f(x) = 2$      11. $f(x) = -5$      12. $f(x) = -4$
   13. $f(x) = \frac{1}{2}$   14. $f(x) = -\frac{3}{2}$   15. $f(x) = -\frac{7}{2}$   16. $f(x) = \frac{1}{3}$
   17. $g(x) = 3\sqrt{2}$   18. $g(x) = 2\sqrt{3}$   19. $h(x) = 0$      20. $h(x) = -\pi$

Use the vertical line test to determine whether or not each graph represents $y$ as a function of $x$.

21. 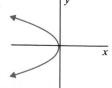     22. 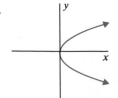     23.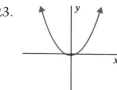

24.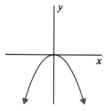

25.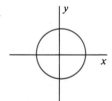

26.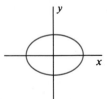

27.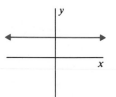

28.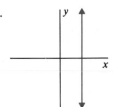

29.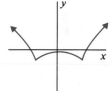

30.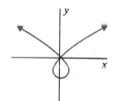

31.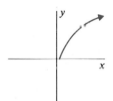

32.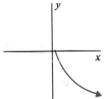

33.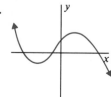

34.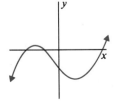

35.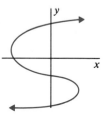

36.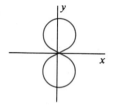

37.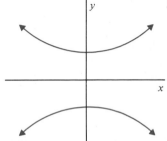

38.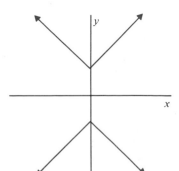

39.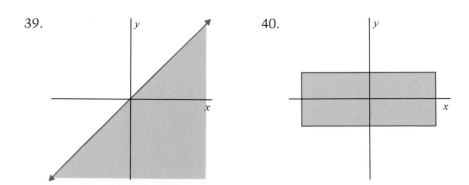

40.

41. The Fahrenheit temperature $T$ in a certain city was recorded each hour $h$ starting at 1 P.M. A graph of the results appears below. Is $T$ a function of $h$?

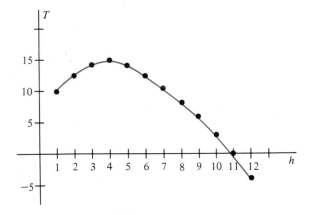

42. **Newton's law of cooling**\* states that the rate at which the temperature of a body changes to meet that of the surrounding medium is directly proportional to the difference in temperature between the body and the medium. The following graph depicts the Fahrenheit temperature $T$ of a hot (212°F) cup of coffee $s$ seconds after it is placed in a room whose temperature is maintained at 70°F. Is $T$ a function of $s$?

\* Named after the English mathematician and physicist Isaac Newton (1642–1727).

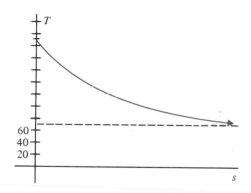

43. The substance radium-226 is present in radioactive wastes. The quantity $Q$ of 100 g of radium-226 that remains after $t$ years is depicted in the graph below. Is $Q$ a function of $t$?

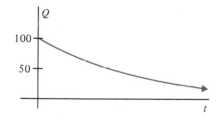

44. The concentration $C$ of a certain drug that remains in the blood-stream $t$ hours after it is injected is depicted in the graph below. Is $C$ a function of $t$?

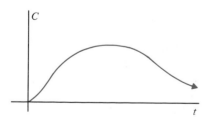

45. The population $p$ of bacteria $t$ hours after a culture is made is depicted in the following graph. Is $p$ a function of $t$?

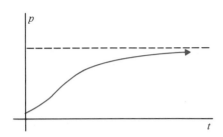

46. The price $p$ of a certain item is related to the quantity demanded $x$ by the graph below. Is $p$ a function of $x$?

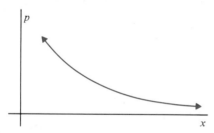

47. What is the range of the function graphed in Problem 41?
48. What is the range of the function graphed in Problem 42?

## Calculator Problems

49. Given the profit function $P$ of Example 3, it can be shown using calculus techniques that *maximum* profit occurs when $x \approx 249$ units. Find and interpret $P(245)$, $P(249)$, and $P(255)$.

50. Graph the constant function $f(x) = \dfrac{\sqrt{317}}{0.87\pi}$.

## Challenge Problems

51. Consider the function $f(x) = \begin{cases} 1, & \text{if } x \text{ is an irrational number,} \\ 0, & \text{if } x \text{ is a rational number.} \end{cases}$

    Find $f(0)$, $f(\pi)$, $f(5)$, $f(-\frac{2}{3})$, and $f(\sqrt{2})$.
52. Approximate the graph of the function in Problem 51.

## *12.4*   LINEAR FUNCTIONS, SLOPE

The next polynomial function in our discussion is the polynomial function of the first degree, or as it is more commonly called, the *linear function*.

---

***Definition***   A **linear function** is any function of the form

$$f(x) = ax + b$$

where $a$ and $b$ are constants and $a \neq 0$.

---

The reason we must stipulate that $a \neq 0$ in the definition above is that if $a = 0$, then the function becomes

$$f(x) = 0 \cdot x + b$$

or

$$f(x) = b,$$

which is a *constant* function, not a linear function.

**EXAMPLE 1**   Graph the linear function $f(x) = 2x + 1$.

This function can also be written as $y = 2x + 1$, and when written in this form it is easily recognized as a linear equation in two variables. From Section 8.2, we know that its graph will be a straight line. In this case the line will not be horizontal but will intersect both axes. We construct the graph by first making a table of values (see next page). Although two ordered pairs are sufficient for our table, it is a good idea to find a third. If the third point lies on the same line as the other two points, then we can be reasonably sure that our table is correct.   □

Since the graph of $y = 2x + 1$ crosses the $x$-axis at the point $(-\frac{1}{2}, 0)$, we say that its **x-intercept** is $-\frac{1}{2}$. Since it crosses the $y$-axis at the point $(0, 1)$, we say that its **y-intercept** is 1.

We can find the $x$-intercepts of the graph of the function $y = f(x)$ (assuming it has any) by setting $f(x) = 0$ and solving for $x$. Similarly, the $y$-intercept can be found (assuming there is one) by setting $x = 0$. Since no vertical line intersects the graph of a function more than once, no function will have more than *one* $y$-intercept. It may, however, have *any* (whole) number of $x$-intercepts.

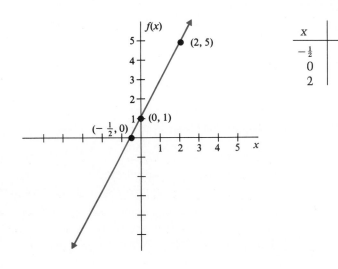

| $x$ | $f(x)$ |
|-----|--------|
| $-\frac{1}{2}$ | 0 |
| 0 | 1 |
| 2 | 5 |

**EXAMPLE 2**   Determine the intercepts of the linear function $f(x) = \frac{1}{3}x - 5$, and then graph the function.

To find the $y$-intercept, we set $x = 0$.

$$f(0) = \frac{1}{3} \cdot 0 - 5$$
$$= -5.$$

The $y$-intercept is $-5$.

To find the $x$-intercept, we set $f(x) = 0$.

$$\frac{1}{3}x - 5 = 0$$
$$\frac{1}{3}x = 5$$
$$x = 15.$$

The $x$-intercept is 15.

Another point is found to check the other two.

$$f(9) = \frac{1}{3} \cdot 9 - 5$$
$$= 3 - 5$$
$$= -2.$$

| $x$ | $f(x)$ |
|-----|--------|
| 0 | $-5$ |
| 15 | 0 |
| 9 | $-2$ |

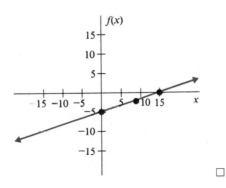

Given any nonvertical line in the plane, we can associate with it a number that measures the *steepness* of the line. Consider for a moment a roof that has a vertical *rise* of 5 feet for each horizontal *run* of 12 feet.

We say that the *slope* of this roof is the ratio of rise to run.* That is,

$$\text{slope} = \frac{\text{rise}}{\text{run}} = \frac{5 \text{ ft}}{12 \text{ ft}} = \frac{5}{12}.$$

Now consider the straight line that passes through the two points $A(3, 6)$ and $B(5, 10)$. An equation for this line is $y = 2x$.

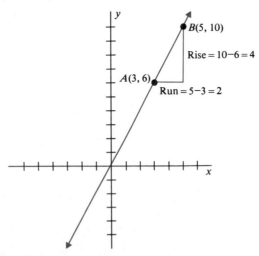

---

* Architects refer to this ratio as the *pitch* of the roof.

The *rise* from $A$ to $B$ is simply the difference of the two $y$-values. The *run* from $A$ to $B$ is the difference of the two $x$-values. If we use the letter $m$ to denote the slope of this line, we can write

$$m = \frac{\text{rise}}{\text{run}} = \frac{10 - 6}{5 - 3} = \frac{4}{2} = 2.$$

Note that we could have reversed the order of the terms in the numerator above if we had done likewise in the denominator. The result would have been the same, since in effect we have simply multiplied numerator and denominator by $-1$. That is,

$$m = \frac{6 - 10}{3 - 5} = \frac{-4}{-2} = 2.$$

Actually, *any* two points on the line above could have been used to determine its slope. For example, suppose the points $D(1, 2)$ and $E(6, 12)$ had been chosen. Then

$$m = \frac{\text{rise}}{\text{run}} = \frac{12 - 2}{6 - 1} = \frac{10}{5} = 2.$$

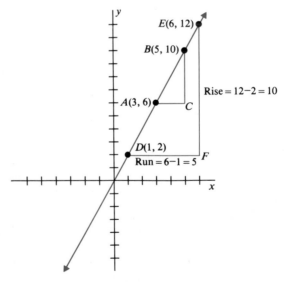

The slope is the same in both cases because the two triangles $ABC$ and $DEF$ are *similar*, and therefore the ratios of their corresponding sides are equal. That is,

$$\frac{EF}{DF} = \frac{BC}{AC}.$$

With this background in mind, we shall formally define the concept of slope.

---

**Definition**   The **slope** $m$ of the line passing through the two points $P_1(x_1, y_1)$ and $P_2(x_2, y_2)$ is given by

$$m = \frac{y_2 - y_1}{x_2 - x_1}.$$

---

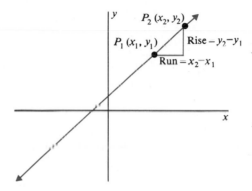

**EXAMPLE 3**   Find the slope of the line below.

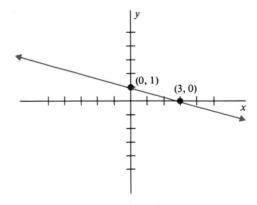

Since the line passes through the two points $(0, 1)$ and $(3, 0)$, the slope is given by

$$m = \frac{1 - 0}{0 - 3} = \frac{1}{-3} = -\frac{1}{3}. \quad \square$$

The slope of the line in Example 3 is a negative number because the line is *decreasing* from left to right.

**EXAMPLE 4** Find the slope of the line below.

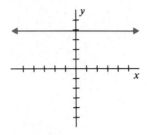

First, we choose two points on the line, say (0, 4) and (5, 4). The slope is then

$$m = \frac{4 - 4}{0 - 5} = \frac{0}{-5} = 0. \quad \square$$

It should be clear from Example 4 that *the slope of every horizontal line is 0.*

**EXAMPLE 5** Find the slope of the line below.

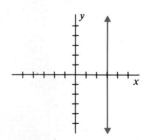

Two points on this line are (3, 0) and (3, 1). Therefore,

$$m = \frac{0 - 1}{3 - 3} = \frac{-1}{0},$$

which is undefined. $\square$

It should be clear from Example 5 that *the slope of every vertical line is undefined.*

We can summarize some of our findings about slope using the four diagrams below.

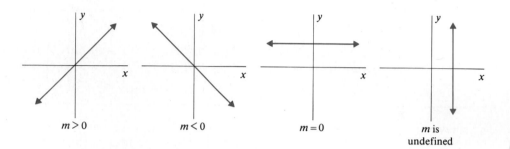

$m > 0$      $m < 0$      $m = 0$      $m$ is
                                          undefined

We shall now see how the slope of a line is related to its equation. Consider the line with slope $m$ and $y$-intercept $b$.

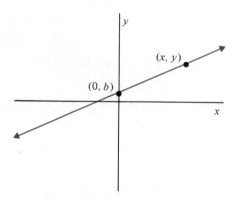

Since the $y$-intercept is $b$, the point $(0, b)$ lies on the line. Therefore, if $(x, y)$ is any arbitrary point on the line except $(0, b)$, we can write the equation

$$\frac{y - b}{x - 0} = m.$$

Simplifying this equation, we have

$$\frac{y - b}{x} = m$$

$$y - b = mx$$

$$y = mx + b.$$

This last equation is also satisfied by the point $(x, y) = (0, b)$, since $b = m \cdot 0 + b$.

---

**Slope-Intercept Form of a Line**

A line has slope $m$ and $y$-intercept $b$ if and only if its equation is of the form

$$y = mx + b.$$

---

**EXAMPLE 6** Determine the slope $m$ and the $y$-intercept $b$ of the line $x + 2y = 10$. Then use this information to graph the line.

In order to determine the slope and $y$-intercept of this line, we put the equation in slope-intercept form. This is done by solving the equation for $y$

$$x + 2y = 10$$
$$2y = -x + 10$$
$$y = -\frac{1}{2}x + 5.$$

Therefore, $m = -\frac{1}{2}$ and $b = 5$.

The graph of the line with $y$-intercept 5 and slope $-\frac{1}{2}$ lies below.

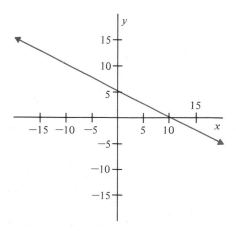

**EXAMPLE 7**   Write an equation for the line that passes through the two points $(1, 5)$ and $(-1, -1)$.

First, we use the two points to determine the slope of the line.

$$m = \frac{5 - (-1)}{1 - (-1)} = \frac{6}{2} = 3.$$

Hence, the equation is of the form $y = 3x + b$.

Then we use the fact that the point $(1, 5)$ is on the line (the point $(-1, -1)$ could have been used just as well) to find the $y$-intercept as follows:

$$5 = 3(1) + b$$
$$2 = b.$$

Therefore, the desired equation is $y = 3x + 2$. □

There is a relationship between the slopes of two lines that are *parallel*. There is also a relationship between the slopes of two lines that are *perpendicular*. These two relationships are stated below without proof.

---

**Parallel and Perpendicular Lines**

Suppose $m_1$ and $m_2$ are the respective slopes of two lines.

1. The two lines are **parallel** if and only if $m_1 = m_2$.

2. The two lines are **perpendicular** if and only if $m_1 = -\dfrac{1}{m_2}$.

---

In other words, *the slopes of parallel lines are equal, while the slopes of perpendicular lines are negative reciprocals of one another.* These relationships do not hold if either line is vertical, of course, since the slope of a vertical line is undefined.

**EXAMPLE 8**   The two lines $y = x$ and $y = x - 3$ are parallel, since they both have a slope of 1. The $y$-intercept of the first line is 0, while the $y$-intercept of the second line is $-3$.

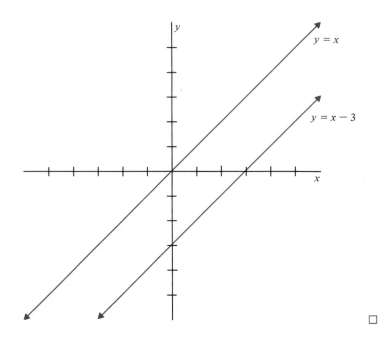

**EXAMPLE 9**   Determine whether the two lines $2x - y = 0$ and $x + 2y = 4$ are parallel, perpendicular, or neither.

We put each line in slope-intercept form.

$$2x - y = 0 \quad x + 2y = 4$$
$$-y = -2x \quad 2y = -x + 4$$
$$y = 2x \qquad y = -\frac{1}{2}x + 2.$$

The slope of the first line is $m_1 = 2$, while the slope of the second line is $m_2 = -\frac{1}{2}$. Since 2 and $-\frac{1}{2}$ are negative reciprocals of each other, the two lines are perpendicular.

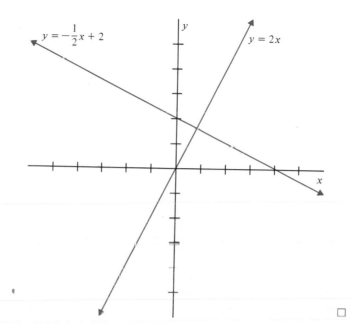

$y = -\frac{1}{2}x + 2$

$y$

$y = 2x$

$x$

The concept of slope is a very important one in mathematics. Besides having numerous applications in its own right, it is a fundamental notion in the study of differential calculus.

## Problem Set 12.4

Find the intercepts and then graph each linear function.

1. $f(x) = 3x + 1$     2. $f(x) = 5x + 1$     3. $f(x) = 4x - 1$     4. $f(x) = 2x - 1$
5. $f(x) = \frac{1}{2}x + 6$     6. $f(x) = \frac{1}{3}x + 6$     7. $g(x) = \frac{1}{5}x$     8. $g(x) = \frac{1}{7}x$
9. $h(x) = -x + 8$     10. $h(x) = -x + 3$

Find the slope of the line passing through each pair of points.

11. $(7, 5)$ and $(3, 2)$                12. $(4, 5)$ and $(1, 3)$
13. $(1, 6)$ and $(2, 4)$                14. $(2, 9)$ and $(3, 6)$
15. $(0, 0)$ and $(5, 1)$                16. $(0, 0)$ and $(7, 1)$
17. $(-3, 8)$ and $(3, -6)$              18. $(-3, 11)$ and $(3, -4)$

19. $(0, -\frac{1}{4})$   and   $(-\frac{11}{12}, -\frac{1}{2})$      20. $(-\frac{11}{24}, -\frac{1}{2})$   and   $(0, -\frac{1}{3})$

21. $(a + b, 3)$   and   $(a - b, 1)$      22. $(6, a - b)$   and   $(2, a + b)$

Determine the slope $m$ and the $y$-intercept $b$ of each line. Then use this information to graph the line.

23. $y = 2x + 3$        24. $y = 3x + 4$        25. $y = 2x$            26. $y = 3x$
27. $4x + y = 2$        28. $6x + y = 3$        29. $x - 3y = 9$        30. $x - 2y = 4$
31. $3x + 2y = 0$       32. $4x + 3y = 0$       33. $5x + 9y = 45$      34. $7x + 12y = 84$
35. $y - 5 = 0$         36. $y - 3 = 0$

37. What is the slope and $y$-intercept of the line $x = 4$? Graph this line.

38. What is the slope and $y$-intercept of the line $x = -1$? Graph this line.

39. Using the same coordinate axes, graph $y = mx$ for
    a) $m = \frac{1}{2}$.      b) $m = 1$.      c) $m = 2$.

40. Using the same coordinate axes, graph $y = mx$ for
    a) $m = -\frac{1}{2}$.      b) $m = -1$.      c) $m = -2$.

41. Using the same coordinate axes, graph $y = -x + b$ for
    a) $b = -2$.      b) $b = 0$.      c) $b = 2$.

42. Using the same coordinate axes, graph $y = x + b$ for
    a) $b = -2$.      b) $b = 0$.      c) $b = 2$.

Write an equation for the line that passes through each pair of points.

43. $(4, 3)$   and   $(5, 5)$         44. $(2, 5)$   and   $(3, 8)$
45. $(-1, 2)$   and   $(5, 4)$        46. $(-3, 4)$   and   $(1, 6)$
47. $(2, -3)$   and   $(-5, 4)$       48. $(-6, 2)$   and   $(4, -8)$
49. $(6, 7)$   and   $(3, 7)$         50. $(8, 8)$   and   $(4, 8)$
51. $(-4, 5)$   and   $(-4, 3)$       52. $(-2, 3)$   and   $(-2, 5)$

Determine whether the given lines are parallel, perpendicular, or neither.

53. $y - 3x = 0,\ \ 6x - 2y = 5$        54. $y - x = 2,\ \ 3x - 3y = 7$
55. $y = 4x + 1,\ \ 3x + 12y = 8$       56. $y = 5x - 1,\ \ 2x + 10y = 0$
57. $2x + 3y = 6,\ \ x - y = -7$        58. $3x + 4y = 6,\ \ x - 2y = -8$

59. Write an equation for the line with $y$-intercept $\frac{3}{7}$ that is
    (a) parallel to $3x + 4y = 20$.      (b) perpendicular to $3x + 4y = 20$.

60. Write an equation for the line with $y$-intercept $-\frac{2}{5}$ that is
    (a) parallel to $2x - 3y = 12$.      (b) perpendicular to $2x - 3y = 12$.

61. The slope of a conical pile of sand is $\frac{2}{3}$. What is the diameter of the base if the height of the pile is 10 ft?

62. Do Problem 61 if the slope of the pile is $\frac{3}{4}$.

63. The **grade** of a road is the ratio of the change in elevation of the road to the corresponding horizontal change (see diagram below). Hence the notion of grade is similar to the notion of slope. If a road rises 15 ft over a horizontal distance of 200 ft, determine the grade of the road.

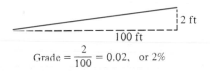

2 ft

100 ft

$$\text{Grade} = \frac{2}{100} = 0.02, \text{ or } 2\%$$

64. A mountain road has a constant grade of 20%. If the drive to the top is 6 mi, how high is the mountain? (*Hint:* See Problem 63, apply the Pythagorean theorem, and then use similar triangles to set up a proportion.)

## Calculator Problems

65. Find the slope of the line passing through (20.288, 10.144) and (28.213, 4.755).

66. A downhill racer takes 39 sec to ski down a mountain that is 1430 ft high and has a slope of $\frac{5}{12}$. Find the skier's average speed in mph.

## Challenge Problems

67. Prove that the diagonals of a square are perpendicular. (*Hint:* Assume that the length of a side is $a$, and place the four vertices of the square at (0, 0), (a, 0), (0, a), and (a, a).)

68. The relationship between Fahrenheit degrees $F$ and Celsius degrees $C$ is linear. Given that water freezes at 0°C or 32°F and boils at 100°C or 212°F, write an equation describing that relationship.

## 12.5  QUADRATIC FUNCTIONS, VERTEX OF A PARABOLA

The next polynomial function we shall consider is the polynomial function of the second degree, or the *quadratic function*.

---

**Definition**    A **quadratic function** is any function of the form

$$f(x) = ax^2 + bx + c$$

where $a$, $b$, and $c$ are constants and $a \neq 0$.

---

Again, if $a = 0$, then $f(x) = ax^2 + bx + c$ reduces to a *linear* function (assuming $b \neq 0$ as well).

Just as the graph of a linear function will always be a straight line, the graph of the quadratic function $f(x) = ax^2 + bx + c$ will always be a *parabola*. As was suggested in Section 11.6, it is of great practical interest to be able to identify the *vertex* of a parabola. This can be done by drawing the graph and estimating the vertex point visually, but this can lead to difficulty, particularly if the coordinates of the vertex are not integers. Therefore we shall now develop a formula that we will use to find the *exact* coordinates of the vertex. We begin this development with two specific examples.

**EXAMPLE 1**   Find the vertex of the quadratic function $f(x) = x^2 - 4x + 5$, and determine whether it is the high point or the low point of the graph.

We begin by grouping the first two terms together.

$$f(x) = (x^2 - 4x) + 5.$$

Then we complete the square on the expression $x^2 - 4x$ by adding $(-\frac{4}{2})^2 = 4$ *inside* the parentheses. To compensate, we also add $-4$ *outside* the parentheses. Our work looks like this:

$$f(x) = (x^2 - 4x + 4) + 5 + (-4)$$
$$f(x) = (x - 2)^2 + 1.$$

Now, $(x - 2)^2 \geq 0$ for any real number $x$. Therefore the *smallest* possible value of $f(x)$ is 1, and that occurs when $x = 2$. For any value of $x$ *not* equal to 2, the value of $f(x)$ will be *larger* than 1. Moreover, the greater the difference between $x$ and 2, the larger the value of $f(x)$. Hence the vertex of this parabola is $V = (2, 1)$, and it is the *low* point of the graph. □

**EXAMPLE 2**    Find the vertex of the quadratic function $f(x) = -2x^2 + 6x - 1$, and determine whether it is the high point or the low point of the graph.

We group the first two terms together and factor out a $-2$.

$$f(x) = (-2x^2 + 6x) - 1$$
$$f(x) = -2(x^2 - 3x) - 1.$$

Then we complete the square on the expression $x^2 - 3x$ by adding $(-\frac{3}{2})^2 = \frac{9}{4}$ inside the parentheses. In doing so, however, we have *actually* added $-2(\frac{9}{4}) = -\frac{9}{2}$ to the right-hand side of the equation. To compensate for this, we must also add $+\frac{9}{2}$ to the right-hand side. Our work looks like this:

$$f(x) = -2\left(x^2 - 3x + \frac{9}{4}\right) - 1 + \frac{9}{2}$$
$$f(x) = -2\left(x - \frac{3}{2}\right)^2 + \frac{7}{2}.$$

Now, $-2(x - \frac{3}{2})^2 \leq 0$ for any real number $x$. Therefore, the *largest* possible $f(x)$-value is $\frac{7}{2}$, and that occurs when $x = \frac{3}{2}$. For any value of $x$ *not* equal to $\frac{3}{2}$, the value of $f(x)$ will be *smaller* than $\frac{7}{2}$. Moreover, the greater the difference between $x$ and $\frac{3}{2}$, the smaller the value of $f(x)$. Hence the vertex of this parabola is $V = (\frac{3}{2}, \frac{7}{2})$, and it is the *high* point of the graph. □

We can always find the vertex of a parabola using the method demonstrated in the previous two examples. However, it will be to our advantage instead to use this method to develop a *formula* that will give us the vertex of *any* quadratic function. Following this method using the general quadratic function, we have

$$f(x) = ax^2 + bx + c \quad (a \neq 0)$$
$$f(x) = a\left(x^2 + \frac{b}{a}x\right) + c$$
$$f(x) = a\left(x^2 + \frac{b}{a}x + \frac{b^2}{4a^2}\right) + c - \frac{b^2}{4a}$$
$$f(x) = a\left(x + \frac{b}{2a}\right)^2 + \frac{4ac - b^2}{4a}.$$

Now, if $a > 0$ then $a(x + b/2a)^2 \geq 0$ for any real number $x$. Therefore, the *smallest* possible $f(x)$-value is $(4ac - b^2)/4a$, and that occurs when $x = -b/2a$.

On the other hand, if $a < 0$ then $a(x + b/2a)^2 \leq 0$ for any real number $x$. In that case, the *largest* possible $f(x)$-value is $(4ac - b^2)/4a$, and that also occurs when $x = -b/2a$.

These results can be summarized in the two diagrams below.

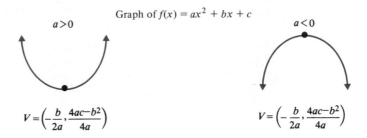

Graph of $f(x) = ax^2 + bx + c$

$a > 0$

$a < 0$

$V = \left(-\dfrac{b}{2a}, \dfrac{4ac-b^2}{4a}\right)$

$V = \left(-\dfrac{b}{2a}, \dfrac{4ac-b^2}{4a}\right)$

**EXAMPLE 3**  Determine the vertex and the intercepts of the quadratic function $y = f(x) = x^2 - 4x + 3$. Then graph the function.

Since $a = 1$, $b = -4$, and $c = 3$, the $x$-value of the vertex is

$$x = -\frac{b}{2a} = -\frac{-4}{2(1)} = 2.$$

We could find the $y$-value of the vertex using the formula $y = (4ac - b^2)/4a$. It is generally easier, though, to simply substitute the $x$-value of the vertex into the function. That is,

$$f(2) = 2^2 - 4 \cdot 2 + 3 = -1.$$

Therefore the vertex is $V = (2, -1)$.

To find the $y$-intercept we set $x = 0$.

$$f(0) = 0^2 - 4 \cdot 0 + 3 = 3.$$

Therefore the $y$-intercept is 3. *Note that the $y$-intercept of $f(x) = ax^2 + bx + c$ is always $c$.*

To find the $x$-intercepts we set $f(x) = 0$.

$$x^2 - 4x + 3 = 0$$
$$(x - 1)(x - 3) = 0$$
$$x = 1 \quad \text{or} \quad x = 3.$$

Therefore the $x$-intercepts are 1 and 3. Note that this graph has *two* $x$-intercepts, indicating that it intersects the $x$-axis at *two* points.

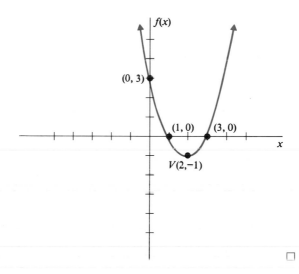

If we wanted the graph above to be more accurate, we could construct a table of values containing additional points. In general, the more points in the table of values, the more accurate the graph is.

**EXAMPLE 4**   Determine the vertex and the intercepts of the quadratic function $y = f(x) = x^2 - 3$. Then graph the function.

Since $a = 1$, $b = 0$, and $c = -3$, the vertex is at

$$x = -\frac{0}{2(1)} = 0,$$
$$f(0) = 0^2 - 3 = -3.$$

Also, the $y$-intercept is $-3$.

To find the $x$-intercepts we set $f(x) = 0$.

$$x^2 - 3 = 0$$
$$x^2 = 3$$
$$x = \pm\sqrt{3}.$$

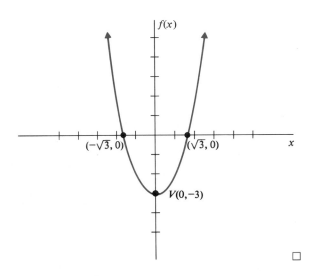

**EXAMPLE 5**   Determine the vertex and the intercepts of the quadratic function $y = f(x) = -\frac{1}{2}x^2 + x - 2$. Then graph the function.

Since $a = -\frac{1}{2}$, $b = 1$, and $c = -2$, the vertex is at

$$x = -\frac{1}{2\left(-\frac{1}{2}\right)} = -\frac{1}{-1} = 1,$$

$$f(1) = -\frac{1}{2}(1)^2 + (1) - 2 = -\frac{3}{2}.$$

The $y$-intercept is $-2$.

To find the $x$-intercepts we set $f(x) = 0$.

$$-\frac{1}{2}x^2 + x - 2 = 0.$$

Multiplying both sides by $-2$ we have

$$x^2 - 2x + 4 = 0.$$

To solve this equation for $x$, we use the quadratic formula.

$$x = \frac{-(-2) \pm \sqrt{(-2)^2 - 4(1)(4)}}{2(1)}$$

$$x = \frac{2 \pm \sqrt{4 - 16}}{2}$$

$$x = \frac{2 \pm \sqrt{-12}}{2}.$$

But these values of $x$ are not real numbers since $\sqrt{-12}$ is not a real number. This means that this parabola has *no* $x$-intercepts and therefore does not touch the $x$-axis at any point. To complete the graph we simply determine several ordered pairs that satisfy the function $f(x) = -\frac{1}{2}x^2 + x - 2$.

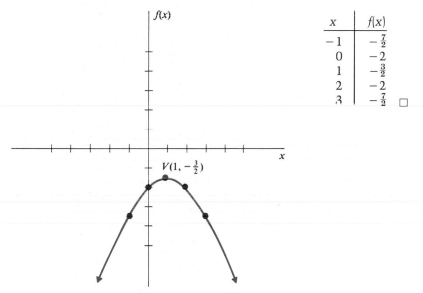

| $x$ | $f(x)$ |
|-----|--------|
| $-1$ | $-\frac{7}{2}$ |
| $0$ | $-2$ |
| $1$ | $-\frac{3}{2}$ |
| $2$ | $-2$ |
| $3$ | $-\frac{7}{2}$ |

We will now see how knowledge of the coordinates of the vertex of a parabola can be put to use in solving an applied problem.

**EXAMPLE 6**  A farmer has 12 miles of fencing with which to bound a rectangular pasture. One side of his property lies at the foot of a straight cliff and needs no fence. What should the dimensions of the pasture be if the area of the pasture is to be a maximum?

Let $A =$ the area of the pasture (the quantity to be maximized),

and $x =$ the width of the pasture.

$$A = x(12 - 2x)$$
$$A = 12x - 2x^2$$
$$A = -2x^2 + 12x.$$

The graph of this function is a parabola that opens downward with vertex at

$$x = -\frac{12}{2(-2)} = -\frac{12}{-4} = 3,$$
$$A = -2(3)^2 + 12(3) = -18 + 36 = 18.$$

Therefore the maximum area of 18 square miles is obtained when the width of the pasture is 3 miles. The corresponding length would be $12 - 2 \cdot 3 = 6$ miles. □

A table of values and a graph for the function of Example 6 lie below.

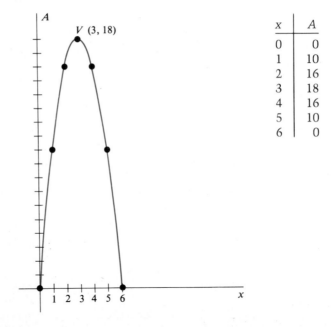

| x | A |
|---|---|
| 0 | 0 |
| 1 | 10 |
| 2 | 16 |
| 3 | 18 |
| 4 | 16 |
| 5 | 10 |
| 6 | 0 |

Since the area $A$ cannot be negative, we do not include the portion of the graph that lies *below* the x-axis.

## Problem Set 12.5

Find the vertex and the intercepts and then graph each quadratic function.

1. $f(x) = x^2 - 6x + 5$
2. $f(x) = x^2 - 6x + 8$
3. $f(x) = x^2 - 2x - 8$
4. $f(x) = x^2 - 2x - 3$
5. $f(x) = 2x^2 - 6x - 8$
6. $f(x) = 2x^2 + 6x - 8$
7. $f(x) = x^2 - 16$
8. $f(x) = x^2 - 1$
9. $f(x) = -x^2 + 16$
10. $f(x) = -x^2 + 1$
11. $f(x) = x^2 - 5$
12. $f(x) = x^2 - 6$
13. $f(x) = x^2 + 3$
14. $f(x) = x^2 + 2$
15. $g(x) = x^2 + x - 1$
16. $g(x) = x^2 - x - 1$
17. $h(x) = -x^2$
18. $h(x) = x^2$
19. $k(x) = \frac{1}{4}x^2$
20. $k(x) = -\frac{1}{4}x^2$
21. $P(x) = -\frac{1}{2}x^2 + 2x - 2$
22. $P(x) = -\frac{1}{2}x^2 + 3x - \frac{9}{2}$
23. $r(x) = -x^2 + 3x - 3$
24. $r(x) = -x^2 + 5x - 7$
25. $g(t) = -4t - 2t^2$
26. $g(t) = -6t - 2t^2$
27. $s = 10t - 6t^2$
28. $s = 8t - 6t^2$

29. If $y = 12x^2 - 8x + 15$, for what value of $x$ is $y$ a minimum?
30. If $y = 15x^2 - 10x + 18$, for what value of $x$ is $y$ a minimum?
31. The daily profit $P(x)$ in hundreds of dollars that is derived from producing $x$ units per day is given by $P(x) = -3x^2 + 24x - 36$. Determine the number of units $x$ that should be produced each day in order to maximize daily profit. What is the maximum daily profit?
32. Do Problem 31 if $P(x) = -3x^2 + 30x - 48$.
33. A farmer wishes to fence in a rectangular pen with 40 ft of fencing. One side of the pen is to lie along a barn and needs no fence. What should the dimensions of the pen be in order to maximize its area?
34. A rancher has 400 yards of fencing with which to bound a rectangular pasture. One side of her property is bordered by another rancher's fence and therefore needs no additional fencing. What should the dimensions of the pasture be in order to maximize its area?
35. A pellet is shot from the top of a building 50 ft high by a slingshot that gives it an initial velocity of 96 ft/sec. Find its maximum height. (*Hint:* See Example 9 of Section 11.1.)
36. An arrow is shot from the top of a cliff 70 ft high using a bow that gives it an initial velocity of 128 ft/sec. Find its maximum height. (*Hint:* See Example 9 of Section 11.1.)

## Calculator Problems

37. Find the vertex and intercepts of the quadratic function $f(x) = x^2 + 2.7x - 20.74$.

38. The daily profit $P(x)$ that is derived from producing $x$ units per day is given by $P(x) = -0.68x^2 + 176.8x - 6807$. Determine the number of units $x$ that should be produced each day in order to maximize daily profit. What is the maximum daily profit?

## Challenge Problems

39. A certain item sells for 50 cents. A market analysis on this item reveals that for each increase of 2 cents in the price, the number of sales per day decreases by 15. If daily sales at 50 cents per item are 795, what should the price of the item be in order to insure a maximum daily revenue?

40. Prove that of all those rectangles having the same fixed perimeter $P$, the square houses the greatest area.

## Chapter Review

True or false.

1. The equation $y = x^2 + 8x - 10$ defines $y$ as a function of $x$.
2. The equation $y^2 - x^2 = 16$ defines $y$ as a function of $x$.
3. The inequality $y < x + 1$ defines $y$ as a function of $x$.
4. The value of the function $f(x) = 1/(x + 1)$ at $x = -\frac{1}{2}$ is 2.
5. The graph of $f(x) = -\frac{1}{17}x^2 + 75x + 100$ is a parabola that opens downward.
6. A polynomial function in $x$ is a function of the form $f(x) = $ a polynomial in $x$.
7. The slope $m$ of the line passing through the two points $P_1(x_1, y_1)$ and $P_2(x_2, y_2)$ is given by $m = (x_2 - x_1)/(y_2 - y_1)$.

Completion.

8. In the equation $y = x^2 + 4x + 10$, $x$ is called the

   _____?_____ variable and $y$ is called the _____?_____
   variable.

9. A rule that assigns to each element $x$ in set $A$ a unique element $y$ in set $B$ is called a _____?_____.

10. If $y$ is a function of $x$, the set of all permissible values that $x$ may assume is called the _____?_____ of the function, while the set of all values taken on by $y$ is called the _____?_____ of the function.

11. The expression $f(x)$ is read _____?_____ and it represents the value of the function $f$ at _____?_____.

12. A function of the form $f(x) = a$ is a(n) _____?_____ function. Its graph is a(n) _____?_____.

13. A function of the form $f(x) = ax + b$ $(a \neq 0)$ is a(n) _____?_____ function. Its graph is a(n) _____?_____.

14. A function of the form $f(x) = ax^2 + bx + c$ $(a \neq 0)$ is a(n) _____?_____ function. Its graph is a(n) _____?_____ whose vertex occurs at $x = $ _____?_____.

15. The degree of the polynomial function $f(x) = ax^3 + bx^2 + cx + d^3$ $(a \neq 0)$ is _____?_____.

16. Vertical Line Test: A graph in the $xy$-plane represents $y$ as a function of $x$ if and only if _____?_____.

17. A line with slope $m$ and $y$-intercept $b$ has equation _____?_____. This equation is known as the _____?_____ form of a line.

18. Suppose $m_1$ and $m_2$ are the respective slopes of two lines. The lines are parallel if and only if _____?_____. The lines are perpendicular if and only if _____?_____.

19. Which of the graphs below represent $y$ as a function of $x$?

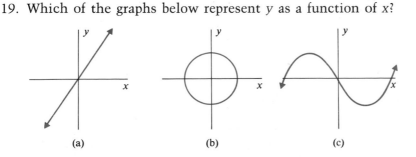

(a)　　　　　　(b)　　　　　　(c)

20. Determine the domain of each function.

    a) $y = 1/(3x^2 + 13x - 10)$     b) $f(x) = \sqrt{6x + 15}$

    c) $g(x) = 5x/\sqrt{1 - x}$

21. Determine the range of each function.

    a) $y = x^2 + 4$     b) $y = \frac{1}{2}x$     c) $h(x) = -x^2$

22. State the domain and range of the function graphed below.

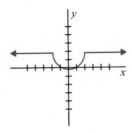

23. Write the slope of each line.

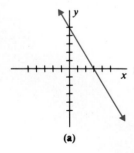

(a)

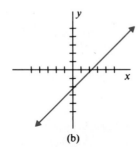

(b)

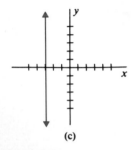

(c)

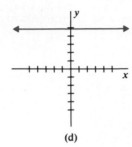

(d)

24. Given $F(x) = x^2 - x + 6$, determine each of the following.
    a) $F(0)$                b) $F(-3)$                c) $F(\frac{1}{2})$                d) $F(t)$
    e) $F(1 + 2)$        f) $F(1) + F(2)$        g) $F(a + b)$        h) $F(x + h)$

25. Find $\dfrac{f(t) - f(x)}{t - x}$ for each function below, and then simplify.
    a) $f(x) = x^2$            b) $f(x) = 8$

26. Determine the slope of the line
    a) that passes through $(-2, 12)$ and $(3, -7)$.
    b) that passes through $(a + b, a)$ and $(a - b, b)$.
    c) that is parallel to the line $2x - 5y = 10$.

27. Determine whether the lines $2y = 1 + 6x$ and $2x - 6y = -1$ are parallel, perpendicular, or neither.

28. Write an equation for the line
    a) that passes through $(\frac{1}{2}, \frac{2}{3})$ and $(-\frac{3}{4}, \frac{1}{3})$.
    b) that is perpendicular to the line $x + 4y = 0$ at the point $(8, -2)$.

29. Determine the slope $m$ and the $y$-intercept $b$ of each line. Then use this information to graph the line.
    a) $y = x$            b) $x + y = -1$            c) $y = 2x + 10$

30. Determine whether the three points $(-1, 13)$, $(8, 5)$, and $(12, 1)$ are *collinear* (i.e., lie on the same straight line).

Graph each function. Label the coordinates of the intercepts and the vertex where appropriate.

31. $f(x) = -2$
33. $h(x) = \frac{1}{4}x - 3$
35. $y = 2x^2 - x - 10$

32. $g(x) = 0$
34. $p(x) = 4x$
36. $f(t) = -8t - 2t^2$

37. Write the surface area $S$ of a cube as a function of its edge $e$.

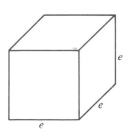

38. Write the area $A$ of the Norman window pictured below as a function of $x$.

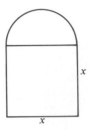

39. A manufacturer can produce watches at a cost of $8.50 per watch plus a daily overhead of $475. If $C(x)$ denotes the total daily cost of producing $x$ watches per day, write a cost function for these watches. Then find and interpret $C(0)$ and $C(65)$.

40. A farmer has 600 yards of fencing with which to construct a rectangular pasture. One side of his property lies along a straight river and needs no fence. What should the dimensions of the pasture be if the area is to be as large as possible?

# Appendixes

# 1 APPENDIX 1: SETS

One of the most significant developments in the history of mathematics was the introduction of *set theory* by a German mathematician named Georg Cantor (1845–1918). Set theory has contributed a foundation which clarifies and unifies the mathematics that we know. A basic knowledge of sets is fundamental to anyone who intends to pursue the study of mathematics.

Intuitively, a **set** is a collection of objects. Other terms that are frequently used synonymously with set are *group, aggregate,* and *class.* The objects in a set are called **elements** or **members** of the set. The elements of a particular set may have some obvious property in common or they may not. For instance, we may speak of the set of whole numbers from 1 to 10, the set of days in a week, or the set of NBA basketball players over seven feet tall. On the other hand, the set whose three elements are the number 1, the name Bob, and the color red is a set whose elements appear to have no connection whatever.

We need some sort of convenient notation to use in writing a set. For this purpose a pair of *braces* is employed to contain the elements of the set, and *commas* are used to separate the elements. The set mentioned above would be written {1, Bob, red}. Note that the commas are necessary, since without them we would not be able to distinguish between the set {1, 2, 3} and the set {123}. The first of these sets has three elements, while the second has but one.

The *order* in which the elements of a set are listed is unimportant. The set {3, 2, 1} is identical to the set {1, 2, 3}. In fact, there are six ways of listing this set: {1, 2, 3}, {2, 1, 3}, {1, 3, 2}, {3, 1, 2}, {2, 3, 1}, {3, 2, 1}.

To facilitate referring to a set in a particular discussion we give it a name, usually in the form of a capital letter. Thus we might write

$$A = \{1, \text{Bob, red}\},$$

meaning $A$ is the name of the set whose three elements are 1, Bob, and red.

The symbol $\in$ is read *is an element of.* Therefore we would be correct in writing $1 \in A$. A *slash mark* is often used in mathematics to *negate* a given symbol. That is, while the symbol $=$ means *is equal to,* the symbol $\neq$ means *is not equal to.* By the same token, the symbol $\notin$ is read *is not an element of.* Using this notation, we could write $2 \notin A$.

**EXAMPLE 1** Using set notation, write the set of whole numbers from 1 to 10.

$$\{1, 2, 3, 4, 5, 6, 7, 8, 9, 10\} \ \square$$

**EXAMPLE 2** Using set notation, write the set of days in the week.

{Sunday, Monday, Tuesday, Wednesday, Thursday, Friday, Saturday} □

The method of writing a set that was used in both of these examples is called the **listing method.** That is, the set was described simply by listing all of its elements. While this method provides a clear description of the set, it would be much too unwieldy to be used in some situations. For example, suppose we wanted to write the set of whole numbers from 1 to 100. For this reason, we introduce another way of writing a set, called the **rule method.** We begin with an example.

**EXAMPLE 3** Using the rule method, write the set of whole numbers from 1 to 100.

$$\{x \mid x \text{ is a whole number between 0 and 101}\} \ \square$$

The expression above is read *the set of all x such that x is a whole number between 0 and 101.* The vertical bar stands for the words *such that.*

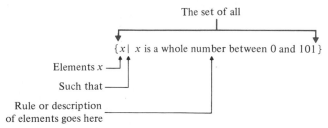

A set may be thought of as a club, with the phrase after the vertical bar being the requirement on $x$ for membership in the club. The letter $x$ is being used as a **variable.** By this we mean that $x$ may represent any one of the elements in the set. Its value is not fixed, but rather, varies. On the other hand, a **constant,** such as 7, remains fixed throughout a particular discussion. In the set above, $x$ represents each of the whole numbers from 1 to 100. Observe that we say "$x$ is *a* whole number between 0 and 101" rather than "x is *all* of the whole numbers between 0 and 101." This simply indicates that x assumes each value one at a time, rather than all of them at once.

**EXAMPLE 4**  Write {a, e, i, o, u} using the rule method.

$$\{y \mid y \text{ is a vowel}\} \quad \square$$

Note that the choice of variable is not important. That is $\{x \mid x$ is a vowel$\}$ and $\{y \mid y$ is a vowel$\}$ represent the same set.

In Example 4, a set was described using the listing method and we were asked to describe the same set using the rule method. The situation may also be reversed.

**EXAMPLE 5**  Write $\{x \mid x$ is a chess piece$\}$ using the listing method.

{pawn, knight, bishop, rook, queen, king}  $\square$

The *listing method* is easier to use when the set is small, or when there is no convenient rule that relates the elements, as is the case with the set {1, Bob, red}. In other cases, the *rule method* will probably prove more convenient.

Suppose we had to write the following set using the listing method:

$$\{x \mid x \text{ is a living unicorn}\}.$$

Since there do not exist any living unicorns, we would have to say that this particular set has no elements. This set is written {  } and is called the **empty set** (or **null set**). Often the symbol $\emptyset$ is used to denote the empty set. That is, $\emptyset = \{ \ \}$.

**EXAMPLE 6**  Using the rule method, describe the empty set in another way.

$$\{x \mid x \text{ is an NBA basketball player over eight feet tall}\} \quad \square$$

A set may be **finite** or **infinite.** That is, it may have a specific number of elements, or its elements may continue without end. The set of months of the year is a finite set; it has a specific number of elements, namely 12. The set of grains of sand in Long Beach, California, is an extremely large set, but it is still finite. One example of an infinite set is the set of whole numbers. Its elements continue without end. We could write the set of whole numbers using the rule method as

$$\{x \mid x \text{ is a whole number}\},$$

or, using the listing method, as

$$\{0, 1, 2, 3, 4, 5, 6, ...\}.$$

Of course, not all of the elements can be listed. The three dots are read *and so on* and mean that the pattern continues without end.

A final note is in order. It is important that we distinguish between symbols such as 3 and {3}. The first represents the *number* 3, while the second represents the *set containing the number* 3. That is 3 ≠ {3}. They are different in the same sort of sense that a hat is different from the same hat placed inside a hatbox.

## Problems

True or false.

1. $5 \in \{5, 7\}$     2. $3 \in \{3, 4, 5\}$     3. $b \notin \{a, b, c\}$
4. yellow $\notin$ {red, blue, yellow, green}
5. $7 \in \{x \mid x$ is an even whole number\}
6. $8 \in \{x \mid x$ is an odd whole number\}
7. ace $\in \{y \mid y$ is a playing card\}
8. deuce $\in \{y \mid y$ is a playing card\}
9. $13 \in \{t \mid t$ is a multiple of 5\}
10. $27 \in \{t \mid t$ is a multiple of 5\}
11. summer $\notin \{x \mid x$ is a season of the year\}
12. Chicago $\notin \{x \mid x$ is a city in the United States\}

Write each of the following sets using the listing method.

13. $\{x \mid x$ is a whole number between 0 and 6\}
14. $\{x \mid x$ is a whole number between 3 and 7\}
15. $\{z \mid z$ is a whole-number multiple of 2\}
16. $\{z \mid z$ is a whole-number multiple of 3\}
17. $\{t \mid t$ is a month of the year\}
18. $\{s \mid s$ is a state in the United States\}
19. $\{y \mid y$ is a whole number between 3 and 4\}
20. $\{y \mid y$ is an odd number divisible by 2\}
21. $\{y \mid y$ is a letter in the word banana\}
22. $\{y \mid y$ is a letter in the word eleven\}
23. $\{x \mid x$ is a dinosaur living in Texas\}
24. $\{x \mid x$ is a female president of the United States\}

25. $\{x \mid x$ is a letter in the word Mississippi$\}$
26. $\{x \mid x$ is a letter in the word Tallahassee$\}$
27. $\{x \mid x$ is an even whole number divisor of 20$\}$
28. $\{x \mid x$ is an odd whole number divisor of 45$\}$
29. $\{2n \mid n$ is a whole number$\}$
30. $\{2n + 1 \mid n$ is a whole number$\}$

Write each of the following sets using the rule method.

31. $\{14, 15, 16, 17, 18, 19\}$        32. $\{7, 8, 9, 10\}$
33. $\{$January, June, July$\}$        34. $\{$Tuesday, Thursday$\}$
35. $\{0, 2, 4, 6, 8, 10, 12, ...\}$        36. $\{1, 3, 5, 7, 9, 11, 13, ...\}$
37. $\{0, 3, 6, 9, 12, 15, 18, ...\}$        38. $\{0, 10, 20, 30, 40, 50, ...\}$
39. $\{5, 15, 25, 35, 45, 55, ...\}$        40. $\{7, 17, 27, 37, 47, 57, ...\}$
41. $\{$Erie, Huron, Michigan, Ontario, Superior$\}$
42. $\{$Africa, Asia, Australia, Europe, North America, South America, Antarctica$\}$

## Calculator Problems

True or false.

43. $1319 \in \{x \mid x$ is a divisor of 2,570,731$\}$.
44. $\pi^4 \in \{y \mid y > 100\}$.

## Challenge Problems

True or false.

45. $\{c\} \in \{a, b, c\}$        46. $c \in \{a, b, \{c\}\}$        47. $\{c\} \in \{a, b, \{c\}\}$

### SUBSETS AND SET OPERATIONS

Suppose that $S$ is the set of students in a class, and $G$ is the set of girls in the same class. Clearly each element of $G$ is also an element of $S$. The set $G$ is said to be a *subset* of the set $S$.

---

| | |
|---|---|
| ***Definition*** | Set $A$ is a **subset** of set $B$ if every element of $A$ is also an element of $B$. |

---

The symbol $\subseteq$ is used to mean *is a subset of*. Thus if $A = \{1, 2, 3\}$ and $B = \{1, 2, 3, 4\}$, we can write $A \subseteq B$. Note that every element of $B$ is *not* an element of $A$, since $4 \in B$ but $4 \notin A$. Therefore $B$ is *not* a subset of $A$, written $B \nsubseteq A$. The relationship between sets $A$ and $B$ is illustrated in the diagram below.[*]

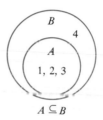

$$A \subseteq B$$

We might ask at this point whether the empty set is a subset of $A$. To answer this we note that $B$ is not a subset of $A$ since $B$ has an element, namely 4, which is not an element of $A$. But the empty set could not have such an element, since it has no elements at all! Therefore $\emptyset \subset A$. As a matter of fact, *the empty set is a subset of every set.* That is, $\emptyset \subset S$ for every set $S$.

**EXAMPLE 1**   List all subsets of the set $\{a, b, c\}$.
There are eight of them.

$$\emptyset \quad \{a\} \quad \{b\} \quad \{c\} \quad \{a, b\} \quad \{a, c\} \quad \{b, c\} \quad \{a, b, c\} \quad \square$$

Note that $\{a, b, c\} \subseteq \{a, b, c\}$. More generally, *every set is a subset of itself.* That is, $S \subseteq S$ for every set $S$.

**EXAMPLE 2**   True or false.

$$\{x \mid x \text{ is a male doctor}\} \subseteq \{x \mid x \text{ is a doctor}\}$$

True. For suppose Jones is an element of the first set. Then Jones is a doctor and Jones is also a male. Therefore, Jones is a doctor. Hence Jones is an element of the second set. Similarly, *every* element of the first set is also an element of the second set. $\square$

---

[*] Diagrams that depict sets as regions are called **Venn diagrams,** after the English logician John Venn (1834–1923).

Sometimes we may be interested in forming new sets from two given sets. Suppose $F$ = {Dan, Jim, Mary} is the set of students who received an A on the first test, and $S$ = {Sue, Jim, Dan, Mike} is the set of students who received an A on the second test. Then {Sue, Dan, Jim, Mary, Mike} is the set of students who received an A on *either* the first test or the second test, or *both* tests. This set is called the *union* of sets $F$ and $S$.

---

**Definition**  Set $A$ **union** set $B$ is the set of all those elements in either $A$ or $B$, or both. Notationally, we write $A \cup B$.

---

**EXAMPLE 3**  Given $A$ = {1, 3, 5} and $B$ = {2, 3, 4}, find $A \cup B$.

$$A \cup B = \{1, 2, 3, 4, 5\}. \ \square$$

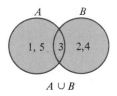

$A \cup B$

Note that the element 3 is listed only *once* in the set $A \cup B$, even though it appears in *both* set $A$ and set $B$.

**EXAMPLE 4**  Given $A$ = {$x$ | $x$ is a male doctor} and $B$ = {$x$ | $x$ is a doctor}, find $A \cup B$.

$$A \cup B = \{x \mid x \text{ is a doctor}\}. \ \square$$

Returning to our previous example, we note that {Jim, Dan} is the set of students who received an A on both tests. This set is called the *intersection* of sets $F$ and $S$.

---

**Definition**  Set $A$ **intersection** set $B$ is the set of all those elements in common to $A$ and $B$. Notationally, we write $A \cap B$.

---

**EXAMPLE 5**   Given $A = \{1, 3, 5\}$ and $B = \{2, 3, 4\}$, find $A \cap B$.

$$A \cap B = \{3\}. \quad \square$$

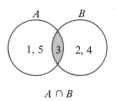

$A \cap B$

**EXAMPLE 6**   Given $W = \{x \mid x$ is a woman in your class$\}$ and $M = \{x \mid x$ is a man in your class$\}$, find $W \cap M$.

$W \cap M = \emptyset$, since these two sets have no elements in common.   $\square$

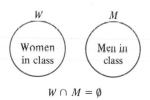

$W \cap M = \emptyset$

When the intersection of two sets is the empty set, the sets are said to be **disjoint sets.** Therefore, the sets $W$ and $M$ of Example 6 are disjoint sets.

**EXAMPLE 7**   Given $S = \{x \mid x$ is a doctor$\}$ and $T = \{x \mid x$ is a female$\}$, find $S \cap T$.

$$S \cap T = \{x \mid x \text{ is a female doctor}\}. \quad \square$$

The set operations of union and intersection can be extended to include *any* number of sets.

**EXAMPLE 8**   Given $A = \{1, 3, 5\}$, $B = \{2, 3, 4\}$, and $C = \{1, 2, 3\}$, find $(A \cap B) \cup C$ and $A \cap (B \cup C)$.

In each case we perform the operation in parentheses first.

$$(A \cap B) \cup C = \{3\} \cup C = \{1, 2, 3\},$$
$$A \cap (B \cup C) = A \cap \{1, 2, 3, 4\} = \{1, 3\}. \quad \square$$

**EXAMPLE 9**   Given that

$$E = \{x \mid x \text{ is an even whole number}\},$$
$$O = \{x \mid x \text{ is an odd whole number}\},$$
$$W = \{x \mid x \text{ is a whole number}\},$$

find: $E \cap O$, $E \cup O$, $E \cap W$, $(E \cup W) \cap O$.

The solutions may be easier to determine if we first visualize the elements of each set.

$$E = \{0, 2, 4, 6, 8, 10, ...\},$$
$$O = \{1, 3, 5, 7, 9, 11, ...\},$$
$$W = \{0, 1, 2, 3, 4, 5, ...\}.$$

With this in mind, we have

$$E \cap O = \emptyset$$
$$E \cup O = W$$
$$E \cap W = E$$
$$(E \cup W) \cap O = W \cap O = O. \quad \square$$

## Problems

True or false.

1. $\{a, b, c\} \subseteq \{a, b, c, d\}$    2. $\{1, 3, 5\} \subseteq \{1, 2, 3, 4, 5\}$    3. $\{6, 7, 8\} \subseteq \{6, 7, 8\}$
4. $\{a, b\} \subseteq \{a, b\}$    5. $\emptyset \subseteq \{\text{ace, king, queen}\}$    6. $\emptyset \subseteq \{a, e, i, o, u\}$
7. $\{\text{Florida, Ohio, New York}\} \subseteq \{x \mid x \text{ is a state in the United States}\}$
8. $\{x \mid x \text{ is a vowel}\} \subseteq \{x \mid x \text{ is a letter in the alphabet}\}$
9. $\{x \mid x \text{ is an odd whole number}\} \subseteq \{x \mid x \text{ is an even whole number}\}$
10. $\{x \mid x \text{ is a doctor}\} \subseteq \{x \mid x \text{ is a lawyer}\}$
11. $\{t \mid t \text{ is a female plumber}\} \subseteq \{t \mid t \text{ is a plumber}\}$
12. $\{t \mid t \text{ is an Italian butcher}\} \subseteq \{t \mid t \text{ is a butcher}\}$
13. $\{a, b, c\} \not\subseteq \{x \mid x \text{ is a letter in the alphabet}\}$
14. $\{x \mid x \text{ lives in Ohio}\} \not\subseteq \{x \mid x \text{ lives in the United States}\}$
15. $\{t \mid t \text{ is a multiple of 2}\} \subseteq \{t \mid t \text{ is a multiple of 3}\}$
16. $\{t \mid t \text{ is a multiple of 2}\} \subseteq \{t \mid t \text{ is a multiple of 4}\}$
17. $\{t \mid t \text{ is a letter in the word banana}\} \subseteq \{t \mid t \text{ is a letter in the word band}\}$
18. $\{t \mid t \text{ is a letter in the word tooth}\} \subseteq \{t \mid t \text{ is a letter in the word hot}\}$

List all subsets of each of the following sets.

19. $\{3\}$                      20. $\{4\}$                      21. $\{5, 6\}$
22. $\{a, b\}$                   23. $\{a, b, c\}$               24. $\{5, 6, 7\}$
25. $\{5, 6, 7, 8\}$             26. $\{a, b, c, d\}$

27. Explain why if $A \subseteq B$ and $B \subseteq C$, then $A \subseteq C$.
28. Explain why if $A \subseteq B$ and $B \subseteq A$, then $A = B$.

Given $A = \{1, 2, 4\}$, $B = \{2, 3, 5, 7\}$, $C = \{6, 3, 5, 8\}$, and
$D = \{1, 4, 8\}$, find:

29. $A \cap B$                   30. $B \cap C$                  31. $B \cup C$
32. $A \cup B$                   33. $A \cup D$                  34. $B \cap D$
35. $A \cap D$                   36. $B \cup D$                  37. $A \cap C$
38. $C \cap D$                   39. $C \cup \emptyset$          40. $D \cup \emptyset$
41. $C \cap \emptyset$           42. $D \cap \emptyset$          43. $A \cup A$
44. $A \cap A$                   45. $A \cup (B \cap C)$         46. $(A \cap B) \cup C$
47. $(D \cup C) \cap A$          48. $(B \cup D) \cap C$         49. $(A \cap C) \cup D$
50. $(B \cap D) \cup A$          51. $A \cap B \cap C$           52. $B \cap C \cap D$
53. $A \cup B \cup C$            54. $B \cup C \cup D$

Given $M = \{x \mid x$ is a male doctor$\}$, $F = \{x \mid x$ is a female doctor$\}$,
and $D = \{x \mid x$ is a doctor$\}$, find:

55. $M \cap F$                   56. $M \cup F$                  57. $M \cap D$
58. $F \cap D$                   59. $M \cup D$                  60. $F \cup D$
61. $(M \cup F) \cap D$          62. $(M \cap F) \cup D$         63. $M \cap F \cap D$
64. $M \cup F \cup D$

True or false.

65. $A \cap B \subseteq A$       66. $A \cap B \subseteq A \cup B$       67. $A \subseteq A \cup B$
68. $\emptyset \subseteq \emptyset$
69. If $A \subseteq B$ and $4 \in B$, then $4 \in A$.
70. If $7 \in A$, then $7 \in A \cap B$.

Completion.

71. If $B \subseteq A$, then $A \cap B = $ _____?_____.

72. If $B \subseteq A$, then $A \cup B = $ _____?_____.

73. If $A$ contains 6 elements, $B$ contains 9 elements, and $A \cap B$ contains

    4 elements, then $A \cup B$ contains _____?_____ (how many)
    elements.

74. If $A$ contains $m$ elements, $B$ contains $n$ elements, and $A \cap B$ contains 3 elements, then $A \cup B$ contains _____?_____ (how many) elements.

## Calculator Problems

75. True or false: $\{m \mid m$ is a multiple of 593$\}$ and $\{d \mid d$ is a divisor of 1,891,893$\}$ are disjoint sets.
76. If a set has $n$ elements, then it will have $2^n$ subsets. Given that set $S$ has 21 elements, how many subsets does $S$ have?

## Challenge Problems

77. True or false: $\{c\} \subseteq \{a, b, \{c\}\}$.
78. Construct sets $F$ and $G$ so that $F \in G$ and $F \subseteq G$.

## 2 | APPENDIX 2: CONVERTING REPEATING DECIMALS TO RATIOS OF INTEGERS

Every nonterminating repeating decimal is a rational number and therefore can be written as a ratio of two integers. The two examples below illustrate a procedure for converting a given repeating decimal to a ratio of two integers.

**EXAMPLE 1**  Express $0.\overline{18}$ as a ratio of two integers.

First, we give the decimal a name, say $x$.

$$x = 0.\overline{18}.$$

Then, in order to move the decimal point two places to the right, we multiply each side of this equation by $10^2$, or 100. We use an exponent of 2 on 10 since there are 2 digits in each repeating block.

$$100x = 18.\overline{18}.$$

Finally, we subtract the first equation from the second and solve for $x$.

$$
\begin{aligned}
100x &= 18.\overline{18} \\
(-)\quad x &= 0.\overline{18} \\
\hline
99x &= 18 \\
x &= \frac{18}{99} = \frac{2}{11}.
\end{aligned}
$$

Therefore, $0.\overline{18} = \frac{2}{11}$. □

**EXAMPLE 2**   Express $4.2\overline{5}$ as a ratio of two integers.

$$\text{Let } x = 4.2\overline{5}.$$

Then

$$
\begin{aligned}
10x &= 42.5\overline{5} \\
(-)\quad x &= 4.2\overline{5} \\
\hline
9x &= 38.3 \\
x &= \frac{38.3}{9}.
\end{aligned}
$$

The numerator of this last fraction is not an integer, but that is easily corrected by multiplying numerator and denominator by 10. Therefore, $4.2\overline{5} = \frac{383}{90}$. □

## Problems

Express each repeating decimal as a ratio of two integers.

| | | | |
|---|---|---|---|
| 1. $0.\overline{36}$ | 2. $0.\overline{45}$ | 3. $0.\overline{07}$ | 4. $0.\overline{08}$ |
| 5. $0.\overline{3}$ | 6. $0.\overline{6}$ | 7. $0.\overline{2}$ | 8. $0.\overline{5}$ |
| 9. $0.\overline{123}$ | 10. $0.\overline{471}$ | 11. $5.\overline{7}$ | 12. $7.\overline{8}$ |
| 13. $9.3\overline{6}$ | 14. $2.5\overline{8}$ | 15. $4.8\overline{13}$ | 16. $3.7\overline{12}$ |
| 17. $0.\overline{6789}$ | 18. $0.\overline{4321}$ | 19. $0.\overline{9}$ | 20. $9.\overline{9}$ |

**3**

# APPENDIX 3: $\sqrt{2}$ IS NOT RATIONAL

Clearly, either $\sqrt{2}$ is rational or $\sqrt{2}$ is not rational. Since we do not know which, let us assume for the sake of argument that $\sqrt{2}$ *is* rational. Then $\sqrt{2}$ can be written as a ratio of two integers *in lowest terms*. That is,

$$\sqrt{2} = \frac{a}{b}$$

where $a$ and $b$ have no common factor. Squaring each side of this last equation gives

$$2 = \frac{a^2}{b^2},$$

or

$$2b^2 = a^2.$$

This equation tells us that $a^2$ must be an even number. Therefore, $a$ itself must be even since the square of an odd integer is odd. Since $a$ is even, it must be true that

$$a = 2k$$

for some integer $k$. Thus

$$a^2 = (2k)^2 = 4k^2.$$

Substituting $4k^2$ for $a^2$ in the equation $2b^2 = a^2$, we have

$$2b^2 = 4k^2,$$

or

$$b^2 = 2k^2.$$

Therefore $b^2$ is even, which means that $b$ is even. But since $a$ is also even this means that $a$ and $b$ have the common factor 2, and thus $a/b$ is *not* in lowest terms. Since our assumption that $\sqrt{2}$ *is* rational led to a contradiction, that assumption must be *false*. Therefore, $\sqrt{2}$ is *not* rational.

## 4 APPENDIX 4: THE METRIC SYSTEM

Early units of measure were often based on parts of the human body. A foot was the length of a man's foot, an inch was the distance from the tip of the thumb to the middle of the first joint, and a mile was 2000 paces. Later, in medieval England, King Henry I decreed that an *ell* (roughly a yard) should be the distance from the tip of his nose to the end of his outstretched thumb. Such units were not very precise, but they did serve a purpose for many years when more accurate scientific measurement was not in great demand. These and other units of measure were organized to form the *English* (or *British*) system of measurement. Because England was dominant in commerce and trade, the English system became the one that was most widely used.

In the English system, length can be measured in inches, feet, yards, or miles. Weight can be measured in ounces, pounds, or tons. Volume can be measured in pints, quarts, or gallons. Over the years these measures have been made more precise and standardized, but conversions between the units themselves have remained awkward. For example, small distances can be measured in inches or feet. Since 1 foot = 12 inches, changing from one of these units to the other requires either multiplying or dividing by 12. That is, 17 feet is $17 \cdot 12 = 204$ inches, and 30 inches is $30 \div 12 = 2.5$ feet. Similarly, 1 yard = 36 inches, 1 mile = 5280 feet, 1 pound = 16 ounces, and 1 gallon = 8 pints.

In spite of its drawbacks, the English system remained popular for many years. But there was still no single, coordinated system acceptable world-wide. Then, in 1790, the French Academy of Science created a simple, scientific standard of weights and measures called the *metric system*. Since this system is based on multiples of ten, converting from one unit in the metric system to another can be accomplished with relative ease. Therein lies one of the major advantages of the metric system over the English system. Another advantage is that in the metric system there is a definite correlation between the units for length, weight, and volume.

One by one, nations have been adopting the metric system as their standard of measurement. It is significant to note that no nation that has adopted the metric system has abandoned it. The United States is now the only major industrial nation in the world that has not officially gone metric. It is almost as if all of the countries in the world are speaking one language and the United States is speaking another. It has been estimated that the United States could save millions of dollars per year in international trade alone by converting to the metric system.

Although the U.S. has not officially gone metric, the system itself is not a complete stranger to its citizens. Olympic track and field and swimming events are measured using the metric system. Athletes speak of the 100 meter dash, the 10,000 meter run, and the 200 meter breaststroke. Many of us have 8 millimeter home movie projectors or 35 millimeter cameras. We may glide down the slopes on skis that are 185 centimeters long, or puff on a 100 millimeter cigarette. Many hospitals are now maintaining patient statistics such as height, weight, and body temperature in metric units, and metric units have long been used for dispensing prescription medicines. Radio and TV stations now report temperature readings in both Fahrenheit and Celsius degrees. Almost all scientific research is done using the metric system, and industries such as electronics, shipbuilding, and even some auto industries have jumped onto the metric bandwagon.

Let's take a look at what we need to know to work successfully with the metric system.

---

**Three Standards** $\begin{cases} \text{meter (m):} & \text{length} \\ \text{liter } (\ell)\text{:} & \text{volume} \\ \text{gram (g):} & \text{mass (weight)} \end{cases}$

**Six Prefixes** $\begin{cases} \text{kilo:} & 1000 \\ \text{hecto:} & 100 \\ \text{deca:} & 10 \\ \text{deci:} & \frac{1}{10} \\ \text{centi:} & \frac{1}{100} \\ \text{milli:} & \frac{1}{1000} \end{cases}$

---

Also, the Celsius scale, which was discussed in Chapter 3, is used for measuring temperature.

To get a *feel* for the standards in the metric system, we can observe that a meter is roughly 3 inches longer than a yard, a liter is just slightly larger than a quart, a gram is about the weight of half of a dime, and an outside temperature of 30° Celsius would send some people scurrying to the beach.

An obvious question that now arises is, "Why were these specific standards chosen?" First, the temperature scale was chosen so that 0° Celsius coincided with the freezing point of water and 100° Celsius coincided with the boiling point of water. The original meter was one ten-millionth of the distance between the North Pole and the equator (measured along the meridian passing through Paris), and the original gram was the weight of one cubic centimeter (a centimeter is one-hundredth of a meter) of water. A liter is the volume contained in a cube that is ten centimeters on each side.

Other units in the metric system, for measuring quantities that are either too large or too small to be measured efficiently using one of the three standards, are created by using one of the six prefixes in conjunction with one of the three standards. The three prefixes that are most commonly used are kilo, centi, and milli. The prefixes hecto, deca, and deci are primarily used in scientific measurements. Thus a kilogram (kg) is 1000 grams (about 2.2 pounds), a centimeter (cm) is $\frac{1}{100}$ of a meter (about the width of a large paper clip), and a milliliter (ml) is $\frac{1}{1000}$ of a liter ($\frac{1}{5}$ of a teaspoon).

Conversions *within* the metric system involve multiplying or dividing by an appropriate power of ten. Hence a conversion can be made simply by moving the decimal point.

**EXAMPLE 1**    Convert 3 meters to centimeters.

Since 1 m = 100 cm,

$$3 \text{ m} = 3 \times 100 \text{ cm} = 300 \text{ cm}. \ \square$$

**EXAMPLE 2**    Convert 55 kilograms to grams.

Since 1 kg = 1000 g,

$$55 \text{ kg} = 55 \times 1000 \text{ g} = 55{,}000 \text{ g}. \ \square$$

**EXAMPLE 3**    Convert 1600 milliliters to liters.

Since

$$1 \text{ m}\ell = \frac{1}{1000} \ell,$$

$$1600 \text{ m}\ell = \frac{1600}{1000} \ell = 1.6 \ \ell. \ \square$$

**EXAMPLE 4**    Convert 2.8 centimeters to millimeters.

Since

$$1 \text{ cm} = 10 \text{ mm},$$

$$2.8 \text{ cm} = 2.8 \times 10 \text{ mm} = 28 \text{ mm}. \ \square$$

Eventually, we should learn to think directly in the metric system without using the English system as a crutch. That is, if someone says that they live 33 kilometers away, we should have an idea of just how far that is. Is it a half-hour drive or a five-hour drive? Is a room 7 meters by 5 meters a small bathroom or a large living room? Is a man who weighs 115 kilograms the size of a defensive tackle or a thoroughbred jockey? Such familiarity only comes with experience. For the time being, we shall have to be content with making conversions between the familiar English system and the somewhat unfamiliar metric system in order to place metric measurements in their proper perspective. In doing so, we shall be on our way to our ultimate goal, which is to "think metric." The conversion table provided below will enable us to make these conversions.

**EXAMPLE 5**   Convert 5 yards to meters.

Yards to meters is an *English to metric* conversion. From the table we see that yards can be converted to meters by multiplying by .9144.

$$5 \text{ yards} = 5 \times .9144 \text{ m} = 4.572 \text{ m}. \quad \square$$

**EXAMPLE 6**   Convert 32 kilograms to pounds.

This is a *metric to English* conversion. From the table we see that we need to multiply by 2.205.

$$32 \text{ kg} = 32 \times 2.205 \text{ pounds} = 70.56 \text{ pounds}. \quad \square$$

| **Metric to English** | | | **English to Metric** | | |
|---|---|---|---|---|---|
| *From* | *To* | *Multiply by* | *From* | *To* | *Multiply by* |
| meters | yards | 1.094 | yards | meters | .9144 |
| meters | feet | 3.281 | feet | meters | .3048 |
| meters | inches | 39.37 | inches | meters | .0254 |
| centimeters | inches | .3937 | inches | centimeters | 2.540 |
| kilometers | miles | .6214 | miles | kilometers | 1.609 |
| grams | ounces | .0353 | ounces | grams | 28.35 |
| kilograms | pounds | 2.205 | pounds | kilograms | .4536 |
| liters | quarts | 1.057 | quarts | liters | .9464 |

## Problems

Make the following conversions within the metric system.

| | | |
|---|---|---|
| 1. 5 m to cm | 2. 7 m to cm | 3. 18 m to mm |
| 4. 13 m to mm | 5. 7.8 m to cm | 6. 5.6 m to cm |
| 7. 16 km to m | 8. 42 km to m | 9. 5200 m to km |
| 10. 6400 m to km | 11. 6200 cm to m | 12. 5700 cm to m |
| 13. 45 mm to m | 14. 75 mm to m | 15. 17.1 cm to mm |
| 16. 20.5 cm to mm | 17. 5 mm to cm | 18. 9 mm to cm |
| 19. 6 kg to g | 20. 11 kg to g | 21. 15,000 g to kg |
| 22. 8000 g to kg | 23. 1.62 kg to g | 24. 3.72 kg to g |
| 25. 8 ℓ to mℓ | 26. 7 ℓ to mℓ | 27. 500 mℓ to ℓ |
| 28. 600 mℓ to ℓ | 29. 37,000 mℓ to ℓ | 30. 42,000 mℓ to ℓ |
| 31. 2.93 ℓ to mℓ | 32. 9.14 ℓ to mℓ | |

Use the table on the previous page to make the conversions indicated. These problems are ideally suited for electronic calculators.

| | | |
|---|---|---|
| 33. 8 yards to m | 34. 2 yards to m | 35. 90 kg to pounds |
| 36. 50 kg to pounds | 37. 3 m to feet | 38. 7 m to feet |
| 39. 350 miles to km | 40. 550 miles to km | 41. 11 ounces to g |
| 42. 9 ounces to g | 43. 23 g to ounces | 44. 17 g to ounces |
| 45. 45 inches to m | 46. 85 inches to m | 47. 200 feet to m |
| 48. 300 feet to m | 49. 7 inches to cm | 50. 9 inches to cm |
| 51. 5 quarts to ℓ | 52. 4 quarts to ℓ | 53. 10 cm to inches |
| 54. 30 cm to inches | 55. 2 m to inches | 56. 5 m to inches |
| 57. 850 pounds to kg | 58. 450 pounds to kg | 59. 30 ℓ to quarts |
| 60. 20 ℓ to quarts | 61. 13 m to yards | 62. 25 m to yards |
| 63. 200 km to miles | 64. 800 km to miles | |

## Challenge Problems

65. Convert 55,000 sq km to square miles.
66. Convert 7200 cu cm to cubic inches.

## Weight Conversion Chart

| Pounds | Kilo-grams | Pounds | Kilo-grams | Pounds | Kilo-grams | Pounds | Kilo-grams |
|---|---|---|---|---|---|---|---|
| 100 | 45.4 | 126 | 57.2 | 150 | 68.0 | 176 | 79.8 |
| 101 | 45.8 | 127 | 57.6 | 151 | 68.5 | 177 | 80.3 |
| 102 | 46.3 | 128 | 58.1 | 152 | 68.9 | 178 | 80.7 |
| 103 | 46.7 | 129 | 58.5 | 153 | 69.4 | 179 | 81.2 |
| 104 | 47.2 | 130 | 59.0 | 154 | 69.9 | 180 | 81.6 |
| 105 | 47.6 | 131 | 59.4 | 155 | 70.3 | 181 | 82.1 |
| 106 | 48.1 | 132 | 59.9 | 156 | 70.8 | 182 | 82.6 |
| 107 | 48.5 | 133 | 60.3 | 157 | 71.2 | 183 | 83.0 |
| 108 | 49.0 | 134 | 60.8 | 158 | 71.7 | 184 | 83.5 |
| 109 | 49.4 | 135 | 61.2 | 159 | 72.1 | 185 | 83.9 |
| 110 | 49.9 | 136 | 61.7 | 160 | 72.6 | 186 | 84.4 |
| 111 | 50.3 | 137 | 62.1 | 161 | 73.0 | 187 | 84.8 |
| 112 | 50.8 | 138 | 62.6 | 162 | 73.5 | 188 | 85.3 |
| 113 | 51.3 | 139 | 63.1 | 163 | 73.9 | 189 | 85.7 |
| 114 | 51.7 | 140 | 63.5 | 164 | 74.4 | 190 | 86.2 |
| 115 | 52.2 | 141 | 64.0 | 165 | 74.8 | 191 | 86.6 |
| 116 | 52.6 | 142 | 64.4 | 166 | 75.3 | 192 | 87.1 |
| 117 | 53.1 | 143 | 64.9 | 167 | 75.8 | 193 | 87.5 |
| 118 | 53.5 | 144 | 65.3 | 168 | 76.2 | 194 | 88.0 |
| 119 | 54.0 | 145 | 65.8 | 169 | 76.7 | 195 | 88.5 |
| 120 | 54.4 | 146 | 66.2 | 170 | 77.1 | 196 | 88.9 |
| 121 | 54.9 | 147 | 66.7 | 171 | 77.6 | 197 | 89.4 |
| 122 | 55.3 | 148 | 67.1 | 172 | 78.0 | 198 | 89.8 |
| 123 | 55.8 | 149 | 67.6 | 173 | 78.5 | 199 | 90.3 |
| 124 | 56.2 | | | 174 | 78.9 | | |
| 125 | 56.7 | | | 175 | 79.4 | | |

## Height Conversion Chart

| Feet | Centi-meters | Feet | Centi-meters | Feet | Centi-meters |
|---|---|---|---|---|---|
| 4' 6" | 137.2 | 5' 3" | 160.0 | 5' 11" | 180.3 |
| 4' 7" | 139.7 | 5' 4" | 162.6 | 6' | 182.9 |
| 4' 8" | 142.2 | 5' 5" | 165.1 | 6' 1" | 185.4 |
| 4' 9" | 144.8 | 5' 6" | 167.6 | 6' 2" | 188.0 |
| 4' 10" | 147.3 | 5' 7" | 170.2 | 6' 3" | 190.5 |
| 4' 11" | 149.9 | 5' 8" | 172.7 | 6' 4" | 193.0 |
| 5' | 152.4 | 5' 9" | 175.3 | 6' 5" | 195.6 |
| 5' 1" | 154.9 | 5' 10" | 177.8 | 6' 6" | 198.1 |
| 5' 2" | 157.5 | | | | |

**Highway Distances in Kilometers**

| | Atlanta | Boston | Chicago | Cleveland | Dallas | Denver | Kansas City | Los Angeles | New Orleans | New York | Portland | Washington |
|---|---|---|---|---|---|---|---|---|---|---|---|---|
| Atlanta | | 1728 | 1175 | 1118 | 1319 | 2270 | 1295 | 3564 | 833 | 1387 | 4315 | 1025 |
| Boston | 1728 | | 1599 | 1015 | 2930 | 3213 | 2339 | 4895 | 2484 | 348 | 4988 | 703 |
| Chicago | 1175 | 1599 | | 549 | 1508 | 1630 | 811 | 3366 | 1519 | 1352 | 3429 | 1146 |
| Cleveland | 1118 | 1015 | 549 | | 2018 | 2198 | 1324 | 3879 | 1697 | 816 | 3973 | 565 |
| Dallas | 1319 | 2930 | 1508 | 2018 | | 1261 | 796 | 2261 | 809 | 2582 | 3310 | 2227 |
| Denver | 2270 | 3213 | 1630 | 2198 | 1261 | | 975 | 1862 | 2071 | 3002 | 2068 | 2751 |
| Kansas City | 1295 | 2339 | 811 | 1324 | 796 | 975 | | 2555 | 1342 | 1945 | 2991 | 1694 |
| Los Angeles | 3564 | 4895 | 3366 | 3879 | 2261 | 1862 | 2555 | | 3065 | 4500 | 1599 | 4262 |
| New Orleans | 833 | 2484 | 1519 | 1697 | 809 | 2071 | 1342 | 3065 | | 2143 | 4119 | 1781 |
| New York | 1387 | 348 | 1352 | 816 | 2582 | 3002 | 1945 | 4500 | 2143 | | 4761 | 368 |
| Portland | 4315 | 4988 | 3429 | 3973 | 3310 | 2068 | 2991 | 1599 | 4119 | 4761 | | 4526 |
| Washington | 1025 | 703 | 1146 | 565 | 2227 | 2751 | 1694 | 4262 | 1781 | 368 | 4526 | |

# VOLUME COMPARISONS

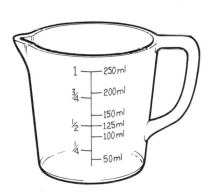

Metric measuring cup — 250 ml

Liter — a little larger than a quart (about 1.06 quarts)

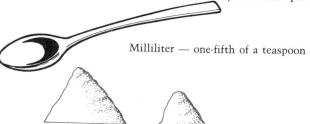

Milliliter — one-fifth of a teaspoon

## TEMPERATURE COMPARISON

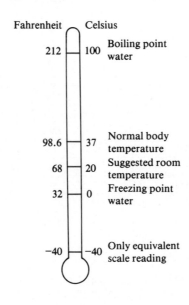

Fahrenheit   Celsius

212   100   Boiling point water

98.6   37   Normal body temperature

68   20   Suggested room temperature

32   0   Freezing point water

−40   −40   Only equivalent scale reading

# Answers
# Answers
# Answers
# Answers

# ANSWERS TO ODD-NUMBERED PROBLEMS AND CHAPTER REVIEWS

**1** CHAPTER ONE

## Problem Set 1.1

1. (a) 5, 173; (b) 5, 173, 0; (c) 5, 173, 0, $-20$, $-1$; (d) All of them
3. $-3$, $+2$
5. $-10$, $+3$
7. 0.5
9. 0.75
11. 0.625
13. $-0.375$
15. $0.66\overline{6}$
17. $-2.25$
19. $0.\overline{2}$
21. $6.\overline{36}$
23. $0.6\overline{81}$
25. $-0.\overline{936}$
27. $3.\overline{142857}$
29. 1.08, $1.\overline{08}$, $\frac{9}{5}$, $1.\overline{8}$
31. $\frac{1}{3}$
33. 5.17365, for example.
35. (a) $\frac{17}{100}$, (b) $\frac{3181}{1000}$
37. (a) $\frac{2}{9}$, (b) $\frac{13}{9}$
39. $0.33\overline{3}$
41. $0.13\overline{8}$
43. $4x$ dollars
45. $37 + 5y$ cards
47. Division by zero is undefined.
49. $0.58\overline{3}$
51. 5
53. HHH, HHT, HTH, HTT, THH, THT, TTH, TTT; 3; Yes

## Problem Set 1.2

1. 1, 2, 3, 6
3. 1, 3, 5, 15
5. 1, 7
7. 1, 2, 3, 4, 6, 8, 12, 24
9. 1, 3, 9, 11, 33, 99
11. No
13. No
15. Yes
17. No
19. No
21. $20 = 2 \cdot 2 \cdot 5$
23. $70 = 2 \cdot 5 \cdot 7$
25. Not factorable
27. $126 = 2 \cdot 3 \cdot 3 \cdot 7$
29. $2520 = 2 \cdot 2 \cdot 2 \cdot 3 \cdot 3 \cdot 5 \cdot 7$
31. 6
33. 6
35. 1
37. 12
39. 26
41. 18
43. 27
45. 16
47. 24
49. 2520
51. 5 and 7, 11 and 13, 17 and 19, for example.
53. $4,294,967,297 = 6,700,417 \cdot 641$
55. 6 and 28, for example.

## Problem Set 1.3A

1.   3.   5.   7.   9.

11. 8   13. 3   15. 5   17. 20   19. 7
21. $\frac{3}{4}$   23. $\frac{2}{3}$   25. $\frac{1}{5}$   27. $\frac{4}{3}$   29. $\frac{4}{5}$
31. $\frac{12}{7}$   33. $\frac{3}{10}$   35. $\frac{9}{10}$   37. 2765
39. $a/b = c/d$ when $ad = bc$ and $b \neq 0$ and $d \neq 0$.

## Problem Set 1.3B

1. $\frac{1}{2}$   3. $\frac{1}{2}$   5. $6\frac{1}{5}$   7. $\frac{11}{12}$   9. $\frac{7}{12}$
11. $\frac{13}{12}$   13. $\frac{29}{40}$   15. $\frac{22}{45}$   17. $\frac{37}{60}$   19. $\frac{53}{504}$
21. $7\frac{419}{1080}$   23. $\frac{3}{5}$   25. $3\frac{2}{9}$   27. $\frac{2}{9}$   29. $\frac{1}{6}$
31. $\frac{13}{5}$   33. $\frac{13}{72}$   35. $\frac{31}{840}$   37. $4\frac{67}{72}$   39. $20\frac{5}{12}$ in.
41. $1\frac{5}{8}$ dollars   43. $4\frac{17}{40}$ ft   45. 0.9953125   47. $\frac{1}{24}, \frac{5}{12}$

## Problem Set 1.3C

1. $\frac{1}{4}$   3. $\frac{3}{20}$   5. $\frac{8}{5}$   7. 25   9. $\frac{7}{4}$
11. $\frac{1}{12}$   13. $\frac{1}{8}$   15. $\frac{25}{12}$   17. $\frac{4}{15}$   19. 3
21. $\frac{6}{7}$   23. $\frac{1192}{473}$   25. 119¢   27. $6\frac{2}{3}\,\ell$   29. $2\frac{1}{5}$ cups
31. 33 bandages   33. $5\frac{3}{4}$ in. by $7\frac{7}{8}$ in.   35. $\frac{47}{90}$   37. $\frac{1}{48}$ cup   39. 0.75
41. $3\frac{7}{32}$ cm

## Problem Set 1.4

1. (a) 5, $-0$, $\frac{3}{4}$, $\sqrt{16}$, $0.07\overline{07}$, 3.14, $-\frac{10}{3}$; (b) $\sqrt{2}$, $\pi$, $\sqrt{10}$, $0.717117111711117 \cdots$
3. 2   5. 7   7. 11   9. 13   11. 30   13. 2.236
15. 7.071   17. 13.30
19. $(2 + 3)^2 = 5^2 = 25$, $2^2 + 3^2 = 4 + 9 = 13$, $(a + b)^2 \neq a^2 + b^2$

21. $(9 - 5)^2 = 4^2 = 16$, $9^2 - 5^2 = 81 - 25 = 56$, $(a - b)^2 \neq a^2 - b^2$
23. 10          25. 15          27. 34          29. 6.403        31. 12.21        33. 20
35. 24          37. 12.49        39. 3          41. 24 ft        43. 15 ft        45. 25 mi
47. (a) 56.40, (b) 24.00, (c) 9.87          49. $529^2 + 2147^2 \neq 2211^2$
51. False. For example, $\sqrt{2} \cdot \sqrt{2} = 2$.

## Problem Set 1.5

1.          3. 7          5. 10          7. 6.5

9. $1\frac{2}{3}$          11. $\sqrt{3}$          13. 0          15. 3          17. $|-5|$          19. $|-5|$
21. $|-\sqrt{2}|$          23. 14          25. 0          27. 11          29. 3          31. 0
33. $-10$          35. $-10$          37. 6          39. 64          41. Undefined          43. 0
45. 2.5          47. 27          49. T          51. F          53. F          55. T
57. F          59. F          61. 0.98          63. F

## Chapter Review

1. T          2. F          3. F          4. T          5. T          6. F
7. F          8. T          9. T          10. F          11. F          12. T
13. T          14. F          15. T          16. T          17. F          18. T
19. T          20. T          21. T          22. T          23. T          24. T
25. Rational                    26. Numerator, denominator
27. Fundamental Law of Fractions          28. Factor (or divisor), multiple
29. Prime, composite              30. 0.375
31. (a) $-5.\overline{18}$, (b) $1.\overline{428571}$          32. (a) $\frac{32}{5}$, (b) $\frac{23}{1000}$
33. $\frac{5}{9}$                      34. 10x cents
35. It is an odd whole number.          36. $2\frac{3}{5}$
37. (a) 3, (b) $\frac{1}{3}$               38. 8
39. $90\sqrt{2} \approx 127.3$ ft          40.

41. $420 = 2 \cdot 2 \cdot 3 \cdot 5 \cdot 7$          42. 63
43. 1008                    44.

45. $\frac{5}{12}$        46. $\frac{29}{30}$        47. $\frac{13}{3}$        48. $\frac{15}{7}$
49. $\frac{9}{25}$        50. $\frac{457}{360}$        51. $7\frac{1}{2}$ in.        52. 2 cups
53. $\frac{17}{24}$

## 2   CHAPTER TWO

### Problem Set 2.1

1. 62    3. 104    5. $\frac{9}{20}$    7. $\frac{19}{60}$    9. 4    11. 1
13. 16    15. 10    17. 10    19. 0    21. 40    23. 36
25. 31    27. 24    29. 250    31. 15.5    33. 25.89    35. 26,600 ft
37. (a) $5(x + 2)$, (b) $5x + 2$      39. Commutative axiom for addition
41. Commutative axiom for multiplication      43. Associative axiom for addition
45. Associative axiom for multiplication      47. Associative axiom for multiplication
49. Commutative axiom for addition      51. Commutative axiom for multiplication
53. Associative axiom for addition      55. Commutative axiom for addition
57. Commutative axiom for multiplication
59. Commutative axiom for addition and commutative axiom for multiplication
61. Commutative axiom for addition
63. $3 + 5 + 2 = 8 + 2 = 10, 3 + 5 + 2 = 3 + 7 = 10, 3 + 5 + 2 = 5 + 5 = 10$
65. $10 + 4 + 12 = 14 + 12 = 26, 10 + 4 + 12 = 10 + 16 = 26, 10 + 4 + 12 = 22$
     $+ 4 = 26$
67. $4 \cdot 6 \cdot \frac{1}{2} = 24 \cdot \frac{1}{2} = 12, 4 \cdot 6 \cdot \frac{1}{2} = 4 \cdot 3 = 12, 4 \cdot 6 \cdot \frac{1}{2} = 2 \cdot 6 = 12$
69. $25 \cdot 6 \cdot 2 = 150 \cdot 2 = 300, 25 \cdot 6 \cdot 2 = 25 \cdot 12 = 300, 25 \cdot 6 \cdot 2 = 50 \cdot 6 = 300$
71. No. $2 - 1 \neq 1 - 2$            73. 29.215            75. 0.257
77. $3 * 5 = 3 \cdot 5 + 3 = 15 + 3 = 18$, but $5 * 3 = 5 \cdot 3 + 5 = 15 + 5 = 20$.

### Problem Set 2.2

1. Identity axiom for addition      3. Inverse axiom for addition
5. Identity axiom for multiplication      7. Inverse axiom for multiplication
9. Inverse axiom for addition      11. Identity axiom for addition

13. Inverse axiom for multiplication
15. Identity axiom for multiplication
17. Inverse axiom for multiplication
19. Inverse axiom for addition

21. $-7$
23. 4
25. $8\frac{1}{2}$
27. 0

29. $-12.5$
31. $\sqrt{7}$
33. $-100$
35. $-t$

37. $\frac{1}{3}$
39. $\frac{1}{10}$
41. 5
43. $\frac{3}{2}$

45. $-\frac{1}{4}$
47. $-1$
49. $\frac{4}{11}$

51. $b/a$, if $a \neq 0$ and $b \neq 0$.

53. 8
55. $\frac{1}{5}$
57. $-2$
59. $\sqrt{2}$

61. 6.9
63. A positive integer
65. $x = 0$

67. $x = 4$
69. $x = 8$
71. $x = 16$
73. $x = 0$

75. $x = 6.6$
77. $x = 2$
79. $x = 3$
81. $x = 8$

83. $x = \frac{15}{4}$
85. $x = 12$
87. $x = 0$
89. $x = 24$

91. (a) 400, (b) 727/1,417,122
93. (a) $x = \frac{7}{3}$, (b) $x = \frac{34}{3}$

95. $1 + a$, if $a \neq 0$.

## Problem Set 2.3

1. $3(1 + 2) = 3(3) = 9$, $3(1 + 2) = 3 \cdot 1 + 3 \cdot 2 = 9$
3. $6(2 + \frac{1}{3}) = 6(\frac{7}{3}) = 14$, $6(2 + \frac{1}{3}) = 6 \cdot 2 + 6 \cdot \frac{1}{3} = 14$
5. $6(17 + 8) = 6(25) = 150$, $6(17 + 8) = 6 \cdot 17 + 6 \cdot 8 = 150$
7. $13(5 + 5) = 13(10) = 130$, $13(5 + 5) = 13 \cdot 5 + 13 \cdot 5 = 130$
9. $12(\frac{1}{3} + \frac{1}{4}) = 12(\frac{7}{12}) = 7$, $12(\frac{1}{3} + \frac{1}{4}) = 12 \cdot \frac{1}{3} + 12 \cdot \frac{1}{4} = 7$
11. $30(\frac{17}{24} + \frac{14}{15}) = 30(\frac{197}{120}) = \frac{197}{4}$, $30(\frac{17}{24} + \frac{14}{15}) = 30 \cdot \frac{17}{24} + 30 \cdot \frac{14}{15} = \frac{85}{4} + 28 = \frac{197}{4}$

13. $3x + 3$
15. $12y + 24$
17. $5z + 1$
19. $4s + 3$

21. $4t + 8$
23. $\frac{15}{2}r$
25. 8
27. $-4.3$

29. 1
31. $-\sqrt{7}$
33. $\frac{4}{5}$
35. $\pi$

37. Like terms
39. Like terms
41. Unlike terms
43. Like terms

45. Like terms
47. Like terms
49. Unlike terms
51. Unlike terms

53. $9x$
55. $19y$
57. $5s$
59. $8z$

61. $8.2t + 1$
63. $20x + 10$
65. $100b^2 + 26b$
67. $\frac{49}{20}s$

69. $37(15.75) + 37(8.50) = 582.75 + 314.50 = \$897.25$,
   $37(15.75) + 37(8.50) = 37(15.75 + 8.50) = 37(24.25) = \$897.25$

71. $\frac{1}{2}hb_1 + \frac{1}{2}hb_2$

73. (a) $1.17(19.72 + 413.57) = 1.17(433.29) = 506.9493$,
       $1.17(19.72 + 413.57) = 1.17(19.72) + 1.17(413.57) = 506.9493$;
   (b) $496(17.012 + 19.763) = 496(36.775) = 18,240.4$,
       $496(17.012 + 19.763) = 496(17.012) + 496(19.763) = 18,240.4$

75. (a) $7534.3x$, (b) $2.0157y$
77. $5 * (3 + 4) = 40$, but $5 * 3 + 5 * 4 = 45$. No.

## Problem Set 2.4A

1.

3.

5.

7.

9.

11.

13.

15. $-14$

17. 3

19. 13
21. $-3$
23. $-20$
25. 12
27. 5
29. $-5$
31. 25
33. 3
35. $-5$
37. 12
39. $-\frac{1}{7}$
41. $-\frac{11}{20}$
43. $-0.5$
45. $-6.8$
47. 13
49. 18
51. \$9.40
53. $-320$ ft
55. 7°
57. Total yardage $= 21$ yd, average gain per carry $= 3$ yd
59. $T = S + 18$
61. Up 27 points
63. Let $a = 7$ and $b = -3$. Then $|a + b| = |7 + (-3)| = |4| = 4$, but $|a| + |b| = |7| + |-3| = 7 + 3 = 10$. $|a + b| = |a| + |b|$ if $a$ and $b$ are both nonnegative numbers or if $a$ and $b$ are both negative numbers.

## Problem Set 2.4B

1. 4
3. $-4$
5. $-9$
7. 7
9. $-4$
11. $-5$
13. 6
15. $-10$
17. $-9$
19. 9
21. 3
23. $-2$
25. 8
27. 12
29. $-15$
31. $-15$
33. $-6$
35. 10
37. 12
39. $-6$
41. $-\frac{1}{6}$
43. $-0.84$
45. $-8.8$
47. $-\frac{19}{7}$
49. 0.4
51. $-8$
53. $-42°$
55. 14,390 ft
57. $T = 10 - 2h$
59. (a) $-896.686$, (b) 60.91
61. $\pi - 2$
63. T

## Problem Set 2.4C

1. $(+3) \cdot (+5) = +15$, $(+2) \cdot (+5) = +10$, $(+1) \cdot (+5) = +5$, $0 \cdot (+5) = 0$, $(-1) \cdot (+5) = -5$, $(-2) \cdot (+5) = -10$, $(-3) \cdot (+5) = -15$

3. $(+3) \cdot (-1) = -3, (+2) \cdot (-1) = -2, (+1) \cdot (-1) = -1, 0 \cdot (-1) = 0, (-1) \cdot (-1) = +1, (-2) \cdot (-1) = +2, (-3) \cdot (-1) = +3$

5. $-20$      7. 30      9. $-12$    11. 12    13. $-88$    15. 0

17. 12      19. $-8$      21. $-255$    23. 693    25. $-\frac{1}{6}$    27. $-1$

29. 6.25      31. $-16$      33. $-8$    35. 16    37. $\frac{1}{9}$    39. 1

41. $-93.13$    43. 2678.106    45. $-23$    47. $-36$    49. 112    51. 180

53. 12      55. $-8.55$ points    57. $-4$ yd    59. 5°F

61. $T = 10 + 4h$, (a) $T = 10 + 4 \cdot 12 = 58°$, (b) $T = 10 + 4(-2) = 2°$, (c) $T = 10 + 4(-3) = -2°$

63. (a) $-17.17$, (b) 34.0044      65. T

## Problem Set 2.4D

1. $(+3) \div (+1) = +3, (+2) \div (+1) = +2, (+1) \div (+1) = +1, 0 \div (+1) = 0, (-1) \div (+1) = -1, (-2) \div (+1) = -2, (-3) \div (+1) = -3$

3. $(+15) \div (-5) = -3, (+10) \div (-5) = -2, (+5) \div (-5) = -1, 0 \div (-5) = 0, (-5) \div (-5) = +1, (-10) \div (-5) = +2, (-15) \div (-5) = +3$

5. $-4$      7. 4      9. $-3$      11. 17          13. 10

15. $-1$      17. 3      19. 0      21. $-10$      23. $-14$

25. $-3.2$    27. 15      29. 10      31. 5         33. $-4$

35. 2      37. $-1$      39. 16      41. $-6/-12 = \frac{1}{2}, -\frac{6}{12} = -\frac{1}{2}$    43. $\frac{2}{5}$

45. $\frac{4}{9}$      47. $-\frac{1}{2}$      49. $x/5$      51. $y/11$      53. $\frac{3}{10}$

55. $-\frac{1}{24}$    57. $-\frac{1}{14}$    59. $-\frac{5}{6}$    61. $-\frac{2}{7}$      63. \$3.40

65. $-2°$      67. 0.353      69. T

## Problem Set 2.5

1. $25x + 15$      3. $-x - 6$      5. $-a + 9$

7. $y - 5$      9. $z + 1$      11. $-2b - 8$

13. $-4c + 20$      15. $6y - 2$      17. $4x - 2$

19. $\frac{1}{6}x - \frac{1}{10}$      21. $5x - 10y + 15$      23. $8.37r - 0.243s + 2.7t$

25. $8x$      27. $2x$      29. $-2a$

31. $-10y$      33. $-3z$      35. 0

37. $2x$      39. $-13b$      41. 0

43. $6y$      45. $-5y$      47. $-6.9q$

49. $6x - 22$
51. $y - 4$
53. $-5z + 21$
55. $-18a + b$
57. $3x - 18$
59. $-12x + 5y$
61. $-7x - 22$
63. $-7x + 10$
65. $-29$
67. $24a + 2$
69. $98a + 12b$
71. $-28a$
73. $(3y - 3)/5$
75. $(x + 4)/10$
77. $(5x - 5)/7$
79. $(-2x + 8)/9$
81. $2x + 12$
83. $(6x - 3)/2$
85. $28.2986c - 4.0964d + 0.0627$
87. $-2.37x - 44.496$
89. Rule for subtraction, distributive axiom, multiplication of signed numbers, rule for subtraction

## Chapter Review

1. F
2. F
3. T
4. T
5. T
6. T
7. T
8. T
9. F
10. T
11. F
12. F
13. F
14. F
15. T
16. T
17. T
18. T
19. F
20. F
21. T
22. T
23. Like
24. $-\frac{10}{23}$
25. 14
26. $-1$
27. $-8$
28. $-11$
29. $-20$
30. $-11$
31. $\frac{1}{6}$
32. 12
33. $-1$
34. $\frac{8}{3}$
35. 0
36. $-64$
37. $-14$
38. 9.9
39. 1
40. $-9$
41. 28
42. $x - 5$
43. $(4x - 24)/3$
44. $3t + 4$
45. $117b^2 + b$
46. $6.8k$
47. $x = 15$
48. $x = 18$
49. $19x - 22y$
50. $2a - 4b$
51. $-9x - 17$
52. A positive integer
53. $3.75x + 4.25y$ dollars
54. $2\pi r^2 + 2\pi rh$
55. $6.25
56. Multiplication axiom for equality
57. Associative axiom for multiplication
58. Inverse axiom for multiplication
59. Identity axiom for multiplication

## 3   CHAPTER THREE

## Problem Set 3.1

1. 3
3. 2
5. 11
7. $-6$
9. 0
11. $\frac{7}{2}$
13. $-4$
15. $-12$
17. 7
19. $-5$
21. $-2$
23. 10

25. 12      27. $-\frac{17}{5}$      29. 4       31. $\frac{13}{17}$      33. $\frac{16}{3}$      35. $-12$
37. $-6$    39. $\frac{8}{3}$        41. $-1$     43. 10         45. $-6$      47. 4
49. 11      51. $-\frac{1}{2}$       53. $-\frac{15}{7}$   55. $-\frac{3}{4}$   57. 0        59. 26
61. 9       63. $-3$                 65. 67.1     67. 2.3        69. 6.82      71. $\frac{8}{3}$
73. Any real number is a solution.

## Problem Set 3.2

1. 4        3. $-3$      5. $-1$      7. 19        9. 11        11. $-3$
13. $-9$    15. $-2$     17. $\frac{5}{2}$    19. 13       21. 0        23. 0
25. $-1$    27. $-3$     29. $-\frac{2}{5}$   31. $-10$    33. $-2$     35. $-\frac{14}{5}$
37. $-15$   39. 17       41. $-\frac{7}{3}$   43. 2.1      45. No solution

## Problem Set 3.3

1. 4        3. $-6$      5. $-7$      7. 5         9. $-6$      11. $\frac{31}{3}$
13. 2       15. $\frac{7}{3}$    17. $-2$     19. 20       21. 225      23. $-4$
25. $-1$    27. $-6$     29. $\frac{27}{4}$   31. 15       33. 55       35. $2152
37. 5600    39. $38      41. 0.814    43. No solution           45. 12

## Problem Set 3.4

1. $P = 22$                    3. $A = 36$             5. $b = 16$
7. $r = 0.04$                  9. $V \approx 47.1$     11. $a = 75$
13. $h = 64$                   15. $h \approx 3.5$
17. (a) $-5°C$, (b) $0°C$, (c) $-20°C$
19. $212°F$                    21. $1\frac{1}{3}$ mi                    23. $24\frac{1}{6}$ nautical mph
25. $25.50                     27. 3 mi
29. (a) 48 ft/sec, (b) 16 ft/sec, (c) $-16$ ft/sec, (d) $-48$ ft/sec. The stone reaches its maxi-
    mum height at $t = 2.5$ sec and strikes the ground at $t = 5$ sec.
31. $987.50                    33. 50.3 ft                             35. 424.1 sq in.
37. 8 gal                      39. 22,619 sq in                        41. 589 cu m

43. 31.7 sq cm

45. $r = V + 32t$

47. $\ell = (P - 2w)/2$

49. $r = d/t$

51. $w = A/\ell$

53. $h = 2A/b$

55. $r = (A - P)/P$

57. $h = (2W + 440)/11$

59. $P = I/rt$

61. $h = 3V/B$

63. $b_1 = (2A - hb_2)/h$

65. $y = -3x + 12$

67. $y = -2x + 3$

69. $y = \frac{1}{2}x + 4$

71. $y = \frac{7}{2}x + \frac{1}{2}$

73. $n = (A - a + d)/d$

75. 9.89 mph

77. 182,700,000 sq mi

79. 21.5 sq cm

81. $y = (ab - bx)/a$

## Problem Set

1. $x + 5$

3. $2x$

5. $3y - 9$

7. $y$ and $23 - y$

9. $n$ and $n + 1$

11. $5(3y) = 15y$

13. $0.05x$

15. $s - 4$

17. $2(r + 7) = 2r + 14$

19. $0.35(30 - z) = 10.5 - 0.35z$

21. $55t$

23. $\frac{1}{2}[n + (n + 2) + (n + 4)] = \frac{3}{2}n + 3$

25. 13 and 17

27. 13 and 26

29. 77 and 78

31. 42, 44, and 46

33. 99

35. 20 bundles

37. Suc is 6, Kathy 18

39. Steve is 12, his brother 6

41. Lisa is 8, Nancy 18

43. 5 in. by 12 in.

45. 8 m by 19 m

47. 17 nickels, 23 dimes

49. 110 adult tickets, 720 student tickets

51. 15 $\ell$ of 60% solution, 25 $\ell$ of 20% solution

53. 6 g

55. $3780 at 8%, $2520 at 12%

57. 7:45 A.M.

59. 6 mph, 8 mph

61. 29.376 kg, 41.985 kg

63. (a) $2n$, (b) $2n + 1$

65. 20 min

## Chapter Review

1. T

2. F

3. T

4. T

5. F

6. T

7. T

8. Equation

9. Conditional

10. Identical

11. $2x + 5$

12. Solution

13. Formula

14. 8

15. $\frac{17}{6}$

16. 9

17. 0

18. $-13$

19. $-\frac{1}{2}$

20. 18

21. 8

22. $-\frac{18}{5}$

23. $w = 5$

24. $a = 135$

25. $r = 0.12$

26. $a = (10 - b)/2$

27. $b = (2M - a)/c$
29. (a) $x + 5 = 27$, (b) $3(x + 2) = 18$
31. 39.9 sq units
33. 17.5 and 35
35. 67, 68, and 69
37. 10 hamburgers, 5 hotdogs
39. Lory is 6, Georganne is 2

28. $n = (D - c + d)/d$
30. 68°F
32. 37.5 min
34. 12 ft, 15 ft, 16 ft
36. $27
38. 27 ft by 78 ft
40. 3 hr

# 4 CHAPTER FOUR

## Problem Set 4.1

1. $5 > 3$
3. $-7 < 0$
5. $-2 > -8$
7. $-10 < 4$
9. $\sqrt{2} > 1$
11. $-\sqrt{2} < -1$
13. $-1001 < -1000$
15. $\pi > 3.14$
17. $\frac{4}{5} > \frac{7}{9}$
19. $\frac{5}{12} < \frac{7}{16}$
21. $-\frac{3}{4} > -\frac{4}{5}$
23. $-\frac{5}{7} < -\frac{7}{10}$
25. T
27. T
29. $b < d < c < a$
31. $\{3, 4, 5, 6, ...\}$
33. $\{..., -2, -1, 0, 1, 2, 3, 4, 5\}$
35. $\{0, 1, 2, 3, 4\}$
37. There are none
39. $\{-3, -2, -1, 0, 1, 2, 3, ...\}$
41. $\{1, 2, 3, 4, 5\}$
43. $\{2, 4, 6, 8, 10\}$
45. $\{-4, -3, -2, -1, 0\}$
47. There are none
49. $\{-6, -5, -4, -3, -2, -1, 0, 1, 2, 3, 4, 5, 6\}$
51. $x \geq 5$ and $x$ is an integer
53. $x \leq -2$ and $x$ is an integer
55. $-3 \leq x \leq 2$ and $x$ is an integer
57. $4 \leq x \leq 14$ and $x$ is even
59. $x \geq 13$ and $x$ is odd
61. $x > 0$
63. $x \geq 0$
65. $x \geq 7$
67. $x + 3 < 9$
69. $5 < r < 6$
71. $-3 \leq y < 15$
73. $t < 4$ min
75. $a \geq 35$ yr
77. $105 \text{ mi} \leq d \leq 165 \text{ mi}$
79. $0 \text{ oz} < w \leq 9 \text{ oz}$
81. T
83. $1635 \text{ sq ft} \leq n \leq 1826 \text{ sq ft}$
85. T

## Problem Set 4.2

1. $6 < 7$ and $-4 < -3$
3. $5 < 11$ and $-5 < 1$
5. $-5 > -15$ and $-15 > -25$
7. $-3 < 10$ and $-13 < 0$
9. $2 < 4$
11. $0 < 12$

13. $-20 > -40$
19. $0 > -12$
25. $x < 10$
31. $x \leqslant 0$
37. $x \geqslant -\frac{7}{2}$
43. $x \leqslant -18$
49. $x \geqslant 2$
55. $x > -6.5$

15. $-16 < 10$
21. $20 < 40$
27. $x \geqslant -7$
33. $x \geqslant -1$
39. $x > 13$
45. $x > \frac{12}{5}$
51. $s \geqslant \$1300$
57. F

17. $-2 > -4$
23. $16 > -10$
29. $x < 2$
35. $x > 5$
41. $x \leqslant 1$
47. $x < -3$
53. $0 \text{ m} < \ell \leqslant 27 \text{ m}$

## Problem Set 4.3

1. $x < 5$
9. $x > 2$
17. $x > 0$
25. $x > -5$
33. $t \leqslant \frac{19}{2}$
41. $7 < x < 9$
49. $5 \leqslant x \leqslant 6$
57. $\frac{1}{3} < p < 5$
63. $\$11.25 \leqslant$ cost per person $\leqslant \$15$
67. More than 1760 items
71. $x \geqslant 1.6$

3. $x > 1$
11. $x \leqslant -4$
19. $x \leqslant 3$
27. $x < 3$
35. $s < \frac{6}{5}$
43. $-8 \leqslant x < 0$
51. $\frac{1}{3} \leqslant x \leqslant \frac{2}{3}$
59. $4 \leqslant q \leqslant 5$

5. $x \leqslant -4$
13. $x < 7$
21. $x \leqslant \frac{9}{4}$
29. $x > \frac{5}{2}$
37. $r < -13$
45. $1 < x \leqslant 5$
53. $-1 \geqslant x \geqslant -5$
61. $t > 10$ min
65. $5° \leqslant F \leqslant 59°$
69. Weight of astronaut $\leqslant 180$ lb

7. $x \geqslant -7$
15. $x \leqslant 0$
23. $x \leqslant 2$
31. $y \geqslant -3$
39. $m \leqslant \frac{76}{3}$
47. $6 \leqslant x \leqslant 14$
55. $2 < n < \frac{19}{6}$

73. Suppose you arrive at the solution $x \geqslant 2$ (if the original inequality involved the symbol $\geqslant$ or $\leqslant$), or $x > 2$ (if the original inequality involved the symbol $>$ or $<$). This solution is correct if (1) substituting 2 for $x$ into the original inequality produces an equality, *and* (2) substituting any number greater than 2 for $x$ into the original inequality produces a true statement.
75. No. of magazines $> 15,000$

## Problem Set 4.4

1.

3.

5.

7.

9.

11.

13.

15.

17.

19.

21.

23.

25.

27.

29.

31.

33. Open half-line

35. Closed half-line

37. Closed interval

39. Open interval

41. (a)

(b)

43. (a)

(b)

45. (a)

(b)

47. (a) No graph

(b)

49. (a) No graph

(b)

51. (a)

(b)

53. (a)

(b)

(c)

55.

57.

59. No graph

## Chapter Review

1. F 2. F 3. T 4. T 5. F 6. T
7. T 8. F 9. T 10. T 11. Inequality 12. Double
13. $a + c < b + c$ 14. $ac > bc$ 15. $ac < bc$

16.

17. $x \leq 2$ and $x$ is an integer

18. (a) $-2 < r < 7$, (b) $4 < s \leq 5$, (c) $d \geq 7'6''$

19. $x \leq 4$  20. $x > -1$  21. $x > 0$  22. $x \leq 4$  23. $r < \frac{20}{3}$  24. $s > 2$

25. $2 \leq x \leq 5$  26. $1 < x < 11$  27. $-\frac{1}{4} \leq h \leq 4$

28. Closed half-line

29. Half-open interval

30. Open half-line

31. Open interval

32. Closed interval

33. No graph

34.

35.

36.

37. $0 \text{ mi} \leq d \leq 9\frac{1}{8} \text{ mi}$

38. $-20° < C < 10°$

39. $s \geq \$1060$

40. No. of items $> 57,500$

# 5 CHAPTER FIVE

## Problem Set 5.1

1. Base $= 4$, exponent $= 3$
3. Base $= -6$, exponent $= 2$
5. Base $= 6$, exponent $= 2$
7. Base $= x$, exponent $= 5$
9. Base $= 5$, exponent $= p$
11. Base $= r + 2$, exponent $= 8$
13. Base $= u/3$, exponent $= 4$
15. Base $= 6a$, exponent $= 11$
17. Base $= \pi$, exponent $= n + 1$
19. Base $= abc$, exponent $= 1 - 3k$
21. 64
23. $-\frac{1}{32}$
25. $-0.343$
27. 75
29. $\frac{1}{2187}$
31. $(-10)^2 = 100$, $-10^2 = -100$
33. $-\frac{3}{16}$
35. $(-2)^7 = -128$, $-2^7 = -128$
37. $(-5)^4 = 625$, $-5^4 = -625$
39. $(-5)^3 = -125$, $-5^3 = -125$
41. $3^2 + 3^4 = 90$, $3^2 \cdot 3^4 = 729$
43. $17^3 - 17^2 = 4624$, $17^3 \div 17^2 = 17$
45. $(2^3)^2 = 64$, $2^{(3^2)} = 512$
47. $9^5$
49. $4^2x^3$
51. $a^3b^4$
53. $(x + 1)^2$
55. $(x - 2)^3$
57. $3a^2 - 2b^3$
59. $x^2y + xy^2$
61. $(3x)^4$

63. $(5a)^2 - a^2b$    65. $(a/b)^3$    67. $(n/2)^5$    69. $(x^2)^3$    71. $(a^3)^4$
73. (a) 0.364, (b) 2.828, (c) 93,648.047, (d) $-0.001$
75. $(2^3)^3 = 512$, but $2^{(3^3)} = 134,217,728$    77. $x = 10$

## Problem Set 5.2

1. $x^7$          3. $a^9$          5. $b^8$          7. $y^{12}$
9. $5^6$          11. $3^{18}$          13. $(x + 2)^6$          15. $(r - 1)^{100}$
17. $8x^3$          19. $4a^6$          21. $24a^4b^4$          23. $-30p^7q^9$
25. $x^{n+1}$          27. $x^2$          29. $a^8$          31. $y^4$
33. $a^2b^{16}$          35. $5^4$          37. $101^{66}$          39. $(x + 2)^4$
41. $5n - 3$          43. $a^{2q}$          45. $x^6$          47. $a^{20}$
49. $b^{60}$          51. $x^{2n}$          53. $a^{3r+3}$          55. $x^3y^3$
57. $a^{10}b^{10}$          59. $125x^3y^3$          61. $16p^2q^2$          63. $a^{r+1}b^{r+1}$
65. $x^5/y^5$          67. $a^{15}/b^{15}$          69. $81/b^4$          71. $-p^3/125$
73. $u^{3s}/v^{3s}$          75. $x^3y^6$          77. $a^8b^{12}$          79. $81x^8y^{12}$
81. $x^{10}/y^5$          83. $27x^{12}/y^6$          85. $16x^{28}/625y^{14}$          87. $200x^8$
89. $48x^4y^3$          91. $-189r^{51}s^{42}$          93. $8,388,608x^{10,833}y^{21,574}$
95. $196,608r^{4323}s^{3993}$          97. $-16a^{4n+1}b^{3m+1}$

## Problem Set 5.3

1. 1          3. 1          5. 1          7. 1
9. $(-4)^0 = 1, -4^0 = -1$          11. 1          13. $\frac{1}{10}$
15. $\frac{1}{1000}$          17. $1/x^5$          19. 8          21. $\frac{49}{4}$
23. $-\frac{125}{27}$          25. 256          27. $y^8$          29. $\frac{1}{9}$
31. $\frac{5}{6}$          33. $\frac{11}{12}$          35. $\frac{73}{576}$          37. $5/x^2$
39. $-13/a^{13}$          41. $10t^4$          43. $-b$          45. $y^2/x^5$
47. $b^4c^6/a^{12}$          49. 1000          51. 0.01          53. 0.1
55. 1,000,000,000          57. 0.00000000001          59. 0.000000000000000001          61. $10^{-2}$
63. $10^{-5}$          65. $10^{14}$          67. $10^{15}$          69. $10^2$
71. $10^5$          73. $x^6$          75. $t^5$          77. $81/p^{12}$
79. $r^9/64s^9$          81. $9/a^3$          83. $16x^6z^4/25y^{12}$
85. (a) 0.0470, (b) 0.0323, (c) 0.0163          87. 1
89. $(1 + 1)^{-1} = 2^{-1} = \frac{1}{2}$, but $1^{-1} + 1^{-1} = 1 + 1 = 2$.

## Problem Set 5.4

1. 300
3. 0.08
5. 410,000
7. 0.00000052
9. 0.000179
11. 214,000,000
13. 3.76
15. $7 \times 10$
17. $5 \times 10^3$
19. $7.3 \times 10^7$
21. $9 \times 10^{-2}$
23. $7.14 \times 10^{-5}$
25. $4.04 \times 10^{-6}$
27. $1.1 \times 10^8$
29. $6.835 \times 10^9$
31. $1.14 \times 10^{-8}$
33. $7.23 \times 10^0$
35. $8 \times 10$
37. $9 \times 10^{-3}$
39. $1.8 \times 10^{-2}$
41. $3.68 \times 10$
43. $3 \times 10^{-2}$
45. $7 \times 10^{-5}$
47. $1.2 \times 10$
49. 25,000,000,000,000
51. $5 \times 10^{20}$
53. 1.3 sec
55. $2^3 = 8$ choices

|  | Game 1 | Game 2 | Game 3 |
|---|---|---|---|
| Choice 1 | Home | Home | Home |
| Choice 2 | Home | Home | Visiting |
| Choice 3 | Home | Visiting | Home |
| Choice 4 | Home | Visiting | Visiting |
| Choice 5 | Visiting | Home | Home |
| Choice 6 | Visiting | Home | Visiting |
| Choice 7 | Visiting | Visiting | Home |
| Choice 8 | Visiting | Visiting | Visiting |

57. (a) \$11,000, (b) \$12,100, (c) \$13,310, (d) \$14,641
59. (a) 140 g, (b) 70 g, (c) 35 g, (d) 17.5 g
61. $5^6$ letters, $5^{10}$ letters     63. $2^{63}$ grains     65. $c = 6.7 \times 10^8$ mi/hr     67. No
69. \$31,071.49     71. $10^{(10^{100})}$

## Problem Set 5.5

1.

| Polynomials | Degree | Leading Coefficient | Constant term | Number of terms |
|---|---|---|---|---|
| a | 3 | 5 | 1 | polynomial |
| c | 7 | 1 | $-1$ | binomial |
| e | 0 | 8 | 8 | monomial |
| g | 1 | $-1$ | 7 | binomial |
| j | 3 | $3^4$ | $-32$ | binomial |
| l | 5 | $\pi$ | 0 | trinomial |
| m | 4 | 8 | 0 | monomial |
| n | 1 | 1 | 2 | binomial |
| o | 100 | $-\frac{1}{10}$ | $\frac{1}{3}$ | trinomial |

3. 5          5. $-1$          7. 3          9. 88          11. 156
13. 1008      15. $-\frac{13}{8}$          17. 13          19. $-89$          21. 7.488
23. 17          25. $-\frac{17}{25}$          27. \$25,588          29. 5050          31. (a) 20, (b) 87.5
33. $h = -16t^2 + 48t + 64$, (a) 96 ft, (b) 96 ft, (c) 64 ft, (d) 0 ft

35. $-7.46$     37. \$121,862.57     39. 296 ft

## Problem Set 5.6

1. $7x^2 + 6x - 1$          3. $11y^3 - 5y^2 - y - 6$          5. $2a^3 - 8a$
7. $12m^3 + m^2 + 12m - 14$          9. $10x^2 + xy - 9y^2$          11. $4x^2 + 5x + 1$
13. $-y^2 - 10y + 10$          15. $2a^3 + 2a^2 + a - 6$          17. $-m^5 - 11m^2 + 1$
19. $2x^3 + 16y^3$          21. $20x^2 + x + 3$          23. $19x^3 - 5x^2 - x + 9$
25. $-2a^2 + 3a - 7$          27. $4x^3 - x^2 - 5x - 2$          29. $2b^2 - 13b - 26$
31. $-x^2 + 16xy - 7y^2$          33. $9a^2 - 15ab - 12b^2$          35. $8x + 3$
37. $10x - 2$          39. $90n + 340$          41. $-3m + 163$ degrees
43. $24.217a^2 + 33.954a - 69.684$
45. $2\pi x^2 + (\sqrt{2} + 3)x + \frac{2}{15}$

## Chapter Review

1. T          2. T          3. F          4. F          5. F          6. T
7. T          8. F          9. T          10. F          11. T          12. T
13. T          14. T          15. T          16. F          17. F          18. F
19. 1          20. $n + 2$          21. 1          22. 4          23. $-2$          24. 3
25. $-625$          26. $\frac{125}{128}$          27. 64          28. 256          29. $3^2x^4y^2 - x^2y^2$
30. $(5x - 1)^3$          31. $x^{19}$          32. $-36x^5y^4$
33. $x + 10$          34. $x^4z^2$          35. $128x^{20}y^{35}/z^{30}$
36. $90,000x^{22}y^8$          37. $-128t^5$          38. 100
39. $6/y^5$          40. $\frac{49}{4}$          41. $11x^3$
42. 0.00304          43. 1000          44. $5.13 \times 10^5$

45. $6.09 \times 10^{-5}$
46. $4.5$
47. $x^{2n}$
48. $b^{3s}$
49. $x^{k+1}y^{k+1}$
50. $5^{2m}/v^{2m}$
51. $(3a + 4)^{r-1}$
52. $\frac{13}{36}$
53. $y^2/x^3$
54. $s^3/5r^3$
55. $b^8/a^8c^8$
56. $516
57. $\frac{7}{3}$
58. $-3x^3 + 6x^2 - 4x - 20$
59. $4x^2yz - xy^2z$
60. $2x^3 + 3x^2 + x - 10$
61. $12a^3 - 13ab - 33b$
62. $-7x^3y^3$
63. $16x + 12$
64. $70,246.40

# 6    CHAPTER SIX

## Problem Set 6.1

1. $x^2 + 5x$
3. $6x^2 - 3x$
5. $x^3 - 4x^2$
7. $8x^3 + 4x^2$
9. $-5x^3y - 5x^2y - 5xy$
11. $x^4y + 2x^3y^2 - x^2y^2$
13. $-7a^4b + 7a^3b^2 - 21a^3$
15. $x^2 + 7x + 10$
17. $x^2 + x - 12$
19. $6x^2 - 13x + 6$
21. $25x^2 + 10x + 1$
23. $x^2 + 2xy + y^2$
25. $4x^2 - 20xy + 25y^2$
27. $x^3 + 8$
29. $3y^3 - 16y^2 + 4y + 5$
31. $a^3 - 2a^2 - 8a + 21$
33. $a^4 - 3a^3 + 3a^2 - 1$
35. $a^3 + 2a^2 - a - 2$
37. $a^3 + a^2b - 4ab^2 - 4b^3$
39. $20c^4 - c^3 - 8c^2 - 17c - 15$
41. $12m^4 + 20m^3 - 31m^2 + 23m - 15$
43. $k^3 + 3k^2 + 3k + 1$
45. $p^3 - 6p^2q + 12pq^2 - 8q^3$
47. $6x^2 + 7x - 3$
49. $V = 456x - 86x^2 + 4x^3$
51. (a) $9.1x^5 + 6.95x^4 - 19.4x^3$, (b) $58,608a^2 + 10,466ab - 17,399b^2$
53. (a) $6x^{3n} - 10x^{2n+1} + 12x^n$, (b) $a^{3k} - 2a^{2k} - 9a^k + 4$

## Problem Set 6.2

1. $x^2 + 5x + 6$
3. $x^2 + 9x + 20$
5. $x^2 + 20x + 99$
7. $x^2 - 11x + 30$
9. $x^2 - 11x + 18$
11. $x^2 - 15x + 56$

13. $y^2 + 2y - 8$

15. $y^2 - 5y - 24$

17. $y^2 - 2y - 120$

19. $a^2 - 25$

21. $a^2 - 100$

23. $b^2 - 1$

25. $b^2 + 14b + 49$

27. $b^2 - 6b + 9$

29. $x^2 - a^2$

31. $x^2 + 2xa + a^2$

33. $81 - y^2$

35. $2x^2 + 7x + 3$

37. $5x^2 + 6x - 8$

39. $3y^2 + y - 2$

41. $2y^2 - 11y - 90$

43. $9x^2 + 6x + 1$

45. $25x^2 - 10x + 1$

47. $36y^2 - 25$

49. $6x^2 + xy - y^2$

51. $10a^2 + 13ab - 3b^2$

53. $a^2 - 4ab + 4b^2$

55. $25x^2 + 20xy + 4y^2$

57. $\frac{3}{25}k^2 + \frac{2}{5}k - \frac{7}{4}$

59. $t^4 - 10t^2 + 9$

61. $-4xy$

63. $6x^2 - x - 12$

65. $51 \cdot 49 = (50 + 1)(50 - 1) = 2499$

67. $3196p^2 - 44{,}720p - 69{,}504$

69. $x^{2n} + 3x^n - 10$

71. Any four consecutive even integers can be denoted by $2n$, $2n + 2$, $2n + 4$, and $2n + 6$, where $n$ is some integer. Doing so, we have:
product of middle two − product of smallest and largest:
$= (2n + 2) \cdot (2n + 4) - 2n \cdot (2n + 6)$
$= 4n^2 + 12n + 8 - 4n^2 - 12n$
$= 8$.

## Problem Set 6.3

1. $5(x^2 + 1)$

3. $4x(x + 2)$

5. $8x(x - 9)$

7. $5(2x + y)$

9. $-3x(x + 2)$

11. $a(a + b)$

13. $-12(x + 2y)$

15. $2y(2y^2 - y + 1)$

17. $3x^2(x^2 - 2x + 4)$

19. $b(b - 1)$

21. $y(y^4 + 1)$

23. $x^2(x^4 - 5x^2 + 1)$

25. $5x^2(x^2 + 3x - 2)$

27. $x^3(x^3 + x^2 + x + 1)$

29. $10z^{72}(z - 10)$

31. $x(y + z)$

33. $12y(x - 2)$

35. $3x^2y^2(y + 7x^2)$

37. $abc(a + b + c)$

39. $-xy^2(y^3 + y^2 - 8)$

41. $2\pi r^2(2r + 3h)$

43. $c + rc = c(1 + r)$

45. $119x(x^2 - 19x + 43)$

47. $(x + y)(x + 5)$

49. $x^3(x^{n+2} + x^n + 1)$

## Problem Set 6.4

1. $(x - 4)(x + 4)$
3. $(x - 9)(x + 9)$
5. $(a - 10)(a + 10)$
7. $(3y - 2)(3y + 2)$
9. Prime
11. $(8x - 3)(8x + 3)$
13. $(7a - 12b)(7a + 12b)$
15. $(z - 1)(z + 1)$
17. $(5x - 11)(5x + 11)$
19. $(2x - y)(2x + y)$
21. $(x - 3)(x + 3)(x^2 + 9)$
23. $(xy - 5)(xy + 5)(x^2y^2 + 25)$
25. $(1 - 10ab)(1 + 10ab)$
27. $(a + b - c)(a + b + c)$
29. $(-x + 6)(5x - 4)$
31. $7(x - 3)(x + 3)$
33. $y(x^3 - 2)(x^3 + 2)$
35. $2(x - 1)(x + 1)(x^2 + 1)$
37. $x(5y - 7x)(5y + 7x)$
39. $x^2y(x - 1)(x + 1)$
41. $6r(r^3 - 4s)(r^3 + 4s)$
43. $25^2 - 15^2 = (25 - 15)(25 + 15) = (10)(40) = 400$
45. $(37x - 99y)(37x + 99y)$
47. $(a^{2m} - b^n)(a^{2m} + b^n)$
49. Since $a - b$, then $a - b - 0$ and hence we cannot divide by $a - b$.

## Problem Set 6.5

1. $(x + 1)(x + 2)$
3. $(x + 3)(x + 4)$
5. $(x + 5)(x + 7)$
7. $(x + 1)^2$
9. Prime
11. $(y - 4)(y - 5)$
13. $(y - 2)(y - 3)$
15. $(y - 4)(y - 8)$
17. $(a - 2)(a + 5)$
19. $(a + 9)(a - 6)$
21. Prime
23. $(b - 7)(b + 6)$
25. $(b + 6)(b - 8)$
27. $(b - 11)(b + 1)$
29. $(x - 45)(x + 1)$
31. $(x - 17)(x + 3)$
33. Prime
35. $(y - 1)(y - 25)$
37. $5(x + 3)(x + 7)$
39. $2(x - 1)(x - 10)$
41. $3(y - 4)(y + 2)$
43. $4(y - 5)^2$
45. $r + 8$
47. $x + 73$
49. $(t^2 + 6)(t - 2)(t + 2)$
51. $k(k - 3)(k + 3)(k^2 + 1)$

## Problem Set 6.6

1. $(2x + 1)(x + 3)$
3. $(3x + 5)(x + 1)$
5. $(5y - 1)(y + 1)$
7. $(11a - 14)(a + 1)$
9. $(2a + 7)^2$
11. Prime
13. $(3x - 1)(4x + 1)$
15. $(3b + 1)^2$
17. Prime
19. $(8x + 1)(2x - 5)$
21. $(4a - 1)(a + 6)$
23. $(4x - y)^2$
25. $(a + 7b)(a - 2b)$
27. $(3a - b)(3a + 4b)$
29. $(4r - 3s)(9r + 8s)$
31. $2x(2x + 1)(x - 3)$
33. $10(2x - 3y)(3x + y)$
35. $4(x - 3y)^2$
37. $3b(4a + b)(a + b)$
39. $k - 1$
41. $136y - 25$
43. (a) $(3t^2 - 5)(2t^2 + 5)$, (b) $(4y^n - 3)(3y^n + 8)$

## Problem Set 6.7

1. $(x + 2)(x^2 - 2x + 4)$
3. $(y - 4)(y^2 + 4y + 16)$
5. $(z + 1)(z^2 - z + 1)$
7. $(3r - 1)(9r^2 + 3r + 1)$
9. $(5s + t)(25s^2 - 5st + t^2)$
11. $(3a - 5b)(9a^2 + 15ab + 25b^2)$
13. $(pq + 1)(p^2q^2 - pq + 1)$
15. $(7u + 6v)(49u^2 - 42uv + 36v^2)$
17. $(x^2 - y)(x^4 + x^2y + y^2)$
19. $(x + 7)(x^2 + 3)$
21. $(b + 13)(a + 2)$
23. $(s - 1)(r + 3)$
25. $(u - 1)(v - 1)$
27. $(s + 8t^2)(s + 6t)$
29. $(x + 3 - y)(x + 3 + y)$
31. $(x + 1 - 2y)(x + 1 + 2y)$
33. $(a - b - 4)(a + b + 4)$
35. $(2r - 5s - 3t)(2r - 5s + 3t)$
37. $(y + 1)(x - 1)(x + 1)$
39. $(p - 4)(p + 4)(q^2 + 9)$
41. $(t + 5)(t - 2)(t^2 + 2t + 4)$
43. $(t + s)^2(t^2 - st + s^2)$
45. $(a + b)(a^2 - ab + b^2) = a^3 - a^2b + ab^2 + ba^2 - ab^2 + b^3 = a^3 + b^3$
47. $(8x + 9)(64x^2 - 72x + 81)$
49. $(s + 53)(19r + 29)$
51. $(s^{2n} - t^m)(s^{4n} + s^{2n}t^m + t^{2m})$

## Problem Set 6.8

1. $3x^5$
3. $-2x^4$
5. $8$
7. $x$
9. $x - y$
11. $x^2 + x$
13. $x + 2$
15. $16x^2 + \frac{3}{4}x - 1$
17. $6y - 2x + 1$
19. $3a^3 + 5ab^2 - 2b^2$
21. $\frac{3}{5}xy^2 - 3y + \frac{1}{5}$
23. $6x^8 - 5x^6 + 4x^2 + 3$
25. $x + 6$
27. $2x - 5$
29. $3x + 4 + 16/(3x - 2)$
31. $2x^2 - x - 1$
33. $4x^2 - 8x + 5$
35. $3a^2 - 6a + 14 - 3/(a + 2)$
37. $y^2 - 3y + 1 + 7/(y + 3)$
39. $x^2 + x + 1$
41. $2m^3 - 4m^2 + 3m - 7$
43. $5x^2 + 3x + \frac{1}{5} + 2/5(5x - 1)$
45. $1/R_1 + 1/R_2 + 1/R_3$
47. $AC = 0.05x + 25 + 1400/x$, (a) \$44, (b) \$52.80
49. $t^2 + 4$ cm/sec
51. $k = 10$
53. $4.9p^2q^2 - 8.18pq + 9.5$
55. $3x^2 - x + 4 + (x + 13)/(2x^2 + 2x - 1)$
57. Any three consecutive integers can be denoted by $n$, $n + 1$, and $n + 2$, where $n$ is some integer. Doing so, we have
$$\text{average of three integers} = \frac{n + (n + 1) + (n + 2)}{3} = \frac{3n + 3}{3} = n + 1.$$

## Chapter Review

| | | | | | |
|---|---|---|---|---|---|
| 1. T | 2. F | 3. T | 4. T | 5. T | 6. T |
| 7. T | 8. F | 9. T | 10. F | 11. F | 12. F |

13. Factored
14. Prime
15. Common factors
16. Descending
17. $18x^3 - 6x^2$
18. $-x^4y + 5x^3y^2 - 4x^2y^3$
19. $6x^3 - 7x^2 - 5x$
20. $a^4 - 3a^3 + 3a^2 - 1$
21. $t^2 - 10t + 25$
22. $16x^2 - 56xy + 49y^2$
23. $a^3 + 12a^2 + 48a + 64$
24. $-18s^3 - 21s^2 + 118s + 176$
25. $a(6a + 1)$
26. $(x - 5)^2$
27. $(x - 10)(x + 10)$
28. $3a^2b(3a^2b^3 - 4ab + 5)$
29. $(x + 9)(x - 6)$
30. $(x + 4)(x + 5)$
31. $5(m - 11)(m + 1)$
32. $(4a - 11b)(4a + 11b)$
33. $x^3y^3(xy - 1)(xy + 1)(x^2y^2 + 1)$
34. $(3s - 4)(s + 6)$
35. $8b(3a + 2)(a - 2)$
36. $14x(5x - 6y)(x + y)$
37. $(a + b - 3c)(a + b + 3c)$
38. $-14c^2d(c^2 + d^2)$
39. $(p + \frac{1}{2})(p^2 - \frac{1}{2}p + \frac{1}{4})$
40. $10(q + 1)(q^2 - q + 1)$
41. $(b + 1)(a^2 + 4)$
42. $(s - t + 9)(s + t - 9)$
43. $w(5u - v^2)(25u^2 + 5uv^2 + v^4)$
44. $(4r - 3s)(16r^2 + 12rs + 9s^2)$
45. $(p + 2q)(p^2 - 2pq + 4q^2)(p + 2)$
46. $(7x - 2y - z)(7x - 2y + z)$
47. $(3t + 4)(4t - 3)$
48. $(1 + r)^2$
49. $-16x^5$
50. $x + y$
51. $x^4 - x^2 + 1$
52. $4a^3b - 5a + \frac{3}{2}$
53. $2x^2 + x + 4$
54. $x^3 - 2x^2 + x - \frac{1}{5} - 4/5(5x + 1)$
55. $\frac{2}{5}k^2 - \frac{29}{60}k - \frac{1}{2}$
56. $12x - 2x^2$
57. $\pi h(R^2 - r^2)$
58. $t^3 - 2t^2 + 4t - 8 + 32/(t + 2)$ cm/sec

---

## 7   CHAPTER SEVEN

## Problem Set 7.1

1. $x = 0$
3. $x = 2$
5. $x = -7$
7. $x = 5, x = -5$
9. $y = 0, y = -8$
11. $a = b, a = -b$

13. $r = 3, r = -4$

15. No value

17. $\frac{3}{4}$

19. $\frac{1}{4}$

21. $2/9a^2$

23. $8a/3$

25. $\frac{5}{7}$

27. $(x - y)/(x + y)$

29. $2/(5x - 1)$

31. $(x + 1)/(x - 1)$

33. $1/(x + 3)$

35. $1/(x + y)^3$

37. $a + b$

39. $(x - y)/(x + y)$

41. $(x - 3)/(x + 3)$

43. $(x - 3)/(x - 1)$

45. $(2x + y)/(x + 5y)$

47. 1

49. $-1$

51. $(a + b)/(a + 3b)$

53. $-1$

55. $(p - 2)/(p + 1)$

57. $3/(q + 2)$

59. (a) $\frac{4}{45}$; (b) $4/5x^2$, $\frac{4}{45}$

61. (a) 4, (b) 4

63. (a) $\frac{6}{5}$; (b) $12/(a - b)$, $\frac{6}{5}$

65. (a) $-1$, (b) $-1$

67. (a) 17; (b) $t + 3$, 17

69. 60

71. 7.75

73. 3.75 cm

75. 2439 persons

77. 2

## Problem Set 7.2

1. $2a^2/27$

3. $4a^2/5b^2$

5. $3a/b$

7. $1/21a$

9. $7a/2$

11. $3(a - b)$

13. $(x - 2)/5x$

15. 1

17. $(x + 3)/8x$

19. $x(x + y)/(x - y)$

21. $30a^2/b^2$

23. $25a^2/12b^2$

25. $a/11b^2$

27. $2a/3(a - 1)$

29. $(a + 1)^2/64(a + 2)$

31. $a(a + 12b)/(a - b)$

33. $(x + 2)/(x - 4)$

35. $(x - 2)/2(x + 4)$

37. $y$

39. $(c + 3)^2/(c - 2)(c + 4)$

41. $(n + r)^3/n^3$

43. $d^2(3k - 2d)/6$

45. $(3x^2 + 26x + 40)/x(x + 2)$

47. (a) 1, (b) 1

49. $(x - 1)y^{k-1}/(y^k + 1)$

## Problem Set 7.3

1. $1/3x$

3. $1/5x$

5. 1

7. $(m - 1)/m^2$

9. $1/k^3$

11. $y/(x - y)$

13. $a + b$

15. $a - b$

17. $(2x + 3)/x(x + 3)$

19. $(r^2 - r + 12)/(r - 1)$

21. $(x^2 + 25)/(x - 5)(x + 5)$

23. $2/(x + 7)$

25. $12x$

27. $40x^2$

29. $x^3y^2$

31. $x + 5$

33. $(x + 2)(x + 3)$

35. $5(r - 4)$

37. $(s - 1)(s + 1)$

39. $12(a - b)(a + b)$

41. $10p(p - 5)(p + 5)$

43. $7(x - 3)(x + 3)$

45. $(x - 9)(x + 2)$

47. $540(3m + 2n)(4m - n)$

49. $(x + 1)^2(x - 1)$

51. $ab(a - b)$

53. $827/x^3$

55. (a) $\dfrac{1}{6x} + \dfrac{1}{6x} = \dfrac{6x + 6x}{6x \cdot 6x} = \dfrac{12x}{36x^2} = \dfrac{1}{3x}$, (b) $\dfrac{a - 3}{a} + \dfrac{3}{a} = \dfrac{(a^2 - 3a) + 3a}{a \cdot a} = \dfrac{a^2}{a^2} = 1$,

(c) $\dfrac{x - y}{x + y} + \dfrac{x - y}{x + y} = \dfrac{(x^2 - y^2) + (x^2 - y^2)}{(x + y)(x + y)} = \dfrac{2(x^2 - y^2)}{(x + y)^2} = \dfrac{2(x - y)}{x + y}$

## Problem Set 7.4

1. 3
9. $a^4 b^5$
17. $s^2 - 8s + 7$
25. $3a^2 - 3ab + 3a - 3b$
33. $(7a - 6b)/a^2 b^2$
37. $(y^2 + 2x^2 - 3xy)/x^2 y^2$
41. $(x^2 + x - 10)/(x + 1)$
45. $(3x + 65)/(x - 5)(x + 5)$
49. $13/3(x + 4)$
53. $3/2(a - 9)$
57. $(b^2 - b + a)/ab(a + b)$
61. $(2x + 1)/(x - 6)$
65. $(3p + 1)/5p(p - 3)$
69. $(-x^2 - x + 4)/(x - 1)$

3. $8x$
11. $r^2 + 9r$
19. $14m - 70$
27. $7/12a$

5. $8xy^2$
13. $s^2$
21. $m^2 - 11m + 30$
29. $7/24b$
35. $(5x^2 + 3x - 1)/x^3$
39. $(x^2 + 9)/x$
43. $(11a + 4)/(a + 2)(a - 4)$
47. $(x^2 + x + 3)/(x - 3)(x + 2)$
51. $3/(x - 1)$
55. $(2a + b + 3)/3(a - b)(a + b)$
59. $3/(x + 3)$
63. $(6r^2 + 4r + 2)/(r - 1)^2(r + 1)$
67. $1/(n - m)$
71. $(-2x - 3)/(x + 3)^2(x + 2)$

7. $b^6$
15. $s^2 + 3s$
23. $8x^2 + 40x$
31. $(1 + 5a)/a^2$

73. Let $x = y = 1$. Then $\frac{1}{x} + \frac{1}{y} = \frac{1}{1} + \frac{1}{1} = 2$, but $1/(x + y) = 1/(1 + 1) = \frac{1}{2}$.

75. $\dfrac{a}{b} + \dfrac{c}{d} = \dfrac{a \cdot d}{b \cdot d} + \dfrac{c \cdot b}{d \cdot b} = \dfrac{ad + bc}{bd}$

77. $2500/r(r + 5)$, (a) 5 hr, (b) $\frac{10}{11}$ hr

79. $1{,}993{,}143/1{,}879{,}981 x^3$
81. $(y^2 + x^2)/xy$
83. $a^2/(a + 1)^2$

## Problem Set 7.5

1. $\frac{4}{15}$
7. $(2b - a)/(2b + a)$
13. $(3x - 1)/x$
19. $-1$
25. $(d - c)/cd$

3. $\frac{11}{4}$
9. $a/b$
15. $(x - 3)/(x + 7)$
21. $s + r$
27. $(m + 3)/(m + 2)$

5. $\frac{13}{6}$
11. $4x/(x - 2)$
17. $x(1 + xy)/y(x - y)$
23. $1/t(t + 1)$
29. $(p + 4)/(p - 4)$

31. $x^2/(x - 1)$      33. $-1/x(x + h)$      35. $(1 - x^2)/2$

37. (a) 8, (b) $\frac{2}{5}$      39. 37.5 mph

41. $\dfrac{2}{\dfrac{1}{a} + \dfrac{1}{b}} = \dfrac{2}{\dfrac{1}{a} + \dfrac{1}{b}} \cdot \dfrac{ab}{ab} = \dfrac{2ab}{b + a}$      43. $\frac{8}{5}$

45. 28.08      47. $(x + 2)/(x - 1)$      49. No solution

## Problem Set 7.6

1. 15    3. 8    5. $-1$    7. 12    9. $\frac{1}{6}$    11. 1

13. $\frac{2}{5}$    15. $-7$    17. 7    19. 2    21. 4    23. $-1$

25. 6    27. 4    29. $-\frac{1}{2}$    31. No solution    33. 2    35. $\frac{1}{2}$

37. 1    39. 1.7    41. $x = (a^2 + ab)/2b$

## Problem Set 7.7

1. 3 ohms    3. 120 ohms    5. $\frac{3}{7}$    7. $\frac{4}{9}$    9. $1\frac{1}{5}$ hr

11. $3\frac{3}{5}$ hr    13. $7\frac{1}{2}$ min    15. 30 mph and 40 mph    17. $1\frac{1}{3}$ mph

19. 56 and 57    21. 224.7 days    23. 280 mi

## Problem Set 7.8

1. $\frac{1}{5}$    3. $\frac{5}{1}$    5. $\frac{2}{3}$    7. $\frac{3}{7}$    9. $\frac{9}{5}$    11. $\frac{5}{8}$

13. $\frac{1}{6}$    15. $\frac{15}{4}$    17. $\frac{12}{25}$    19. $\pi$    21. $\frac{78}{95}$

23. $x/16 = 3/4,\ x = 12$    25. $5/7 = 20/x,\ x = 28$    27. $3/5 = x/4,\ x = 12/5$

29. $12/x = 8/2,\ x = 3$    31. $x/(x + 3) = 42/48,\ x = 21$    33. 48 ft

35. 1170 boys    37. $7\frac{1}{2}$ in.    39. 18 bulbs    41. 5.7 ft

43. 13 mi    45. 750 envelopes    47. \$2550 and \$3570    49. 465 deer

51. (a) $x = 11{,}361$, (b) $x = 0.2755$    53. $(1 + \sqrt{5})/2 \approx 1.618,\ \frac{8}{5} = 1.6$

55. $12\frac{1}{2}$ in. by $17\frac{1}{2}$ in.

## Chapter Review

1. T   2. T   3. F   4. T   5. F   6. T
7. T   8. F   9. T   10. T   11. T   12. T
13. F   14. F   15. F   16. F   17. T   18. F
19. T   20. T   21. Rational expression
22. Complex fraction   23. $2/(1/x + 1/y)$   24. Proportion
25. $x + 1$ and 3, $x$ and 4   26. $x = 6$   27. No value
28. $r = \frac{2}{3}, r = -1$   29. $-\frac{17}{3}$   30. $(x - 2)/(x - 3)$
31. $-5$   32. $(p + q)/(p - q)$   33. $5m/(6m - 5n)$
34. $5k^3$   35. $3c^2 - 24c + 36$   36. $m(m - 1)^2(m + 1)$
37. $14(r + 3s)(r - 4s)$   38. $3/5a$   39. $(x^2 + xy - y^2)/x^2y^2$
40. $3x/(x - 2)(x + 1)$   41. $(-y - 8)/(y - 4)(y + 4)$   42. $a/2$
43. $4(x + 5)/(x + 3)$   44. $\frac{5}{2}$   45. $b(a - b)/(a + b)$
46. $(x^2 + 17x - 17)/(x + 17)$   47. $2/(m + 2)^2(m + 3)$   48. $(k + 3)/(k + 5)$
49. $5/2(y + 3)$   50. $4/(x + 8)(x + 4)$
51. $-c(c + d)(c + 1)/(c - d)(c - 2)$
52. $\frac{1}{25}$   53. $x/y$   54. $(r + 5)/(r + 2)$   55. $x^2/(x + 1)$
56. $\frac{3}{7}$   57. $-8$   58. $\frac{34}{5}$   59. $\frac{13}{3}$
60. No solution   61. 31   62. $\frac{48}{5}$
63. (a) $x/5 = 12/18, x = 10/3$; (b) $x/(x + 1) = 48/64, x = 3$   64. $-8/x(x + h)$
65. 0.004   66. $\frac{1}{3}$, 3   67. 9 mph   68. 72 ohms
69. $\frac{13}{19}$   70. $3\frac{3}{7}$ hr   71. 549 girls   72. $3710 and $4770
73. $2\frac{4}{7}$ mph   74. $70\frac{1}{2}$ ft

## 8  CHAPTER EIGHT

## Problem Set 8.1

1.

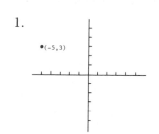

3.

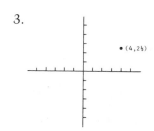

5.

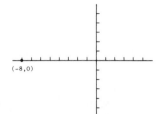

(−8,0)

7.

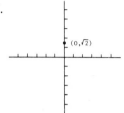

$(0, \sqrt{2})$

9. $A(5, 2)$, $B(2, -3)$, $C(-3, 2)$, $D(-1, -1)$, $E(-5, 0)$, $F(0, 4)$, $G(0, 0)$, $H(2, 5)$
11. (a) IV, (b) III, (c) I or IV or it is on the positive $x$-axis, (d) III or IV or it is on the negative $y$-axis

13 to 25.

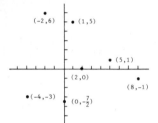

27 to 31.

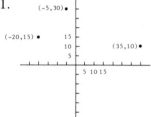

33 to 37.

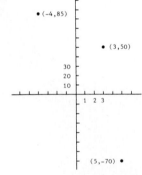

39. (a)

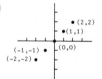

(b) Infinite number    (c)

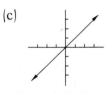

41. (a)

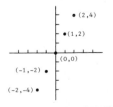

(b) Infinite number    (c)

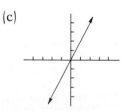

43.

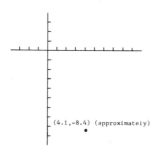

(4.1,-8.4) (approximately)

45. 9.1

47. (a) $P(6) = \frac{5}{36}$, (b) $P(n < 6) = \frac{5}{18}$, (c) $P(16) = 0$, (d) $P(1 < n < 13) = 1$, (e) 7, (f) 2 or 12, (g) 216 outcomes

## *Problem Set 8.2*

1. (a) Linear, (b) Not linear, (c) Not linear, (d) Linear, (e) Not linear
3. (a) Yes, (b) No, (c) Yes, (d) Yes, (e) Yes
5. (a) Yes, (b) Yes, (c) No, (d) Yes, (e) Yes
7. (a) Yes, (b) No, (c) Yes, (d) No, (e) Yes
9. (a) $(0, 1)$, (b) $(1, 6)$, (c) $(3, 16)$, (d) $(-2, -9)$, (e) $(\frac{1}{5}, 2)$
11. (a) $(0, 10)$, (b) $(1, 12)$, (c) $(4, 18)$, (d) $(-5, 0)$, (e) $(\frac{1}{2}, 11)$
13. (a) $(0, 0)$, (b) $(-2, 6)$, (c) $(4, -12)$, (d) $(\frac{1}{3}, -1)$, (e) $(-\frac{2}{3}, 2)$

15.

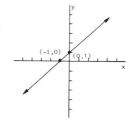

17.

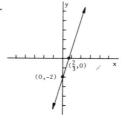

19.

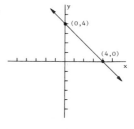

21.

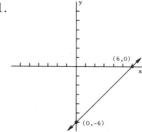

23.

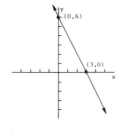

25.

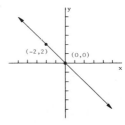

27.
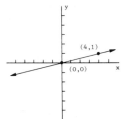

29.
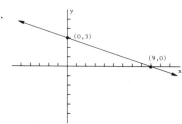

31.
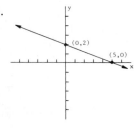

33.
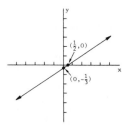

35.
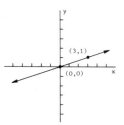

37.
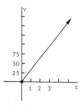

39.
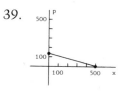

41. $C = 2x + 20$
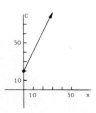

43. $20x + 30y = 600$

45. $y = x$

47. $t = 2s$

49. Yes

51.
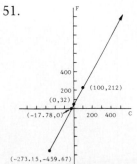

53. $d = 15t$
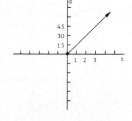

## *Problem Set 8.3*

1. (a) (0, 4), (1, 4), (2, 4), (3, 4), (4, 4); (b) Infinite number;
   (c)

3. (a) (−2, 0), (−2, 1), (−2, 2), (−2, 3), (−2, 4); (b) Infinite number;
   (c)
   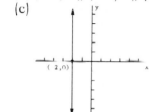

5. (a) (0, 0), (1, 0), (2, 0), (3, 0), (4, 0); (b) Infinite number;
   (c)

7.

9.

11.

13.

15.
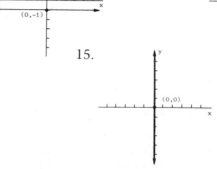

17.
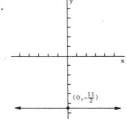

19.
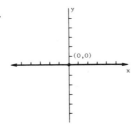

21.
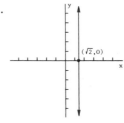

23. $y = 1$     25. $x = -2$     27. $(4, -3)$

29.
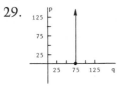

31.
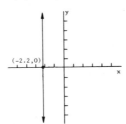

33.
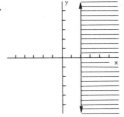

## Problem Set 8.4

1. (a) $(4, 0)$, $(5, 0)$, $(4, 1)$, $(5, 1)$, $(4, 3)$;
   (b)
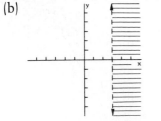

3. (a) $(0, -2)$, $(0, -3)$, $(0, -4)$, $(0, -5)$, $(10, -2)$;
   (b)

5. (a) $(1, 0)$, $(0, 1)$, $(2, 0)$, $(0, 2)$, $(1, 1)$;
   (b)
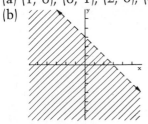

7.
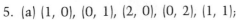

9.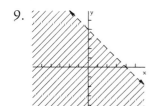

11.

13.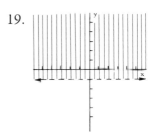

15.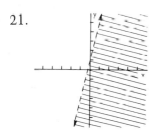

17.

19.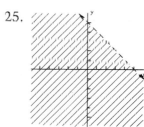

21.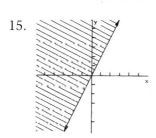

23.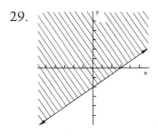

25.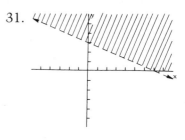

27.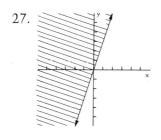

29.

31.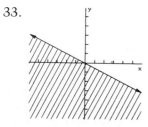

33.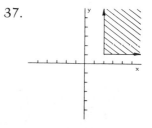

35. $x > 0$

37.

39. $4x + 5y \geqslant 12$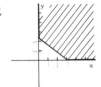

41.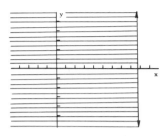

43.

45.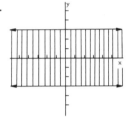

## Chapter Review

| | | | | | |
|---|---|---|---|---|---|
| 1. T | 2. T | 3. T | 4. T | 5. T | 6. T |
| 7. T | 8. F | 9. F | 10. T | 11. T | 12. T |
| 13. T | 14. F | 15. F | 16. T | 17. F | 18. T |
| 19. T | 20. T | 21. T | 22. F | 23. T | 24. Origin |

25. Quadrants

26. Coordinates

27. $A(0, 0)$, $B(3, 10)$, $C(3, -15)$

28.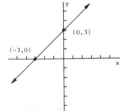

29.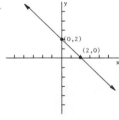

30.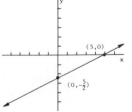

31.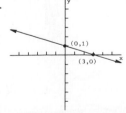

32.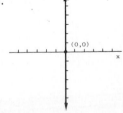

33.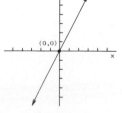

34.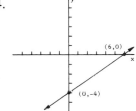

35.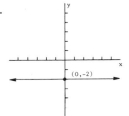

36.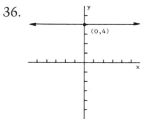

37.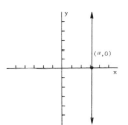

38.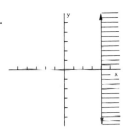

39.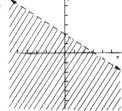

40.

41.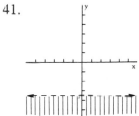

42.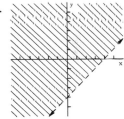

43.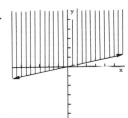

44. $y = -2$

45. $t = s + 1$

46.

47.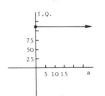

48. $100x + 150y \leq 300$

49.  $C = 0.50x + 10$

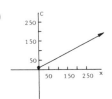

50.

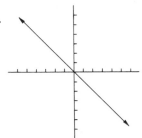

51.

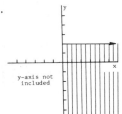

y-axis not
included

52.

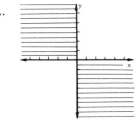

9  **CHAPTER NINE**

**Problem Set 9.1**

1.

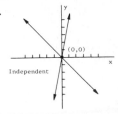

(3,1)

Independent

3.

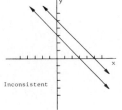

Inconsistent

5.

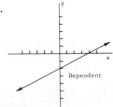

Dependent

7.

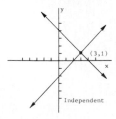

(0,0)

Independent

9.

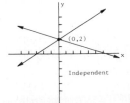

(0,2)

Independent

11.

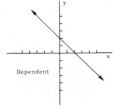

Dependent

13.

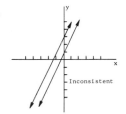

Inconsistent

15.

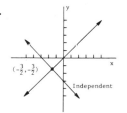

$(-\frac{3}{2}, -\frac{3}{2})$

Independent

17.

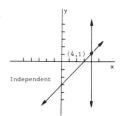

$(4, 1)$

Independent

23. $(4.4, 6.5)$ is a solution.

19.

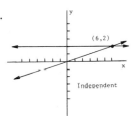

$(6, 2)$

Independent

21.

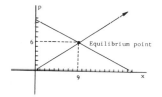

6

Equilibrium point

9

25.

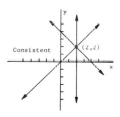

Consistent

$(2, 2)$

## Problem Set 9.2

1. $(3, 0)$     3. $(4, 1)$     5. $(1, -3)$     7. $(-1, 1)$     9. $(7, 2)$
11. $(2, 0)$     13. $(\frac{8}{5}, -\frac{6}{5})$     15. $(\frac{1}{2}, \frac{1}{2})$     17. $(-3, 6)$     19. $(\frac{1}{2}, -8)$
21. $(\frac{1}{7}, \frac{4}{7})$     23. $(0, 0)$     25. $(0, \frac{2}{3})$     27. $(-\frac{57}{16}, \frac{21}{8})$     29. $p = 39, q = 73$
31. $(604, 135)$
33. Dependent system. Solution consists of all ordered pairs $(x, y)$ on the line $4x - 5y = 8$.
35. $(\frac{7}{2}, -\frac{3}{2})$

## Problem Set 9.3

1. $(3, 1)$     3. $(3, 2)$     5. $(5, -3)$     7. $(-2, 6)$     9. $(5, 2)$
11. $(-\frac{1}{3}, 3)$     13. $(-3, 1)$     15. $(\frac{1}{2}, \frac{1}{3})$     17. $(-\frac{5}{2}, 2)$     19. $(-6, \frac{11}{8})$

21. $(\frac{11}{5}, \frac{1}{2})$     23. $(-4, 0)$     25. $(1, 1)$     27. $(-2, 5)$     29. $(9, -8)$
31. $(0, 1)$     33. $(-6, 0)$     35. $(11, 15)$     37. $x = 26, y = 16$     39. $(0.10, 0.30)$
41. Inconsistent system. No solution.     43. $(\frac{3}{4}, \frac{3}{2})$

## Problem Set 9.4

1. 22 and 41                          3. 26 and 28                    5. 73 and 75
7. 7 and 51                           9. 5 oz of A and 3 oz of B
11. $27,000                          13. $1350 and $2650     15. 9 ft and 15 ft
17. 17 nickels and 11 dimes      19. 29 dimes and 8 quarters
21. 14 lb of $.85 nuts and 6 lb of $1.35 nuts
23. 25 gal of 20% solution and 75 gal of 60% solution
25. $18,000 at 5% and $7000 at 7%
27. Alberto travels 3 mi and Rosie 4 mi
29. 42 mph and 57 mph       31. 8.8 oz of A and 4.4 oz of B       33. 83

## Problem Set 9.5

1. 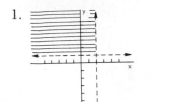     3. 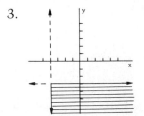     5.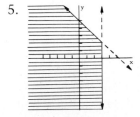

7. 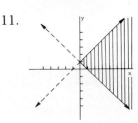     9. 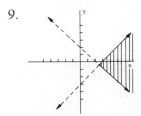     11.

41. $(-0.069, 0.213)$ is a solution.     43.       45.

## Chapter Review

1. T                2. T                3. F                4. T
5. F                6. F                7. F                8. T
9. Inconsistent     10. Dependent       11. Independent

12. 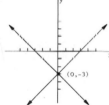                13.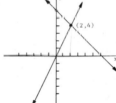

14. $(-2, 5)$           15. $(1, \frac{9}{2})$           16. $(1, -1)$           17. No solution
18. $(-21, 4)$          19. $(\frac{32}{3}, -\frac{23}{6})$           20. $(-51, -85)$

21. 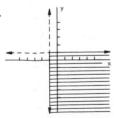                22. 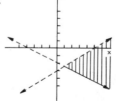                23.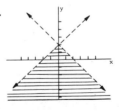

24. 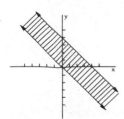           25. $(2, 8)$      26. 37 and 39        27. 38 and 96

28. 40 gal of 25% solution and 10 gal of 75% solution

13.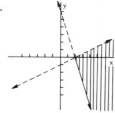

15.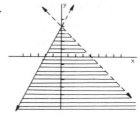

17.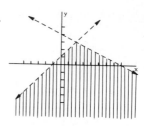

19.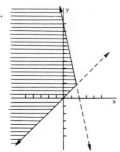

21.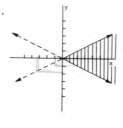

23.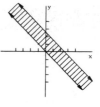

25.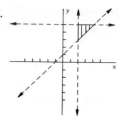

27.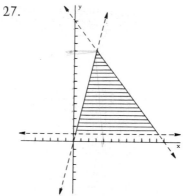

29.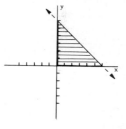

31. No graph

33. $x \geqslant 2$
    $y \leqslant -1$

35. $t \leqslant s$
    $t \geqslant 0$
    $s < 3$

37.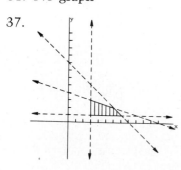

39. $x + 2y < 8$
    $x < \frac{2}{3}y$
    $x \geqslant 0$
    $y \geqslant 0$

29. 5 oz of A and 4 oz of B

30. $2x + 5y \leqslant 30$
$4x \leqslant 20$
$x \geqslant 0$
$y \geqslant 0$

31. 40 mph and 60 mph

32.     $t \geqslant s$
$0 \leqslant s \leqslant 4$
$t < 5$

# *10*  CHAPTER TEN

## *Problem Set 10.1*

1. 6      3. $-9$      5. $\pm 8$      7. 1      9. $-12$
11. $\frac{2}{11}$      13. $\frac{3}{4}$      15. 0.1      17. 0.06      19. 1.3
21. Not a real number      23. 5      25. 7      27. $\pm 5$
29. $-2$      31. 2      33. Not a real number      35. 0.1
37. $-4$      39. 8      41. 2      43. 5      45. $x$
47. $-x$      49. $x^2$      51. $2x^3$      53. $5xy^4$      55. $s^2t^2$
57. $3a^4b$      59. $x + y$      61. $y + 2$
63. $\sqrt{16} + \sqrt{9} = 7$, but $\sqrt{16 + 9} = 5$. Conclusion: $\sqrt{a + b} \neq \sqrt{a} + \sqrt{b}$
65. $\sqrt{289} - \sqrt{225} = 2$, but $\sqrt{289 - 225} = 8$. Conclusion: $\sqrt{a - b} \neq \sqrt{a} - \sqrt{b}$
67. (a) 0.5 sec, (b) 1 sec, (c) 2.5 sec
69. $\pi/2$ sec    71. 147.431      73. 4.451
75. (a) Approximately 5 hr, (b) 4.2 yr        77. $r^{k+1}$

## *Problem Set 10.2*

1. $2\sqrt{3}$      3. $3\sqrt{5}$      5. $20\sqrt{2}$      7. $-10\sqrt{2}$
9. $\pm 4\sqrt{10}$      11. $2x^2\sqrt{7}$      13. $12x\sqrt{15y}$      15. $2\sqrt[3]{6}$

17. $x\sqrt[3]{3}$

19. $3\sqrt[4]{5}$

21. $-12\sqrt{5}$

23. $60\sqrt{30}$

25. $5a^2\sqrt{3a}$

27. $xy^3\sqrt[3]{x^2}$

29. $6a^4b\sqrt{3b}$

31. $(a + 8)\sqrt{a + 8}$

33. $90x^6y^3\sqrt{x}$

35. $s\sqrt{t - s}$

37. 11

39. $15\sqrt{2}$

41. 5

43. $2\sqrt{15}$

45. $11\sqrt{14}$

47. $5\sqrt{5}$

49. $3x + 1$

51. $60\sqrt{3}$

53. $2\sqrt[3]{25}$

55. $2\sqrt[4]{15}$

57. $a^3\sqrt{5}$

59. $42x^4y^2\sqrt{2xy}$

61. $t(r + s)$

63. $10\sqrt{6} \approx 24.49$

65. $100\sqrt{13} \approx 360.6$

67. $5\sqrt{70} \approx 41.83$

69. $40\sqrt{3} \approx 69.28$

71. $6\sqrt{33} \approx 34.47$

73. $2\sqrt{34}$ cm

75. $80\sqrt{2}$ volts

77. $\sqrt{1369 \cdot 2209} = \sqrt{3{,}024{,}121} = 1739 = 37 \cdot 47 = \sqrt{1369} \cdot \sqrt{2209}$

79. $x^{k+1}\sqrt{x}$

81. $s = \frac{1}{2}(x + x + x) = 3x/2$. Therefore, $A = \sqrt{s(s - a)(s - b)(s - c)}$

$$= \sqrt{\frac{3x}{2}\left(\frac{3x}{2} - x\right)\left(\frac{3x}{2} - x\right)\left(\frac{3x}{2} - x\right)}$$

$$= \sqrt{\frac{3x^4}{16}}$$

$$= \frac{x^2}{4}\sqrt{3}.$$

## Problem Set 10.3

1. $\frac{1}{3}$

3. $\frac{2}{5}$

5. $\pm\frac{11}{6}$

7. $\sqrt{5}/4$

9. $\sqrt{3}/7$

11. $\frac{1}{4}$

13. $\frac{2}{3}$

15. $xy^2\sqrt{3y}/5$

17. $2\sqrt{3}/5$

19. $5\sqrt{2}/3$

21. $2y\sqrt[3]{4y}/5$

23. $2\sqrt{7}/3$

25. $\pm 4\sqrt{2}/15$

27. $\dfrac{r\sqrt{r}}{st^3}$

29. 2

31. 12

33. 10

35. $\sqrt{3}$

37. $5\sqrt{10}$

39. $2\sqrt{2}$

41. $13x^2y^2$

43. 2

45. $x\sqrt[3]{5}$

47. $\dfrac{3\sqrt{a}}{b}$

49. $\dfrac{\sqrt{3}}{3} \approx 0.577$

51. $\dfrac{2\sqrt{7}}{7} \approx 0.756$

53. $5\sqrt{2} \approx 7.07$

55. $\dfrac{\sqrt{10}}{2} \approx 1.58$

57. $\dfrac{\sqrt{6}}{3} \approx 0.816$

59. $\dfrac{\sqrt{10}}{10} \approx 0.316$

61. $(\pi/2)\sqrt{3}$ sec

63. $3\sqrt{47}/94$ amps

65. $\sqrt{\dfrac{a}{b}} = \sqrt{\dfrac{7056}{3136}} = \sqrt{2.25} = 1.5 = \dfrac{84}{56} = \dfrac{\sqrt{7056}}{\sqrt{3136}}$

67. $\dfrac{x^{n+1}}{y^{n}}$

69. $t_m = t_s\sqrt{1 - \dfrac{v^2}{c^2}} = t_s\sqrt{\dfrac{c^2 - v^2}{c^2}} = \dfrac{t_s\sqrt{c^2 - v^2}}{c}$

## Problem Set 10.4

1. $7\sqrt{5}$

3. $12\sqrt{2}$

5. $5\sqrt{19}$

7. $13\sqrt{3}$

9. Cannot be simplified

11. $-2\sqrt{2}$

13. $5\sqrt{2} - 4\sqrt{3}$

15. Cannot be simplified

17. $6\sqrt{13x}$

19. $12\sqrt[3]{9y}$

21. $3\sqrt{17}/4$

23. $4\sqrt{x} + 2y$

25. $6\sqrt{2}$

27. $5\sqrt{2}$

29. $8\sqrt{3y}$

31. $7\sqrt{5}$

33. $3\sqrt{7r}$

35. $23\sqrt[3]{3}$

37. $\dfrac{7\sqrt{2}}{3}$

39. $5a\sqrt{5ab}$

41. $9\sqrt{s}$

43. $11\sqrt{5}/5$

45. $7\sqrt{6}/3$

47. $4\sqrt{3} + 4$

49. $20\sqrt{5} - 10$

51. $21\sqrt{11} + 7\sqrt{15}$

53. $\sqrt{6} + 2$

55. $2\sqrt{10} - 50$

57. $x + x\sqrt{y}$

59. $t^2 - 5$

61. $5 + 2\sqrt{6}$

63. $13 + 2\sqrt{10}$

65. $10c + 30\sqrt{2c} + 45$

67. $2 + \sqrt[3]{12}$

69. $2 + \sqrt{3}$

71. $(\sqrt{7} - 2)/3$

73. $(\sqrt{x} + \sqrt{y})/(x - y)$

75. $1 + \sqrt{5}$

77. $1 + \sqrt{3}$

79. $4 + \sqrt{15}$

81. $1/(\sqrt{t} + 2)$

83. $(-5 \pm \sqrt{17})/2$

85. $(3 \pm \sqrt{15})/2$

87. $(-4 \pm \sqrt{-4})/2$, which are not real numbers

89. $\dfrac{\sqrt{7} - 2}{3} \approx 0.21525$

91. $x - y$

## Problem Set 10.5

1. 16

3. 5

5. 6

7. No solution

9. $-3$

11. No solution

13. 54

15. $\frac{16}{9}$

17. 8

19. No solution

21. 7

23. $\frac{2}{7}$

25. $-\frac{7}{2}$

27. $\frac{1}{3}$

29. $-\frac{7}{9}$

31. 3

33. 49

35. $-\frac{4}{3}$

37. $32/\pi^2$ ft

39. $W = 18{,}000$ watts

41. 38

43. $A = \pi r^2$

45. 4.03

47. $\frac{13}{2}$

49. The 12th floor

## Problem Set 10.6

1. 9
3. 27
5. 27
7. 10
9. 2
11. $-2$
13. 2
15. 1024
17. $-2$
19. Not a real number
21. 1
23. 625
25. 16
27. $-1$
29. $x$
31. $2ab^2\sqrt{3}$
33. $\frac{1}{8}$
35. $\frac{1}{5}$
37. $\frac{1}{3}$
39. $\frac{1}{243}$
41. $\frac{1}{27}$
43. $-\frac{1}{2}$
45. $\frac{1}{25}$
47. $1/x$
49. $1/\sqrt{2}$
51. $1/5\sqrt{5}$
53. $1/3\sqrt{5}$
55. $1/3a^2b^4$
57. $\frac{9}{4}$
59. $\frac{7}{10}$
61. $\sqrt[3]{x^2}$
63. $\sqrt{x^2+1}$
65. $1/\sqrt[5]{(5p-3)^3}$
67. $\sqrt[3]{3pq^2}$
69. $x^{1/4}$
71. $y^{3/2}$
73. $(a-4)^{1/2}$
75. $(13ab^2)^{1/3}$
77. (a) $100\sqrt{2}$ g, (b) 100 g, (c) $50\sqrt{2}$ g
79. (a) $R = 100$, (b) $R = 21.6$

81. (a) 5.62, (b) 0.01
83. $\dfrac{1}{((x+(x+x^{1/2})^{1/3})^{1/4}}$
85. $50\sqrt[3]{4}$ g

## Problem Set 10.7

1. $x$
3. $x^2$
5. $x^{7/12}$
7. $x^3$
9. 1
11. $(r-7)^{7/6}$
13. $x$
15. $x^{1/2}$
17. $(x+2)^2$
19. $a^3$
21. $a^8$
23. $a^{1/6}$
25. $\sqrt{5}$
27. $\sqrt{7}$
29. $-4p^2$
31. $a^3b^2$
33. $3ab$
35. $a/b^2$
37. $a^6/b^9$
39. $yz^3$
41. $x^4y^6/z^2$
43. $y^5/x^2z^3$
45. $p^6/rq^3$
47. $2m^{5/3}$
49. $b^{3/2}/a^{13}$
51. $X^{5/2}$
53. (a) 480 widgets, (b) $480\sqrt[3]{10}$ widgets
55. $p^{1961}/q^{893}$
57. $x^{2/3}$
59. $\sqrt[6]{a^5}$

## Chapter Review

1. T
2. T
3. F
4. T
5. F
6. F
7. T
8. T
9. T
10. T
11. T
12. T
13. T
14. F
15. T
16. $b^n = a$, principal, index, radicand, radical sign
17. Conjugates
18. $\pm 1.1$
19. 3
20. 5

21. 2001

22. 9

23. $x^6$

24. $4x^2y^3$

25. $2s^2t^3$

26. $a + 3$

27. $12\sqrt{5}$

28. $3\sqrt[3]{3x}$

29. $-20xy\sqrt{2x}$

30. $(p + q)^2\sqrt{p + q}$

31. $54s^4t^4\sqrt{st}$

32. $a^3\sqrt{b - a}$

33. $4\sqrt{2}$

34. $210\sqrt{6}$

35. $r^4\sqrt{15}$

36. $4x + 10$

37. $6\sqrt[3]{5}$

38. $\pm\sqrt{13}/9$

39. $3\sqrt{3}$

40. $-6\sqrt{3}/7$

41. $5a^2b\sqrt{3b}/14$

42. $12x$

43. $14\sqrt[4]{3}$

44. $3st^2\sqrt[3]{s}$

45. $7\sqrt{5}$

46. $8\sqrt{2} - 4\sqrt{5}$

47. $4\sqrt[3]{5r}$

48. $\sqrt{11}/3$

49. $9\sqrt{s}/4$

50. $11 - 3\sqrt{55}$

51. $\sqrt[3]{20} - 5$

52. $1 + 2\sqrt{y} + y$

53. $\sqrt{35}/5$

54. $2\sqrt{13}/13$

55. $3(3 - \sqrt{5})/2$

56. $(x + \sqrt{xy})/(x - y)$

57. 2

58. 512

59. 9

60. $\frac{1}{32}$

61. $-1$

62. $1/6\sqrt{6}$

63. $\frac{5}{6}$

64. $x\sqrt[3]{x}$

65. $1/\sqrt[3]{2p - q}$

66. $y^{3/4}$

67. $(q^2 + 1)^{1/3}$

68. $-1 + \sqrt{5}$

69. $\frac{1}{4}$

70. 1

71. $x^{1/3}$

72. $x - 3$

73. $16p^2$

74. $9a^2b$

75. $x^4/y^3z$

76. $2p^2q^3$

77. $2ab^2\sqrt{5}$

78. $1/m^2n^{4/3}$

79. $10\sqrt{23} \approx 47.96$

80. $2\sqrt{3} \approx 3.464$

81. $\frac{5}{2}$

82. No solution

83. 4

84. 4

85. $(3 \pm \sqrt{5})/8$

86. $\frac{7}{2}$ m

87. Diameter $= 20\sqrt{7/\pi}$ ft

88. $90\sqrt{2}$ volts

89. 100 ft

90. $72/\pi^2$ ft

91. (a) $250\sqrt[3]{4}$ g, (b) $250\sqrt{2}$ g, (c) 250 g, (d) $125\sqrt{2}$ g

92. (a) 720 widgets, (b) $192\sqrt[3]{4}$ widgets

# 11   CHAPTER ELEVEN

## Problem Set 11.1

1. $a = 2, b = 9, c = 4$

3. $a = 1, b = -4, c = 4$

5. $a = 1, b = -1, c = 0$

7. $a = 9, b = 0, c = -25$

9. $a = 4, b = 0, c = -1$

11. $a = 1, b = -5, c = 5$

13. 1, 3         15. $-2, -3$      17. 2, 4         19. $-6, 2$
21. 2            23. 3, $-\frac{7}{2}$      25. $\frac{1}{3}, -\frac{1}{2}$      27. $-\frac{5}{2}$
29. 0, $-5$      31. 0, 8          33. 4, $-4$      35. 3, $-3$
37. $\frac{5}{2}, -\frac{5}{2}$      39. $\frac{5}{3}, -\frac{1}{2}$      41. 9, $-6$       43. $\frac{5}{4}, -\frac{8}{9}$
45. 0, 1, 2      47. 0, $-2, -3$   49. 0, $\frac{1}{2}, -5$      51. 0, $\frac{1}{2}, -\frac{1}{2}$
53. 0, 3, 4      55. 0, 10, $-10$   57. 1, 2         59. 4 sec
61. 0 or 5       63. No solution   65. $x = 0$ or $x = 2a$      67. 0, 853
69. 2            71. 2, 3, $\frac{5}{2}$

## Problem Set 11.2

1. 2, $-3$          3. $-2, -3$        5. 5             7. $\frac{2}{3}, -\frac{1}{2}$
9. 4, $-3$         11. $-\frac{2}{5}$        13. $-2, -4$       15. 0, 8
17. 0, $-\frac{1}{9}$       19. 9, $-9$        21. $\frac{1}{6}, -\frac{1}{6}$        23. 0, $\frac{2}{3}$
25. 2, $-\frac{3}{2}$       27. 8, $-8$        29. 11, $-11$      31. $\frac{1}{3}, -\frac{1}{3}$
33. $\frac{2}{5}, -\frac{2}{5}$       35. $\frac{10}{9}, -\frac{10}{9}$      37. $\sqrt{7}, -\sqrt{7}$      39. $\sqrt{11}, -\sqrt{11}$
41. $\sqrt{3}/2, -\sqrt{3}/2$      43. $2\sqrt{3}, -2\sqrt{3}$      45. No real solution
47. 3, $-5$        49. $-1 + \sqrt{3}, -1 - \sqrt{3}$        51. 8, $-2$
53. $3 + \sqrt{11}, 3 - \sqrt{11}$         55. $2 + 5\sqrt{2}, 2 - 5\sqrt{2}$
57. No real solution         59. $a + \sqrt{b}$ and $a - \sqrt{b}$ if $b \geqslant 0$
61. 4 ft/sec       63. 10%           65. 10 sides       67. 4 sec
69. 3 or $\frac{1}{3}$       71. $r = \sqrt{A/\pi}$       73. $v = \sqrt{2K/m}$       75. $a = \pm\sqrt{c^2 - b^2}$
77. 13.04 m        79. 3.34 sec       81. $d = \sqrt{km_1m_2/F}$       83. 4, $\frac{3}{7}$
85. 3, $-3$

## Problem Set 11.3

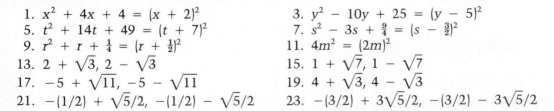

1. $x^2 + 4x + 4 = (x + 2)^2$          3. $y^2 - 10y + 25 = (y - 5)^2$
5. $t^2 + 14t + 49 = (t + 7)^2$          7. $s^2 - 3s + \frac{9}{4} = (s - \frac{3}{2})^2$
9. $r^2 + r + \frac{1}{4} = (r + \frac{1}{2})^2$          11. $4m^2 = (2m)^2$
13. $2 + \sqrt{3}, 2 - \sqrt{3}$          15. $1 + \sqrt{7}, 1 - \sqrt{7}$
17. $-5 + \sqrt{11}, -5 - \sqrt{11}$          19. $4 + \sqrt{3}, 4 - \sqrt{3}$
21. $-(1/2) + \sqrt{5}/2, -(1/2) - \sqrt{5}/2$          23. $-(3/2) + 3\sqrt{5}/2, -(3/2) - 3\sqrt{5}/2$

25. $\frac{1}{2}$, $-\frac{3}{2}$                            27. $5 + 2\sqrt{3}$, $5 - 2\sqrt{3}$

29. $3 + \sqrt{31}/2$, $3 - \sqrt{31}/2$                  31. $1/3 + \sqrt{7}/3$, $1/3 - \sqrt{7}/3$

33. No real solution

35. At $t = 3 - \sqrt{5} \approx 0.76$ sec and at $t = 3 + \sqrt{5} \approx 5.24$ sec

37. $s = (1 + \sqrt{13})/2$ or $s = (1 - \sqrt{13})/2$

39. $x^2 + 5798x + 8{,}404{,}201 = (x + 2899)^2$

41. $x^2 + 4x - 12 - 0$                    43. $x^2 - 4x = 0$

## Problem Set 11.4

1. $-1$, $-3$          3.  2, 1          5. $-3$, $\frac{1}{3}$        7. 5

9. 0, 5                  11. 0, $\frac{1}{9}$          13. $\frac{5}{2}$, $-\frac{5}{2}$

15. $(-1 + \sqrt{13})/2$, $(-1 - \sqrt{13})/2$        17. $(3 + \sqrt{5})/2$, $(3 - \sqrt{5})/2$

19. $(-3 + \sqrt{17})/4$, $(-3 - \sqrt{17})/4$        21. $1 + \sqrt{2}$, $1 - \sqrt{2}$

23. $(-3 + \sqrt{3})/3$, $(-3 - \sqrt{3})/3$        25. $1 + \sqrt{7}$, $1 - \sqrt{7}$

27. $6 + \sqrt{11}$, $6 - \sqrt{11}$                29. No real solution

31. No real solution                      33. $2 + \sqrt{5}$, $2 - \sqrt{5}$

35. $(-2 + \sqrt{7})/3$, $(-2 - \sqrt{7})/3$        37. No real solution

39. $(1 + \sqrt{3})/3$, $(1 - \sqrt{3})/3$        41. $\sqrt{3}/2$, $-\sqrt{3}$

43. (a) At $t = (2 - \sqrt{3})/2 \approx 0.13$ sec and at $t = (2 + \sqrt{3})/2 \approx 1.87$ sec; (b) Never

45. $p = (5 + \sqrt{21})/2$ or $p = (5 - \sqrt{21})/2$

47. 2.1, $-0.8$                              49. $x = (1 + \sqrt{5})/2$

## Problem Set 11.5

1. 5 and 7              3. 11 and 12          5. 11 and 13        7. 10 and 11

9. 6 in. by 11 in.      11. 10 m by 26 m      13. 1 ft            15. 14 in. by 14 in.

17. $x = 3 - \sqrt{5} \approx 0.76$ in. or $x = 3 + \sqrt{5} \approx 5.24$ in.

19. $(5 + \sqrt{17})/2 \approx 4.56$ hr, $(3 + \sqrt{17})/2 \approx 3.56$ hr

21. 50 mph              23. (20, 0.75)            25. 1.85 and 7.74      27. $3\sqrt{2} \approx 4.24$ in.

## *Problem Set 11.6*

1.
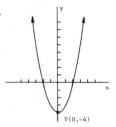

3.
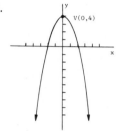

5.
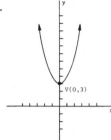

7.
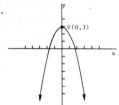

9.
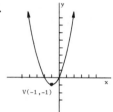

11.
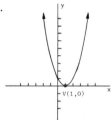

13.
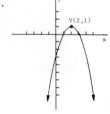

15.
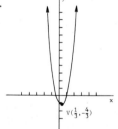

17.
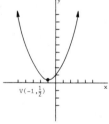

19.
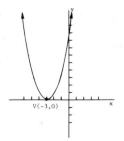

21.
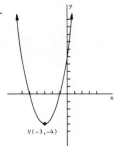

23.
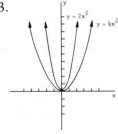

25.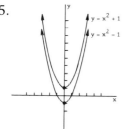

27.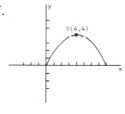

29. $A = s^2, s \geq 0$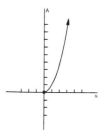

31.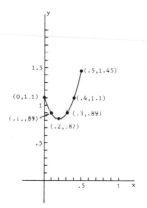

33. $x = \dfrac{1}{2}\left( \dfrac{-b + \sqrt{b^2 - 4ac}}{2a} \quad | \quad \dfrac{-b - \sqrt{b^2 - 4ac}}{2a} \right) = \dfrac{1}{2}\left( \dfrac{-2b}{2a} \right) = \dfrac{-b}{2a}$

## Chapter Review

1. T
2. F
3. T
4. Quadratic, second-degree, standard
5. $a = 0, b = 0$
6. Two
7. Factoring, extraction of roots, completing the square, quadratic formula
8. Parabola, up, down, vertex, vertex, axis of symmetry
9. $a = 2, b = -1, c = 12$
10. $a = 3, b = 0, c = -20$
11. $y^2 - 16y + 64 = (y - 8)^2$
12. $t^2 + 5t + \frac{25}{4} = (t + \frac{5}{2})^2$
13. $-5$
14. $\frac{1}{5}, -4$
15. $\frac{7}{3}, -\frac{7}{3}$
16. 0, 5
17. 10, $-10$
18. $3\sqrt{2}, -3\sqrt{2}$

19. No real solution
20. $4, -20$
21. $3 + \sqrt{6}, 3 - \sqrt{6}$
22. $(-1 + \sqrt{3})/2, (-1 - \sqrt{3})/2$
23. $(-3 + \sqrt{13})/2, (-3 - \sqrt{13})/2$
24. $2 + 2\sqrt{2}, 2 - 2\sqrt{2}$
25. $(3 - \sqrt{3})/4, (-3 - \sqrt{3})/4$
26. $0, 4, -4$
27. $0, \frac{3}{4}, -\frac{8}{9}$
28. $0, (2 + \sqrt{6})/2, (2 - \sqrt{6})/2$

29.

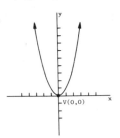

30.

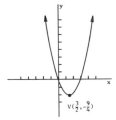

31.

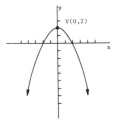

32.

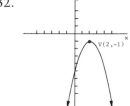

33. $(16, 0.75)$
34. $x = 5a/4$ or $x = -3a$
35. No real solution
36. $r = \sqrt{S/4\pi}$
37. 10%
38. 1 or 4
39. $7 + \sqrt{37} \approx 13.08$ hr   and   $5 + \sqrt{37} \approx 11.08$ hr
40. 40 mph
41. (a) 5 sec, (b) Never
42. 56 ft

## *12*  CHAPTER TWELVE

### Problem Set 12.1

1. Yes
3. Yes
5. Yes
7. No
9. No
11. Yes
13. Yes
15. No

17. Yes
19. No
21. Yes
23. Yes
25. Yes
27. No
29. No
31. All real numbers
33. All real numbers
35. All real numbers
37. $x \neq 2$
39. $x \neq 5, -5$
41. $x \neq 8, -8$
43. $x \neq 2, 3$
45. $x \neq 0, 7$
47. $x \geq 0$
49. $x \geq 6$
51. $x \geq 4$
53. $x \geq -3$
55. $x \geq \frac{13}{5}$
57. $x < \frac{3}{2}$
59. All real numbers
61. $y \geq 0$
63. $y \geq 1$
65. All real numbers
67. $y \leq 10$
69. All real numbers
71. $y \geq 100$
73. Yes
75. Yes
77. Yes
79. No
81. No
83. $V = \frac{4}{3}\pi r^3,\ r \geq 0$
85. $d = 16t^2,\ t \geq 0$
87. $E = 100 + 0.15s,\ s \geq 0$
89. $x \geq 63.88$
91. $-3 \leq x \leq 3$
93. (a) $A = \pi r^2$, (b) Quadruples it

## *Problem Set 12.2*

1. 0
3. 16
5. 16
7. $\frac{1}{4}$
9. 5
11. $a^2$
13. $a^2 + 2a + 1$
15. $a^2 + 2ab + b^2$
17. 1
19. 77
21. 85
23. $\frac{7}{4}$
25. $26 - \sqrt{5}$
27. $5a^2 - a + 1$
29. $5a^2 + 9a + 5$
31. $5x^2 + 10xh + 5h^2 - x - h + 1$
33. Undefined
35. $\frac{1}{4}$
37. $-\frac{1}{4}$
39. 2
41. $\sqrt{5}/5$
43. $1/a$
45. $1/(a + 1)$
47. $1/(x - h)$
49. 22
51. 24
53. 42
55. 20
57. 1
59. Undefined
61. 200
63. 73
65. 18
67. 73
69. 2
71. $t + x$
73. $V(0) = 1087$ ft/sec and $V(25) = 1137$ ft/sec are the velocities of sound through air having a temperature of 0°C and 25°C, respectively.
75. $h(t) = -16t^2 + 132t$; $h(2) = 200$ ft and $h(5) = 260$ ft are the heights of the arrow at $t = 2$ sec and $t = 5$ sec, respectively.
77. $C(x) = 8x + 350$; $C(0) = \$350$ and $C(125) = \$1350$ are the costs of producing 0 motors and 125 motors, respectively.
79. (a) $-1.864$, (b) 130,524, (c) 1.669        81. (a) $-5a - 2$, (b) $a^4 + 1$, (c) 48
83. (a) 7, (b) 0, (c) 3, (d) $-3$

## Problem Set 12.3

1. (a) Degree 2, (b) Degree 3, (c) Degree 0, (d) Not a polynomial function, (e) Not a polynomial function, (f) Degree 5
3. $C(30) = 3590$ is the cost of producing 30 units.
5. $f(3) = 7$, $f(0) = 7$, $f(7) = 7$, $f(-1) = 7$, $f(\sqrt{2}) = 7$, $f(\pi) = 7$, $f(a) = 7$, $f(a^2) = 7$, $f(a + 1) = 7$, $f(x + h) = 7$
7. $g(a + b) = 6$, while $g(a) + g(b) = 6 + 6 = 12$.

9. 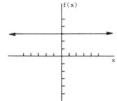   11. 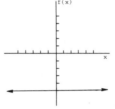   13.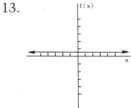

15. 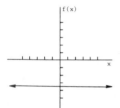   17. 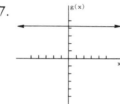   19.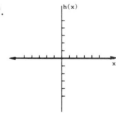

21. No     23. Yes     25. No     27. Yes     29. Yes     31. Yes
33. Yes     35. No     37. No     39. No     41. Yes     43. Yes
45. Yes     47. $-5 \le T \le 15$
49. $P(245) = 337{,}426.75$, $P(249) = 337{,}557.03$, and $P(255) = 337{,}274.25$ are the profits derived from 245 units, 249 units, and 255 units, respectively.
51. $f(0) = 0$, $f(\pi) = 1$, $f(5) = 0$, $f(-\frac{2}{3}) = 0$, $f(\sqrt{2}) = 1$

## Problem Set 12.4

1. 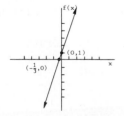   3. 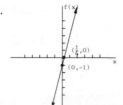   5.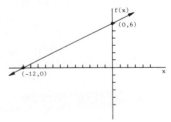

7.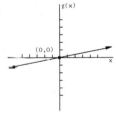

9.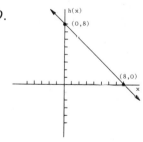

11. $\frac{3}{4}$

13. $-2$

15. $\frac{1}{5}$

17. $-\frac{7}{3}$

19. $\frac{3}{11}$

21. $1/b$

23.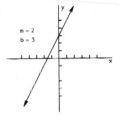

25.

27.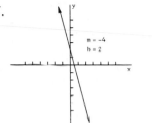

29.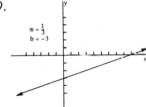

31.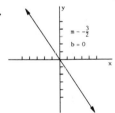

33.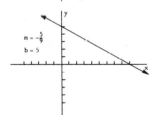

35.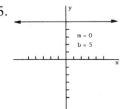

37.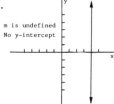

39.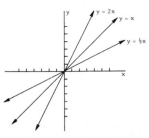

41.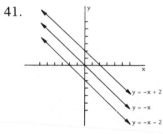

43. $y = 2x - 5$     45. $y = \frac{1}{3}x + \frac{7}{3}$     47. $y = -x - 1$

49. $y = 7$     51. $x = -4$     53. Parallel

55. Perpendicular     57. Neither

59. (a) $y = -\frac{3}{4}x + \frac{3}{7}$, (b) $y = \frac{4}{3}x + \frac{3}{7}$     61. 30 ft

63. $\frac{3}{40} = 0.075 = 7.5\%$     65. $-0.68$

67. $m_1 = (a - 0)/(a - 0) = 1$ and $m_2 = (a - 0)/(0 - a) = -1$, so $m_1 \cdot m_2 = -1$.

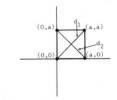

## Problem Set 12.5

1.

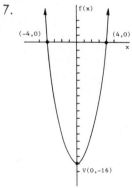

3.

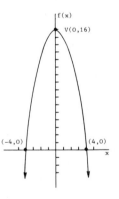

5.

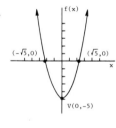

7.

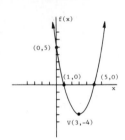

9.

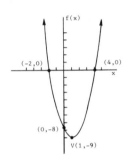

11.

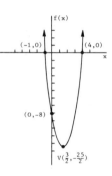

13.

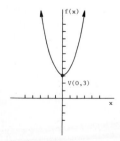

15.

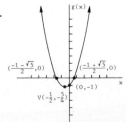

17.

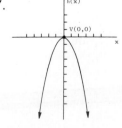

19.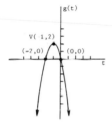

21.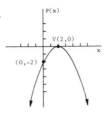

23.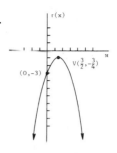

25.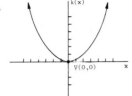

27.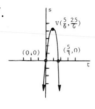

29. $x = \frac{1}{3}$

31. $x = 4$ units, $P(4) = \$1200$      33. 10 ft by 20 ft
35. 194 ft
37. $V(-1.35, -22.5625)$, $y$-intercept is $-20.74$, $x$-intercepts are 3.4 and $-6.1$
39. 78 cents

## Chapter Review

1. T
2. F
3. F
4. T
5. T
6. T
7. F
8. Independent, dependent
9. Function from A to B
10. Domain, range
11. *f of x, x*
12. Constant, horizontal line through $(0, a)$
13. Linear, line
14. Quadratic, parabola, $-b/2a$
15. 3

16. No vertical line intersects the graph at more than one point
17. $y = mx + b$, slope-intercept
18. $m_1 = m_2$, $m_1 \cdot m_2 = -1$
19. (a) Yes, (b) No, (c) Yes
20. (a) $x \neq \frac{2}{3}$, $-5$; (b) $x \geq -\frac{5}{2}$; (c) $x < 1$
21. (a) $y \geq 4$, (b) All real numbers, (c) $h(x) \leq 0$
22. Domain is all reals, range is $0 \leq y \leq 2$
23. (a) $-\frac{5}{3}$, (b) 1, (c) Undefined, (d) 0
24. (a) 6, (b) 18, (c) $\frac{23}{4}$, (d) $t^2 - t + 6$, (e) 12, (f) 14, (g) $a^2 + 2ab + b^2 - a - b + 6$, (h) $x^2 + 2xh + h^2 - x - h + 6$
25. (a) $t + x$, (b) 0
26. (a) $-\frac{19}{5}$, (b) $(a - b)/2b$, (c) $\frac{2}{5}$
27. Neither
28. (a) $y = \frac{4}{15}x + \frac{8}{15}$, (b) $y = 4x - 34$
29. (a) $m = 1$, $b = 0$;        (b) $m = -1$, $b = -1$;        (c) $m = 2$, $b = 10$

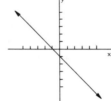

30. They are not collinear

31.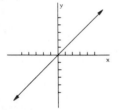

32.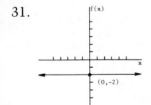

33.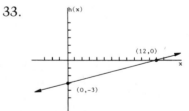

34.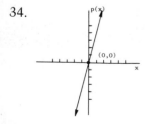

35.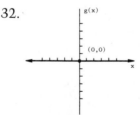

36.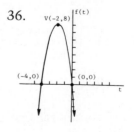

37. $S = 6e^2$
38. $A = (\pi + 8)x^2/8$
39. $C(x) = 8.5x + 475$; $C(0) = \$475$ and $C(65) = \$1027.50$ are the costs of producing 0 watches and 65 watches, respectively.
40. 150 yd by 300 yd

# APPENDIXES

## Appendix 1: Sets — Set Notation

1. T        3. F        5. F        7. T        9. F        11. F
13. {1, 2, 3, 4, 5}                    15. {0, 2, 4, 6, 8, 10, 12, ...}
17. {January, February, March, April, May, June, July, August, September, October, November, December}
19. $\emptyset$                        21. {b, a, n}
23. $\emptyset$                        25. {M, i, s, p}
27. {2, 4, 10, 20}                    29. {0, 2, 4, 6, 8, ...}
31. {$x \mid x$ is a whole number between 13 and 20}
33. {$x \mid x$ is a month beginning with the letter "J"}
35. {$x \mid x$ is an even whole number}
37. {$x \mid x$ is a whole number multiple of 3}
39. {$x \mid x$ is a whole number ending in 5}
41. {$x \mid x$ is a Great Lake}        43. T        45. F        47. T

## Appendix 1: Sets — Subsets and Set Operations

1. T        3. T        5. T        7. T        9. F        11. T
13. F        15. F        17. T        19. $\emptyset$, {3}        21. $\emptyset$, {5}, {6}, {5, 6}
23. $\emptyset$, {a}, {b}, {c}, {a, b}, {a, c}, {b, c}, {a, b, c}
25. $\emptyset$, {5}, {6}, {7}, {8}, {5, 6}, {5, 7}, {5, 8}, {6, 7}, {6, 8}, {7, 8}, {5, 6, 7}, {5, 6, 8}, {5, 7, 8}, {6, 7, 8}, {5, 6, 7, 8}

27. Suppose $x$ represents any element in set $A$. That is, $x \in A$. Then $x$ must also be an element of set $B$, since $A \subseteq B$. That is, $x \in B$. But then $x$ must also be an element of set $C$, since $B \subseteq C$. Therefore, for each element $x \in A$, we must also have that $x \in C$. That is, $A \subseteq C$.

29. $\{2\}$     31. $\{2, 3, 5, 6, 7, 8\}$     33. $\{1, 2, 4, 8\}$     35. $\{1, 4\}$

37. $\emptyset$     39. $C$     41. $\emptyset$     43. $A$     45. $\{1, 2, 3, 4, 5\}$

47. $\{1, 4\}$     49. $D$     51. $\emptyset$     53. $\{1, 2, 3, 4, 5, 6, 7, 8\}$

55. $\emptyset$     57. $M$     59. $D$     61. $D$     63. $\emptyset$     65. T

67. T     69. F     71. $B$     73. 11     75. T     77. F

## Appendix 2: Converting Repeating Decimals to Ratios of Integers

1. $\frac{4}{11}$     3. $\frac{7}{99}$     5. $\frac{1}{3}$     7. $\frac{2}{9}$     9. $\frac{41}{333}$     11. $\frac{52}{9}$

13. $\frac{281}{30}$     15. $\frac{953}{198}$     17. $\frac{2263}{3333}$     19. $\frac{1}{1} = 1$

## Appendix 4: The Metric System

1. 500 cm     3. 18,000 mm     5. 780 cm     7. 16,000 m     9. 5.2 km

11. 62 m     13. 0.045 m     15. 171 mm     17. 0.5 cm     19. 6000 g

21. 15 kg     23. 1620 g     25. 8000 m$\ell$     27. 0.5 $\ell$     29. 37 $\ell$

31. 2930 m$\ell$     33. 7.315 m     35. 198.5 lb     37. 9.843 ft     39. 563.2 km

41. 311.8 g     43. 0.8119 oz     45. 1.143 m     47. 60.96 m     49. 17.78 cm

51. 4.732 $\ell$     53. 3.937 in.     55. 78.74 in.     57. 385.6 kg     59. 31.71 qt

61. 14.22 yd     63. 124.3 mi     65. 21,240 sq mi

# Indexes
# Indexes
# Indexes
# Indexes

Index of Applications
Subject Index

## INDEX OF APPLICATIONS

## Astronomy and Space

## Biology, Medicine, and Psychology

## Ecology and Social Sciences

## Sports, Recreation, and Entertainment

## Consumer Mathematics

## Word Problems

## Pure Geometry

## Miscellaneous

## Subject Index